Stephen Crane

An Omnibus

STEPHEN CRANE *1871–1900*

Stephen Crane

An Omnibus

EDITED, WITH INTRODUCTION AND NOTES, BY

ROBERT WOOSTER STALLMAN

1970

NEW YORK ALFRED A. KNOPF

L. C. CATALOG CARD NUMBER: 52–6416

THIS IS A BORZOI BOOK,
PUBLISHED BY ALFRED A. KNOPF, INC.

FIRST COLLECTED EDITION
PUBLISHED NOVEMBER 10, 1952
REPRINTED SIX TIMES
EIGHTH PRINTING, FEBRUARY 1970

FOR

CLIFTON WALLER BARRETT

EDITOR'S FOREWORD

THIS NEW EDITION of Stephen Crane brings together for the first time his best works in a single volume: three of his novels, ten of his short stories, and sixteen poems. The works are grouped according to their subject-matter or setting—very simply as *Bowery Tales, War Tales, A Tale of the Sea, Western Tales, Whilomville Stories,* and *Poems.* Crane's journalism is represented by four of his articles: each of the first three parts of this book concludes with one of these articles. In Part VII I have collected fifty-seven letters never before published, in addition to letters reprinted from periodicals and books in which they first appeared. A dozen of the letters are from the collection of Mr. H. B. Collamore, and three others (one an inscription) from that of Mr. Josiah K. Lilly. Nine of the new letters are the gift of Mr. Odell S. Hathaway, Jr.

I am indebted to Mr. Clifton Waller Barrett for photostat copies of twenty-seven new Crane letters and the original handwritten manuscripts of *The Red Badge of Courage.* No part of these manuscripts has been previously reproduced in America. My collation of these manuscripts deals chiefly with the critically significant variants. It represents no more than a first attempt at a full comparative study. My account of the history of these manuscripts is the first full account of the composition of *The Red Badge.*

This selection of Crane's best works has been determined by critical standards, not by mere personal taste. I have tried to establish grounds for the critical importance of every piece comprised in it. My introductions and preface pieces to each section contain analytical readings of several short stories and poems and a new interpretation of *The Red Badge of Courage.* This anthology should help to upset the prevailing notion of Crane as a one-book genius. My purpose is to provide a re-valuation of Crane's art and achievement.

Crane's fiction, apart from *The Red Badge*, has been available only in *Twenty Stories*, edited by Carl Van Doren in 1940. They are not Crane's best, and it is difficult to say what principle that selection was based upon. The editor's job, I think, is to isolate the best from the worst. *Selected Prose and Poetry* (1950) contributes little to differentiate it from Van Doren's collection. The definitive edition—*The Work of Stephen Crane* (1925-7), edited by Wilson Follett in twelve volumes and furnished with introductions by Crane's friends and admirers—helped to establish Crane's standing as an American classic. But there his good things got lost under an avalanche of rubbish. Sherwood Anderson, in his Introduction to Volume XI of the *Work,* called Crane "an explosion" and exclaimed: "The thing to do is to have all his books on your shelves." But these books, alas for the poor reader, sold only in sets costing ninety dollars. It is frequently said that a writer cannot be understood in any full sense of the word unless we have his complete works. On the contrary, I think that one grain of sand can best be understood when isolated from the avalanche; a mountain is at its top! The best of Crane is not very much, and it does not take the whole body of his writings to understand any single perfection.

Crane has been discovered twice since he died, in 1900—more than any other American author except Henry James. But our discovery of James and our revivals of Hawthorne and Melville have been accompanied by critical exploration of their works, whereas scholarship and criticism of Crane is still negligible. Since his death what has been written about him is chiefly biographical—250 articles or books, which amounts to just half the number of writings on his contemporary A. E. Housman. American literary historians, until lately, continued to ignore or slight his art and achievement; no critical examination of his works has ever been made. The biography of Crane has been written three times,[1] yet the

---

[1] In 1923 by Thomas Raymond and by Thomas Beer, and in 1950 by John Berryman. Bibliographies include Vincent Starrett's (1923),

chronology of his life and writings still remains incomplete. His letters have never before been collected, and his best works are brought together here for the first time. I do not think that it can be questioned that Crane has been critically neglected. *The Cambridge History of American Literature* (1923) gives Crane one page. Matthiessen's *American Renaissance* (1941) ignored Crane, though two biographies and two bibliographies had already appeared. In the business of documenting literature for "trends" and "influences," Crane gets crowded out. The sociology of American life can be documented better from Norris and Dreiser. Professor Robert Spiller's appraisal of Crane in the *Literary History of the United States* (1948) helps to correct this distorted perspective, but on the other hand Crane gets no appraisal whatever—only three scant cross-references—in Professor Alexander Cowie's *Rise of the American Novel* (1948); there is not a word about Crane's importance in the history of American fiction in this volume of 754 pages!

Nor has Crane received attention in our critical journals, where one might expect to find him, except in a couple of articles. Of these Wilson Follett's review of Crane's reputation, appearing in 1929, is one of the best. As he said then, with most of Crane's works out of print for a quarter of a century, "It is not strange that to a wholly false image of the man there should gradually have been added an equally false impression of his work: namely, that it consists of (a) *The Red Badge of Courage* and (b) negligible odds and ends, to be classified as the ephemeral by-products of a reporter and war correspondent." [2] In England, where he had been lionized, his books—out of print for thirty years—became "as rare as a gold sovereign," and in America Hemingway occupied the place that Crane filled thirty years before. His revival in the twenties, for which

---

B. J. R. Stolper's (1930), and the Ames Williams and Vincent Starrett *Stephen Crane: A Bibliography* (John Valentine, 1948).

[2] "The Second Twenty-Eight Years: A Note on Stephen Crane, 1871–1900," *Bookman*, 68 (January 1929), 532–7.

Thomas Beer's *Stephen Crane* (1923) was largely responsible,
was initiated by Vincent Starrett's selection of short stories
(*Men, Women and Boats*, 1921), by which the public was reminded that Crane wrote something more than just *The Red
Badge*. The recognition he won was not because of *The Red
Badge*, though wartime interest in his novel helped, but because there was the shock of recognition by the artists of the
1920's that their art had kinship in technique and theme with
Crane's timeless art. Crane was rediscovered not by literary
historians but by creative writers (Joseph Hergesheimer, Willa
Cather, Hemingway, and Sherwood Anderson). In Crane, a
writer's writer, they recognized a contemporary. Henry Hazlitt's edition of *Maggie and Other Stories* (1931) started Crane
into the sociological thirties. Sales of this book all but stopped
by 1937, and though *Maggie* had another edition in 1933, reviewers were asking the same question about Crane's popularity that had been asked in 1917—"today who reads Crane?"
In the forties Crane came to the front again—beginning with
Twenty Stories, the reprint of Beer's biography with an introduction by Joseph Conrad, (*Stephen Crane*, 1923) in his
Hanna, Crane, and The Mauve Decade (1941), and the re-
appearance of H. G. Wells's important summing up of Crane
("From an English Standpoint") in *The Shock of Recognition*
(1943). When Edmund Wilson compiled this anthology, he
complained that American critics had nothing better to offer.
One had to go abroad to find the best critical piece on Stephen
Crane. The Introductions by Hergesheimer and H. L. Mencken
in the *Work*, however, deserve mention. And Mencken's
short piece on Crane in the Baltimore *Sun* (1924), reprinted
in *A Mencken Chrestomathy* (1949). On the poetry there is
Harriet Monroe's note in *Poetry* for 1919, which is much better
than Amy Lowell's sentimentalized sketch prefacing Volume VI of the *Work*, and there is Horace Gregory's perceptive
chapter on Crane in his *History of American Poetry* (1946).
Mr. John Berryman psychoanalyzes the poems in his *Stephen*

Crane (1950). Apart from this, critical understanding of Crane's works remains pretty much the same as in 1900 when Wells lamented that criticism had not yet done "justice to the unsurpassable beauty of Crane's best writing."

One of Scott Fitzgerald's critics remarks that "there is not always as much to say about his works as critics would like" (Alfred Kazin, in *F. Scott Fitzgerald,* 1951, p. 17). The case with Crane is just the obverse: critically there is so much to say, and so little of it has yet been said. No Crane critic, from Beer to Berryman, has yet printed anything that is relevant to the criticism of the works *as* works of art, and every commentator to the present has committed the characteristic heresy of biographical criticism—the equation of the works with life itself. In his Introduction to the Heritage Press edition of *The Red Badge* (1944), Carl Van Doren discusses Henry Fleming, the soldier hero of the novel and of its sequel story *The Veteran,* as though Henry were a living person, a G.I. in the flesh and blood. In John T. Winterich's Introduction to the Folio Society edition (1951), the novel is interpreted to be no more than a document on the Civil War. The same misreading appeared in the reviews of 1895. In 1945 an Armed Services edition gave the book its largest circulation so far, but the reason for its popularity was the same as in 1917, when soldiers were first introduced to *The Red Badge* in an Over the Top edition by Guy Empey—"the greatest war novel ever written."

Mr. John Berryman's *Stephen Crane* brings Beer up to date, pieces together the facts for new insights and discoveries, and reconstructs the chronology. But his book is Beer all over again, in both theme and style. He reworks Beer's theme, his reading of fear in the works *and* fear in the life, and he emulates Beer in style and method. Far better is Beer's impressionist portrait of Crane. Literary biography is here lifted to the level of art. But Beer is not reliable. The facts are distorted, and gaps in the chronology are disguised by Beer's tricks of camera, by kaleidoscopic effects and cinematic shadow-work.

Beer's stylized portrait gives equal weight to every detail, dramatizes every episode, and sentimentalizes. There is need for a new critical-biographical study of Crane, and the time is ripe for a corrected perspective.

NOTE & ACKNOWLEDGMENTS

MY SELECTION of Crane, based on a total reading of his works, aims to present only his best. The questions I have asked of every story are: has it any meaning or theme, and what is the structure by which it is formed? The critical test of any literary work is language and form. Nothing in *The Sullivan County Sketches* is worth mentioning in these terms. I had thought to reprint here a miscellany of Crane to illustrate the range and variety of his writings—namely, the satire, *An Illusion in Red and White*; the fable, *How the Donkey Lifted the Hills*; and the comic sketch, *The Holler Tree* from *The Sullivan County Sketches*. The purpose of this book, however, is to represent achievement rather than range; consequently range gets only incidental notice. Range can be represented only by including second-best things. *The Monster, Death and the Child, The Price of the Harness,* and several other favorites belong to that category.

Every anthology wants to be a longer book; every anthologist wants to include more choices from his bulky author than space permits. A critical selection of Crane must defend itself on other grounds. Crane is bulky, but not at his best.

I wish to thank the several persons whose assistance has made this volume possible: Miss Josephine La Vecchia for typing my research notes; my wife, Virginia, for typing the manuscript; and for constant help in bibliographical matters Miss Roberta Smith, Reference Librarian of the University of Connecticut. I owe a considerable debt to Mr. Charles Ede, editor of the Folio Society, for providing me with galley proof of the Folio Society edition of *The Red Badge of Courage*.

For correspondence and kind suggestions I wish to thank Mr. A. S. W. Rosenbach; Miss Evelyn O'Connor; Professor Howard Vincent; Professor W. L. Werner; Mr. Jay Leyda; Mr.

Paul Revere Reynolds; Mr. Sy Kahn; Mr. Malcolm Cowley; Professor Robert Heilman; Mr. Max J. Herzberg of the *Newark News*; Miss Gladys Love, Head of the Reference Division of the Rochester Public Library; Mr. John B. Kaiser, Director of the Reference Department of the Public Library of Newark, New Jersey; Mr. T. E. Norton, Librarian of Lafayette College; Mr. Charles D. Abbott, Director of Libraries at the University of Buffalo; Mr. Richard T. Morris, Assistant Director of the Buffalo Public Library; Mr. David Randall; Mr. Roger B. Francis, Executive Assistant at the New York Public Library; Mrs. Althea Green Wilson, of the Yale University Library; Mr. John D. Holmes, of the Library of Congress; Mr. Wharton Miller, Director, and Mr. Lester Wells, Curator of the Stephen Crane Collection at the Syracuse University Library. I wish to thank Mr. Wells for his many kindnesses. In order to assist me in permission matters, Mr. Wells visited the executor of the Stephen Crane Estate.

For permission to reprint Stephen Crane letters and for kind correspondence on permission matters, I wish to thank Mr. Spencer Curtis Brown; Mr. Tyrus Harmsen, of the Department of Manuscripts at the Huntington Library; Mr. John D. Gordan, Curator of the Berg Collection, and Mr. Paul North Rice, Chief of the Reference Department, at the New York Public Library; and Mr. Harold Rugg, Librarian of Dartmouth College; and Mr. Donald C. Gallup, of the Yale Collection of American Literature at the Yale University Library. I owe a considerable debt to Mr. Josiah K. Lilly for his generous gift of copies of three new Crane letters (one an inscription) and to LCDR Melvin Schoberlin for photostat copy of one letter originally published in a pamphlet that is rare now and practically impossible to obtain. Mr. H. B. Collamore granted me use of his Stephen Crane Collection and gave me photostat copies of thirteen letters and the Stephen Crane Notebook. I wish to thank also Mr. Odell S. Hathaway, Jr., for giving me copies of nine previously unpublished Crane letters.

I am deeply grateful to Mr. Clifton Waller Barrett for his

extraordinary gift of photostat copies of the manuscripts of *The Red Badge of Courage* and a magnificent set of new Crane letters and the manuscripts of some unpublished Crane stories. The letters have never before been published, and the manuscripts of *The Red Badge* are produced here for the first time. Mr. Barrett further aided me by reading the manuscript of my introductions to this book and offering several suggestions toward improvement. For advice and encouragement I have also to thank my editor, Mr. Herbert Weinstock, of Alfred A. Knopf, Inc. For help toward establishing the text of *The Red Badge* as a faithful copy of the first American edition, I wish to thank Professor Richard M. Ludwig, of Princeton University.

CONTENTS

PART IV: WESTERN TALES

PART V: WHILOMVILLE STORIES

PART VI: POEMS

PART VII: LETTERS

INTRODUCTION

Luckless in everything else, Crane had the great luck—
phenomenal among writers—to write two works of art having
major importance in American letters and to write them both
before he was twenty-two. Though he died when he was but
twenty-eight, he left behind him more than enough perfec-
tions to place him solidly among the half-dozen major artists
of American fiction in the nineteenth century—not in the first
rank with Hawthorne and Melville and Henry James but,
counting work for work, in the second rank with Poe and
Howells and Twain. Not counting his detective fiction, Poe
is at his best in but a couple of short stories and one novel,
The Narrative of A. Gordon Pym. Crane perfected more works
than either Poe or Twain. He first broke new ground with
Maggie: A Girl of the Streets, the then sordid realism of that
work initiating the literary trend of the next generation.
Maggie is a tone painting rather than a realistic photograph
of slum life, but it opened the door to the Norris-Dreiser-
Farrell school of sociological realism. The sensational success
of *The Red Badge of Courage* (a best-seller in England and
in America, it outsold Zola and Tolstoy and even Kipling)
brought him into instantaneous and meteoric renown. In *The
Red Badge,* an impressionistic painting notable for its bold
innovations in technique and style, and in *The Open Boat,*
that flawless construct of paradox and symbol, Crane established himself among the foremost engineers in the techniques
of modern fiction. *The Open Boat* (1897) is a perfect fusion
of the impressionistic realism of *Maggie* (1893) and the symbolic realism of *The Red Badge of Courage* (1895). The two
main technical movements of modern fiction—realism and symbolism—have their beginnings here in these achievements of
Stephen Crane.

Crane is frequently spoken of as the most legendary figure in American letters since Edgar Allan Poe. "A genius as singular as Poe" and "destined from the first to be a present-day Poe"—Hamlin Garland concluded after meeting him—"a singular and daring soul, irresponsible as the wind." A whole mythology of bizarre tales, some of them not entirely untrue, surrounds his elusive and enigmatic personality, and it is difficult to distinguish the real Crane from the mythical Crane when so much of the factual is itself fantastic. The fantastic pursued him beyond the grave in the fact that after he died his widow—an extraordinary woman and a faithful wife—returned to her former trade in Jacksonville, Florida, where as the madam of a bawdyhouse she presided over a mansion modeled on Brede Place, the semi-medieval residence of the Cranes in England.[1] Crane, by nature overgenerous, had a trigger-quick love for the underdog—Bowery bums and streetwalkers—and an immense capacity for friendship. His friendship was shared by the literary great—Conrad, Henry James, H. G. Wells, Ford Madox Ford, William Dean Howells, Hamlin Garland, and others. Conrad affectionately attended him during his fatal illness, and Henry James, waiting upon him with oversolicitous devotion, treated him as though he were another Keats—a pet lamb in a sentimental tragedy. He lived violently and he died young, but even while he lived, the real Crane was being converted into the conventional legend of the artist—luckless, penniless, creative only when fever-ridden or drunk. There is this folk version of the wayward genius, under which Crane's myth-making personality has been likened to Poe's, and there is the more classical version of the "stricken boy," the genius who dies young—Chatterton, Keats, Schubert, Beardsley.

The Crane portrait hangs, as it were, between calumny and idolatry; seen from this latter point of view (viz. Ford Madox Ford's) we get a sentimentalized impression: "I took him at

---

[1] See Chapter xxx of *The St. Johns* by Branch Cabell and A. J. Hanna (1943).

once to be a god—an Apollo with starry eyes." The reputation of Crane is as contradictory as the man himself. Not fame alone but scandal attached to his name, and by 1896 he was "the most thoroughly abused writing man" in America. To champion a woman of the streets and get into a tangle with the police was bad taste in the 1890's, and Crane's unearned ill repute among certain editors and his scandalous reputation with the public contributed to the neglect into which his works fell after 1900. An author who shows "bad taste" in his life cannot show "good taste" in his writings—it is the same moral whip that is even today used against Poe and Byron. The abuse of Crane's name came solely from the American press, and in 1897 he settled in England because of it.

There seem so many of them in America who want to kill, bury and forget me purely out of unkindness and envy—and my unworthiness, if you choose. All the hard things they say of me affect me principally because I think of mine own people—you and Teddie and the families. It is nothing, bless you. Now Dick Davis for instance has come to like the abuse. He accepts it as a tribute to his excellence. But he is a fool. Now I want you to promise to never pay any attention to it, even in your thought. It is too immaterial and foolish. Your little brother is neither braggart or a silent egotist but he knows that he is going on steadily to make his simple little place and he can't be stopped, he can't even be retarded. He is coming. [Letter to William, October 29, 1897.]

But there was another reason for Crane's going to England. He had reason to fear malicious gossip about his marriage to, or his living with, a woman who had once been associated with a "house of joy."

He had suffered out the public indifference to *Maggie* (as late as 1930 that book remained practically unknown in America), but critical ridicule heaped on *The Black Riders*—published just before *The Red Badge,* and preferred by Crane as his "more ambitious effort"—must have added to his embitterment.

Fame descended upon Crane in 1896, in January, when he

was living with his brother at Hartwood, Sullivan County, New York, and a few months before he died he wrote from England to an American editor, Joseph O'Connor: "I have only one pride—and that is that the English edition of 'The Red Badge of Courage' has been received with great praise by the English reviewers. I am proud of this simply because the remoter people would seem more just and harder to win." [2] No man of his generation was more admired and loved or received greater critical recognition, but that was in another country.

The chief impetus for Crane's American success was provided by British praise, and the tumultuous reception accorded *The Red Badge* by the British journals was first heralded at home by Harold Frederic's London dispatch to the *New York Times* on January 26, 1896: "Stephen Crane's Triumph—London Curious About the Identity of America's New Writer." (Crane wrote Hitchcock about it: "delighted with Frederic's letter in the Times.") Then, once America got wind of it, but not until then, his book early the next year "swept the country," leading the best-seller lists by March and April in sixteen cities and going through fourteen American printings that year. At home derision and heated contention accompanied the praise, the American press taking offense at being told that Crane had been "first praised in England." What a controversy *The Red Badge* stirred up! What critical warfare it ignited! The *Critic* in January 1897 counterblasted against the *Daily News* that Crane had been reviewed "from Maine to California before a single English reviewer had received the book," and it reminded these ignorant English editors that some half-dozen other authors had also been first "discovered" or "boomed" here in America. Behind the blurred truth, however, it was exactly as the *Daily News* asserted: "After English praise, the author's countrymen reconsidered their verdict." The book did pretty well for the first three

---

[2] Published in the *Rochester Post-Express*, April 18, 1900, p. 4; reprinted in part in the *Literary Digest*, June 23, 1900.

months, but at first it sold very slowly. "Mr. Hitchcock tells me," Crane wrote in a letter of December 24, 1895, "that the book does not sell much in New York. It has gone to about 4,500, though, and many of them have been sent west." He remarked to a friend: "Oh, of course, I should be glad if everybody, Canadians, Feejees, Hottentots, wild men of Borneo, would buy *The Red Badge*—four copies of it—but they won't; so what's the use of thinking of the reader?"

"Who is this man Crane, anyway?" The question was asked in the editorial offices of the *Philadelphia Press,* where in December 1894 *The Red Badge* was making its first appearance—serialized from December 3 to 8. "Well, if he keeps this up, we'll all know him in a few years." Appleton brought out the book-length version early in October 1895, and two months later (during the week of November 30) Heinemann published it in England. The Muse on Publisher's Hill showed prophetic wit in putting *The Red Badge of Courage* into Heinemann's "*Pioneer* Series of *Modern* Fiction." Or again in crowning the first American edition with a gilt top! The flash and blast that the book made, the shock and excitement, the sensation it produced were at once "unprecedented and irresistible." As Conrad, H. G. Wells, Mencken, and Hergesheimer testify, it detonated on the public—to use Conrad's trope—with "the impact and force of a twelve-inch shell charged with a very high explosive." What caused the explosion, particularly upon his more perceptive readers, was the explosive style of the book, Crane's own bombardment of similes and metaphors.

Sentimental critics have shed literary tears over Crane's early death, but his death at twenty-eight resulted in no loss to literature. He had exhausted his genius. By 1900 the whirligig of taste had replaced Crane with Frank Norris, and the *Bookman*—reviewing *McTeague,* which had appeared the year before—piously admonished Norris "to walk humbly" amidst "the warning of Mr. Crane's obvious failure to meet the expectations he excited." Hamlin Garland, shifting away

now from his former praise, wrote in *Roadside Meetings*
(p. 206) that Crane "was too brilliant, too fickle, too erratic to
last. He could not go on doing stories like *The Red Badge of
Courage.*" But this is misleading and it ignores the fact that
Crane went on doing not more *Red Badge*'s but other kinds
of stories just as good or, in *The Open Boat*, better. Two opposite points of view, both of them mistaken, argue that (1) his
last works show "no diminution of literary powers" and
(2) that he died young "without fulfilling his wonderful promise." It seems to be the occupational disease of critics to concern themselves more with an author's future promise than
with his present achievement, and consequently no American
author "succeeds" because he inevitably "fails." As for Crane's
failure to live up to the fulfillments that his work "promised,"
he excited no expectations but those he fulfilled in the works
that excited them. It is not true that he "expended himself"
with the creation of *Maggie* and *The Red Badge*, not yet; but
after his initial achievements—*Maggie*, a little later *The Red
Badge*, *George's Mother*, and then *The Open Boat*—he wrote
no more than a half-dozen first-rate tales, and in poetry, after
The Black Riders, there was the same falling off, the late work
sharply declining from the early. He produced too much, he
kept repeating himself, and he never developed. His writings
fill twelve volumes—eighty-six sketches and tales, five brief
novels, three volumes of verse, and a mass of journalistic
stuff (one hundred and twenty-eight articles). The greater
part of all this work is second-rate. The artist had succumbed
to the journalist (for example, *Active Service*, *The O'Ruddy*,
Great Battles of the World), though some of the pure Crane
shone even at the end of his cometlike career. As Sherwood
Anderson said: "Suppose he did put a pretty little patent-
leather finish on some of his later tales. Take him for what he
was—his importance."

What killed Crane was not literary neglect—he died, so the
popular notion has it, "tragically young," "a boy, spiritually
killed by neglect"—but rather his own will to burn himself out,

his Byronic craving to make his body "a testing ground for all
the sensations of life." He aimed not to live very long (thirty-
five at best, he wrote Nellie Crouse), and knowing that his
time was short, he had no time to lose. *He lived in desperation
against time.* Like F. Scott Fitzgerald, who wrote (to quote
Malcolm Cowley) "in a room full of clocks and calendars,"
Crane feared time if he feared anything. (It is curious that he
should describe his mother in terms of time: "She spoke as
slowly as a big clock ticks and her effects were impromptu.")
He died at the same sinister hour as Fitzgerald, three in the
morning. His life was again like Fitzgerald's in this: though
filled with adventure, it was neither thrilling nor romantic,
but actually somewhat banal. "Even his war adventures," as
H. L. Mencken says, "were far less thrilling in fact than in
his florid accounts of them." [3] What D. H. Lawrence remarked
about Melville is true also of Crane: "The artist was so much
greater than the man."

Crane was intense, volatile, spontaneous—what he wrote
came unwatched from his pen. He wrote as he lived, and his
life was shot through with ironies. Seeing life from a water-
soaked dinghy, as it were, the sea tossing him about this way
and that, he saw it as an angry or indifferent sea—"the grim
waves menacing" and "most wrongfully and barbarously
abrupt." If he won any "grace" from that cold voyage it was,
I think, the artist's gift of ironic outlook, that grace of irony
which is so central to his art. Irony is Crane's chief technical
instrument. It is the key to our understanding of the man and
of his works. He wrote with the intensity of a poet's emotion,
the compressed emotion that bursts into symbol and paradox.

2

Crane wasted his genius. Under the mistaken notion that only
those who have suffered shipwreck can become its interpreters, he expended himself in a search for experience. Will-

[3] In *A Mencken Chrestomathy* (1949), p. 497.

fully and needlessly he risked his life—among bandits in Mexico, under shellfire in Cuba and Greece as war correspondent,
and off the Florida seacoast as a filibustering seaman in the
disaster that befell him when he survived shipwreck only after
suffering thirty hours at sea in a ten-foot dinghy. It was natural that Crane should want to see actual warfare after writing about it, and four years later as war correspondent in the
Greco-Turkish War he tested the psychological truth of his
imagined picture. "My picture was all right!" he told Conrad.
"I have found it as I imagined it." But at what a cost! Exposures endured in Cuba wrecked his health and impaired
his art. Nothing vital came from his war experiences. His imagination, as one friend said, "worked better in a room than
on a battlefield." [4] And the pity of it all is that it could have
been otherwise. He could have lived in one of his brothers'
homes and done his writing there; he could have retreated
from life to calculate it from a distance as Hawthorne and
James did. Instead, he chose to get as close to life as possible.
Garland, meeting him in McClure's office one day, said to him
earnestly:

Crane, why don't you cut loose from your associations here? Go to
your brother's farm in Sullivan County and get back your tone. You
don't look well. Settle down to the writing of a single big book up
there, and take your time to do it.—
    Impulsively thrusting out his hand to me, he said—I'll do it.—
Alas! He did not. He took a commission to go to Greece and report
a war. On his return from Greece he went to Cuba.[5]

---

[4] C. Lewis Hind in *Authors and I* (1921), pp. 73–4. The same opinion
is given by H. G. Wells, Hamlin Garland, and others.
    [5] *Roadside Meetings*, pp. 203–4. Beer states that Crane could have
retreated to his brother's home "and stayed as a pensioner until, somehow, he had established himself with a public. But Crane's independence
had a bent almost savage and ungracious." *Hanna, Crane, and The
Mauve Decade*, pp. 277–8. (All references to Beer are to this volume.)
Crane's niece argues *contra* Beer that Crane's brothers were not oversolicitous about him: "My Uncle, Stephen Crane," *American Mercury*, 31
(January 1924), 24. This article fills in the situation but does not change
the fact that, while his brothers may not have been oversolicitous about

Writing from London in 1897 to his brother William, Crane said: "My idea is to come finally to live at Port Jervis or Hartwood. I am a wanderer now and I must see enough but—afterwards—I think of P. J. & Hartwood."

He wanted to get at the real thing, and so he stood all night in a blizzard in order to write *Men in the Storm*; to get at the real thing he spent a night in a Bowery flophouse in order to write *An Experiment in Misery*; to get at the real thing he traveled across the Western prairies, and out of it he got *The Blue Hotel* and *The Bride Comes to Yellow Sky*; out of Mexico he got *Horses—One Dash!* and other sketches; and out of Cuba and Greece impressions of war for *Wounds in the Rain*, stories like *Death and the Child*, and the novel *Active Service*. But was there any need for Crane to experience a blizzard in order to write *Men in the Storm*? Would not an imaginary rather than an actual blizzard have served just as well, the germinal idea of the story being a *symbolic* storm—the storm of social strife? Familiarizing himself with New York tenement life certainly was not necessary for the germinal idea of *An Auction*, in which he depicts the social shame of a poor couple whose household goods are auctioned off amidst the derisive mockery of a parrot and a gaping crowd. No personal experience of Bret Harte's country was needed to write parodies of Bret Harte's Californian tales—in *Moonlight in the Snow, Twelve O'Clock,* and *A Self-Made Man*. Much of Crane's anecdotal material might just as well have originated in other people's experience, and in fact some of it did—for example, the incident used in *The Lone Charge of Francis B. Perkins* was taken from Ralph Paine.

In his quest for and immersion in experience, Crane stands at the headstream of what has been defined as the dominant American theme and literary trend[6]—exemplified in Heming-

---

him, still they would have taken him in as they had before. There was no necessity for Crane's sleeping in Bowery flophouses. He went to them by choice.

[6] See Philip Rahv's *Image and Idea* (1949), p. 8.

way, Anderson, and Thomas Wolfe, who put the same pre-
mium on personal experience. Considering how much personal experience he had to draw upon, he put it to very little
significant use. At his best he used not the experienced event
but the event distilled for its thematic potentialities. The exception is *The Open Boat,* but here—as with Conrad in *Heart
of Darkness,* which is taken straight from life—the personal
experience served simply as the canvas for the re-created picture. The only work Conrad ever wrote immediately after
an actual experience on the spot was *The Idiots* (*Life and
Letters,* I, 164). *The Open Boat* was an immediate transcript
of personal experience, but it is personal experience trans-
formed into an impersonal and symbolic representation of
life—the plight of mankind tossed upon an indifferent sea. The
calculated design and significance of the story can be explained by no source other than the conceiving imagination
of the artist. Crane excels in the portrayal of mental turmoil,
and for this psychological realism his creative imagination required no first-hand experience. *The Open Boat* and *Horses—
One Dash!* are his most directly autobiographical tales, but
most of his fiction is only remotely autobiographical. Contacts with reality, for Conrad and Crane alike, provoked hints
for characters, details of locality, and the like; but it is seldom
that Crane presents minute descriptions of people or scenes,
and details of locality are not photographically recorded. The
locality of *The Blue Hotel* has symbolic import and could
have been painted with no first-hand knowledge of it. He
could have written *The Blue Hotel* without leaving New
York City. The fight that he witnessed and tried to stop during an incident in Lincoln, Nebraska, became the fight de-
picted in *The Blue Hotel,* but the germinal idea for the story
might just as well have had a literary source. *The Blue Hotel*
has been called "a Hemingway story," but in germinal conception it follows Robert Louis Stevenson's formula: a certain
scene and atmosphere suggest the correlative action and persons for that particular locality, and they are so used as to

express and symbolize it. The atmosphere of the old blue hotel, the psychic quality of its screaming blue, impels and
foreshadows the action that expresses it—the murder of the
Swede.

Crane's two greatest works—*The Red Badge of Courage* and
The Open Boat—represent two opposite methods of creation:
from imagined experience and from actual experience. In contradiction to his theory that the artist can write about life only
after first experiencing it, Crane reproduced the immediacies
of battle in *The Red Badge of Courage* long before he had
seen and suffered actual shellfire. The single marvel he wrung
from personal experience was *The Open Boat,* and the marvel
of it is that he manipulated the whole experience into art
without altering the facts. Yet a paradox is here established,
for the masterpiece that he salvaged from his expense of greatness could have been conceived without the personal experience—as *The Red Badge of Courage* is there to testify.

They all insist—said Crane, referring to the reviewers of his *Red
Badge*—that I am a veteran of the civil war, whereas the fact is, as
you know, I never smelled even the powder of a sham battle. I
know what the psychologists say, that a fellow can't comprehend a
condition that he has never experienced, and I argued that many
times with the Professor. Of course, I have never been in a battle,
but I believe that I got my sense of the rage of conflict on the football field, or else fighting is a hereditary instinct, and I wrote intuitively; for the Cranes were a family of fighters in the old days,
and in the Revolution every member did his duty. But be that as it
may, I endeavoured to express myself in the simplest and most concise way. If I failed, the fault is [not] mine.[7]

Discovery that the author had been born six years after Appo-
mattox provoked "universal surprise." Harold Frederic, discussing this question in his *Times* article on Crane, pointed
out *why* it is that the best accounts of battles have been written by novelists who never saw warfare, and the least realistic

---

[7] Letter to John N. Hilliard, written from England. Reprinted in *New
York Times, Supplement,* July 14, 1900, p. 466.

accounts by trained correspondents who were on the spot. Between them, Frederic found, "The line between journalism and literature obtruded itself." This same point holds true of most of the war tales Crane wrote after he himself had witnessed a battle; there is very little difference between the war tales written before he had experienced war and the war tales written after his experience of it except that the later ones are often more journalism than literature. Frederic, himself a novelist and a journalist, put his finger on the paradox of art:

It seems as if the actual sight of a battle has some dynamic quality in it which overwhelms and crushes the literary faculty in the observer. At best, he gives us a conventional account of what happened; but on analysis you find that this is not what he really saw, but what all his reading has taught him that he must have seen. In the same way battle painters depict horses in motion, not as they actually move, but as it has been agreed by numberless generations of draughtsmen to say that they move. At last, along comes a Muybridge, with his instantaneous camera, and shows that the real motion is entirely different.[8]

Comparison between Crane's description of war and a painter's was noted in the New York *World* the next month (February 1896): Zola, "rather than Mr. Crane, is the Verestchagin of literature."

The critical point to make about the notion that artists cannot reproduce the actualities of life without first experiencing them is that the exact obverse is, in fact, the truth. "I decided that the nearer a writer gets to life, the greater he becomes as an artist." Yet Crane's own art was at its greatest when he wrote at some distance from the reality he had experienced or when, on the other hand, he wrote out of no personal experience at all. His best works do not vindicate or support the creative principle that generated them.

What are the proper uses of personal experience? Thomas Wolfe, learning from wasted experience, tried to find the an-

---

[8] *New York Times, Supplement*, January 26, 1896, p. 22.

swer—too late to be of use to him. "And now I really believe that *so far as the artist is concerned* [italics mine], the unlimited extent of human experience is not so important for him as the depth and intensity with which he experiences things." [9] And *imagines* things! The depth and intensity of the artist's personal experience does not distinguish him *as* artist. Fitzgerald likewise exploited personal experience, sometimes shamefully, but he was an artist who knew how to convert it into an imaginative construct. Mark Twain's explanation for not continuing to write novels was that "capital"—personal experience—was not sufficient by itself.

3

There is an ironic contradiction between Crane's art and his theory of art. There is, furthermore, a duality in his theory. He argued for personal experience as the basis of art, but he also argued for imaginative experience. At the same time he also believed that the greater the obstacles an artist had to overcome—the harder the conditions he had to meet—the greater his art would be. In the letter in which he says that he wrote *The Red Badge* "intuitively," he explains: "It was an effort born of pain, and I believe that it was beneficial to it as a piece of literature. It seems a pity that this should be so— that art should be a child of suffering; and yet such seems to be the case." [1] Crane (unwittingly) echoed Keats—and with the same inconsistency; for Keats, too, believed in Inspiration and simultaneously held that art is not born without pain. It is difficult to reconcile Crane as Inspirational Artist with the calculated design of *The Red Badge*, every impression in it being preconceived. His casual remarks about art, as one writer says, have an offhand air "designed to deceive his readers into believing that for him art was a matter of no great moment,

---

[9] *The Story of a Novel*, in *The Portable Thomas Wolfe* (1948), p. 586.

[1] Letter to John N. Hilliard in *New York Times, Supplement*, July 14, 1900, p. 466.

that creation was a natural function, hardly worth comment
or appraisal." [2] Like Conrad and Chekhov, Crane spoke of the
artist as being "nothing but a powerful memory that can move
itself at will through certain experiences sideways, and every
artist must be in some things powerless as a dead snake."
Chekhov said that a writer should depend solely upon memory,
he should never keep a notebook. "When he died the drawer
of his writing-table was found to be stuffed with notebooks."
I am quoting here Edwin Mitchell, whose *Art of Authorship*
(1935) was first to announce the existence of a Stephen Crane
Notebook.[3] According to Crane's niece, manuscripts were often
returned by publishers with the demand: " 'Take the swear
words out of it, and we will publish it.' His reply was unvary-
ing: 'I can't, as that is how such men talk.' He had a passion
for truth, and felt that to make such a change would not be
sincere." [4] Crane did a good deal of revising, however, and he
revised even after his work had been published. My point is
that as soon as an author corrects so much as a comma he is
no longer a purely inspirational creator. As for Crane's moral
megrim that revisions are "dishonest" and "insincere," that
scruple too contradicts the view of the artist as a conscious
architect, and Crane *was* such an artist. As Yeats aptly put it:
"The correction of prose, because it has no fixed laws, is endless; a poem comes right with a click like a closing box." [5]

Crane's poems came just that way. "Personally I like my
little book of poems, *The Black Riders*, better than I do *The*

---

[2] *The Art of Stephen Crane,* unpublished Cornell University dissertation by Jean Elizabeth Whitehead (1944), p. 71.

[3] Photostat copy of Crane's Notebook is in my possession, the gift of
Mr. H. B. Collamore. The Notebook, pocket size, contains first drafts of
unpublished sketches and articles, scraps of description and dialogue, and
the opening pages of *A Desertion*. One of Crane's notes is a quotation
from Emerson: "Congratulate yourselves if you have done something
strange and extravagant and have broken the monotony of a decorous
age."

[4] Edna Crane Sidbury: "My Uncle, Stephen Crane," *Literary Digest,*
4 (March 1926), 250.

[5] *Letters to Dorothy Wellesley* (1940), p. 24.

Red Badge of Courage. The reason is, I suppose, that the former is the more ambitious effort." [6] Crane was at his *most* inspirational in writing his poems; "ambitious effort" is contradictory. And though he preferred his poetry to his fiction, he said elsewhere about *The Black Riders*: "Some of the pills are darned dumb, anyhow." As another instance of self-contradiction, he concealed whatever moral meaning his stories intended—"I let the reader find it for himself." But, like Conrad, Crane put little stock in the reader's perceptiveness, and according to his friend Herbert P. Williams, "he does not think to trust the imagination of any one who reads."

—Trust their imaginations? Why, they haven't got any! They are used to having everything detailed for them. Our imaginations are defunct for lack of use, like our noses. So whether I say a thing or suggest it, I try to put it in the most forcible way.—

Singular declaration, this, for a man whose books appeal chiefly to men of powerful imagination. [7]

While no systematic point of view can be extracted from Crane's remarks and written commentaries, he subscribed to one theory again and again, Hamlin Garland's "veritism." But even this theory does not account for his art.

The creed of veritism which Garland preached—the theory that art is founded on personal experience and copies reality—Crane echoed when, not long before his death, he told a friend: "You can never do anything good aesthetically—and you can never do anything that's any good except aesthetically —unless it has at one time meant something important to you." And in an early letter (1895), taking issue with one of Henry James's critical tenets, he said: "What, though, does the man

---

[6] Letter to John N. Hilliard (1897). Again, in a letter written late in 1895 and published the next year in *Leslie's Weekly*, Crane said: "I suppose I ought to be thankful to *The Red Badge*, but I am much fonder of my little book of poems, *The Black Riders*. The reason, perhaps, is that it was a more ambitious effort."

[7] "Mr. Crane as a Literary Artist," *Illustrated American*, July 18, 1896, p. 126.

mean by disinterested contemplation? It won't wash. If you care enough about a thing to study it, you are interested and have stopped being disinterested." He told Reginald Kauffman: "I could never do what I didn't feel like doing—not even writing." In *Crumbling Idols* (1894), which Crane most likely read, Garland advised young writers: "Write of those things of which you know most, and for which you care most. By doing so you will be true to yourself, true to your locality, and true to your time" (p. 35). While Crane was still at college (he was not there very long), he told a school chum who wanted to write but could not "get down the real thing":

Treat your notions like that—he said, scooping up a handful of sand and tossing it to the brisk sea-breeze—Forget what you think about it and tell how you feel about it.—And then years later, when this same aspiring writer queried Crane whether he would now revise the advice he had given him that day on the beach, Crane said emphatically—No. You've got to feel the things you write if you want to make an impact on the world.[8]

And so, "to make an impact on the world," he studied the demi-world of New York: he spent several nights in a Mills Hotel "in search of material." His training as a newspaper reporter accounts in part for the theory he believed in. Such contacts with life set him apart from William Dean Howells. The very places Crane went slumming in—Bowery saloons, flophouses, and police stations—Howells prudishly avoided even when he was a reporter: "abhorrent contacts" he called them (in *Years of My Youth*).[9] At the other extreme was Jack London, who championed "the exalting of the life that is in me over Art, or any other extraneous thing." For Crane, on the contrary, life was but fuel for his kiln.

---

[8] Arthur Oliver quoting Crane in "Jersey Memories—Stephen Crane," *New Jersey Historical Society*, 16 (1931), 454–5, 460.

[9] As Van Wyck Brooks mentions in *A Chilmark Miscellany* (1949), pp. 236–7, Howells had "a morbid horror of the sordid and ugly; and this squeamishness had grown on the tender-minded Howells with his life in Venice and later in Cambridge and Boston."

Crane's infrequent comments on art amount to no more than the standard of *truth and sincerity* that Conrad and Henry James and Howells promulgated. Truth is the sum of James's critical theory; fidelity is the chief tenet in Conrad's code of the artist. Their art, however, always was several jumps ahead of their theory, and contradicted it. They are not realists. Their art does not copy reality; it is impressionistic and symbolic. "Realism" to Howells and Henry James and Conrad meant truth and fidelity to the facts of experience, and almost everything that Crane wrote was motivated by this principle. It was an ethical-and-æsthetic principle, and Howells had announced it in his 1891 volume, *Criticism and Fiction*:

> I confess that I do not care to judge any work of the imagination without first of all applying this test to it. We must ask ourselves before we ask anything else, Is it true?—true to the motives, the impulses, the principles that shape the life of actual men and women? This truth, which necessarily includes the highest morality and the highest artistry—this truth given, the book cannot be wicked and cannot be weak; and without it all graces of style and feats of invention and cunning of construction are so many superfluities of naughtiness. . . . In the whole range of fiction I know of no true picture of life—that is, of human nature—which is not also a masterpiece of literature, full of divine and natural beauty. (P. 241.)

Art, said Garland in *Crumbling Idols*, is an individual thing. It's a question of "one man facing certain facts and telling his individual relations to them." It is a question of conscience, of artistic integrity. You will find Conrad and Henry James dealing with this theme not only in their prefaces, but also in their fiction. The artist must create his vision with the utmost fidelity to what Conrad called "the image of truth abiding in facts" (*Life and Letters*, I, 280). Crane expressed the same conviction: "To keep close to my honesty is my supreme ambition. . . . This aim in life struck me as being the only thing worth while. A man is sure to fail at it, but there is something in the failure." Again: "a man is born into the world with his

own pair of eyes and he is not at all responsible for his vision—
he is merely responsible for his quality of personal honesty." [1]
That, too, rings with Howells's voice. Writing is a test of moral
courage, he told Crane. "A writer of skill cannot be defeated
because he remains true to his conscience." In Lowell's remark to Howells, Hawthorne comes to mind: "After all, the
barriers are very thin. They are paper. If a man has his conscience and one or two friends who can help him, it becomes
very simple at last." Crane had plenty of friends, and they all
believed in his genius. Genius for Crane amounted to *inspiration* ("I write what is in me"), and *truth* to life and *honesty* of
conscience or *sincerity* of purpose.

The one thing that deeply pleases me in my literary life [he wrote
an editor-friend after the publication of his *Red Badge of Courage*]
—brief and inglorious as it is—is the fact that men of sense believe
me to be sincere. "Maggie," published in paper covers, made me the
friendship of Hamlin Garland and W. D. Howells, and the one
thing that makes my life worth living in the midst of all this abuse
and ridicule is the consciousness that never for an instant have those
friendships at all diminished. Personally I am aware that my work
does not amount to a string of dried beans—I always calmly admit
it. But I also know that I do the best that is in me, without regard
to cheers or damnation. [Letter to O'Connor, written 1898?]

Sincerity was Garland's idol, and truth and beauty were
somehow one. "If we insist on sincerity, the question of dignity will take care of itself. Truth is a fine preparation for dignity, and for beauty as well" (*Idols*, p. 35). So Zola seemed to
Crane "a sincere writer" and Stevenson "insincere." And that
was that. Purely subjective criteria. But then, Crane was not
a critic and did not profess to be. "My judgment in the case
is not worth burning straw," Crane once wrote, "but I give it
as portentously as if kingdoms toppled while awaiting it under

---

[1] Letter to Joseph O'Connor, literary editor of the *Rochester Post-
Express*, published in the *Post-Express* April 18, 1900. Reprinted in "Some
Letters of Stephen Crane," *New York Times, Supplement*, July 14, 1900,
and in the *Academy*, August 11, 1900, p. 116.

anxious skies." [2] Crane was even less of a critic than myself, said Conrad. "Criticism is very much a matter of vocabulary very consciously used; with us it was the intonation that mattered. The tone of a grunt could convey an infinity of meaning between us." Once in a while, however, Crane got off some good grunts. Of Stevenson, whom he parodied in *The O'Ruddy,* he exclaimed to Ford Madox Ford: "By God! when Stevenson wrote 'With interjected finger he *delayed* the action of the *timepiece,*' meaning [as Ford explains it] 'he put the clock back,' Stevenson put back the clock of English fiction one hundred and fifty years!" Crane was conceited by streaks, more often modest than not, and quite unpredictable.

From Howells and Garland, Crane received not only personal encouragement and public praise, but also a creed to go by. Garland as a young man making his first visit to the East had been befriended by Howells and, in turn, he became Crane's greatest benefactor. The copy of *Maggie* that Garland sent Howells went unread until Crane wrote him "a heart-breaking note to the effect that he saw I didn't care for his book. On this I read it, and found I did care for it immensely." [3] He was enough impressed so that in the *New York Press* (April 15, 1894) "The Greatest Living American Writer" called it "a remarkable book. There is so much realism of a certain kind in it that unfits it for general reading, but once in a while it will do to tell the truth as completely as Maggie does."

Garland's 1893 review of *Maggie*—of immense value to Crane because it was his first—applauded the author for writing about *the life he had lived* and for writing about it *truthfully,* not mincingly as others had done. In *Maggie* and *George's Mother* Crane had already written the novel Howells was asking for: the novel of social and moral intent which adjusts "perspectives" by portraying—in Emerson's words—

---

[2] Quoted by Beer in his Introduction to Vol. VII of the *Work,* p. xiv.

[3] Letter from Howells to Mrs. Stephen Crane, in the *Academy,* 59 (August 1900), 123.

not "the great, the remote, the romantic," but "the familiar and
the low." (Emerson, implicit in Howells's creed, is traceable
throughout much of Crane's writings.) "I had no other purpose
in writing *Maggie* than to show people as they seem to me.
If that be evil, make the most of it." [4] *Maggie* was "evil" because it exposed—without the custom-built moralizing of the
contemporary novel—what it was forbidden to expose. Howells, as Crane quoted him in the *Times*, said that "a novel
should never preach and berate and storm." Crane said the
same thing a few years later:

Preaching is fatal to art in literature. I try to give to readers a slice
out of life; and, if there is any moral lesson in it, I do not try to
point it out. I let the reader find it for himself.[5]

And then (echoing Howells) he added: "As Emerson said,
'there should be a long logic beneath the story, but it should
be carefully kept out of sight.'" Howells's insistence that "A
man should mean something when he writes" is echoed in
Crane's insistence of May 1895 about *The Black Riders*: "But
I meant what I said." In *Maggie* he meant what he said, and
what he meant was "to show that environment is a tremendous
thing in this world, and often shapes lives regardlessly."

Howells was not shocked by *Maggie* (it shocked Richard
Watson Gilder, who rejected it for the *Century*), but he
thought its realism too realistic and he advised the young man
to remove the profanities, "which I thought would shock the
public." Howells was often squeamish about getting the whole
truth—"perhaps it is better not to recognize the facts." De Forest's novels were too grim, and Howells shuddered. The
realism he got in Crane and Frank Norris was more than he
had bargained for. His own brand, the "romance of the commonplace," seemed to the new century all too namby-pamby,
"kittenish" (as Mencken calls it). And Garland, finding Crane's

---

[4] Letter to Catherine Harris dated November 12, 1896. Quoted in
Beer, pp. 312–13.
[5] Letter to John N. Hilliard (1897).

philosophy too pessimistic ("a realist or verist is really an optimist"), cooled off. What he wrote after 1900 was not inspired by the program of realism he had formerly professed.

Crane did not start out as a writer in the Howells-Garland camp, and during his career he changed styles several times. *The Monster* is not in the style of *The Open Boat* nor the style of *The Sullivan County Sketches*. The first change came in 1892, shortly after he completed *The Sullivan County Sketches* ("How I wish I had dropped them into the wastebasket!"). It began when he suddenly "renounced the clever school in literature":

You know [he wrote to Lily Brandon on February 20, 1896] when I left you [1892, autumn], I renounced the clever school in literature. It seemed to me that there must be something more in life than to sit and cudgel one's brains for clever and witty expedients. So I developed all alone a little creed of art which I thought was a good one. Later I discovered that my creed was *identical* [italics mine] with the one of Howells and Garland and in this way I became involved in the beautiful war between those who say that art is man's substitute for nature and we are the most successful in art when we approach the nearest to nature and truth, and those who say—well, I don't know what they say . . . they fight villianously and keep Garland and I out of the big magazines. Howells, of course, is too powerful for them.

If I had kept to my clever Rudyard-Kipling style, the road might have been shorter but, ah, it wouldn't be the true road. The two years of fighting have been well-spent. And now I am almost at the end of it. This winter fixes me firmly. We have proved too formidable for them, confound them.[6]

Crane says that he "developed all alone a little creed of art," but it is more than probable that he knew Howells's *Criticism and Fiction* some time after its publication in 1891. His acknowledgment to Howells for his "re-adjustment" in critical outlook is not made in this letter, but it is made in his inscrip-

---

[6] Quoted in Melvin Schoberlin's Introduction to *The Sullivan County Sketches* (Syracuse University Press, 1950), p. 19. Reproduced here by permission of the Syracuse University Library and Melvin Schoberlin.

tion written in a presentation copy of *Maggie*: "as a token of
the veneration and gratitude of Stephen Crane for many things
he has learned of the common man and, above all, for a certain re-adjustment of his point of view victoriously concluded
some time in 1892." Crane was very much in Howells's debt.
The resemblance between his creed and Howells's has been
denied by Crane's latest biographer (cf. John Berryman's
Stephen Crane, p. 54), but Crane's confession of faith—"identical"—pins it down. The creeds of Crane and Howells *are*
identical, both in social philosophy and in æsthetic principle.

4

What makes Crane of such exceptional critical interest is the
great range and number of comparisons with other artists,
echoes, and parallelisms that suggest themselves to any critic
who has studied the man and his art. The range of cross-
references extends from Flaubert and Hawthorne to Mark
Twain and Rudyard Kipling, or—in terms of his influence on
twentieth-century fiction—beyond his contemporaries Frank
Norris and Theodore Dreiser to Dos Passos and Hemingway.
While Crane's influence can be documented by a formidable
catalogue of specific echoes in later American fiction, it per-
sists more significantly in less subtilized form—that is, his nat-
uralistic outlook in modern novels of slum life, his concept of
the soldier as Everyman in modern novels of war. Maggie's
brother (as other critics have pointed out) is a forebear of
Studs Lonigan, and Crane in several of his stories (*An Episode
of War* is one example) foremirrors Hemingway. Modern
American literature has its beginnings in Mark Twain and
Stephen Crane. Crane in his use of dialect and in his stories
of childhood links with Twain, Kipling, and Booth Tarkington. Crane's own Tom Sawyer is Jimmie Trescott (in *Making
an Orator*), and his *Sullivan County Sketches* and *Whilomville Stories* had their inspirational source in Twain's *Roughing It* and *Life on the Mississippi* (Crane's favorite book).
More important is the kinship they establish in the history of

American literature: they each brought new subject-matter
into fiction and perfected the techniques for manipulating it.
Technically, *The Red Badge of Courage* stands in legitimate
comparison with *Huckleberry Finn*. They have the same form
—namely, repetitions of ironic episodes—and they deal with
heroes in quest of selfhood. In *Huckleberry Finn* every episode
is built upon the themes of death and deception or betrayal,
and the same themes or leitmotivs are central in *The Red
Badge*.

The numerous artists who collect or radiate around Crane
form, as it were, a literary cartwheel. The spokes that com-
pose it include: the legendary Poe and Robert Louis Stevenson, the adventurer and sketch-writer Robert Cunninghame
Graham, the realists Howells and Garland, the naturalists
Norris and Dreiser, the impressionists Chekhov and Katherine
Mansfield and Conrad and Henry James, and the writers
on warfare, including Tolstoy, Zola, Ambrose Bierce, J. W.
De Forest, Rudyard Kipling, and Henri Barbusse. Kipling's
war tales and poems paved the way for Crane's *Red Badge*;
his soldier hero, as British reviewers detected, seemed not
unrelated to Tommy Atkins. Crane's earliest style was Kipling-
esque, as in some of *The Sullivan County Sketches* (for example, *Killing His Bear*), and something of Kipling's influence infected certain later pieces such as *The Quest for Virtue*,
God Rest Ye, Merry Gentlemen, and *Kim Up!*—one of his very
last tales. Kipling's subject is similar to Crane's and Conrad's.
The key to the whole work of Kipling, as Edmund Wilson defines it, is that "the great celebrant of physical courage should
prove in the long run to convey his most moving and convincing effects in describing moral panic." Kipling was one of the
three or four influences that Crane admitted, though not always publicly. "If I had kept to my clever Rudyard-Kipling
style, the road might have been shorter but, ah, it wouldn't
be the true road." Kipling's ballads, read to Crane by Irving
Bacheller, brought forth a burst of excitement. Chance made
their careers run similarly too. Both became celebrities while

still youths: Kipling in 1887, when he was twenty-two, and
Crane—"a sort of American Kipling"—when twenty-four. Both
had been journalists before becoming authors, and both
wrote about warfare they had never seen. By further coincidence, their greatest recognition came only after their books
had reached England, and both suffered their greatest abuse
here in America—Kipling, hurt and bewildered, fled from Vermont. Kipling might have expressed the same sad and bitter
note that Crane felt, the same lament:

Now that I have reached the goal [he wrote in a letter from
England three years before he died] I suppose that I ought to be
contented; but I am not. I was happier in the old days when I was
always dreaming of the thing I have now attained. I am disappointed with success, and I am tired of abuse. Over here, happily,
they don't treat you as if you were a dog, but give everyone an
honest measure of praise or blame. There are no disgusting personalities.[7]

It was Conrad who first identified similarities between
Crane's artistic temperament and his own and who first identified *The Red Badge of Courage,* with its psychological inquiry into the moral problem of conduct, with his own *Nigger
of the "Narcissus."* (Crane's enthusiasm for this story led him
to seek out Conrad in England and thereby become his friend
and later his neighbor.) Conrad might have noted further
similarities had he known Crane's *An Experiment in Misery*
and *Maggie,* for the short story carries the Conradian theme
of Solidarity (the theme also of *The Open Boat*), and *Maggie*
the Conradian theme of Fidelity—*Maggie* being a study in in-
fidelity or betrayal. Crane and Conrad are closely akin not
only in temperament, but also in artistic code and in thematic
range and ironic outlook or tone. Both treat the subject of
heroism ironically and both contrive for their heroes, usually
weak or defeated men, unequal contests against outside forces,

---

[7] Letter to John N. Hilliard, reprinted from the *New York Times,
Supplement,* July 14, 1900, p. 466.

pitting them against the sublime obstacles of hostile or indifferent nature. *The Open Boat* epitomizes this subject for
Crane, *Typhoon* for Conrad.

The Red Badge of Courage is readily identifiable with *Lord
Jim*, but their differences are, I think, more instructive.
Whereas Lord Jim has an innate capacity for heroism, Henry
Fleming has it thrust upon him by chance and at the wrong
moment. For Crane, as *The End of the Battle* testifies, heroism
is not a predictable possession, but an impersonal gift thrust
upon man with ironic consequences. The whole intention of
his fable *A Mystery of Heroism* is to explode the myth of
heroism. The soldier Collins does a heroic deed, but, as in
Kipling, it is "the heroism of moral fortitude on the edge of
a nervous collapse." Collins runs under shellfire to get water
at a well and once there he is a hero, "an intruder in the land
of fine deeds," but once there the poor hero is cut off (both
literally and symbolically) from his fellow men, and the empti-
ness of his vainglorious triumph is symbolized by the bucket
from which the wasted water spills as he nervously makes his
way back to the men. Crane's characters are always common,
insignificant, and virtually nameless persons; no Crane character is heroic, none is a leader, none is an ideal. When compared
with Conrad's, Crane's concept of man's nature seems shallow.
It is neither penetrating nor magnanimous.

5

Crane stands in close kinship to Conrad and Henry James,
the masters of the impressionist school. Edward Garnett, in
1898, hailed Crane as "the chief impressionist of the age,"
adding that "Mr. Crane's talent is unique." All three aimed
to create (to use Henry James's phrase) "a direct impression
of life." Their credo is voiced by Conrad in his celebrated
Preface to *The Nigger of the "Narcissus"*—it is "by the power
of the written word, to make you hear, to make you feel—it is,
before all, to make you *see*." Their aim was to immerse the
reader in the created experience so that its impact on him

would occur simultaneously with the discovery of it by the characters themselves. Instead of panoramic views of a battle-field, Crane paints not the whole scene but disconnected seg-ments of it, all that a participant in an action or a spectator of a scene can possibly take into his view at any one moment. Crane is a master at creating illusions of reality by means of a fixed point of vision, through a specifically located observer.

From their position as they again faced toward the place of fighting, they could of course comprehend a greater amount of battle than when their visions had been blurred by the hurling smoke of the line. They could see dark stretches winding along the land, and on one cleared space there was a row of guns making gray clouds, which were filled with large flashes of orange-colored flame (*The Red Badge of Courage*, p. 333).

"None of them knew the colour of the sky"—that famous opening sentence of *The Open Boat* defines the restricted point of view of the four men in the wave-tossed dinghy, their line of vision being shut off by the menacing walls of angry water. Busy at the oars, they knew the color of the sky only by the color of the sea, and "they knew it was broad day because the colour of the sea changed from slate to emerald-green, streaked with amber lights, and the foam was like tumbling snow." Everything is keyed in a state of tension—even their speech, which is abrupt and composed of "disjointed sentences." Crane's style is itself composed of disjointed sentences, dis-connected sense-impressions, chromatic vignettes by which the reality of the adventure is evoked in all its point-present immediacy.

Crane's style has been likened to a unique instrument that no one after his death has ever been able to play. *The Red Badge of Courage* seems unprecedented and non-comparable. But Chekhov, who was almost of an age with Crane, and a little later Katherine Mansfield, who adopted the method of Chekhov, were both masters of the same instrument. In its episodic structure and impressionistic style Chekhov's *The*

Cherry Orchard suggests a parallel to *The Red Badge of Courage*. All three artists had essentially the same literary aim and method: intensity of vision, objectivity in rendering it. All three aimed at a depersonalization of art: they aimed to get outside themselves completely in order "to find the greatest truth of the idea" and "see the thing as it really is"; to keep themselves aloof from their characters, not to become emotionally involved with their subjects, and to comment on them not by statement, but by evocation in picture and tone. "Sentiment is the devil," said Crane (and in this he echoed Flaubert).

A great stylist, Crane puts language to poetic uses, which is to use it reflexively and symbolically. *The works that employ this reflexive and symbolic language constitute what is permanent of Crane.*

Crane's language is the language of symbol and paradox: the wafer-like sun in *The Red Badge*; or in *The Open Boat* the paradox of "cold, comfortable sea-water," an image that calls to mind the poetry of Yeats, with its fusion of contradictory emotions. This single image evokes the sensation of the whole experience of the men in the dinghy, but it suggests furthermore another telltale significance, one applicable to Stephen Crane. What is readily recognizable in this paradox of "cold, comfortable sea-water" is that irony of opposites which constituted the personality of the man who wrote it. It is the subjective correlative of his own plight. The enigma of the man is symbolized by his enigmatic style.[8]

---

[8] Portions of this Introduction first appeared in the Introduction to the Modern Library edition of *The Red Badge of Courage*, copyright 1951 by Random House, Inc., and used here by courtesy of Random House, Inc.

PART I

Bowery Tales

INTRODUCTION

CRANE was born with printer's ink in his veins: both his parents were writers and two of his brothers were newspaper reporters. His ancestry comprised clergymen and soldiers, and his literary work (as Clarence Peaslee first pointed out) shows the hereditary influence of these two professions: "the one furnishing the basis of style, the other of incident." [1] At school Crane took a course in the Bible, but homework for that course must have come easy for him, as his father was pastor of the Methodist church and his mother, a newspaper reporter on church affairs and lecturer on Temperance and Woman's Rights, was the daughter of Reverend George Peck, at one time editor of the *Christian Advocate* (the official organ of the Methodist Episcopal Church), and the niece of Bishop Jesse Peck, one of the founders of Syracuse University. His father, editor of various church periodicals, was a learned divine and "a writer of rare ability, adorning his discourses with a style of rich beauty." Stephen got from his parents not only a natural bent for writing but a marked predilection for casting his ideas, incidents, and sometimes even his style in Biblical form. Several of his parable poems deal with Christ; *The Red Badge of Courage* is shot through with religious symbolism; and scriptural allusion and metaphor occur in *Maggie, George's Mother, An Experiment in Misery,* and *The Open Boat.* The only thing he found to praise in a story sent him by a young writer for his criticism was its religious motif, and he singled it out—"You will never hold the cross toward me"—with the comment: "That, I think is very effective." [2] Another woman once asked him what Hamlin Garland looked like, and his answer was: "Oh, like a nice Jesus Christ."

---

[1] "Stephen Crane's College Days," *Monthly Illustrator,* 13 (1895–7), 27–30.

[2] See letter to Miss Walker, pp. 653–4.

Crane's father was a noted wit, and the comic characterizes much of Crane's writings. Reverend Jonathan Townley Crane had such a sense of humor that his congregation proposed to publish a book of his witticisms. Stephen wrote stories when but eight years old; at sixteen he was doing newspaper reporting for his mother's column in the *New York Tribune*, ghostwriting for his elder brother, Townley, the *Tribune*'s New Jersey correspondent, and sometimes writing up stuff for his brother Wilbur, also with the *Tribune*. Crane was born, so to speak, on Park Row.

For three summers (1888–90) Townley, in charge of a news bureau for several newspapers, had Stephen write up "Shore News" about resorts along the New Jersey coast, collecting space-rate for it as though it were his own. In the spring of 1891—Stephen was then a freshman at Syracuse University—he was hired by Willis Johnson as city correspondent for the *Tribune*. He had spent the fall term at Lafayette College, but he preferred baseball to mining-engineering, and in theme-writing he got zero; so he transferred in January to Syracuse University and arrived at the Delta Upsilon Fraternity "in a cab and a cloud of tobacco smoke." Here, too, he lasted just one term.[3] Athletic but also literary, an omnivorous reader, he used to retreat to the cupola of the chapter house and, smoking his prized water-pipe, read or write sketches.[4] The most important thing that happened to him at the university was his writing a story about a streetwalker.

Crane got his "artistic education" (as he put it) on the Bowery. But at nineteen when he wrote this draft of what was

---

[3] See letter p. 627.

[4] Crane is reported to have placed some of these sketches in the *Detroit Free Press*, but neither these sketches nor the "first fiction" Crane said he wrote for the *Tribune* at eighteen have ever been traced. The only known piece published under Crane's name before 1892 was a story called *The King's Favor*, which appeared in the Syracuse *University Herald* in May 1891. His first appearance in a professional magazine was in *Cosmopolitan Magazine* with *A Tent in Agony*, published in December 1892. Five of his Sullivan County sketches were published in the *Tribune* during the summer of this year.

to become *Maggie: A Girl of the Streets,* he knew very little about the Bowery, slum life, and prostitutes. *Maggie,* it has always been taken for granted (by Hitchcock, Starrett, and others), is a record of what Crane observed as a newspaper reporter in New York. But he was not a New York reporter until 1892, and he had already written his study of slum life months before exploring the scene of his novel. Garland in his *Arena* review said "it is written by one who has lived the life. The young author . . . has grown up in the very scenes he describes." But that is inaccurately put, for *Maggie* was composed before personal experience. So too with *George's Mother* and *The Red Badge of Courage*: after he invented them he tested them for their truth to life and injected into their plots some personal episodes experienced during the progress of composition. "The vaunted Crane realism," as Harvey Wickham pointed out, "was never of the photographic sort. Thus the only incident which really happened [in *George's Mother*] was George's amazing lunch—a charlotte russe and a beer." George and his mother were drawn from two relatives of Wickham, "Crane transposing them to the slums, preserving only the characters—a plausible and worthless young man with an indulgent and credulous parent." Wickham's relative, whose real name was Frank, actually gave "George's lunch," and Crane watched him consume it in a Fourteenth Street resort opposite Tammany Hall.[5] Disputing Beer's opinion that Crane had invented the plot of *Maggie,* Frederic Lawrence (in a letter written in 1923) claimed that both *Maggie* and *George's Mother* were drawn "from our own observations and adventures." Crane of course knew the Bowery intimately and had considerable experiences with prostitutes, but not until he had written one or two drafts of *Maggie.*

Robert Davis has described for us one of Crane's encounters

---

[5] "Stephen Crane at College," *American Mercury,* 7 (March 1926), 291–7. Wickham, a college friend of Crane, corrects Beer in this article. Beer had suggested (1923) that the characters in *George's Mother* were nothing more than a coarsened Stephen Crane and his mother.

with Bowery streetwalkers: a girl they met one night was asked by Crane, when he spotted her as she crossed the street: "A stranger here?"

—Well, suppose I am a stranger. Can you show me anything?—
—Yes—replied the author of *Maggie*.—I can show you the way out, but if you prefer to remain—Crane made another gesture with his felt hat and bowed with an air of magnificent finality.

The girl suddenly found an extra button at the throat of her coat and fastened herself in. The light seemed to go out of Stephen Crane's eyes as though some one had turned down a lamp from within.

—You shouldn't hang out here, kid—said Maggie in a throaty voice.—You look cold. You can't stand it. This fat guy can.—[6]

It looks like an episode right out of his own book!

It is impossible to say where Crane got the stuff and craft of *Maggie*. Either he invented the plot or he took it from Zola's *L'Assommoir*. It is not certain, however that he read that book. Crane said he began *Maggie* at twenty and "finished it when I was somewhat beyond 21." He also said he wrote it "in two days before Christmas," and his niece reports that he wrote it "at our house in two or three nights." According to Berryman, Crane had "unconscious aggressions" to discharge against his mother and so he chose "the subject of *Maggie*, his first work, following immediately upon his mother's death," and he represented his mother there as Maggie, a fallen woman. But the facts inconvenience that theory, for *Maggie* was conceived as early as April or May 1891, months before his mother died (December 7). The draft Crane wrote "in two days before Christmas" was a second draft. "One day in the summer of 1891," says Willis Johnson (day editor of the *Tribune* and a friend of the Crane family), "he brought me a big bundle of manuscript, and asked me to read it and tell him what to do with it. I found it to be not a Sullivan County sketch, but a tale of the slums of New York, the first draft of

---

[6] *Work*, II, xviii–xix.

Maggie: A Girl of the Streets." Johnson was impressed by Crane's "mastery of the speech and manners of the denizens of the New York slums, *although he had spent little time in that city and had enjoyed little opportunity for observation of its ways.*" [7] As Crane made trips to New York from his brother's place at Lake View that fall and explored the Bowery with his friend Wallis McHarg in January, Johnson must be correct in saying that he first saw the manuscript—at least some fragment of the novel—in the summer of 1891. Frank Noxon testifies that Crane's fraternity brothers at Syracuse saw the manuscript. Crane wrote this first draft of *Maggie* at the Delta Upsilon house. Sheets of it, carelessly left scattered about his front-corner room, were "picked up and read by droppers-in." [8] His fraternity brothers, says Clarence Peaslee, advised him about the plot of *Maggie*. He told them about it, "putting it in various lights and constructions, and then asking which was more effective."

After writing a story—another friend, R. G. Vosburgh, tells us—he would put it away for two or three weeks, and work on something else until his mind was thoroughly clear for a fresh consideration of it. When the story was taken out for revision it would be turned over to his friends for criticism, and Crane would argue with them about the objections they would make. He often accepted suggestions for changes but it always seemed as though these changes were those he had already decided upon himself before they were mentioned by others. This was also characteristic of the discussions of *The Red Badge of Courage*. He convinced himself; others might help him, but he arrived at his own conclusions. [9]

That summer, and again in 1892, Crane beachcombed Asbury Park for the *Tribune*. Early in 1892 he worked for the

[7] "The Launching of Stephen Crane," *Literary Digest International Book Review*, 4 (April 1926), 289.

[8] "The Real Stephen Crane," *Step Ladder* [Chicago], 14 (January 1928), 4–9.

[9] "The Darkest Hour in the Life of Stephen Crane," *Book Lover*, 2 (Summer 1901), 339. For further discussion of Crane's creative process see my Introductions, pp. xxvii–xxxiii and *passim*; 203–13, 217–24.

Herald, but he was fired in February, and in August the *Trib-une* fired him and Townley for an article in his brother's column ("On the New Jersey Coast") which gave offense not only to *Tribune* readers, but also to its owner and editor, Whitelaw Reid, then running for the vice-presidency of the United States. It jeopardized the election of his boss. Visiting Hamlin Garland a few days after the Sunday it appeared (August 21), Crane told him he had lost his job. "You see, I made a report of a labor parade the other day, which slipped in over the managing editor's fence." The paraders of the Junior Order of United American Mechanics were insulted by the *Tribune's* corrosive account: "probably . . . the most awkward, ungainly, uncut and uncarved procession that ever raised clouds of dust on sun-beaten streets." The throng that watched them march got ridiculed too, and even the town: "Asbury Park creates nothing. It does not make; it merely amuses." Crane's article was not calculated to please either the marchers or their employers, and if the marchers thought there was some praise for them ("The visitors were men who possessed principles"), that was only because they were not used to finding irony in a newspaper column.

It belonged in the novel this bright college boy was writing, but as a budding journalist the ironic was quite misplaced. So, too, was his contempt of these galley-slaves of capitalistic oppressors: "They merely plodded along, not seeming quite to understand, stolid, unconcerned and, in a certain sense, dignified—a pace and a bearing emblematic of their lives. [Crane had a symbolic bent even here!] They smiled occasionally and from time to time greeted friends in the crowd on the sidewalk. Such an assemblage of the spraddle-legged men of the middle class, whose hands were bent and shoulders stooped from delving and construction, had never appeared to an Asbury Park summer crowd, and the latter was vaguely amused." But not Crane. Garland asked him what he expected by writing such a thing, and Crane smiled with bitter reflection—"I was so hot at the sight of those poor misshapen fools shouting

for monopoly that I gave no thought to its effect upon my own
master. I don't know that it would have made much difference
if I had. I wanted to say those things anyway." (Crane's picture of the Asbury Park parade seems echoed in his description
of the workingmen in episode 7 of *Maggie*.) The *Tribune* got
a telegram from the United American Mechanics informing
Reid that his newspaper had better eat its words or he had
better retire as candidate. "You'd hardly think," Crane told
Arthur Oliver, "a little innocent chap like me could have stirred
up such a row in American politics. It shows what innocence
can do if it has the opportunity!" [1] "What innocence can do"
is the crux of *The Bride Comes to Yellow Sky*; what innocence
must do is the crux of *The Red Badge of Courage*. Innocence
thwarted and betrayed by environment is the sum of *Maggie*.
Innocence debased and deluded is *George's Mother*.

So Crane got a theme for fiction out of this experience. It
was the turning-point in his career, Willis Johnson thought,
for it was he who advised Crane to give up newspaper work,
not to waste his talent competing with penny-a-liners. It would
have been the turning-point had Crane taken Johnson's advice.
But the typesetting rooms where Crane had spent much of his
spare time as an undergraduate had inspired him to become a
journalist, and he was determined to stick to that profession.
"I could never do what I didn't feel like doing—not even writing," he told a friend, "but as I felt more often and more intensely like writing than anything else, I thought I'd better
try newspaper work." [2] William Dean Howells, beginning like
Crane as a typesetter, turned his back on journalism; but Crane
wanted to study "unvarnished" human nature and he liked to
experience things and not just write about them, and so he became a space-paid reporter rambling through the Bowery and
trudging from one editor's office to another trying to place an

---

[1] In "Jersey Memories—Stephen Crane," *New Jersey Historical Society
Proceedings*, 16 (1931), 459–60. The quotation preceding this one is
taken from "Stephen Crane, ex-'94," by M. Ellwood Smith, in the
Syracusan, 10 (December 1, 1917), 4.

[2] Reginald Kauffman in *Modern Culture*, October 1900, pp. 143–5.

occasional article at five dollars a column. One of the editors who hired him (Ed Marshall, later famous as a war correspondent in Cuba) said that Crane's article on tenement-house fire panics "was one of the best things that he or any other man ever did." Crane himself thought that some of his short sketches of New York city street life were among his best things, and he intended to have them published "in book form under the title 'Midnight Sketches.'" (They were collected, most of them, under that title in Vol. XI of the collected *Work.*) Some of these sketches perished beneath the scissors of Crane's editors. There was one called "Sixth Avenue" which would have provoked libel from advertisers in the *New York Press,* and after Curtis Brown crossed out the offending phrases, another editor threw it away as not exciting enough (*Contacts,* page 260). In the spring of 1893, at the time of beginning *The Red Badge of Courage,* he wrote sketches of East Side children (one of these was *An Ominous Baby*), but he could not sell them until the next year. Neither could he sell *The Reluctant Voyagers* and *The Pace of Youth* when they were written. Through Garland he got a commission from the Wilson Newspaper Syndicate to write a story about New York lodging-houses, and so Crane and one of his artist friends spent a night and two days (according to Vosburgh) as tramps on the Bowery. Seen there in March, he was pointed out as an eccentric wasting his time in Bowery dives, the outcast son of an Episcopal minister.

But the outcast in *An Experiment in Misery* is not Stephen Crane. "Mrs. Howells was right," Crane wrote in 1896, replying to Miss Catherine Harris's letter about *Maggie,* "in telling you that I have spent a great deal of time on the East Side and that I have no opinion of missions. . . . In a story of mine called *An Experiment in Misery* I tried to make plain that the root of Bowery life is a sort of cowardice. Perhaps I mean a lack of ambition or to willingly be knocked flat and accept the licking." To the young man in the story the noise of the city was "the confusion of strange tongues, babbling heedlessly;

it was the clink of coin, the voice of the city's hopes, which were to him no hopes." Environment—"*unholy* atmospheres"—is the antagonist, but the young man does nothing to change it. In the flophouse the naked bums take "splendid poses, standing massively like chiefs."

An Experiment in Misery, like *Maggie,* combines irony and pity. There are tracings here of the same leitmotivs—"unholy atmospheres"—and the same imagery—"wreathed in a red grin" —that Crane reused in *The Red Badge of Courage,* and in touching upon the theme of solidarity *An Experiment in Misery* anticipates *The Open Boat.* But in this earlier piece Crane has not patterned the imagery or made it consistently metaphorical, and details that might have been converted to evoke symbolic overtones are wastefully misspent. The opinion that *An Experiment in Misery* is "far more important than the more famous and accessible *Red Badge of Courage* or such stories of mere physical accident as *The Open Boat,*" as Ludwig Lewisohn would have it, can be dismissed without further comment. (*The Monster,* another social study, has also received undeserved acclaim. I don't think it needs to be demonstrated that *The Monster* is not a unified structural whole.) *An Experiment in Misery,* as Edward Garnett aptly noted, reveals in its "nervous audacity of phrasing . . . the quality of chiaroscuro of a master's etching." That Crane had always been "an ardent admirer of fine paintings" (as a college friend mentions) is evident in his language, in the brush-strokes of his style. The subject of *George's Mother,* so the *Book Buyer* (1896) complained, "seems more suitable for drawing in shades of gray, while Mr. Crane's brushes are full of red and yellow paint." And *Maggie* shows the same "blinding glare of primary colors" as *The Red Badge of Courage,* "a panorama of illumination."

The Men in the Storm, written at the same time as *An Experiment in Misery* (March 1893?), is filled with "social calculation." Homeless wanderers, some down-and-outers and Bowery bums, stand in a blizzard at the closed doors of a charitable house. They are waiting (symbolically) for "the

open door"—for a social change. "Oh, let us in fer Gawd's
sake!" Across the street is a stout and well-clothed rich man,
with "a beard like the Prince of Wales. He stood in an attitude
of magnificent reflection. He slowly stroked his moustache
with a certain grandeur of manner, and looked down at the
snow-crusted mob." Crane here *evokes by picture* his criticism
of the rich. Flaubert's *Madame Bovary*, which Crane had no
doubt read, employs the same technique of submerged commentary: for example, the picture of the Comte de Vaubyes-
sard's ball (Chapter i, page viii). Similarly, at the end of the
story Crane's description of the blizzard is loaded with a
significance that is pictured, not stated: "The snow beat with
merciless persistence *upon the bowed heads of those who
waited.*" It is a snowstorm of social strife that beats down on
the men. "A street lamp on the curb *struggled to illuminate,*
but it was reduced to impotent blindness by the swift gusts of
sleet crusting its panes."

The Men in the Storm is a far more richly packed piece of
symbolism than *An Experiment in Misery*, but it is spoiled by
some passages of direct statement: "There were men of undoubted patience, industry, and temperance, who in time of
ill-fortune, do not habitually rail at the state of society, snarling at the arrogance of the rich, and bemoaning the cowardice
of the poor, but who at these times are apt to wear a sudden
and singular meekness, as if they saw the world's progress
marching from them, and were trying to perceive where they
had failed, what they lacked, to be thus vanquished in the
race." That is bad writing and bad artistry.

The *Press* printed *An Experiment in Misery* the next April,
and Garland mailed both *An Ominous Baby* and *The Men in
the Storm* to the *Arena* (published there in 1894) with a note
to the editor to be generous because "the author is hungry."
It was Garland who had suggested that Crane should study
East Side life. "I remember talking with him about 'the bread
lines,' which regularly formed each night at certain bakeries

which gave away their stale bread, and at my suggestion he went down one winter's evening [in a March blizzard, 1893], joined one of these lines, and made a study which he afterwards called *The Men in the Storm,* a fine sketch. . . . And yet in spite of my aid and these promising activities, he remained almost as needy as ever. Thin and seedy, he still slept on the floor—according to his own story, smoking incessantly and writing in any possible corner." Depressed, Crane soberly told Garland one day: "I'd trade my entire future for twenty-three dollars in cash." In 1896 Crane inscribed a copy of *George's Mother:* "To my friend Eddie in memory of our days of suffering and trouble. . . ."

Nothing Crane had written was published in 1893 except *Maggie.* Like Hawthorne's first novel, it was published at the author's expense (William Crane gave him one thousand dollars) and under an assumed name: "Johnston Smith." Crane first made it "Johnson Smith," these being the two most numerous names in the city directory, but finally inserted the "t" in the former name so that (as Crane whimsically explained it to Willis Johnson) "neither Mr. Podsnap nor Mrs. Grundy might suspect him of being the guilty author!" He planned to wait, so he told somebody else, "until all the world was pyrotechnic about Johnston Smith's *Maggie* and then I was going to flop down like a trapeze performer from the wire and, coming forward with all the modest grace of a consumptive nun, say, I am he, friends!" Beer, quoting this last, says that few of Crane's friends had read the manuscript. But the fact is that most of his friends had read it—Noxon and Peaslee, Harvey Wickham, Louis Senger and his cousin Linson in Crane's room, Corwin Linson in his studio, and others elsewhere. Garland, getting a copy of the paper-bound, mustard-colored pamphlet in his mail, immediately wrote to accuse Crane of being the author, and soon afterwards he came and "confessed his crime." The printer, too, played it safe. He refused his name to the book. It was too frank and might get him into trouble. The frightened printer probably made "about $700 out of me. . . . A firm of religious and medical printers did me the dirt." Ironically enough, it was a religious house. "Will made me get the thing copyrighted. I had not even that much sense." So he sent one dollar and a typewritten title-page to the Librarian of Congress on January 19, 1893, for copyrighting the as yet unpublished book. This title-page bore Crane's name but omitted "Maggie" from the title. It was William who had christened it a couple of months before (in November, says Beer): "Maggie: A Girl of the Streets." He had persuaded Stephen that characters in a novel ought to be given names. In revising *The Red Badge of Courage*, however, his procedure was just the reverse. While he followed his brother's advice during composition of the first drafts of *The Red Badge*, when he came to revise the final handwritten manuscript he recast the names of his soldiers and reduced them to anonymity.

Maggie was published this spring (1893), and Garland reviewed it in the June issue of the *Arena*. "The three months which have passed have been months of very hard work to S. Crane. . . . I wrote a book." So Crane informed Lily Brandon. Beginning *Maggie* at Syracuse and finishing it at Lake View in December 1891, he then revised it in March 1892, and then he recast it for the fourth time during the winter of 1892–3. On the 23rd of March he took the manuscript to Richard Watson Gilder, who thought *Maggie* too "cruel" for the *Century*. Johnson sent Crane to Ripley Hitchcock at Appleton and Co., who told Johnson: "That boy has the real stuff in him." He rejected *Maggie*, but accepted *The Red Badge of Courage* two years later and then, because that novel was a sensational success, he got Appleton to reissue *Maggie*; and so it appeared for the first time between hard covers in June 1896. An English edition of *George's Mother* appeared that same month, and later that year Heinemann published *Maggie* with "An Appreciation" by William Dean Howells. Crane, correcting the proofs and writing a preface for Appleton, asked Hitchcock to "watch for bad grammatical form and bad spelling. I am too jaded

with Maggie to be able to see it." But he "carefully plugged at
the words which hurt. Seems to me the book wears quite a
new aspect from very slight omissions. . . ."

2

George's Mother, not published until 1896 (issued one week
before *Maggie*), was begun in 1893 and completed late in
1894. Crane wrote Garland on November 15, 1894: "I have
just completed a New York book that leaves *Maggie* at the
post. It is my best thing. Since you are not here, I am going
to see if Mr. Howells will not read it." Howells, interviewed
by Crane for the *New York Times* in October 1894 ("Fears
Realists Must Wait"), must have had *George's Mother* in mind
when he said: "I like to see the novelists treating some of the
other important things of life—the relation of mother and
son. . . . The other [i.e., the relation of man to maid] can be
but fragmentary." Reviewing "New York Low Life in Fiction"
for the New York *World* two years later, he praised Crane's
honesty with the reader for what we would today call his
social realism: the pathos of the underprivileged "rendered
without one maudlin touch." Whereas *Maggie* is a full study,
George's Mother "is the study of a situation merely: a poor,
inadequate woman, of a commonplace religiosity, whose son
goes to the bad. The wonder of it is the courage which deals
with persons so absolutely average, and the art that graces
them with the beauty of the author's compassion for everything that errs and suffers."

George's Mother had its title changed several times after
Howells first saw the manuscript. It was "A Woman without
Weapons" when the *Bookman*, in May 1895, referred to it by
that title as one of Crane's manuscripts now in the publisher's
hands. Upon publication, *George's Mother* was reviewed by
Harry Thurston Peck in the *Bookman* for July, but he was no
more perceptive than Howells in seeing what the novel is
really about. He was right, however, in his conjecture about
the date of its composition: "from a consideration of the internal

evidence, we should say that its first draft must belong to the time when he wrote and published *Maggie*. Judged by the qualities of style and strength we should, in fact, pronounce it to be even earlier, and probably one of Mr. Crane's first attempts at serious composition; for it is altogether crude and unsatisfactory." Howells's verdict, made that same month in the New York *World*, placed *Maggie* and *George's Mother* above *The Red Badge of Courage*, and in *Harper's Magazine* almost two decades later he reckoned from his Editor's Easy Chair that *The Red Badge* was the best seller of its day "possibly because it was his worst book." It was Howells's critical creed that influenced Crane to reconstruct *Maggie*, an influence that he acknowledged—"a certain re-adjustment of his point of view victoriously concluded some time in 1892." It is not improbable that Howells's opinion of *The Red Badge* had something to do with Crane's own feelings about it: "People may just as well discover now that the high dramatic key of *The Red Badge* cannot be sustained. I don't think *The Red Badge* to be any great shakes but then the very theme of it gives it an intensity that a writer can't reach every day." Garland said the same thing, but he waited until Crane was dead and buried before he printed it—in the *Saturday Evening Post* for July 28, 1900.

Garland in the *Arena* (June 1893) thought that *Maggie* "fails of rounded completeness. It is only a fragment." But "It is the voice of the slums. . . . His book is the most truthful and unhackneyed study of the slums I have yet read, fragment though it is." And that was why he thought it important. "It is important because it voices the blind rebellion of Rum Alley and Devil's Row. It creates the atmosphere of the jungles, where vice festers and crime passes gloomily by, where outlawed human nature rebels against God and man." Rupert Hughes, in *Godey's Magazine* (October 1895), echoed Garland and argued that to write books that arouse "sympathy for the unfortunates who must fill the cellar of the tenement we call life . . . is far better even than to be artistic." Evidently the ladies of Port Jervis did not see it that way, for they didn't think it proper to permit Stephen Crane into their homes. (Beer, page 389). The latest opinion on *Maggie* (1951) is that it is "a short, murky novel." [3]

Howells, not agreeing with Garland in this, thought *Maggie* and *George's Mother* superior to *The Red Badge of Courage* "as pieces of art," and then, grounding his verdict on his own canon, added that "as representations of life their greater fidelity cannot be questioned." No wonder Crane felt obliged to test the imagined reality of *The Red Badge* by experiencing the real thing, as though *that* would prove its worth! Crane's social studies won Howells's praise because they squared with his creed. "Mr. Crane has the skill to show how evil is greatly the effect of ignorance and imperfect civilization." Present-day Marxian and sociological critics judge novels on the same ground: novels should deal with the fundamental realities of American life. In *The O'Ruddy* Crane, who began as a social critic, ended as a romanticist, and even as the realist of slum life he kept repeating himself. Two years before he died his coauthor for this last novel prophesied that Crane "was most likely to produce the great American novel" (Robert Barr in the *Bookman*, July 1900). Perhaps he had already written it. According to Ben Hecht, *Maggie* and *George's Mother* constitute "the great American novel."

3

All Crane stories end in irony. Some end in a minor note, like *Maggie* and *George's Mother*—"not with a bang but a whimper." Every Crane story worth mentioning is designed upon a single ironic incident, a crucial paradox or irony of opposites. All of them are built out of anecdotal material, and all are concerned with virtually the same problem—the moral problem of conduct. It is the same in Conrad. In method of construction, however, Crane's closer affinities are with Chekhov.

---

[3] John T. Winterich, Introduction to Folio Society edition of *The Red Badge of Courage*, p. 14.

They were among the first to eliminate plot. Crane constructs his stories, like Chekhov, by building up to a crucial moment of impasse and collapse. A Crane story consists of that moment when the characters confront the inescapable impasse of a situation by which they are boxed in, and then—the moment of spiritual collapse—"nothing happens," and they are left with a sense of loss or insignificance or defeat, futility or disillusionment.

Crane is a master of the contradictory effect. The scene of Maggie at the theater (episode number 8) epitomizes the design of the whole story: illusions and ideals shattered by realities. Crane's Maggie is a Bowery version of Flaubert's Emma Bovary. Maggie at the theater and Emma at the opera parallel each other in ironic intent and structural purpose. Not logic but mood defines the relationship between the various episodes of *Maggie*. *The Red Badge of Courage* and *The Open Boat*, like *Madame Bovary*, are constructed of alternating moods, each built-up mood of hope or illusion being canceled out by contradictory moods of futility, disillusionment, or despair. This method of the double mood was Flaubert's major technical innovation. It is the form of Joyce's *Portrait of the Artist as a Young Man* and of *Dubliners* (notably *The Dead*), and almost all of Katherine Mansfield's and Chekhov's short stories are in this form. It is the form of Melville's masterpiece, *Benito Cereno*, and of Hawthorne's Kafka-like parable, *My Kinsman, Major Molineux*. Crane constructs his stories to effect a single mood (*The Upturned Face* is one example), or by a series of moods with each unit composed of a contrast. *Maggie*, a sentimental melodrama that borders upon travesty, concludes with the orgy of melodramatic emotion which Maggie's mother gives vent to over the death of the daughter whom she has brutalized and driven into the streets. The final turnabout is a parody of pious sentiment—"Oh, yes, I'll fergive her! I'll fergive her!" The grotesque buffoonery of this mock lamentation is comic enough, but tragedy underlies it in the theme that all is sham, even between mother and daughter.

George Kelcey in *George's Mother* is his mother's ideal, and she is deluded. (It is significant that Crane at first called this novel "A Woman without Weapons.") Her whole life sacrificed to his well-being, she anticipates the time when her son shall become "a white and looming king among men." She worships him with all the devotion of a sweetheart, and with the blind devotion of a religious fanatic she dies still believing in him. Like Crane's own mother, Mrs. Kelcey is a member of the W.C.T.U. and is filled with religious zeal. Her great grief is that her son refuses to attend prayer-meetings. These conventicles are her shrine, and a "smiling saloon" is George's. Each one has found a place of refuge from the world's harsh realities, where the chosen few congregate and are saved. For George it is whisky that is prophetic. In a ritual of emptying and refilling of glasses, he holds communion with his coreligionists behind the closed doors of little back rooms at night. He partakes too much and loses his job as a consequence, whereupon his friends forsake him. Sometimes he dreams "of the indefinite woman and the fragrance of roses that came from her hair," but she too forsakes him. The forsaken mother, broken and deranged, is tormented by visions. "She was staring off at something sinister." The devils of sin she had warred against all her life have at last overpowered her. It is the demon world making final onslaught against that visionary hope she worshipped as her son. He too has been possessed and destroyed. She tried to save him, but when he entered the chapel that one time he resentfully consented to accompany her there, "he felt a sudden quaking. His knees shook. It was an awesome place to him." And in the chamber of death where his mother cries to him unheeded, there too he quakes, becoming so nervous "that he could not hear the chatter from the bed, but he was always conscious of the ticking of the little clock out on the kitchen shelf." The ticking clock signifies life dissipated and unconverted. It is "emblematic of the life of the city." City and church, George and his mother—they are counterparts.

The conflict between George and his mother is summed up in Crane's symbolic picture of city and church. The conflict between them (reality versus illusion) is symbolically pictured in Part XI:

In a dark street the little chapel sat humbly between two towering apartment-houses.

The city overpowers the church.

A red street-lamp stood in front. It threw a marvellous reflection upon the wet pavements. It was like the death-stain of a spirit.

The red street-lamp shines; the church is humble. George is "the death-stain of a spirit."

Farther up, the brilliant lights of an avenue made a span of gold across the black street. A roar of wheels and a clangour of bells came from this point, interwoven into a sound emblematic of the life of the city.

In Part XVII the ticking clock replaces the clangor of bells. George belongs to the noisy world of brilliant lights.

It seemed somehow to affront this solemn and austere little edifice. It suggested an approaching barbaric invasion. The little church, pierced, would die with a fine illimitable scorn for its slayers.

The little church signifies Christ—"pierced." George not only turns his back on the church but, ironically, immediately after experiencing it, goes to the Devil—and faster than ever before.[4]

---

[4] *George's Mother* was discussed in similar terms by the *Critic* in June 1896, and I have drawn some phrasings from this review and others, including the *Academy* and the *New York Press* reviews of the same year. Nothing has been written on *George's Mother* since then that even approximates exegesis, and no insight whatsoever is exhibited in what few commentaries Crane's critics have written about this work from 1896 to the present.

ON THE NEW JERSEY COAST.[1]

☼ ☼ ☼

Guests Continue to Arrive in Large Numbers.

Parades and Entertainments—Well-Known
People Who are Registered at the Various Hotels.

ASBURY PARK, N. J., Aug. 20 (Special).—The parade of the
Junior Order of United American Mechanics here on Wednesday afternoon was a deeply impressive one to some persons.
There were hundreds of the members of the order, and they
wound through the streets to the music of enough brass bands
to make furious discords. It probably was the most awkward,
ungainly, uncut and uncarved procession that ever raised
clouds of dust on sun-beaten streets. Nevertheless, the spectacle of an Asbury Park crowd confronting such an aggregation
was an interesting sight to a few people.

Asbury Park creates nothing. It does not make; it merely
amuses. There is a factory where nightshirts are manufactured,
but it is some miles from town. This is a resort of wealth and
leisure, of women and considerable wine. The throng along
the line of march was composed of summer gowns, lace para-
sols, tennis trousers, straw hats and indifferent smiles. The
procession was composed of men, bronzed, slope-shouldered,
uncouth and begrimed with dust. Their clothes fitted them

---

[1] Reprinted from the *New York Tribune*, August 21, 1892. Crane's
article was attacked in the *Asbury Park Journal* and in the *Daily Spray*,
where it was reprinted in full. It is reprinted in Melvin Schoberlin's Introduction to *The Sullivan County Sketches of Stephen Crane* (1949)
and discussed there in detail. Its first book appearance was in *The Public
Papers of a Bibliomaniac*, by Charles Honce (Golden Eagle Press, 1942).
Beer's account is corrected by Willis Fletcher Johnson in *Literary Digest
International Book Review*, 4 (April 1926), 290. See also Victor Elconin
in *American Literature*, 20 (November 1948), 275–90.

illy, for the most part, and they had no ideas of marching. They merely plodded along, not seeming quite to understand, stolid, unconcerned and, in a certain sense, dignified—a pace and a bearing emblematic of their lives. They smiled occasionally and from time to time greeted friends in the crowd on the sidewalk. Such an assemblage of the spraddle-legged men of the middle class, whose hands were bent and shoulders stooped from delving and constructing, had never appeared to an Asbury Park summer crowd, and the latter was vaguely amused.

The bona fide Asbury Parker is a man to whom a dollar, when held close to his eye, often shuts out any impression he may have had that other people possess rights. He is apt to consider that men and women, especially city men and women, were created to be mulcted by him. Hence the tan-colored, sun-beaten honesty in the faces of the members of the Junior Order of United American Mechanics is expected to have a very staggering effect upon them. The visitors were men who possessed principles. . . .

THE MEN IN THE STORM

THE BLIZZARD began to swirl great clouds of snow along the streets, sweeping it down from the roofs, and up from the pavements, until the faces of pedestrians tingled and burned as from a thousand needle-prickings. Those on the walks huddled their necks closely in the collars of their coats, and went along stooping like a race of aged people. The drivers of vehicles hurried their horses furiously on their way. They were made more cruel by the exposure of their position, aloft on high seats. The street cars, bound up-town, went slowly, the horses slipping and straining in the spongy brown mass that lay between the rails. The drivers, muffled to the eyes, stood erect, facing the wind, models of grim philosophy. Overhead, trains rumbled and roared, and the dark structure of the elevated railroad, stretching over the avenue, dripped little streams and drops of water upon the mud and snow beneath.

All the clatter of the street was softened by the masses that lay upon the cobbles, until, even to one who looked from a window, it became important music, a melody of life made necessary to the ear by the dreariness of the pitiless beat and sweep of the storm. Occasionally one could see black figures of men busily shovelling the white drifts from the walks. The sounds from their labour created new recollections of rural experiences which every man manages to have in a measure. Later, the immense windows of the shops became aglow with light, throwing great beams of orange and yellow upon the pavement. They were infinitely cheerful, yet in a way they accentuated the force and discomfort of the storm, and gave a meaning to the pace of the people and the vehicles, scores of pedestrians and drivers, wretched with cold faces, necks, and feet, speeding for scores of unknown doors and entrances, scattering to an infinite variety of shelters, to places which the imagination made warm with the familiar colours of home.

There was an absolute expression of hot dinners in the pace of the people. If one dared to speculate upon the destination of those who came trooping, he lost himself in a maze of social calculation; he might fling a handful of sand and attempt to follow the flight of each particular grain. But as to the suggestion of hot dinners, he was in firm lines of thought, for it was upon every hurrying face. It is a matter of tradition; it is from the tales of childhood. It comes forth with every storm.

However, in a certain part of a dark west-side street, there was a collection of men to whom these things were as if they were not. In this street was located a charitable house where for five cents the homeless of the city could get a bed at night, and in the morning coffee and bread.

During the afternoon of the storm, the whirling snows acted as drivers, as men with whips, and at half-past three the walk before the closed doors of the house was covered with wanderers of the street, waiting. For some distance on either side of the place they could be seen lurking in the doorways and behind projecting parts of buildings, gathering in close bunches in an effort to get warm. A covered wagon drawn up near the curb sheltered a dozen of them. Under the stairs that led to the elevated railway station, there were six or eight, their hands stuffed deep in their pockets, their shoulders stooped, jiggling their feet. Others always could be seen coming, a strange procession, some slouching along with the characteristic hopeless gait of professional strays, some coming with hesitating steps, wearing the air of men to whom this sort of thing was new.

It was an afternoon of incredible length. The snow, blowing in twisting clouds, sought out the men in their meagre hiding-places, and skilfully beat in among them, drenching their persons with showers of fine stinging flakes. They crowded together, muttering, and fumbling in their pockets to get their red inflamed wrists covered by the cloth.

New-comers usually halted at one end of the groups and

addressed a question, perhaps much as a matter of form, "Is it open yet?"

Those who had been waiting inclined to take the questioner seriously and became contemptuous. "No; do yeh think we'd be standin' here?"

The gathering swelled in numbers steadily and persistently. One could always see them coming, trudging slowly through the storm.

Finally, the little snow plains in the street began to assume a leaden hue from the shadows of evening. The buildings up-reared gloomily save where various windows became brilliant figures of light, that made shimmers and splashes of yellow on the snow. A street lamp on the curb struggled to illuminate, but it was reduced to impotent blindness by the swift gusts of sleet crusting its panes.

In this half-darkness, the men began to come from their shelter-places and mass in front of the doors of charity. They were of all types, but the nationalities were mostly American, German, and Irish. Many were strong, healthy, clear-skinned fellows, with that stamp of countenance which is not frequently seen upon seekers after charity. There were men of undoubted patience, industry, and temperance, who, in time of ill-fortune, do not habitually turn to rail at the state of society, snarling at the arrogance of the rich, and bemoaning the cowardice of the poor, but who at these times are apt to wear a sudden and singular meekness, as if they saw the world's progress marching from them, and were trying to perceive where they had failed, what they had lacked, to be thus vanquished in the race. Then there were others, of the shifting Bowery element, who were used to paying ten cents for a place to sleep, but who now came here because it was cheaper.

But they were all mixed in one mass so thoroughly that one could not have discerned the different elements, but for the fact that the labouring men, for the most part, remained silent and impassive in the blizzard, their eyes fixed on the windows of the house, statues of patience.

The sidewalk soon became completely blocked by the bodies of the men. They pressed close to one another like sheep in a winter's gale, keeping one another warm by the heat of their bodies. The snow came upon this compressed group of men until, directly from above, it might have appeared like a heap of snow-covered merchandise, if it were not for the fact that the crowd swayed gently with a unanimous rhythmical motion. It was wonderful to see how the snow lay upon the heads and shoulders of these men, in little ridges an inch thick perhaps in places, the flakes steadily adding drop and drop, precisely as they fall upon the unresisting grass of the fields. The feet of the men were all wet and cold, and the wish to warm them accounted for the slow, gentle rhythmical motion. Occasionally some man whose ear or nose tingled acutely from the cold winds would wriggle down until his head was protected by the shoulders of his companions.

There was a continuous murmuring discussion as to the probability of the doors being speedily opened. They persistently lifted their eyes toward the windows. One could hear little combats of opinion.

"There's a light in th' winder!"

"Naw; it's a reflection f'm across th' way."

"Well, didn't I see 'em light it?"

"You did?"

"I did!"

"Well, then, that settles it!"

As the time approached when they expected to be allowed to enter, the men crowded to the doors in an unspeakable crush, jamming and wedging in a way that, it seemed, would crack bones. They surged heavily against the building in a powerful wave of pushing shoulders. Once a rumour flitted among all the tossing heads.

"They can't open th' door! Th' fellers er smack up agin 'em."

Then a dull roar of rage came from the men on the outskirts; but all the time they strained and pushed until it appeared to

be impossible for those that they cried out against to do anything but be crushed into pulp.

"Ah, git away f'm th' door!"

"Git outa that!"

"Throw 'em out!"

"Kill 'em!"

"Say, fellers, now, what th' 'ell? G've 'em a chance t' open th'
door!"

"Yeh damn pigs, give 'em a chance t' open th' door!"

Men in the outskirts of the crowd occasionally yelled when
a boot-heel of one of trampling feet crushed on their freezing
extremities.

"Git off me feet, yeh clumsy tarrier!"

"Say, don't stand on me feet! Walk on th' ground!"

A man near the doors suddenly shouted: "O-o-oh! Le' me
out—le' me out!" And another, a man of infinite valour, once
twisted his head so as to half face those who were pushing behind him. "Quit yer shovin', yeh"—and he delivered a volley
of the most powerful and singular invective, straight into the
faces of the men behind him. It was as if he was hammering
the noses of them with curses of triple brass. His face, red with
rage, could be seen, upon it an expression of sublime disregard
of consequences. But nobody cared to reply to his imprecations; it was too cold. Many of them snickered, and all continued to push.

In occasional pauses of the crowd's movement the men had
opportunities to make jokes; usually grim things, and no doubt
very uncouth. Nevertheless, they were notable—one does not
expect to find the quality of humour in a heap of old clothes
under a snowdrift.

The winds seemed to grow fiercer as time wore on. Some of
the gusts of snow that came down on the close collection of
heads cut like knives and needles, and the men huddled, and
swore, not like dark assassins, but in a sort of American fashion, grimly and desperately, it is true, but yet with a wondrous
under-effect, indefinable and mystic, as if there was some kind

of humour in this catastrophe, in this situation in a night of snow-laden winds.

Once the window of the huge dry-goods shop across the street furnished material for a few moments of forgetfulness. In the brilliantly lighted space appeared the figure of a man. He was rather stout and very well clothed. His beard was fashioned charmingly after that of the Prince of Wales. He stood in an attitude of magnificent reflection. He slowly stroked his moustache with a certain grandeur of manner, and looked down at the snow-encrusted mob. From below, there was denoted a supreme complacence in him. It seemed that the sight operated inversely, and enabled him to more clearly regard his own delightful environment.

One of the mob chanced to turn his head, and perceived the figure in the window. "Hello, look-it 'is whiskers," he said genially.

Many of the men turned then, and a shout went up. They called to him in all strange keys. They addressed him in every manner, from familiar and cordial greetings to carefully worded advice concerning changes in his personal appearance. The man presently fled, and the mob chuckled ferociously, like ogres who had just devoured something.

They turned then to serious business. Often they addressed the stolid front of the house.

"Oh, let us in fer Gawd's sake!"

"Let us in, or we'll all drop dead!"

"Say, what's th' use o' keepin' us poor Indians out in th' cold?"

And always some one was saying, "Keep off my feet."

The crushing of the crowd grew terrific toward the last. The men, in keen pain from the blasts, began almost to fight. With the pitiless whirl of snow upon them, the battle for shelter was going to the strong. It became known that the basement door of the foot of a little steep flight of stairs was the one to be opened, and they jostled and heaved in this direction like labouring fiends. One could hear them panting and groaning in their fierce exertion.

Usually some one in the front ranks was protesting to those in the rear—"O-o-ow! Oh, say now, fellers, let up, will yeh? Do yeh wanta kill somebody?"

A policeman arrived and went into the midst of them, scolding and berating, occasionally threatening, but using no force but that of his hands and shoulders against these men who were only struggling to get in out of the storm. His decisive tones rang out sharply—"Stop that pushin' back there! Come, boys, don't push! Stop that! Here you, quit yer shovin'! Cheese that!"

When the door below was opened, a thick stream of men forced a way down the stairs, which were of an extraordinary narrowness, and seemed only wide enough for one at a time. Yet they somehow went down almost three abreast. It was a difficult and painful operation. The crowd was like a turbulent water forcing itself through one tiny outlet. The men in the rear, excited by the success of the others, made frantic exertions, for it seemed that this large band would more than fill the quarters, and that many would be left upon the pavements. It would be disastrous to be of the last, and accordingly men with the snow biting their faces writhed and twisted with their might. One expected that, from the tremendous pressure, the narrow passage to the basement door would be so choked and clogged with human limbs and bodies that movement would be impossible. Once indeed the crowd was forced to stop, and a cry went along that a man had been injured at the foot of the stairs. But presently the slow movement began again, and the policeman fought at the top of the flight to ease the pressure of those that were going down.

A reddish light from a window fell upon the faces of the men when they, in turn, arrived at the last three steps and were about to enter. One could then note a change of expression that had come over their features. As they stood thus upon the threshold of their hopes, they looked suddenly contented and complacent. The fire had passed from their eyes and the snarl had vanished from their lips. The very force of the crowd in the rear, which had previously vexed them, was regarded from another point of view, for it now made it inevitable that they should go through the little doors into the place that was cheery and warm with light.

The tossing crowd on the sidewalk grew smaller and smaller. The snow beat with merciless persistence upon the bowed heads of those who waited. The wind drove it up from the pavements in frantic forms of winding white, and it seethed in circles about the huddled forms passing in one by one, three by three, out of the storm.

AN EXPERIMENT IN MISERY [1]

I T was late at night, and a fine rain was swirling softly down, causing the pavements to glisten with hue of steel and blue and yellow in the rays of the innumerable lights. A youth was trudging slowly, without enthusiasm, with his hands buried deep in his trousers pockets, toward the downtown places where beds can be hired for coppers. He was clothed in an aged and tattered suit, and his derby was a marvel of dust-covered crown and torn rim. He was going forth to eat as the wanderer may eat, and sleep as the homeless sleep. By the time he had reached City Hall Park he was so completely plastered with yells of "bum" and "hobo," and with various unholy epithets that small boys had applied to him at intervals, that he was in a state of the most profound dejection. The sifting rain saturated the old velvet collar of his overcoat, and as the wet cloth pressed against his neck, he felt that there no

---

[1] This story had a different beginning and ending in the version appearing in the *New York Press* for April 22, 1894. They are reprinted here for the first time. In its original version the story began this way:

Two men stood regarding a tramp.

"I wonder how he feels," said one, reflectively. "I suppose he is homeless, friendless, and has, at the most, only a few cents in his pocket. And if this is so, I wonder how he feels."

The other, being the elder, spoke with an air of authoritative wisdom. "You can tell nothing of it unless you are in that condition yourself. It is idle to speculate about it from this distance."

"I suppose so," said the younger man, and then he added as from an inspiration: "I think I'll try it. Rags and tatters, you know, a couple of dimes, and hungry, too, if possible. Perhaps I could discover his point of view or something near it."

"Well, you might," said the other, and from those words begins this veracious narrative of an experiment in misery.

The youth went to the studio of an artist friend, who, from his store, rigged him out in an aged suit and a brown derby hat that had been made long years before. And then the youth went forth to try to eat as the tramp may eat, and sleep as the wanderers sleep.

longer could be pleasure in life. He looked about him searching for an outcast of highest degree that they two might share
miseries, but the lights threw a quivering glare over rows and
circles of deserted benches that glistened damply, showing
patches of wet sod behind them. It seemed that their usual
freights had fled on this night to better things. There were
only squads of well-dressed Brooklyn people who swarmed
toward the bridge.

The young man loitered about for a time and then went
shuffling off down Park Row. In the sudden descent in style
of the dress of the crowd he felt relief, and as if he were at last
in his own country. He began to see tatters that matched his
tatters. In Chatham Square there were aimless men strewn
in front of saloons and lodging-houses, standing sadly, patiently, reminding one vaguely of the attitudes of chickens in
a storm. He aligned himself with these men, and turned slowly
to occupy himself with the flowing life of the great street.

Through the mists of the cold and storming night, the cable
cars went in silent procession, great affairs shining with red
and brass, moving with formidable power, calm and irresistible, dangerful and gloomy, breaking silence only by the loud
fierce cry of the gong. Two rivers of people swarmed along
the sidewalks, spattered with black mud which made each
shoe leave a scar-like impression. Overhead, elevated trains
with a shrill grinding of the wheels stopped at the station,
which upon its leg-like pillars seemed to resemble some monstrous kind of crab squatting over the street. The quick fat
puffings of the engines could be heard. Down an alley there
were sombre curtains of purple and black, on which street
lamps dully glittered like embroidered flowers.

A saloon stood with a voracious air on a corner. A sign leaning against the front of the doorpost announced "Free hot
soup to-night!" The swing doors, snapping to and fro like
ravenous lips, made gratified smacks as the saloon gorged
itself with plump men, eating with astounding and endless
appetite, smiling in some indescribable manner as the men

came from all directions like sacrifices to a heathenish super-
stition.

Caught by the delectable sign, the young man allowed himself to be swallowed. A bartender placed a schooner of dark
and portentous beer on the bar. Its monumental form up-
reared until the froth atop was above the crown of the young
man's brown derby.

"Soup over there, gents," said the bartender affably. A little
yellow man in rags and the youth grasped their schooners
and went with speed toward a lunch-counter, where a man
with oily but imposing whiskers ladled genially from a kettle
until he had furnished his two mendicants with a soup that
was steaming hot, and in which there were little floating suggestions of chicken. The young man, sipping his broth, felt
the cordiality expressed by the warmth of the mixture, and he
beamed at the man with oily but imposing whiskers, who
was presiding like a priest behind an altar. "Have some more,
gents?" he inquired of the two sorry figures before him. The
little yellow man accepted with a swift gesture, but the youth
shook his head and went out, following a man whose wondrous seediness promised that he would have a knowledge of
cheap lodging-houses.

On the sidewalk he accosted the seedy man. "Say, do you
know a cheap place to sleep?"

The other hesitated for a time, gazing sideways. Finally he
nodded in the direction of the street. "I sleep up there," he
said, "when I've got the price."

"How much?"

"Ten cents."

The young man shook his head dolefully. "That's too rich
for me."

At that moment there approached the two a reeling man in
strange garments. His head was a fuddle of bushy hair and
whiskers, from which his eyes peered with a guilty slant. In a
close scrutiny it was possible to distinguish the cruel lines of
a mouth which looked as if its lips had just closed with satis-

faction over some tender and piteous morsel. He appeared like
an assassin steeped in crimes performed awkwardly.

But at this time his voice was tuned to the coaxing key of
an affectionate puppy. He looked at the men with wheedling
eyes, and began to sing a little melody for charity. "Say, gents,
can't yeh give a poor feller a couple of cents t' git a bed? I got
five, an' I gits anudder two I gits me a bed. Now, on th' square,
gents, can't yeh jest gimme two cents t' git a bed? Now, yeh
know how a respecterble gentlem'n feels when he's down on
his luck, an' I—"

The seedy man, staring with imperturbable countenance at
a train which clattered overhead, interrupted in an expression-
less voice: "Ah, go t' hell!"

But the youth spoke to the prayerful assassin in tones of
astonishment and inquiry. "Say, you must be crazy! Why
don't yeh strike somebody that looks as if they had money?"

The assassin, tottering about on his uncertain legs, and at
intervals brushing imaginary obstacles from before his nose,
entered into a long explanation of the psychology of the situation. It was so profound that it was unintelligible.

When he had exhausted the subject, the young man said
to him: "Let's see th' five cents."

The assassin wore an expression of drunken woe at this
sentence, filled with suspicion of him. With a deeply pained
air he began to fumble in his clothing, his red hands trembling. Presently he announced in a voice of bitter grief, as if
he had been betrayed: "There's on'y four."

"Four," said the young man thoughtfully. "Well, look-a
here, I'm a stranger here, an' if ye'll steer me to your cheap
joint I'll find the other three."

The assassin's countenance became instantly radiant with
joy. His whiskers quivered with the wealth of his alleged emotions. He seized the young man's hand in a transport of delight and friendliness.

"B' Gawd," he cried, "if ye'll do that, b' Gawd, I'd say yeh
was a damned good fellow, I would, an' I'd remember yeh

all m' life, I would, b' Gawd, an' if I ever got a chance I'd
return the compliment"—he spoke with drunken dignity—
"b' Gawd, I'd treat yeh white, I would, an' I'd allus remember
yeh."

The young man drew back, looking at the assassin coldly.
"Oh, that's all right," he said. "You show me th' joint—that's
all you've got t' do."

The assassin, gesticulating gratitude, led the young man
along a dark street. Finally he stopped before a little dusty
door. He raised his hand impressively. "Look-a here," he said,
and there was a thrill of deep and ancient wisdom upon his
face, "I've brought yeh here, an' that's my part, ain't it? If th'
place don't suit yeh, yeh needn't git mad at me, need yeh?
There won't be no bad feelin', will there?"

"No," said the young man.

The assassin waved his arm tragically, and led the march
up the steep stairway. On the way the young man furnished
the assassin with three pennies. At the top a man with benevolent spectacles looked at them through a hole in a board. He
collected their money, wrote some names on a register, and
speedily was leading the two men along a gloom-shrouded
corridor.

Shortly after the beginning of this journey the young man
felt his liver turn white, for from the dark and secret places
of the building there suddenly came to his nostrils strange
and unspeakable odours, that assailed him like malignant dis-
eases with wings. They seemed to be from human bodies
closely packed in dens; the exhalations from a hundred pairs
of reeking lips; the fumes from a thousand bygone debauches;
the expression of a thousand present miseries.

A man, naked save for a little snuff-coloured undershirt, was
parading sleepily along the corridor. He rubbed his eyes and,
giving vent to a prodigious yawn, demanded to be told the
time.

"Half-past one."

The man yawned again. He opened a door, and for a mo-

ment his form was outlined against a black, opaque interior.
To this door came the three men, and as it was again opened
the unholy odours rushed out like fiends, so that the young
man was obliged to struggle as against an overpowering wind.

It was some time before the youth's eyes were good in the
intense gloom within, but the man with benevolent spectacles
led him skilfully, pausing but a moment to deposit the limp
assassin upon a cot. He took the youth to a cot that lay tranquilly by the window, and showing him a tall locker for
clothes that stood near the head with the ominous air of a
tombstone, left him.

The youth sat on his cot and peered about him. There was a
gas-jet in a distant part of the room, that burned a small flick-
ering orange-hued flame. It caused vast masses of tumbled
shadows in all parts of the place; save where, immediately
about it, there was a little grey haze. As the young man's eyes
became used to the darkness, he could see upon the cots that
thickly littered the floor the forms of men sprawled out, lying
in death-like silence, or heaving and snoring with tremendous
effort, like stabbed fish.

The youth locked his derby and his shoes in the mummy-
case near him, and then lay down with an old and familiar
coat around his shoulders. A blanket he handled gingerly,
drawing it over part of the coat. The cot was covered with
leather, and as cold as melting snow. The youth was obliged
to shiver for some time on this affair, which was like a slab.
Presently, however, his chill gave him peace, and during this
period of leisure from it he turned his head to stare at his
friend the assassin, whom he could dimly discern where he
lay sprawled on a cot in the abandon of a man filled with
drink. He was snoring with incredible vigour. His wet hair
and beard dimly glistened, and his inflamed nose shone with
subdued lustre like a red light in a fog.

Within reach of the youth's hand was one who lay with
yellow breast and shoulders bare to the cold draughts. One
arm hung over the side of the cot, and the fingers lay full

length upon the wet cement floor of the room. Beneath the
inky brows could be seen the eyes of the man, exposed by the
partly opened lids. To the youth it seemed that he and this
corpse-like being were exchanging a prolonged stare, and
that the other threatened with his eyes. He drew back, watching his neighbour from the shadows of his blanket-edge. The
man did not move once through the night, but lay in this stillness as of death like a body stretched out expectant of the
surgeon's knife.

And all through the room could be seen the tawny hues
of naked flesh, limbs thrust into the darkness, projecting beyond the cots; upreared knees, arms hanging long and thin
over the cot-edges. For the most part they were statuesque,
carven, dead. With the curious lockers standing all about like
tombstones, there was a strange effect of a graveyard where
bodies were merely flung.

Yet occasionally could be seen limbs wildly tossing in fantastic nightmare gestures, accompanied by guttural cries,
grunts, oaths. And there was one fellow off in a gloomy corner,
who in his dreams was oppressed by some frightful calamity,
for of a sudden he began to utter long wails that went almost
like yells from a hound, echoing wailfully and weird through
this chill place of tombstones where men lay like the dead.

The sound, in its high piercing beginnings that dwindled
to final melancholy moans, expressed a red and grim tragedy
of the unfathomable possibilities of the man's dreams. But to
the youth these were not merely the shrieks of a vision-
pierced man: they were an utterance of the meaning of the
room and its occupants. It was to him the protest of the
wretch who feels the touch of the imperturbable granite
wheels, and who then cries with an impersonal eloquence,
with a strength not from him, giving voice to the wail of a
whole section, a class, a people. This, weaving into the young
man's brain, and mingling with his views of the vast and
sombre shadows that, like mighty black fingers, curled around
the naked bodies, made the young man so that he did not

sleep, but lay carving the biographies for these men from his meagre experience. At times the fellow in the corner howled in a writhing agony of his imaginations.

Finally a long lance-point of grey light shot through the dusty panes of the window. Without, the young man could see roofs drearily white in the dawning. The point of light yellowed and grew brighter, until the golden rays of the morning sun came in bravely and strong. They touched with radiant colour the form of a small fat man who snored in stuttering fashion. His round and shiny bald head glowed suddenly with the valour of a decoration. He sat up, blinked at the sun, swore fretfully, and pulled his blanket over the ornamental splendours of his head.

The youth contentedly watched this rout of the shadows before the bright spears of the sun, and presently he slumbered. When he awoke he heard the voice of the assassin raised in valiant curses. Putting up his head, he perceived his comrade seated on the side of the cot engaged in scratching his neck with long fingernails that rasped like files.

"Hully Jee, dis is a new breed. They've got can-openers on their feet." He continued in a violent tirade.

The young man hastily unlocked his closet and took out his shoes and hat. As he sat on the side of the cot lacing his shoes, he glanced about and saw that daylight had made the room comparatively commonplace and uninteresting. The men, whose faces seemed stolid, serene, or absent, were engaged in dressing, while a great crackle of bantering conversation arose.

A few were parading in unconcerned nakedness. Here and there were men of brawn, whose skins shone clear and ruddy. They took splendid poses, standing massively like chiefs. When they had dressed in their ungainly garments there was an extraordinary change. They then showed bumps and deficiencies of all kinds.

There were others who exhibited many deformities. Shoulders were slanting, humped, pulled this way and pulled that way. And notable among these latter men was the little fat man who had refused to allow his head to be glorified. His pudgy form, builded like a pear, bustled to and fro, while he swore in fishwife fashion. It appeared that some article of his apparel had vanished.

The young man attired himself speedily, and went to his friend the assassin. At first the latter looked dazed at the sight of the youth. This face seemed to be appealing to him through the cloud-wastes of his memory. He scratched his neck and reflected. At last he grinned, a broad smile gradually spreading until his countenance was a round illumination. "Hello, Willie," he cried cheerily.

"Hello," said the young man. "Are yeh ready t' fly?"

"Sure." The assassin tied his shoe carefully with some twine and came ambling.

When he reached the street the young man experienced no sudden relief from unholy atmospheres. He had forgotten all about them, and had been breathing naturally, and with no sensation of discomfort or distress.

He was thinking of these things as he walked along the street, when he was suddenly startled by feeling the assassin's hand, trembling with excitement, clutching his arm, and when the assassin spoke, his voice went into quavers from a supreme agitation.

"I'll be hully, bloomin' blowed if there wasn't a feller with a nightshirt on up there in that joint."

The youth was bewildered for a moment, but presently he turned to smile indulgently at the assassin's humour. "Oh, you're a damned liar," he merely said.

Whereupon the assassin began to gesture extravagantly and take oath by strange gods. He frantically placed himself at the mercy of remarkable fates if his tale were not true. "Yes, he did! I cross m' heart thousan' times!" he protested, and at the moment his eyes were large with amazement, his mouth wrinkled in unnatural glee. "Yessir! A nightshirt! A hully white nightshirt!"

"You lie!"

"No, sir! I hope ter die b'fore I kin git anudder ball if there wasn't a jay wid a hully, bloomin' white nightshirt!"

His face was filled with the infinite wonder of it. "A hully white nightshirt," he continually repeated.

The young man saw the dark entrance to a basement restaurant. There was a sign which read "No mystery about our hash!" and there were other age-stained and world-battered legends which told him that the place was within his means. He stopped before it and spoke to the assassin. "I guess I'll git somethin' t' eat."

At this the assassin, for some reason, appeared to be quite embarrassed. He gazed at the seductive front of the eating-place for a moment. Then he started slowly up the street. "Well, good-bye, Willie," he said bravely.

For an instant the youth studied the departing figure. Then he called out, "Hol' on a minnet." As they came together he spoke in a certain fierce way, as if he feared that the other would think him to be charitable. "Look-a here, if yeh wanta git some breakfas' I'll lend yeh three cents t' do it with. But say, look-a here, you've gotta git out an' hustle. I ain't goin' t' support yeh, or I'll go broke b'fore night. I ain't no millionaire."

"I take me oath, Willie," said the assassin earnestly, "th' on'y thing I really needs is a ball. Me t'roat feels like a fryin'-pan. But as I can't get a ball, why, th' next bes' thing is break-fast, an' if yeh do that for me, b' Gawd, I say yeh was th' whitest lad I ever see."

They spent a few moments in dexterous exchanges of phrases, in which they each protested that the other was, as the assassin had originally said, "a respecterble gentlem'n." And they concluded with mutual assurances that they were the souls of intelligence and virtue. Then they went into the restaurant.

There was a long counter, dimly lighted from hidden sources. Two or three men in soiled white aprons rushed here and there.

The youth bought a bowl of coffee for two cents and a roll for one cent. The assassin purchased the same. The bowls were webbed with brown seams, and the tin spoons wore an air of having emerged from the first pyramid. Upon them were black moss-like encrustations of age, and they were bent and scarred from the attacks of long-forgotten teeth. But over their repast the wanderers waxed warm and mellow. The assassin grew affable as the hot mixture went soothingly down his parched throat, and the young man felt courage flow in his veins.

Memories began to throng in on the assassin, and he brought forth long tales, intricate, incoherent, delivered with a chattering swiftness as from an old woman. "—great job out 'n Orange. Boss keep yeh hustlin', though, all time. I was there three days, and then I went an' ask 'im t' lend me a dollar. 'G-g-go ter the devil,' he says, an' I lose me job.

"South no good. Damn niggers work for twenty-five an' thirty cents a day. Run white man out. Good grub, though. Easy livin'.

"Yas; useter work little in Toledo, raftin' logs. Make two or three dollars er day in the spring. Lived high. Cold as ice, though, in the winter.

"I was raised in northern N' York. O-o-oh, yeh jest oughto live there. No beer ner whisky, though, 'way off in the woods. But all th' good hot grub yeh can eat. B' Gawd, I hung around there long as I could till th' ol' man fired me. 'Git t' hell outa here, yeh wuthless skunk, git t' hell outa here, an' go die,' he says. 'You're a hell of a father,' I says, 'you are,' an' I quit 'im."

As they were passing from the dim eating-place, they encountered an old man who was trying to steal forth with a tiny package of food, but a tall man with an indomitable moustache stood dragon-fashion, barring the way of escape. They heard the old man raise a plaintive protest. "Ah, you always want to know what I take out, and you never see that I usually bring a package in here from my place of business."

As the wanderers trudged slowly along Park Row, the assassin began to expand and grow blithe. "B' Gawd, we've been livin' like kings," he said, smacking appreciative lips.

"Look out, or we'll have t' pay fer it t'-night," said the youth with gloomy warning.

But the assassin refused to turn his gaze toward the future. He went with a limping step, into which he injected a suggestion of lamb-like gambols. His mouth was wreathed in a red grin.

In City Hall Park the two wanderers sat down in the little circle of benches sanctified by traditions of their class. They huddled in their old garments, slumbrously conscious of the march of the hours which for them had no meaning.

The people of the street hurrying hither and thither made a blend of black figures, changing, yet frieze-like. They walked in their good clothes as upon important missions, giving no gaze to the two wanderers seated upon the benches. They expressed to the young man his infinite distance from all that he valued. Social position, comfort, the pleasures of living were unconquerable kingdoms. He felt a sudden awe.

And in the background a multitude of buildings, of pitiless hues and sternly high, were to him emblematic of a nation forcing its regal head into the clouds, throwing no downward glances; in the sublimity of its aspirations ignoring the wretches who may flounder at its feet. The roar of the city in his ear was to him the confusion of strange tongues, babbling heedlessly; it was the clink of coin, the voice of the city's hopes, which were to him no hopes.

He confessed himself an outcast, and his eyes from under the lowered rim of his hat began to glance guiltily, wearing the criminal expression that comes with certain convictions.[2]

---

[2] The original version included the following final part:

"Well," said the friend, "did you discover his point of view?"

"I don't know that I did," replied the young man; "but at any rate I think mine own has undergone a considerable alteration."

STEPHEN CRANE.

MAGGIE: A GIRL OF THE STREETS

I

A VERY little boy stood upon a heap of gravel for the honour
of Rum Alley. He was throwing stones at howling urchins from
Devil's Row, who were circling madly about the heap and
pelting him. His infantile countenance was livid with the fury
of battle. His small body was writhing in the delivery of oaths.

"Run, Jimmie, run! Dey'll git yehs!" screamed a retreating
Rum Alley child.

"Naw," responded Jimmie with a valiant roar, "dese mugs
can't make me run."

Howls of renewed wrath went up from Devil's Row throats.
Tattered gamins on the right made a furious assault on the
gravel-heap. On their small convulsed faces shone the grins of
true assassins. As they charged, they threw stones and cursed
in shrill chorus.

The little champion of Rum Alley stumbled precipitately
down the other side. His coat had been torn to shreds in a
scuffle, and his hat was gone. He had bruises on twenty parts
of his body, and blood was dripping from a cut in his head.
His wan features looked like those of a tiny insane demon. On
the ground, children from Devil's Row closed in on their antagonist. He crooked his left arm defensively about his head
and fought with madness. The little boys ran to and fro, dodging, hurling stones, and swearing in barbaric trebles.

From a window of an apartment-house that uprose from
amid squat ignorant stables there leaned a curious woman.
Some labourers, unloading a scow at a dock at the river,
paused for a moment and regarded the fight. The engineer of
a passive tugboat hung lazily over a railing and watched.
Over on the island a worm of yellow convicts came from the

shadow of a grey ominous building and crawled slowly along the river's bank.

A stone had smashed in Jimmie's mouth. Blood was bubbling over his chin and down upon his ragged shirt. Tears made furrows on his dirt-stained cheeks. His thin legs had begun to tremble and turn weak, causing his small body to reel. His roaring curses of the first part of the fight had changed to a blasphemous chatter. In the yells of the whirling mob of Devil's Row children there were notes of joy like songs of triumphant savagery. The little boys seemed to leer gloatingly at the blood upon the other child's face.

Down the avenue came boastfully sauntering a lad of sixteen years, although the chronic sneer of an ideal manhood already sat upon his lips. His hat was tipped over his eye with an air of challenge. Between his teeth a cigar-stump was tilted at the angle of defiance. He walked with a certain swing of the shoulders which appalled the timid. He glanced over into the vacant lot in which the little raving boys from Devil's Row seethed about the shrieking and tearful child from Rum Alley.

"Gee!" he murmured with interest, "a scrap. Gee!" He strode over to the cursing circle, swinging his shoulders in a manner which denoted that he held victory in his fists. He approached at the back of one of the most deeply engaged of the Devil's Row children. "Ah, what d' hell," he said, and smote the deeply engaged one on the back of the head.

The little boy fell to the ground and gave a tremendous howl. He scrambled to his feet, and perceiving, evidently, the size of his assailant, ran quickly off, shouting alarms. The entire Devil's Row party followed him. They came to a stand a short distance away and yelled taunting oaths at the boy with the chronic sneer.

The latter, momentarily, paid no attention to them. "What's wrong wi'che, Jimmie?" he asked of the small champion.

Jimmie wiped his blood-wet features with his sleeve. "Well,

it was dis way, Pete, see? I was goin' teh lick dat Riley kid, an' dey all pitched on me."

Some Rum Alley children now came forward. The party stood for a moment exchanging vainglorious remarks with Devil's Row. A few stones were thrown at long distances, and words of challenge passed between small warriors. Then the Rum Alley contingent turned slowly in the direction of their home street. They began to give, each to each, distorted versions of the fight. Causes of retreat in particular cases were magnified. Blows dealt in the fight were enlarged to catapultian power, and stones thrown were alleged to have hurtled with infinite accuracy. Valour grew strong again, and the little boys began to brag with great spirit. "Ah, we blokies kin lick d' hull damn Row," said a child, swaggering.

Little Jimmie was trying to stanch the flow of blood from his cut lips. Scowling, he turned upon the speaker. "Ah, where was yehs when I was doin' all deh fightin'?" he demanded. "Youse kids makes me tired."

"Ah, go ahn!" replied the other argumentatively.

Jimmie replied with heavy contempt. "Ah, youse can't fight, Blue Billie! I kin lick yeh wid one han'."

"Ah, go ahn!" replied Billie again.

"Ah!" said Jimmie threateningly.

"Ah!" said the other in the same tone.

They struck at each other, clinched, and rolled over on the cobble-stones.

"Smash 'im, Jimmie, kick d' face off 'im!" yelled Pete, the lad with the chronic sneer, in tones of delight.

The small combatants pounded and kicked, scratched and tore. They began to weep, and their curses struggled in their throats with sobs. The other little boys clasped their hands and wriggled their legs in excitement. They formed a bobbing circle about the pair.

A tiny spectator was suddenly agitated. "Cheese it, Jimmie, cheese it! Here comes yer fader," he yelled.

The circle of little boys instantly parted. They drew away and waited in ecstatic awe for that which was about to happen. The two little boys, fighting in the modes of four thousand years ago, did not hear the warning.

Up the avenue there plodded slowly a man with sullen eyes. He was carrying a dinner-pail and smoking an apple-wood pipe. As he neared the spot where the little boys strove, he regarded them listlessly. But suddenly he roared an oath and advanced upon the rolling fighters. "Here, you Jim, git up, now, while I belt yer life out, yeh disorderly brat." He began to kick into the chaotic mass on the ground. The boy Billie felt a heavy boot strike his head. He made a furious effort and disentangled himself from Jimmie. He tottered away.

Jimmie arose painfully from the ground and, confronting his father, began to curse him. His parent kicked him. "Come home, now," he cried, "an' stop yer jawin', er I'll lam the everlasting head off yehs."

They departed. The man paced placidly along with the apple-wood emblem of serenity between his teeth. The boy followed a dozen feet in the rear. He swore luridly, for he felt that it was degradation for one who aimed to be some vague kind of soldier, or a man of blood with a sort of sublime licence, to be taken home by a father.

II

Eventually they entered a dark region where, from a careening building, a dozen gruesome doorways gave up loads of babies to the street and the gutter. A wind of early autumn raised yellow dust from cobbles and swirled it against a hundred windows. Long streamers of garments fluttered from fire-escapes. In all unhandy places there were buckets, brooms, rags, and bottles. In the street infants played or fought with other infants or sat stupidly in the way of vehicles. Formidable women, with uncombed hair and disordered dress, gossiped while leaning on railings, or screamed in frantic quarrels. Withered persons, in curious postures of submission to something, sat smoking pipes in obscure corners. A thousand odours of cooking food came forth to the street. The building quivered and creaked from the weight of humanity stamping about in its bowels.

A small ragged girl dragged a red, bawling infant along the crowded ways. He was hanging back, baby-like, bracing his wrinkled, bare legs. The little girl cried out: "Ah, Tommie, come ahn. Dere's Jimmie and fader. Don't be a-pullin' me back." She jerked the baby's arm impatiently. He fell on his face, roaring. With a second jerk she pulled him to his feet, and they went on. With the obstinacy of his order, he protested against being dragged in a chosen direction. He made heroic endeavours to keep on his legs, denounced his sister, and consumed a bit of orange-peeling which he chewed between the times of his infantile orations.

As the sullen-eyed man, followed by the blood-covered boy, drew near, the little girl burst into reproachful cries. "Ah, Jimmie, youse bin fightin' agin."

The urchin swelled disdainfully. "Ah, what d' hell, Mag. See?"

The little girl upbraided him. "Youse allus fightin', Jimmie, an' yeh knows it puts mudder out when yehs come home half dead, an it's like we'll all get a poundin'." She began to weep. The babe threw back his head and roared at his prospects.

"Ah," cried Jimmie, "shut up er I'll smack yer mout'. See?" As his sister continued her lamentations, he suddenly struck her. The little girl reeled, and, recovering herself, burst into tears and quaveringly cursed him. As she slowly retreated, her brother advanced, dealing her cuffs.

The father heard, and turned about. "Stop that, Jim, d'yeh hear? Leave yer sister alone on the street. It's like I can never beat any sense into yer wooden head."

The urchin raised his voice in defiance to his parent, and continued his attacks. The babe bawled tremendously, protesting with great violence. During his sister's hasty manœuvres he was dragged by the arm.

Finally the procession plunged into one of the gruesome doorways. They crawled up dark stairways and along cold, gloomy halls. At last the father pushed open a door, and they entered a lighted room in which a large woman was rampant.

She stopped in a career from a seething stove to a pan-covered table. As the father and children filed in she peered at them. "Eh, what? Been fightin' agin!" She threw herself upon Jimmie. The urchin tried to dart behind the others, and in the scuffle the babe, Tommie, was knocked down. He protested with his usual vehemence because they had bruised his tender shins against a table leg.

The mother's massive shoulders heaved with anger. Grasping the urchin by the neck and shoulder she shook him until he rattled. She dragged him to an unholy sink, and, soaking a rag in water, began to scrub his lacerated face with it. Jimmie screamed in pain, and tried to twist his shoulders out of the clasp of the huge arms.

The babe sat on the floor watching the scene, his face in contortions like that of a woman at a tragedy. The father, with a newly ladened pipe in his mouth, sat in a backless chair near the stove. Jimmie's cries annoyed him. He turned about and bellowed at his wife. "Let the kid alone for a minute, will yeh, Mary? Yer allus poundin' 'im. When I come nights I can't get no rest 'cause yer allus poundin' a kid. Let up, d'yeh hear? Don't be allus poundin' a kid." The woman's operations on the urchin instantly increased in violence. At last she tossed him to a corner, where he limply lay weeping.

The wife put her immense hands on her hips, and with a chieftain-like stride approached her husband. "Ho!" she said, with a great grunt of contempt. "An' what in the devil are you stickin' your nose for?" The babe crawled under the table, and, turning, peered out cautiously. The ragged girl retreated, and the urchin in the corner drew his legs carefully beneath him.

The man puffed his pipe calmly and put his great muddied

boots on the back part of the stove. "Go t' hell," he said tranquilly.

The woman screamed, and shook her fists before her husband's eyes. The rough yellow of her face and neck flared suddenly crimson. She began to howl.

He puffed imperturbably at his pipe for a time, but finally arose and went to look out the window into the darkening chaos of back yards. "You've been drinkin', Mary," he said. "You'd better let up on the bot', ol' woman, or you'll git done."

"You're a liar. I ain't had a drop," she roared in reply. They had a lurid altercation.

The babe was staring out from under the table, his small face working in his excitement. The ragged girl went stealthily over to the corner where the urchin lay. "Are yehs hurted much, Jimmie?" she whispered timidly.

"Not a little bit. See?" growled the little boy.

"Will I wash d' blood?"

"Naw!"

"Will I—"

"When I catch dat Riley kid I'll break 'is face! Dat's right! See?" He turned his face to the wall as if resolved grimly to bide his time.

In the quarrel between husband and wife the woman was victor. The man seized his hat and rushed from the room, apparently determined upon a vengeful drunk. She followed to the door and thundered at him as he made his way downstairs.

She returned and stirred up the room until her children were bobbing about like bubbles. "Git outa d' way," she bawled persistently, waving feet with their dishevelled shoes near the heads of her children. She shrouded herself, puffing and snorting, in a cloud of steam at the stove, and eventually extracted a frying-pan full of potatoes that hissed. She flourished it. "Come t' yer suppers, now," she cried with sudden exasperation. "Hurry up, now, er I'll help yeh!"

The children scrambled hastily. With prodigious clatter they arranged themselves at table. The babe sat with his feet dangling high from a precarious infant's chair and gorged his small stomach. Jimmie forced, with feverish rapidity, the grease-enveloped pieces between his wounded lips. Maggie, with side glances of fear of interruption, ate like a small pursued tigress.

The mother sat blinking at them. She delivered reproaches, swallowed potatoes, and drank from a yellow-brown bottle. After a time her mood changed, and she wept as she carried little Tommie into another room and laid him to sleep, with his fists doubled, in an old quilt of faded red-and-green grandeur. Then she came and moaned by the stove. She rocked to and fro upon a chair, shedding tears and crooning miserably to the two children about their "poor mother" and "yer fader, damn 'is soul."

The little girl plodded between the table and the chair with a dishpan on it. She tottered on her small legs beneath burdens of dishes. Jimmie sat nursing his various wounds. He cast furtive glances at his mother. His practised eye perceived her gradually emerge from a mist of muddled sentiment until her brain burned in drunken heat. He sat breathless.

Maggie broke a plate.

The mother started to her feet as if propelled. "Good Gawd!" she howled. Her glittering eyes fastened on her child with sudden hatred. The fervent red of her face turned almost to purple. The little boy ran to the halls, shrieking like a monk in an earthquake. He floundered about in darkness until he found the stairs. He stumbled, panic-stricken, to the next floor.

An old woman opened a door. A light behind her threw a flare on the urchin's face. "Eh, child, what is it dis time? Is yer fader beatin' yer mudder, or yer mudder beatin' ye fader?"

III

Jimmie and the old woman listened long in the hall. Above the muffled roar of conversation, the dismal wailings of babies at night, the thumping of feet in unseen corridors and rooms, and the sound of varied hoarse shoutings in the street and the rattling of wheels over cobbles, they heard the screams of the child and the roars of the mother die away to a feeble moaning and a subdued bass muttering.

The old woman was a gnarled and leathery personage who could don at will an expression of great virtue. She possessed a small music-box capable of one tune, and a collection of "God bless yeh's" pitched in assorted keys of fervency. Each day she took a position upon the stones of Fifth Avenue, where she crooked her legs under her and crouched, immovable and hideous, like an idol. She received daily a small sum in pennies. It was contributed, for the most part, by persons who did not make their homes in that vicinity. Once, when a lady had dropped her purse on the sidewalk, the gnarled woman had grabbed it and smuggled it with great dexterity beneath her cloak. When she was arrested she had cursed the lady into a partial swoon, and with her aged limbs, twisted from rheumatism, had kicked the breath out of a huge policeman whose conduct upon that occasion she referred to when she said, "The police, damn 'em!"

"Eh, Jimmie, it's a shame," she said. "Go, now, like a dear, an' buy me a can, an' if yer mudder raises 'ell all night yehs can sleep here." Jimmie took a tendered tin pail and seven pennies and departed. He passed into the side door of a saloon and went to the bar. Straining up on his toes he raised the pail and pennies as high as his arms would let him. He saw two hands thrust down to take them. Directly the same hands let down the filled pail, and he left.

In front of the gruesome doorway he met a lurching figure. It was his father, swaying about on uncertain legs. "Give me deh can. See?" said the man.

"Ah, come off! I got dis can fer dat ol' woman, an' it 'ud be dirt teh swipe it. See?" cried Jimmie.

The father wrenched the pail from the urchin. He grasped it in both hands and lifted it to his mouth. He glued his lips to the under edge and tilted his head. His throat swelled until it seemed to grow near his chin. There was a tremendous gulping movement and the beer was gone. The man caught his breath and laughed. He hit his son on the head with the empty pail.

As it rolled clanging into the street, Jimmie began to scream, and kicked repeatedly at his father's shins. "Look at deh dirt what yeh done me," he yelled. "Deh ol' woman 'll be t'rowin' fits." He retreated to the middle of the street, but the old man did not pursue. He staggered toward the door. "I'll paste yeh when I ketch yeh!" he shouted, and disappeared.

During the evening he had been standing against a bar drinking whiskies, and declaring to all comers confidentially: "My home reg'lar livin' hell! Why do I come an' drin' whisk' here thish way? 'Cause home reg'lar livin' hell!"

Jimmie waited a long time in the street and then crept warily up through the building. He passed with great caution the door of the gnarled woman, and finally stopped outside his home and listened. He could hear his mother moving heavily about among the furniture of the room. She was chanting in a mournful voice, occasionally interjecting bursts of volcanic wrath at the father, who, Jimmie judged, had sunk down on the floor or in a corner.

"Why deh blazes don' cher try teh keep Jim from fightin'? I'll break yer jaw!" she suddenly bellowed.

The man mumbled with drunken indifference, "Ah, w'at's hitin' yeh? Wa'a 's odds? W'a' makes kick?"

"Because he tears 'is clothes, yeh fool!" cried the woman in supreme wrath.

The husband seemed to become aroused. "Go chase yerself!" he thundered fiercely in reply. There was a crash against the door, and something broke into clattering fragments. Jimmie partially suppressed a yell and darted down the stairway. Below he paused and listened. He heard howls and curses, groans and shrieks—a confused chorus as if a battle were raging. With it all there was the crash of splintering furniture. The eyes of the urchin glared in his fear that one of them would discover him.

Curious faces appeared in doorways, and whispered comments passed to and fro. "Ol' Johnson's playin' horse agin."

Jimmie stood until the noises ceased and the other inhabitants of the tenement had all yawned and shut their doors. Then he crawled upstairs with the caution of an invader of a panther's den. Sounds of laboured breathing came through the broken door-panels. He pushed the door open and entered, quaking.

A glow from the fire threw red hues over the bare floor, the cracked and soiled plastering, and the overturned and broken furniture. In the middle of the floor lay his mother asleep. In one corner of the room his father's limp body hung across the seat of a chair.

The urchin stole forward. He began to shiver in dread of awakening his parents. His mother's great chest was heaving painfully. Jimmie paused and looked down at her. Her face was inflamed and swollen from drinking. Her yellow brows shaded eyelids that had grown blue. Her tangled hair tossed in waves over her forehead. Her mouth was set in the same lines of vindictive hatred that it had, perhaps, borne during the fight. Her bare red arms were thrown out above her head in an attitude of exhaustion, something, mayhap, like that of a sated villain.

The urchin bent over his mother. He was fearful lest she should open her eyes, and the dread within him was so strong that he could not forbear to stare, but hung as if fascinated over the woman's grim face. Suddenly her eyes opened. The urchin found himself looking straight into an expression which, it would seem, had the power to change his blood to salt. He howled piercingly and fell backward.

The woman floundered for a moment, tossed her arms about her head as if in combat, and again began to snore. Jimmie crawled back into the shadows and waited. A noise in the next room had followed his cry at the discovery that his mother was awake. He grovelled in the gloom, his eyes riveted upon the intervening door. He heard it creak, and then the sound

of a small voice came to him. "Jimmie! Jimmie! Are yehs dere?"
it whispered. The urchin started. The thin white face of his
sister looked at him from the doorway of the other room. She
crept to him across the floor.

The father had not moved, but lay in the same deathlike
sleep. The mother writhed in an uneasy slumber, her chest
wheezing as if she were in the agonies of strangulation. Out at
the window a florid moon was peering over dark roofs, and in
the distance the waters of a river glimmered pallidly.

The small frame of the ragged girl was quivering. Her features were haggard from weeping, and her eyes gleamed with
fear. She grasped the urchin's arm in her little trembling hands
and they huddled in a corner. The eyes of both were drawn,
by some force, to stare at the woman's face, for they thought
she need only to awake and all the fiends would come from
below. They crouched until the ghost mists of dawn appeared
at the window, drawing close to the panes, and looking in at
the prostrate, heaving body of the mother.

IV

The babe, Tommie, died. He went away in an insignificant
coffin, his small waxen hand clutching a flower that the girl,
Maggie, had stolen from an Italian.

She and Jimmie lived.

The inexperienced fibres of the boy's eyes were hardened at
an early age. He became a young man of leather. He lived
some red years without labouring. During that time his sneer
became chronic. He studied human nature in the gutter, and
found it no worse than he thought he had reason to believe it.
He never conceived a respect for the world, because he had
begun with no idols that it had smashed.

He clad his soul in armour by means of happening hilariously
in at a mission church where a man composed his sermons of
"you's." Once a philosopher asked this man why he did not say
"we" instead of "you." The man replied, "What?" While they got
warm at the stove he told his hearers just where he calculated

they stood with the Lord. Many of the sinners were impatient over the pictured depths of their degradation. They were waiting for soup-tickets. A reader of the words of wind-demons might have been able to see the portions of a dialogue pass to and fro between the exhorter and his hearers. "You are damned," said the preacher. And the reader of sounds might have seen the reply go forth from the ragged people: "Where's our soup?" Jimmie and a companion sat in a rear seat and commented upon the things that didn't concern them, with all the freedom of English tourists. When they grew thirsty and went out, their minds confused the speaker with Christ.

Momentarily, Jimmie was sullen with thoughts of a hopeless altitude where grew fruit. His companion said that if he should ever go to heaven he would ask for a million dollars and a bottle of beer. Jimmie's occupation for a long time was to stand at street corners and watch the world go by, dreaming blood-red dreams at the passing of pretty women. He menaced mankind at the intersections of streets. At the corners he was in life and of life. The world was going on and he was there to perceive it.

He maintained a belligerent attitude toward all well-dressed men. To him fine raiment was allied to weakness, and all good coats covered faint hearts. He and his orders were kings, to a certain extent, over the men of untarnished clothes, because these latter dreaded, perhaps, to be either killed or laughed at. Above all things he despised obvious Christians and ciphers with the chrysanthemums of aristocracy in their buttonholes. He considered himself above both of these classes. He was afraid of nothing.

When he had a dollar in his pocket his satisfaction with existence was the greatest thing in the world. So, eventually, he felt obliged to work. His father died, and his mother's years were divided up into periods of thirty days.

He became a truck-driver. There was given to him the charge of a painstaking pair of horses and a large rattling truck. He invaded the turmoil and tumble of the downtown streets, and learned to breathe maledictory defiance at the police, who occasionally used to climb up, drag him from his perch, and punch him. In the lower part of the city he daily involved himself in hideous tangles. If he and his team chanced to be in the rear he preserved a demeanour of serenity, crossing his legs and bursting forth into yells when foot passengers took dangerous dives beneath the noses of his champing horses. He smoked his pipe calmly, for he knew that his pay was marching on. If his charge was in the front, and if it became the key-truck of chaos, he entered terrifically into the quarrel that was raging to and fro among the drivers on their high seats, and sometimes roared oaths and violently got himself arrested.

After a time his sneer grew so that it turned its glare upon all things. He became so sharp that he believed in nothing. To him the police were always actuated by malignant impulses, and the rest of the world was composed, for the most part, of despicable creatures who were all trying to take advantage of him, and with whom, in defence, he was obliged to quarrel on all possible occasions. He himself occupied a downtrodden position, which had a private but distinct element of grandeur in its isolation.

The greatest cases of aggravated idiocy were, to his mind, rampant upon the front platforms of all the street-cars. At first his tongue strove with these beings, but he eventually became superior. In him grew a majestic contempt for those strings of street-cars that followed him like intent bugs. He fell into the habit, when starting on a long journey, of fixing his eye on a high and distant object, commanding his horses to start, and then going into a trance of oblivion. Multitudes of drivers might howl in his rear, and passengers might load him with opprobrium, but he would not awaken until some blue policeman turned red and began frenziedly to seize bridles and beat the soft noses of the responsible horses.

When he paused to contemplate the attitude of the police toward himself and his fellows, he believed that they were the only men in the city who had no rights. When driving about, he felt that he was held liable by the police for anything that might occur in the streets, and that he was the common prey of all energetic officials. In revenge, he resolved never to move out of the way of anything, until formidable circumstances or a much larger man than himself forced him to it.

Foot passengers were mere pestering flies with an insane disregard for their legs and his convenience. He could not comprehend their desire to cross the streets. Their madness smote him with eternal amazement. He was continually storming at them from his throne. He sat aloft and denounced their frantic leaps, plunges, dives, and straddles. When they would thrust at, or parry, the noses of his champing horses, making them swing their heads and move their feet, and thus disturbing a stolid, dreamy repose, he swore at the men as fools, for he himself could perceive that Providence had caused it to be clearly written that he and his team had the inalienable right to stand in the proper path of the sun-chariot and, if they so minded, to obstruct its mission or take a wheel off. And if the god driver had had a desire to step down, put up his flame-coloured fists, and manfully dispute the right of way, he would have probably been immediately opposed by a scowling mortal with two sets of hard knuckles.

It is possible, perhaps, that this young man would have derided, in an axle-wide alley, the approach of a flying ferry-boat. Yet he achieved a respect for a fire-engine. As one charged toward his truck, he would drive fearfully upon a sidewalk, threatening untold people with annihilation. When an engine struck a mass of blocked trucks, splitting it into fragments as a blow annihilates a cake of ice, Jimmie's team could usually be observed high and safe, with whole wheels, on the sidewalk. The fearful coming of the engine could break up the most intricate muddle of heavy vehicles at which the police had been storming for half an hour. A fire-engine was enshrined in his heart as an appalling thing that he loved with a distant, dog-like devotion. It had been known to overturn a street-car. Those leaping horses, striking sparks from the cobbles in their forward lunge, were creatures to be ineffably admired. The clang of the gong pierced his breast like a noise of remembered war.

When Jimmie was a little boy he began to be arrested. Before he reached a great age, he had a fair record. He developed too great a tendency to climb down from his truck and fight with other drivers. He had been in quite a number of miscellaneous fights, and in some general barroom rows that had become known to the police. Once he had been arrested for assaulting a Chinaman. Two women in different parts of the city, and entirely unknown to each other, caused him considerable annoyance by breaking forth, simultaneously, at fateful intervals, into wailings about marriage and support and infants.

Nevertheless, he had, on a certain star-lit evening, said wonderingly and quite reverently, "Deh moon looks like hell, don't it?"

V

The girl, Maggie, blossomed in a mud-puddle. She grew to be a most rare and wonderful production of a tenement district, a pretty girl. None of the dirt of Rum Alley seemed to be in her veins. The philosophers, upstairs, downstairs, and on the same floor, puzzled over it. When a child, playing and fighting with gamins in the street, dirt disgusted her. Attired in tatters and grime, she went unseen.

There came a time, however, when the young men of the vicinity said, "Dat Johnson goil is a putty good looker." About this period her brother remarked to her: "Mag, I'll tell yeh dis! See? Yeh've eeder got t'go on d' toif er go t' work!" Whereupon she went to work, having the feminine aversion to the alternative. By a chance, she got a position in an establishment where they made collars and cuffs. She received a stool and a machine in a room where sat twenty girls of various shades of yellow discontent. She perched on the stool and treadled at her machine all day, turning out collars with a name which might have been noted for its irrelevancy to anything connected with collars. At night she returned home to her mother.

Jimmie grew large enough to take the vague position of head of the family. As incumbent of that office, he stumbled upstairs late at night, as his father had done before him. He reeled about the room, swearing at his relations, or went to sleep on the floor.

The mother had gradually risen to such a degree of fame that she could bandy words with her acquaintances among the police justices. Court officials called her by her first name. When she appeared they pursued a course which had been theirs for months. They invariably grinned, and cried out, "Hello, Mary, you here again?" Her grey head wagged in many courts. She always besieged the bench with voluble excuses, explanations, apologies, and prayers. Her flaming face and rolling eyes were a familiar sight on the island. She measured time by means of sprees, and was swollen and dishevelled.

One day the young man Pete, who as a lad had smitten the Devil's Row urchin in the back of the head and put to flight the antagonists of his friend Jimmie, strutted upon the scene. He met Jimmie one day on the street, promised to take him to a boxing match in Williamsburg, and called for him in the evening.

Maggie observed Pete.

He sat on a table in the Johnson home, and dangled his checked legs with an enticing nonchalance. His hair was curled down over his forehead in an oiled bang. His pugged nose seemed to revolt from contact with a bristling moustache of short, wire-like hairs. His blue double-breasted coat, edged with black braid, was buttoned close to a red puff tie, and his patent leather shoes looked like weapons. His mannerisms stamped him as a man who had a correct sense of his personal superiority. There were valour and contempt for circumstances in the glance of his eye. He waved his hands like a man of the world who dismisses religion and philosophy, and says "Rats!"

He had certainly seen everything, and with each curl of his lip he declared that it amounted to nothing. Maggie thought he must be a very "elegant" bartender.

He was telling tales to Jimmie. Maggie watched him furtively, with half-closed eyes lit with a vague interest.

"Hully gee! Dey makes me tired," he said. "Mos' e'ry day some farmer comes in an' tries t' run d' shop. See? But d' gits t'rowed right out. I jolt dem right out in d' street before dey knows where dey is. See?"

"Sure," said Jimmie.

"Dere was a mug come in d' place d' odder day wid an idear he was goin' t' own d' place. Hully gee! he was goin' t' own d' place. I see he had a still on, an' I didn' wanna giv 'im no stuff, so I says, 'Git outa here an' don' make no trouble,' I says like dat. See? 'Git outa here an' don' make no trouble'; like dat. 'Git outa here,' I says. See?"

Jimmie nodded understandingly. Over his features played an eager desire to state the amount of his valour in a similar crisis, but the narrator proceeded.

"Well, deh blokie he says: 'T' blazes wid it! I ain' lookin' for no scrap,' he says—see?—'but,' he says, 'I'm 'spectable cit'zen an' I wanna drink, an' quick, too.' See? 'Aw, go ahn!' I says, like dat. 'Aw, go ahn,' I says. See? 'Don' make no trouble,' I says, like dat. 'Don' make no trouble.' See? Den d' mug, he squared off an' said he was fine as silk wid his dukes—see?—an' he wan'ed a drink—quick. Dat's what he said. See?"

"Sure," repeated Jimmie.

Pete continued. "Say, I jes' jumped d' bar, an' d' way I plunked dat blokie was outa sight. See? Dat's right! In d' jaw! See? Hully gee! he t'rowed a spittoon t'rough d' front windee. Say, I t'ought I'd drop dead. But d' boss, he comes in after, an' he says: 'Pete, yehs done jes' right! Yeh've gotta keep order, an' it's all right.' See? 'It's all right,' he says. Dat's what he said."

The two held a technical discussion.

"Dat bloke was a dandy," said Pete in conclusion, "but he hadn' oughta made no trouble. Dat's what I says t' dem: 'Don'

come in here an' make no trouble,' I says, like dat. 'Don' make
no trouble.' See?"

As Jimmie and his friend exchanged tales descriptive of their
prowess, Maggie leaned back in the shadow. Her eyes dwelt
wonderingly and rather wistfully upon Pete's face. The broken
furniture, grimy walls, and general disorder and dirt of her
home of a sudden appeared before her and began to take a
potential aspect. Pete's aristocratic person looked as if it
might soil. She looked keenly at him, occasionally wondering
if he was feeling contempt. But Pete seemed to be enveloped
in reminiscence.

"Hully gee!" said he, "dose mugs can't feaze me. Dey knows
I kin wipe up d' street wid any t'ree of dem."

When he said, "Ah, what d' hell!" his voice was burdened
with disdain for the inevitable and contempt for anything that
fate might compel him to endure.

Maggie perceived that here was the ideal man. Her dim
thoughts were often searching for far-away lands where the
little hills sing together in the morning. Under the trees of her
dream-gardens there had always walked a lover.

VI

Pete took note of Maggie. "Say, Mag, I'm stuck on yer shape.
It's outa sight," he said parenthetically, with an affable grin.

As he became aware that she was listening closely, he grew
still more eloquent in his description of various happenings in
his career. It appeared that he was invincible in fights. "Why,"
he said, referring to a man with whom he had had a misunderstanding, "dat mug scrapped like a dago. Dat's right. He was
dead easy. See? He t'ought he was a scrapper. But he foun' out
diff'ent. Hully gee!"

He walked to and fro in the small room, which seemed then
to grow even smaller and unfit to hold his dignity, the attribute
of a supreme warrior. That swing of the shoulders which had
frozen the timid when he was but a lad had increased with
his growth and education in the ratio of ten to one. It, com-

bined with the sneer upon his mouth, told mankind that there
was nothing in space which could appal him. Maggie marvelled at him and surrounded him with greatness. She vaguely
tried to calculate the altitude of the pinnacle from which he
must have looked down upon her.

"I met a chump deh odder day way up in deh city," he said.
"I was goin' teh see a frien' of mine. When I was a-crossin' deh
street deh chump runned plump inteh me, an' den he turns
aroun' an' says, 'Yer insolen' ruffin!' he says, like dat. 'Oh, gee!'
I says, 'oh, gee! git off d' eart'!' I says, like dat. See? 'Git off d'
eart'!' like dat. Den deh blokie he got wild. He says I was a
contempt'ble scoun'el, er somethin' like dat, an' he says I was
doom' teh everlastin' pe'dition, er somethin' like dat. 'Gee!' I
says, 'gee! Yer joshin' me,' I says. 'Yer joshin' me.' An' den I
slugged 'im. See?"

With Jimmie in his company, Pete departed in a sort of
blaze of glory from the Johnson home. Maggie, leaning from
the window, watched him as he walked down the street. Here
was a formidable man who disdained the strength of a world
full of fists. Here was one who had contempt for brass-clothed
power; one whose knuckles could ring defiantly against the
granite of law. He was a knight.

The two men went from under the glimmering street lamp
and passed into shadows. Turning, Maggie contemplated the
dark, dust-stained walls, and the scant and crude furniture of
her home. A clock, in a splintered and battered oblong box
of varnished wood, she suddenly regarded as an abomination.
She noted that it ticked raspingly. The almost vanished flowers
in the carpet pattern, she conceived to be newly hideous. Some
faint attempts which she had made with blue ribbon to
freshen the appearance of a dingy curtain, she now saw to be
piteous.

She wondered what Pete dined on.

She reflected upon the collar-and-cuff factory. It began to
appear to her mind as a dreary place of endless grinding.
Pete's elegant occupation brought him, no doubt, into con-

tact with people who had money and manners. It was probable that he had a large acquaintance with pretty girls. He must have great sums of money to spend.

To her the earth was composed of hardships and insults. She felt instant admiration for a man who openly defied it. She thought that if the grim angel of death should clutch his heart, Pete would shrug his shoulders and say, "Oh, ev'ryt'ing goes."

She anticipated that he would come again shortly. She spent some of her week's pay in the purchase of flowered cretonne for a lambrequin. She made it with infinite care, and hung it to the slightly careening mantel over the stove in the kitchen. She studied it with painful anxiety from different points in the room. She wanted it to look well on Sunday night when, perhaps, Jimmie's friend would come. On Sunday night, however, Pete did not appear. Afterward the girl looked at it with a sense of humiliation. She was now convinced that Pete was superior to admiration for lambrequins.

A few evenings later Pete entered with fascinating innovations in his apparel. As she had seen him twice and he wore a different suit each time, Maggie had a dim impression that his wardrobe was prodigious.

"Say, Mag," he said, "put on yer bes' duds Friday night an' I'll take yehs t' d' show. See?" He spent a few moments in flourishing his clothes, and then vanished without having glanced at the lambrequin.

Over the eternal collars and cuffs in the factory Maggie spent the most of three days in making imaginary sketches of Pete and his daily environment. She imagined some half-dozen women in love with him, and thought he must lean dangerously toward an indefinite one whom she pictured as endowed with great charms of person, but with an altogether contemptible disposition. She thought he must live in a blare of pleasure. He had friends and people who were afraid of him. She saw the golden glitter of the place where Pete was to take her. It would be an entertainment of many hues and many melodies, where she was afraid she might appear small and mouse-coloured.

Her mother drank whisky all Friday morning. With lurid face and tossing hair she cursed and destroyed furniture all Friday afternoon. When Maggie came home at half-past six her mother lay asleep amid the wreck of chairs and a table. Fragments of various household utensils were scattered about the floor. She had vented some phase of drunken fury upon the lambrequin. It lay in a bedraggled heap in the corner.

"Hah!" she snorted, sitting up suddenly, "where yeh been? Why don' yeh come home earlier? Been loafin' 'round d' streets. Yer gettin' t' be a reg'lar devil."

When Pete arrived, Maggie, in a worn black dress, was waiting for him in the midst of a floor strewn with wreckage. The curtain at the window had been pulled by a heavy hand and hung by one tack, dangling to and fro in the draught through the cracks at the sash. The knots of blue ribbons appeared like violated flowers. The fire in the stove had gone out. The displaced lids and open doors showed heaps of sullen grey ashes. The remnants of a meal, ghastly, lay in a corner. Maggie's mother, stretched on the floor, blasphemed, and gave her daughter a bad name.

VII

An orchestra of yellow silk women and bald-headed men, on an elevated stage near the centre of a great green-hued hall, played a popular waltz. The place was crowded with people grouped about little tables. A battalion of waiters slid among the throng, carrying trays of beer-glasses, and making change from the inexhaustible vaults of their trousers pockets. Little boys, in the costumes of French chefs, paraded up and down the irregular aisles vending fancy cakes. There was a low rumble of conversation and a subdued clinking of glasses. Clouds of tobacco smoke rolled and wavered high in air above the dull gilt of the chandeliers.

The vast crowd had an air throughout of having just quitted labour. Men with calloused hands, and attired in garments that showed the wear of an endless drudging for a living, smoked their pipes contentedly and spent five, ten, or perhaps fifteen cents for beer. There was a mere sprinkling of men who smoked cigars purchased elsewhere. The great body of the crowd was composed of people who showed that all day they strove with their hands. Quiet Germans, with maybe their wives and two or three children, sat listening to the music, with the expressions of happy cows. An occasional party of sailors from a war-ship, their faces pictures of sturdy health, spent the earlier hours of the evening at the small round tables. Very infrequent tipsy men, swollen with the value of their opinions, engaged their companions in earnest and confidential conversation. In the balcony, and here and there below, shone the impassive faces of women. The nationalities of the Bowery beamed upon the stage from all directions.

Pete walked aggressively up a side aisle and took seats with Maggie at a table beneath the balcony. "Two beehs!" Leaning back, he regarded with eyes of superiority the scene before them. This attitude affected Maggie strongly. A man who could regard such a sight with indifference must be accustomed to very great things. It was obvious that Pete had visited this place many times before, and was very familiar with it. A knowledge of this fact made Maggie feel little and new.

He was extremely gracious and attentive. He displayed the consideration of a cultured gentleman who knew what was due. "Say, what's eatin' yeh? Bring d' lady a big glass! What use is dat pony?"

"Don't be fresh, now," said the waiter, with some warmth, as he departed.

"Ah, git off d' eart'!" said Pete, after the other's retreating form.

Maggie perceived that Pete brought forth all his elegance

and all his knowledge of high-class customs for her benefit. Her heart warmed as she reflected upon his condescension.

The orchestra of yellow silk women and bald-headed men gave vent to a few bars of anticipatory music, and a girl, in a pink dress with short skirts, galloped upon the stage. She smiled upon the throng as if in acknowledgment of a warm welcome, and began to walk to and fro, making profuse gesticulations, and singing, in brazen soprano tones, a song the words of which were inaudible. When she broke into the swift rattling measures of a chorus some half-tipsy men near the stage joined in the rollicking refrain, and glasses were pounded rhythmically upon the tables. People leaned forward to watch her and to try to catch the words of the song. When she vanished there were long rollings of applause. Obedient to more anticipatory bars, she reappeared among the half-suppressed cheering of the tipsy men. The orchestra plunged into dance music, and the laces of the dancer fluttered and flew in the glare of gas-jets. She divulged the fact that she was attired in some half-dozen skirts. It was patent that any one of them would have proved adequate for the purpose for which skirts are intended. An occasional man bent forward, intent upon the pink stockings. Maggie wondered at the splendour of the costume and lost herself in calculations of the cost of the silks and laces.

The dancer's smile of enthusiasm was turned for ten minutes upon the faces of her audience. In the finale she fell into some of those grotesque attitudes which were at the time popular among the dancers in the theatres up-town, giving to the Bowery public the diversions of the aristocratic theatre-going public at reduced rates.

"Say, Pete," said Maggie, leaning forward, "dis is great."

"Sure!" said Pete, with proper complacence.

A ventriloquist followed the dancer. He held two fantastic dolls on his knees. He made them sing mournful ditties and say funny things about geography and Ireland.

"Do dose little men talk?" asked Maggie.

"Naw," said Pete, "it's some big jolly. See?"

Two girls, set down on the bills as sisters, came forth and sang a duet which is heard occasionally at concerts given under church auspices. They supplemented it with a dance, which, of course, can never be seen at concerts given under church auspices.

After they had retired, a woman of debatable age sang a negro melody. The chorus necessitated some grotesque waddlings supposed to be an imitation of a plantation darky, under the influence, probably, of music and the moon. The audience was just enthusiastic enough over it to make her return and sing a sorrowful lay, whose lines told of a mother's love, and a sweetheart who waited, and a young man who was lost at sea under harrowing circumstances. From the faces of a score or so in the crowd the self-contained look faded. Many heads were bent forward with eagerness and sympathy. As the last distressing sentiment of the piece was brought forth, it was greeted by the kind of applause which rings as sincere.

As a final effort, the singer rendered some verses which described a vision of Britain annihilated by America, and Ireland bursting her bonds. A carefully prepared climax was reached in the last line of the last verse, when the singer threw out her arms and cried, "The star-spangled banner." Instantly a great cheer swelled from the throats of this assemblage of the masses, most of them of foreign birth. There was a heavy rumble of booted feet thumping the floor. Eyes gleamed with sudden fire, and calloused hands waved frantically in the air.

After a few moments' rest, the orchestra played noisily, and a small fat man burst out upon the stage. He began to roar a song and to stamp back and forth before the footlights, wildly waving a silk hat and throwing leers broadcast. He made his face into fantastic grimaces until he looked like a devil on a Japanese kite. The crowd laughed gleefully. His short, fat legs were never still a moment. He shouted and roared and bobbed his shock of red wig until the audience broke out in excited applause.

Pete did not pay much attention to the progress of events upon the stage. He was drinking beer and watching Maggie. Her cheeks were blushing with excitement and her eyes were glistening. She drew deep breaths of pleasure. No thoughts of the atmosphere of the collar-and-cuff factory came to her.

With the final crash of the orchestra they jostled their way to the sidewalk in the crowd. Pete took Maggie's arm and pushed a way for her, offering to fight with a man or two. They reached Maggie's home at a late hour and stood for a moment in front of the gruesome doorway.

"Say, Mag," said Pete, "give us a kiss for takin' yeh t' d' show, will yer?"

Maggie laughed, as if startled, and drew away from him. "Naw, Pete," she said, "dat wasn't in it."

"Ah, why wasn't it?" urged Pete.

The girl retreated nervously.

"Ah, go ahn!" repeated he.

Maggie darted into the hall and up the stairs. She turned and smiled at him, then disappeared.

Pete walked slowly down the street. He had something of an astonished expression upon his features. He paused under a lamp-post and breathed a low breath of surprise. "Gee!" he said, "I wonner if I've been played fer a duffer."

VIII

As thoughts of Pete came to Maggie's mind, she began to have an intense dislike for all of her dresses. "What ails yeh? What makes ye be allus fixin' and fussin'?" her mother would frequently roar at her. She began to note with more interest the well-dressed women she met on the avenues. She envied elegance and soft palms. She craved those adornments of person which she saw every day on the street, conceiving them to be allies of vast importance to women. Studying faces, she thought many of the women and girls she chanced to meet smiled with serenity as though for ever cherished and watched over by those they loved.

The air in the collar-and-cuff establishment strangled her. She knew she was gradually and surely shrivelling in the hot, stuffy room. The begrimed windows rattled incessantly from the passing of elevated trains. The place was filled with a whirl of noises and odours. She became lost in thought as she looked at some of the grizzled women in the room, mere mechanical contrivances sewing seams and grinding out, with heads bent over their work, tales of imagined or real girlhood happiness, or of past drunks, or the baby at home, and unpaid wages. She wondered how long her youth would endure. She began to see the bloom upon her cheeks as something of value. She imagined herself, in an exasperating future, as a scrawny woman with an eternal grievance. She thought Pete to be a very fastidious person concerning the appearance of women.

She felt that she should love to see somebody entangle their fingers in the oily beard of the fat foreigner who owned the establishment. He was a detestable character. He wore white socks with low shoes. He sat all day delivering orations in the depths of a cushioned chair. His pocket-book deprived them of the power of retort. "What do you sink I pie fife dolla a week for? Play? No, py tamn!"

Maggie was anxious for a friend to whom she could talk about Pete. She would have liked to discuss his admirable mannerisms with a reliable mutual friend. At home, she found her mother often drunk and always raving. It seemed that the world had treated this woman very badly, and she took a deep revenge upon such portions of it as came within her reach. She broke furniture as if she were at last getting her rights. She swelled with virtuous indignation as she carried the lighter articles of household use, one by one, under the shadows of the three gilt balls, where Hebrews chained them with chains of interest.

Jimmie came when he was obliged to by circumstances over

which he had no control. His well-trained legs brought him staggering home and put him to bed some nights when he would rather have gone elsewhere.

Swaggering Pete loomed like a golden sun to Maggie. He took her to a dime museum, where rows of meek freaks astonished her. She contemplated their deformities with awe, and thought them a sort of chosen tribe. Pete, racking his brains for amusement, discovered the Central Park Menagerie and the Museum of Arts. Sunday afternoons would sometimes find them at these places. Pete did not appear to be particularly interested in what he saw. He stood around looking heavy, while Maggie giggled in glee.

Once at the menagerie he went into a trance of admiration before the spectacle of a very small monkey threatening to thrash a cageful because one of them had pulled his tail and he had not wheeled about quickly enough to discover who did it. Ever after Pete knew that monkey by sight, and winked at him, trying to induce him to fight with other and larger monkeys.

At the museum, Maggie said, "Dis is outa sight!"

"Aw, rats!" said Pete; "wait till next summer an' I'll take yehs to a picnic."

While the girl wandered in the vaulted rooms, Pete occupied himself in returning, stony stare for stony stare, the appalling scrutiny of the watch-dogs of the treasures. Occasionally he would remark in loud tones, "Dat jay has got glass eyes," and sentences of the sort. When he tired of this amusement he would go to the mummies and moralize over them.

Usually he submitted with silent dignity to all that he had to go through, but at times he was goaded into comment. "Aw!" he demanded once. "Look at all dese little jugs! Hundred jugs in a row! Ten rows in a case, an' 'bout a t'ousand cases! What d' blazes use is dem?"

In the evenings of week days he often took her to see plays in which the dazzling heroine was rescued from the palatial home of her treacherous guardian by the hero with the beauti-

ful sentiments. The latter spent most of his time out at soak
in pale-green snow-storms, busy with a nickel-plated revolver
rescuing aged strangers from villains. Maggie lost herself in
sympathy with the wanderers swooning in snow-storms beneath happy-hued church windows, while a choir within sang
"Joy to the World." To Maggie and the rest of the audience
this was transcendental realism. Joy always within, and they,
like the actor, inevitably without. Viewing it, they hugged
themselves in ecstatic pity of their imagined or real condition.
The girl thought the arrogance and granite-heartedness of the
magnate of the play were very accurately drawn. She echoed
the maledictions that the occupants of the gallery showered on
this individual when his lines compelled him to expose his extreme selfishness.

Shady persons in the audience revolted from the pictured
villainy of the drama. With untiring zeal they hissed vice and
applauded virtue. Unmistakably bad men evinced an apparently sincere admiration for virtue. The loud gallery was over-
whelmingly with the unfortunate and the oppressed. They
encouraged the struggling hero with cries, and jeered the
villain, hooting and calling attention to his whiskers. When
anybody died in the pale-green snow-storms, the gallery
mourned. They sought out the painted misery and hugged it
as akin.

In the hero's erratic march from poverty in the first act to
wealth and triumph in the final one, in which he forgives all
the enemies that he has left, he was assisted by the gallery,
which applauded his generous and noble sentiments and
confounded the speeches of his opponents by making irrelevant but very sharp remarks. Those actors who were cursed
with the parts of villains were confronted at every turn by
the gallery. If one of them rendered lines containing the most
subtile distinctions between right and wrong, the gallery was
immediately aware that the actor meant wickedness, and denounced him accordingly. The last act was a triumph for the
hero, poor and of the masses, the representative of the audi-

ence, over the villain and the rich man, his pockets stuffed
with bonds, his heart packed with tyrannical purposes, imperturbable amid suffering.

Maggie always departed with raised spirits from these
melodramas. She rejoiced at the way in which the poor and
virtuous eventually overcame the wealthy and wicked. The
theatre made her think. She wondered if the culture and re-
finement she had seen imitated, perhaps grotesquely, by the
heroine on the stage, could be acquired by a girl who lived in
a tenement house and worked in a shirt factory.

IX

A group of urchins were intent upon the side door of a saloon. Expectancy gleamed from their eyes. They were twisting
their fingers in excitement. "Here she comes!" yelled one of
them suddenly. The group of urchins burst instantly asunder
and its individual fragments were spread in a wide, respectable
half-circle about the point of interest. The saloon door opened
with a crash, and the figure of a woman appeared upon the
threshold. Her grey hair fell in knotted masses about her
shoulders. Her face was crimsoned and wet with perspiration.
Her eyes had a rolling glare. "Not a cent more of me money
will yehs ever get—not a red! I spent me money here fer t'ree
years, an' now yehs tells me yeh'll sell me no more stuff! Go
fall on yerself, Johnnie Murckre! 'Disturbance'? Disturbance
be blowed! Go fall on yerself, Johnnie—"

The door received a kick of exasperation from within, and
the woman lurched heavily out on the sidewalk. The gamins
in the half-circle became violently agitated. They began to
dance about and hoot and yell and jeer. A wide dirty grin
spread over each face.

The woman made a furious dash at a particularly outrageous
cluster of little boys. They laughed delightedly, and scampered
off a short distance, calling out to her over their shoulders.
She stood tottering on the kerb-stone and thundered at them.
"Yeh devil's kids!" she howled, shaking her fists. The little boys

whooped in glee. As she started up the street they fell in behind and marched uproariously. Occasionally she wheeled about and made charges on them. They ran nimbly out of reach and taunted her.

In the frame of a gruesome doorway she stood for a moment cursing them. Her hair straggled, giving her red features a look of insanity. Her great fists quivered as she shook them madly in the air. The urchins made terrific noises until she turned and disappeared. Then they filed off quietly in the way they had come.

The woman floundered about in the lower hall of the tenement house, and finally stumbled up the stairs. On an upper hall a door was opened and a collection of heads peered curiously out, watching her. With a wrathful snort the woman confronted the door, but it was slammed hastily in her face and the key was turned.

She stood for a few minutes, delivering a frenzied challenge at the panels. "Come out in deh hall, Mary Murphy, if yehs want a scrap! Come ahn! yeh overgrown terrier, come ahn!" She began to kick the door. She shrilly defied the universe to appear and do battle. Her cursing trebles brought heads from all doors save the one she threatened. Her eyes glared in every direction. The air was full of her tossing fists. "Come ahn! deh hull gang of yehs, come ahn!" she roared at the spectators. An oath or two, catcalls, jeers, and bits of facetious advice were given in reply. Missiles clattered about her feet.

"What's wrong wi'che?" said a voice in the gathered gloom, and Jimmie came forward. He carried a tin dinner-pail in his hand and under his arm a truckman's brown apron done in a bundle. "What's wrong?" he demanded.

"Come out! all of yehs, come out," his mother was howling. "Come ahn an' I'll stamp yer faces t'rough d' floor."

"Shet yer face, an' come home, yeh old fool!" roared Jimmie at her. She strode up to him and twirled her fingers in his face. Her eyes were darting flames of unreasoning rage, and her frame trembled with eagerness for a fight.

"An' who are youse? I ain't givin' a snap of me fingers fer youse!" she bawled at him. She turned her huge back in tremendous disdain and climbed the stairs to the next floor.

Jimmie followed, and at the top of the flight he seized his mother's arm and started to drag her toward the door of their room. "Come home!" he gritted between his teeth.

"Take yer hands off me! Take yer hands off me!" shrieked his mother. She raised her arm and whirled her great fist at her son's face. Jimmie dodged his head, and the blow struck him in the back of the neck. "Come home!" he gritted again. He threw out his left hand and writhed his fingers about her middle arm. The mother and the son began to sway and struggle like gladiators.

"Whoop!" said the Rum Alley tenement house. The hall filled with interested spectators. "Hi, ol' lady, dat was a dandy!" "T'ree t' one on d' red!" "Ah, quit yer scrappin'!"

The door of the Johnson home opened and Maggie looked out. Jimmie made a supreme cursing effort and hurled his mother into the room. He quickly followed and closed the door. The Rum Alley tenement swore disappointedly and retired.

The mother slowly gathered herself up from the floor. Her eyes glittered menacingly upon her children.

"Here now," said Jimmie, "we've had enough of dis. Sit down, an' don' make no trouble."

He grasped her arm and, twisting it, forced her into a creaking chair.

"Keep yer hands off me!" roared his mother again.

"Say, yeh ol' bat! Quit dat!" yelled Jimmie, madly. Maggie shrieked and ran into the other room. To her there came the sound of a storm of crashes and curses. There was a great final thump and Jimmie's voice cried: "Dere, now! Stay still." Maggie opened the door now, and went warily out. "Oh, Jimmie!"

He was leaning against the wall and swearing. Blood stood upon bruises on his knotty forearms where they had scraped against the floor or the walls in the scuffle. The mother lay screeching on the floor, the tears running down her furrowed face.

Maggie, standing in the middle of the room, gazed about her. The usual upheaval of the tables and chairs had taken place. Crockery was strewn broadcast in fragments. The stove had been disturbed on its legs, and now leaned idiotically to one side. A pail had been upset and water spread in all directions.

The door opened and Pete appeared. He shrugged his shoulders. "Oh, gee!" he observed. He walked over to Maggie and whispered in her ear: "Ah, what d' hell, Mag? Come ahn and we'll have a outa-sight time."

The mother in the corner upreared her head and shook her tangled locks. "Aw, yer bote no good, needer of yehs," she said, glowering at her daughter in the gloom. Her eyes seemed to burn balefully. "Yeh've gone t' d' devil, Mag Johnson, yehs knows yehs have gone t' d' devil. Yer a disgrace t' yer people. An' now, git out an' go ahn wid dat doe-faced jude of yours. Go wid him, curse yeh, an' a good riddance. Go, an' see how yeh likes it."

Maggie gazed long at her mother.

"Go now, an' see how yeh likes it. Git out. I won't have sech as youse in me house! Git out, d' yeh hear! Damn yeh, git out!"

The girl began to tremble.

At this instant Pete came forward. "Oh, what d' hell, Mag, see?" whispered he softly in her ear. "Dis all blows over. See? D' ol' woman'ill be all right in d' mornin'. Come ahn out wid me! We'll have a outa-sight time."

The woman on the floor cursed. Jimmie was intent upon his bruised forearms. The girl cast a glance about the room filled with a chaotic mass of *débris,* and at the writhing body of her mother.

"Git th' devil outa here."

Maggie went.

X

Jimmie had an idea it wasn't common courtesy for a friend to come to one's home and ruin one's sister. But he was not sure how much Pete knew about the rules of politeness.

The following night he returned home from work at a rather late hour in the evening. In passing through the halls he came upon the gnarled and leathery old woman who possessed the music-box. She was grinning in the dim light that drifted through dust-stained panes. She beckoned to him with a smudged forefinger.

"Ah, Jimmie, what do yehs t'ink I tumbled to, las' night! It was deh funnies' t'ing I ever saw," she cried, coming close to him and leering. She was trembling with eagerness to tell her tale. "I was by me door las' night when yer sister and her jude feller came in late, oh, very late. An' she, the dear, she was a-cryin' as if her heart would break, she was. It was deh funnies' t'ing I ever saw. An' right out here by me door she asked him did he love her, did he. An' she was a-crying as if her heart would break, poor t'ing. An' him, I could see be deh way what he said it dat she had been askin' orften; he says, 'Oh, gee, yes,' he says, says he. 'Oh, gee, yes.' "

Storm-clouds swept over Jimmie's face, but he turned from the leathery old woman and plodded on upstairs.

" 'Oh, gee, yes,' " she called after him. She laughed a laugh that was like a prophetic croak.

There was no one in at home. The rooms showed that attempts had been made at tidying them. Parts of the wreckage of the day before had been repaired by an unskilled hand. A chair or two and the table stood uncertainly upon legs. The floor had been newly swept. The blue ribbons had been restored to the curtains, and the lambrequin, with its immense sheaves of yellow wheat and red roses of equal size, had been returned, in a worn and sorry state, to its place at the mantel. Maggie's jacket and hat were gone from the nail behind the door.

Jimmie walked to the window and began to look through the blurred glass. It occurred to him to wonder vaguely, for an instant, if some of the women of his acquaintance had brothers.

Suddenly, however, he began to swear. "But he was me frien'! I brought 'im here! Dat's d' devil of it!" He fumed about the room, his anger gradually rising to the furious pitch. "I'll kill deh jay! Dat's what I'll do! I'll kill deh jay!"

He clutched his hat and sprang toward the door. But it opened, and his mother's great form blocked the passage. "What's d' matter wid yeh?" exclaimed she, coming into the rooms.

Jimmie gave vent to a sardonic curse and then laughed heavily. "Well, Maggie's gone teh d' devil! Dat's what! See?"

"Eh?" said his mother.

"Maggie's gone teh d' devil! Are yehs deaf?" roared Jimmie, impatiently.

"Aw, git out!" murmured the mother, astounded.

Jimmie grunted, and then began to stare out the window. His mother sat down in a chair, but a moment later sprang erect and delivered a maddened whirl of oaths. Her son turned to look at her as she reeled and swayed in the middle of the room, her fierce face convulsed with passion, her blotched arms raised high in imprecation.

"May she be cursed for ever!" she shrieked. "May she eat nothin' but stones and deh dirt in deh street. May she sleep in deh gutter an' never see deh sun shine again. D' bloomin'—"

"Here now," said her son. "Go fall on yerself, an' quit dat."

The mother raised lamenting eyes to the ceiling. "She's d' devil's own chil', Jimmie," she whispered. "Ah, who would t'ink such a bad girl could grow up in our fambly, Jimmie, me son. Many d' hour I've spent in talk wid dat girl an' tol' her if she ever went on d' streets I'd see her damned. An' after all her bringin'-up an' what I tol' her and talked wid her, she goes teh d' bad, like a duck teh water."

The tears rolled down her furrowed face. Her hands trembled. "An den when dat Sadie MacMallister next door to us was sent teh d' devil by dat feller what worked in d' soap factory, didn't I tell our Mag dat if she—"

"Ah, dat's anudder story," interrupted the brother. "Of course, dat Sadie was nice an' all dat—but—see?—it ain't dessame as if—well, Maggie was diff'ent—see?—she was diff'ent." He was trying to formulate a theory that he had always unconsciously held, that all sisters excepting his own could, advisedly, be ruined.

He suddenly broke out again. "I'll go t'ump d' mug what done her d' harm. I'll kill 'im! He t'inks he kin scrap, but when he gits me a-chasin' 'im he'll fin' out where he's wrong, d' big stiff! I'll wipe up d' street wid 'im." In a fury he plunged out the doorway.

As he vanished the mother raised her head and lifted both hands, entreating. "May she be cursed for ever!" she cried.

In the darkness of the hallway Jimmie discerned a knot of women talking volubly. When he strode by they paid no attention to him. "She allus was a bold thing," he heard one of them cry in an eager voice. "Dere wasn't a feller come teh deh house but she'd try teh mash 'im. My Annie says deh shameless t'ing tried teh ketch her feller, her own feller, what we useter know his fader."

"I could 'a' tol' yehs dis two years ago," said a woman, in a key of triumph. "Yes, sir, it was over two years ago dat I says teh my ol' man, I says, 'Dat Johnson girl ain't straight,' I says. 'Oh, rats!' he says. 'Oh, hell!' 'Dat's all right,' I says, 'but I know what I knows,' I says, 'an' it'll come out later. You wait an' see,' I says, 'you see.'"

"Anybody what had eyes could see dat dere was somethin' wrong wid dat girl. I didn't like her actions."

On the street Jimmie met a friend. "What's wrong?" asked the latter.

Jimmie explained. "An' I'll t'ump 'im till he can't stand."

"Oh, go ahn!" said the friend. "What's deh use! Yeh'll git pulled in! Everybody'ill be on to it! An' ten plunks! Gee!"

Jimmie was determined. "He t'inks he kin scrap, but he'll fin' out diff'ent."

"Gee!" remonstrated the friend, "what's d' use?"

XI

On a corner a glass-fronted building shed a yellow glare upon the pavements. The open mouth of a saloon called seductively to passengers to enter and annihilate sorrow or create rage.

The interior of the place was papered in olive and bronze tints of imitation leather. A shining bar of counterfeit massiveness extended down the side of the room. Behind it a great mahogany-imitation sideboard reached the ceiling. Upon its shelves rested pyramids of shimmering glasses that were never disturbed. Mirrors set in the face of the sideboard multiplied them. Lemons, oranges, and paper napkins, arranged with mathematical precision, sat among the glasses. Many-hued decanters of liquor perched at regular intervals on the lower shelves. A nickel-plated cash-register occupied a place in the exact centre of the general effect. The elementary senses of it all seemed to be opulence and geometrical accuracy.

Across from the bar a smaller counter held a collection of plates upon which swarmed frayed fragments of crackers, slices of boiled ham, dishevelled bits of cheese, and pickles swimming in vinegar. An odour of grasping, begrimed hands and munching mouths pervaded all.

Pete, in a white jacket, was behind the bar bending expectantly toward a quiet stranger. "A beeh," said the man. Pete drew a foam-topped glassful, and set it dripping upon the bar.

At this moment the light bamboo doors at the entrance swung open and crashed against the wall. Jimmie and a companion entered. They swaggered unsteadily but belligerently toward the bar, and looked at Pete with bleared and blinking eyes.

"Gin," said Jimmie.

"Gin," said the companion.

Pete slid a bottle and two glasses along the bar. He bent his head sideways as he assiduously polished away with a napkin at the gleaming wood. He wore a look of watchfulness.

Jimmie and his companion kept their eyes upon the bartender and conversed loudly in tones of contempt.

"He's a dandy masher, ain't he?" laughed Jimmie

"Well, ain't he!" said the companion, sneering. "He's great, he is. Git on to deh mug on deh blokie. Dat's enough to make a feller turn handsprings in 'is sleep."

The quiet stranger moved himself and his glass a trifle farther away and maintained an attitude of obliviousness.

"Gee! ain't he hot stuff?"

"Git on to his shape!"

"Hey!" cried Jimmie, in tones of command. Pete came along slowly, with a sullen dropping of the under lip.

"Well," he growled, "what's eatin' yehs?"

"Gin," said Jimmie.

"Gin," said the companion.

As Pete confronted them with the bottle and the glasses they laughed in his face. Jimmie's companion, evidently overcome with merriment, pointed a grimy forefinger in Pete's direction. "Say, Jimmie," demanded he, "what's dat behind d' bar?"

"Looks like some chump," replied Jimmie. They laughed loudly.

Pete put down a bottle with a bang and turned a formidable face toward them. He disclosed his teeth, and his shoulders heaved restlessly. "You fellers can't guy me," he said. "Drink yer stuff an' git out an' don' make no trouble."

Instantly the laughter faded from the faces of the two men, and expressions of offended dignity immediately came. "Aw, who has said anyt'ing t' you?" cried they in the same breath.

The quiet stranger looked at the door calculatingly.

"Ah, come off," said Pete to the two men. "Don't pick me up fer no jay. Drink yer rum an' git out an' don' make no trouble."

"Aw, go ahn!" airily cried Jimmie.

"Aw, go ahn!" airily repeated his companion.

"We goes when we git ready! See?" continued Jimmie.

"Well," said Pete in a threatening voice, "don' make no trouble."

Jimmie suddenly leaned forward with his head on one side. He snarled like a wild animal. "Well, what if we does? See?" said he.

Hot blood flushed into Pete's face, and he shot a lurid glance at Jimmie. "Well, den we'll see who's d' bes' man, you or me," he said.

The quiet stranger moved modestly toward the door.

Jimmie began to swell with valour. "Don' pick me up fer no tenderfoot. When yeh tackles me yeh tackles one of d' bes' men in d' city. See? I'm a scrapper, I am. Ain't dat right, Billie?"

"Sure, Mike," responded his companion in tones of conviction.

"Aw!" said Pete, easily. "Go fall on yerself."

The two men again began to laugh.

"What is dat talking?" cried the companion.

"Don' ast me," replied Jimmie with exaggerated contempt.

Pete made a furious gesture. "Git outa here now, an' don' make no trouble. See? Youse fellers er lookin' fer a scrap, an' it's like yeh'll fin' one if yeh keeps on shootin' off yer mout's. I know yehs! See? I kin lick better men dan yehs ever saw in yer lifes. Dat's right! See? Don' pick me up fer no stiff, er yeh might be jolted out in d' street before yeh knows where yeh is. When I comes from behind dis bar, I t'rows yehs bote inteh d' street. See?"

"Ah, go ahn!" cried the two men in chorus.

The glare of a panther came into Pete's eyes. "Dat's what I said! Unnerstan'?"

He came through a passage at the end of the bar and swelled down upon the two men. They stepped promptly forward and crowded close to him. They bristled like three roosters. They moved their heads pugnaciously and kept their shoulders braced. The nervous muscles about each mouth twitched with a forced smile of mockery.

"Well, what yer goin' t' do? gritted Jimmie.

Pete stepped warily back, waving his hands before him to keep the men from coming too near.

"Well, what yer goin' t' do?" repeated Jimmie's ally. They kept close to him, taunting and leering. They strove to make him attempt the initial blow.

"Keep back now! Don' crowd me," said Pete ominously.

Again they chorused in contempt. "Aw, go ahn!"

In a small, tossing group, the three men edged for positions like frigates contemplating battle.

"Well, why don' yeh try t' t'row us out?" cried Jimmie and his ally with copious sneers.

The bravery of bulldogs sat upon the faces of the men. Their clenched fists moved like eager weapons. The allied two jostled the bartender's elbows, glaring at him with feverish eyes and forcing him toward the wall.

Suddenly Pete swore furiously. The flash of action gleamed from his eyes. He threw back his arm and aimed a tremendous, lightning-like blow at Jimmie's face. His foot swung a step forward and the weight of his body was behind his fist. Jimmie ducked his head, Bowery-like, with the quickness of a cat. The fierce answering blows of Jimmie and his ally crushed on Pete's bowed head.

The quiet stranger vanished.

The arms of the combatants whirled in the air like flails. The faces of the men, at first flushed to flame-coloured anger, now began to fade to the pallor of warriors in the blood and heat of a battle. Their lips curled back and stretched tightly over the gums in ghoul-like grins. Through their white, gripped teeth struggled hoarse whisperings of oaths. Their eyes glittered with murderous fire.

Each head was huddled between its owner's shoulders, and arms were swinging with marvellous rapidity. Feet scraped to and fro with a loud scratching sound upon the sanded floor. Blows left crimson blotches upon the pale skin. The curses of the first quarter-minute of the fight died away. The breaths of the fighters came wheezing from their lips and the three chests were straining and heaving. Pete at intervals gave vent to low, laboured hisses, that sounded like a desire to kill. Jimmie's ally gibbered at times like a wounded maniac. Jimmie was silent, fighting with the face of a sacrificial priest. The rage of fear shone in all their eyes, and their blood-coloured fists whirled.

At a critical moment a blow from Pete's hand struck the ally, and he crashed to the floor. He wriggled instantly to his feet and, grasping the quiet stranger's beer-glass from the bar, hurled it at Pete's head.

High on the wall it burst like a bomb, shivering fragments flying in all directions. Then missiles came to every man's hand. The place had heretofore appeared free of things to throw, but suddenly glasses and bottles went singing through the air. They were thrown point-blank at bobbing heads. The pyramids of shimmering glasses, that had never been disturbed, changed to cascades as heavy bottles were flung into them. Mirrors splintered to nothing.

The three frothing creatures on the floor buried themselves in a frenzy for blood. There followed in the wake of missiles and fists some unknown prayers, perhaps for death.

The quiet stranger had sprawled very pyrotechnically out on the sidewalk. A laugh ran up and down the avenue for the half of a block. "Dey've t'rowed a bloke inteh deh street."

People heard the sound of breaking glass and shuffling feet within the saloon and came running. A small group, bending down to look under the bamboo doors, and watching the fall of glass and three pairs of violent legs, changed in a moment to a crowd. A policeman came charging down the sidewalk and bounced through the doors into the saloon. The crowd bent and surged in absorbing anxiety to see.

Jimmie caught the first sight of the oncoming interruption. On his feet he had the same regard for a policeman that, when on his truck, he had for a fire-engine. He howled and ran for the side door.

The officer made a terrific advance, club in hand. One comprehensive sweep of the long night-stick threw the ally to the floor and forced Pete to a corner. With his disengaged hand he made a furious effort at Jimmie's coat-tails. Then he regained his balance and paused. "Well, well, you are a pair of pictures. What have ye been up to?"

Jimmie, with his face drenched in blood, escaped up a side street, pursued a short distance by some of the more law-loving or excited individuals of the crowd.

Later, from a safe dark corner, he saw the policeman, the ally, and the bartender emerge from the saloon. Pete locked the doors and then followed up the avenue in the rear of the crowd-encompassed policeman and his charge.

At first Jimmie, with his heart throbbing at battle heat, started to go desperately to the rescue of his friend, but he halted. "Ah, what's d' use?" he demanded of himself.

XII

In a hall of irregular shape sat Pete and Maggie drinking beer. A submissive orchestra dictated to by a spectacled man with frowsy hair and in soiled evening dress, industriously followed the bobs of his head and the waves of his baton. A ballad-singer, in a gown of flaming scarlet, sang in the inevitable voice of brass. When she vanished, men seated at the tables near the front applauded loudly, pounding the polished wood with their beer-glasses. She returned attired in less gown, and sang again. She received another enthusiastic encore. She reappeared in still less gown and danced. The deafening rumble of glasses and clapping of hands that followed her exit indicated an overwhelming desire to have her come on for the fourth time, but the curiosity of the audience was not gratified.

Maggie was pale. From her eyes had been plucked all look of self-reliance. She leaned with a dependent air toward her companion. She was timid, as if fearing his anger or displeasure. She seemed to beseech tenderness of him.

Pete's air of distinguished valour had grown upon him until it threatened to reach stupendous dimensions. He was infinitely gracious to the girl. It was apparent to her that his condescension was a marvel. He could appear to strut even while sitting still, and he showed that he was a lion of lordly characteristics by the air with which he spat.

With Maggie gazing at him wonderingly, he took pride in commanding the waiters, who were, however, indifferent or deaf. "Hi, you, git a russle on yehs! What yehs lookin' at? Two more beehs, d' yeh hear?" He leaned back and critically regarded the person of a girl with a straw-coloured wig who was flinging her heels about upon the stage in somewhat awkward imitation of a well-known *danseuse.*

At times Maggie told Pete long confidential tales of her former home life, dwelling upon the escapades of the other members of the family and the difficulties she had had to combat in order to obtain a degree of comfort. He responded in the accents of philanthropy. He pressed her arm with an air of reassuring proprietorship.

"Dey was cursed jays," he said, denouncing the mother and brother.

The sound of the music which, through the efforts of the frowsy-headed leader, drifted to her ears in the smoke-filled atmosphere, made the girl dream. She thought of her former Rum Alley environment and turned to regard Pete's strong protecting fists. She thought of a collar-and-cuff manufactory and the eternal moan of the proprietor: "What een hale do you sink I pie fife dolla a week for? Play? No, py tamn!" She contemplated Pete's man-subduing eyes and noted that wealth and prosperity were indicated by his clothes. She imagined a future rose-tinted because of its distance from all that she had experienced before.

As to the present she perceived only vague reasons to be miserable. Her life was Pete's, and she considered him worthy of the charge. She would be disturbed by no particular apprehensions so long as Pete adored her as he now said he did. She did not feel like a bad woman. To her knowledge she had never seen any better.

At times men at other tables regarded the girl furtively. Pete, aware of it, nodded at her and grinned. He felt proud. "Mag, yer a bloomin' good looker," he remarked, studying her face through the haze. The men made Maggie fear, but she blushed at Pete's words as it became apparent to her that she was the apple of his eye.

Grey-headed men, wonderfully pathetic in their dissipation, stared at her through clouds. Smooth-cheeked boys, some of them with faces of stone and mouths of sin, not nearly so pathetic as the grey heads, tried to find the girl's eyes in the smoke-wreaths. Maggie considered she was not what they thought her. She confined her glances to Pete and the stage.

The orchestra played negro melodies, and a versatile drummer pounded, whacked, clattered, and scratched on a dozen machines to make noise.

Those glances of the men, shot at Maggie from under half-closed lids, made her tremble. She thought them all to be worse men than Pete. "Come, let's go," she said.

As they went out Maggie perceived two women seated at a table with some men. They were painted, and their cheeks had lost their roundness. As she passed them the girl, with a shrinking movement, drew back her skirts.

XIII

Jimmie did not return home for a number of days after the fight with Pete in the saloon. When he did, he approached with extreme caution.

He found his mother raving. Maggie had not returned home. The parent continually wondered how her daughter could come to such a pass. She had never considered Maggie as a pearl dropped unstained into Rum Alley from Heaven, but she could not conceive how it was possible for her daughter to fall so low as to bring disgrace upon her family. She was terrific in denunciation of the girl's wickedness.

The fact that the neighbours talked of it maddened her. When women came in, and in the course of their conversation casually asked, "Where's Maggie dese days?" the mother shook her fuzzy head at them and appalled them with curses. Cunning hints inviting confidence she rebuffed with violence.

"An' wid all d' bringin'-up she had, how could she?" moaningly she asked of her son. "Wid all d' talkin' wid her I did an' d' t'ings I tol' her to remember. When a girl is bringed up d' way I bringed up Maggie, how kin she go teh d' devil?"

Jimmie was transfixed by these questions. He could not conceive how, under the circumstances, his mother's daughter and his sister could have been so wicked.

His mother took a drink from a bottle that sat on the table. She continued her lament. "She had a bad heart, dat girl did, Jimmie. She was wicked t' d' heart an' we never knowed it."

Jimmie nodded, admitting the fact.

"We lived in d' same house wid her an' I brought her up, an' we never knowed how bad she was."

Jimmie nodded again.

"Wid a home like dis an' a mudder like me, she went teh d' bad," cried the mother, raising her eyes.

One day Jimmie came home, sat down in a chair, and began to wriggle about with a new and strange nervousness. At last he spoke shamefacedly. "Well, look-a-here, dis t'ing queers us! See? We're queered! An' maybe it 'ud be better if I—well, I t'ink I kin look 'er up an'—maybe it 'ud be better if I fetched her home an'—"

The mother started from her chair and broke forth into a storm of passionate anger. "What! Let 'er come an' sleep under deh same roof wid her mudder agin? Oh, yes, I will, won't I! Sure! Shame on yehs, Jimmie Johnson, fer sayin' such a t'ing teh yer own mudder! Little did I t'ink when yehs was a baby playin' about me feet dat ye'd grow up teh say sech a t'ing teh yer mudder—yer own mudder. I never t'ought—"

Sobs choked her and interrupted her reproaches.

"Dere ain't nottin' teh make sech trouble about," said Jimmie. "I on'y says it 'ud be better if we keep dis t'ing dark, see? It queers us! See?"

His mother laughed a laugh that seemed to ring through the city and be echoed and re-echoed by countless other laughs. "Oh, yes, I will, won't I? Sure!"

"Well, yeh must take me fer a damn fool," said Jimmie, indignant at his mother for mocking him. "I didn't say we'd make 'er inteh a little tin angel, ner nottin', but deh way it is now she can queer us! Don'che see?"

"Ay, she'll git tired of deh life atter a while, an' den she'll wanna be a-comin' home, won' she, deh beast! I'll let 'er in den, won't I?"

"Well, I didn't mean none of dis prod'gal bus'ness anyway," explained Jimmie.

"It wa'n't no prod'gal daughter, yeh fool," said the mother. "It was prod'gal son, anyhow."

"I know dat," said Jimmie.

For a time they sat in silence. The mother's eyes gloated on the scene which her imagination called before her. Her lips were set in a vindictive smile. "Ay, she'll cry, won' she, an' carry on, an' tell how Pete, or some odder feller, beats 'er, an' she'll say she's sorry an' all dat, an' she ain't happy, she ain't, an' she wants to come home agin, she does." With grim humour the mother imitated the possible wailing notes of the daughter's voice. "Den I'll take 'er in, won't I? She kin cry 'er two eyes out on deh stones of deh street before I'll dirty d' place wid her. She abused an' ill-treated her own mudder—her own mudder what loved her, an' she'll never git anodder chance."

Jimmie thought he had a great idea of women's frailty, but he could not understand why any of his kin should be victims. "Curse her!" he said fervidly. Again he wondered vaguely if some of the women of his acquaintance had brothers. Nevertheless, his mind did not for an instant confuse himself with those brothers nor his sister with theirs.

After the mother had, with great difficulty, suppressed the neighbours, she went among them and proclaimed her grief.

"May Heaven forgive dat girl," was her continual cry. To attentive ears she recited the whole length and breadth of her woes. "I bringed 'er up deh way a daughter oughta be bringed up, an' dis is how she served me! She went teh deh devil deh first chance she got! May Heaven forgive her."

When arrested for drunkenness she used the story of her daughter's downfall with telling effect upon the police justices. Finally one of them said to her, peering down over his spectacles: "Mary, the records of this and other courts show that you are the mother of forty-two daughters who have been ruined. The case is unparalleled in the annals of this court, and this court thinks—"

The mother went through life shedding large tears of sorrow. Her red face was a picture of agony.

Of course Jimmie publicly damned his sister that he might appear on a higher social plane. But, arguing with himself, stumbling about in ways that he knew not, he, once, almost came to a conclusion that his sister would have been more firmly good had she better known how. However, he felt that he could not hold such a view. He threw it hastily aside.

XIV

In a hilarious hall there were twenty-eight tables and twenty-eight women and a crowd of smoking men. Valiant noise was made on a stage at the end of the hall by an orchestra composed of men who looked as if they had just happened in. Soiled waiters ran to and fro, swooping down like hawks on the unwary in the throng; clattering along the aisles with trays covered with glasses; stumbling over women's skirts and charging two prices for everything but beer, all with a swiftness that blurred the view of the coconut palms and dusty monstrosities painted upon the walls of the room. A "bouncer," with an immense load of business upon his hands, plunged about in the crowd, dragging bashful strangers to prominent chairs, ordering waiters here and there, and quarrelling furiously with men who wanted to sing with the orchestra.

The usual smoke-cloud was present, but so dense that heads and arms seemed entangled in it. The rumble of conversation was replaced by a roar. Plenteous oaths heaved through the air. The room rang with the shrill voices of women bubbling over with drink-laughter. The chief element in the music of the orchestra was speed. The musicians played in intent fury. A woman was singing and smiling upon the stage, but no one took notice of her. The rate at which the piano, cornet, and violins were going seemed to impart wildness to the half-drunken crowd. Beer-glasses were emptied at a gulp and conversation became a rapid chatter. The smoke eddied and swirled like a shadowy river hurrying toward some unseen falls. Pete and Maggie entered the hall and took chairs at a table near the door. The woman who was seated there made an attempt to occupy Pete's attention, and, failing, went away.

Three weeks had passed since the girl had left home. The air of spaniel-like dependence had been magnified and showed its direct effect in the peculiar off-handedness and ease of Pete's ways toward her. She followed Pete's eyes with hers, anticipating with smiles gracious looks from him.

A woman of brilliance and audacity, accompanied by a mere boy, came into the place and took a seat near them. At once Pete sprang to his feet, his face beaming with glad surprise. "Hully gee, dere's Nellie!" he cried. He went over to the table and held out an eager hand to the woman.

"Why, hello, Pete, me boy, how are you?" said she, giving him her fingers.

Maggie took instant note of the woman. She perceived that her black dress fitted her to perfection. Her linen collar and cuffs were spotless. Tan gloves were stretched over her well-shaped hands. A hat of a prevailing fashion perched jauntily upon her dark hair. She wore no jewellery and was painted with no apparent paint. She looked clear-eyed through the stares of the men.

"Sit down, and call your lady friend over," she said to Pete.

At his beckoning Maggie came and sat between Pete and the mere boy.

"I t'ought yeh was gone away fer good," began Pete, at once. "When did yeh git back? How did dat Buff'lo business turn out?"

The woman shrugged her shoulders. "Well, he didn't have as many stamps as he tried to make out, so I shook him, that's all."

"Well, I'm glad teh see yehs back in deh city," said Pete, with gallantry. He and the woman entered into a long converation, exchanging reminiscences of days together. Maggie sat still, unable to formulate an intelligent sentence as her addition to the conversation, and painfully aware of it.

She saw Pete's eyes sparkle as he gazed upon the handsome stranger. He listened smilingly to all she said. The woman was familiar with all his affairs, asked him about mutual friends, and knew the amount of his salary. She paid no attention to Maggie, looking toward her once or twice and apparently seeing the wall beyond.

The mere boy was sulky. In the beginning he had welcomed the additions with acclamations. "Let's all have a drink! What'll you take, Nell? And you, Miss What's-your-name. Have a drink, Mr. —— you, I mean." He had shown a sprightly desire to do the talking for the company and tell all about his family. In a loud voice he declaimed on various topics. He assumed a patronizing air toward Pete. As Maggie was silent, he paid no attention to her. He made a great show of lavishing wealth upon the woman of brilliance and audacity.

"Do keep still, Freddie! You talk like a clock," said the woman to him. She turned away and devoted her attention to Pete. "We'll have many a good time together again, eh?"

"Sure, Mike," said Pete, enthusiastic at once.

"Say," whispered she, leaning forward, "let's go over to Billie's and have a time."

"Well, it's dis way! See?" said Pete. "I got dis lady frien' here."

"Oh, g'way with her," argued the woman.

Pete appeared disturbed.

"All right," said she, nodding her head at him. "All right for you! We'll see the next time you ask me to go anywheres with you."

Pete squirmed. "Say," he said, beseechingly, "come wid me a minute an' I'll tell yer why."

The woman waved her hand. "Oh, that's all right, you needn't explain, you know. You wouldn't come merely because you wouldn't come, that's all." To Pete's visible distress she turned to the mere boy, bringing him speedily out of a terrific rage. He had been debating whether it would be the part of a man to pick a quarrel with Pete, or would he be justified in striking him savagely with his beer-glass without warning. But he recovered himself when the woman turned to renew her smilings. He beamed upon her with an expression that was somewhat tipsy and inexpressibly tender.

"Say, shake that Bowery jay," requested he, in a loud whisper.

"Freddie, you are so funny," she replied.

Pete reached forward and touched the woman on the arm. "Come out a minute while I tells yeh why I can't go wid yer. Yer doin' me dirt, Nell! I never t'ought ye'd do me dirt, Nell. Come on, will yer?" He spoke in tones of injury.

"Why, I don't see why I should be interested in your explanations," said the woman, with a coldness that seemed to reduce Pete to a pulp.

His eyes pleaded with her. "Come out a minute while I tells yeh. On d' level, now."

The woman nodded slightly at Maggie and the mere boy, saying, " 'Scuse me."

The mere boy interrupted his loving smile and turned a shrivelling glare upon Pete. His boyish countenance flushed and he spoke in a whine to the woman: "Oh, I say, Nellie, this ain't a square deal, you know. You aren't goin' to leave me and go off with that duffer, are you? I should think—"

"Why, you dear boy, of course I'm not," cried the woman, affectionately. She bent over and whispered in his ear. He smiled again and settled in his chair as if resolved to wait patiently.

As the woman walked down between the rows of tables, Pete was at her shoulder talking earnestly, apparently in explanation. The woman waved her hands with studied airs of indifference. The doors swung behind them, leaving Maggie and the mere boy seated at the table.

Maggie was dazed. She could dimly perceive that something stupendous had happened. She wondered why Pete saw fit to remonstrate with the woman, pleading forgiveness with his eyes. She thought she noted an air of submission about her leonine Pete. She was astounded.

The mere boy occupied himself with cocktails and a cigar. He was tranquilly silent for half an hour. Then he bestirred himself and spoke. "Well," he said, sighing, "I knew this was the way it would be. They got cold feet." There was another stillness. The boy seemed to be musing. "She was pulling m' leg. That's the whole amount of it," he said, suddenly. "It's a bloomin' shame the way that girl does. Why, I've spent over two dollars in drinks to-night. And she goes off with that plugugly, who looks as if he had been hit in the face with a coin die. I call it rocky treatment for a fellah like me. Here, waiter, bring me a cocktail, and make it strong."

Maggie made no reply. She was watching the doors.

"It's a mean piece of business," complained the mere boy. He explained to her how amazing it was that anybody should treat him in such a manner. "But I'll get square with her, you bet. She won't get far ahead of yours truly, you know," he added, winking. "I'll tell her plainly that it was bloomin' mean business. And she won't come it over me with any of her 'now-Freddie-dear's.' She thinks my name is Freddie, you know, but of course it ain't. I always tell these people some name like that, because if they got on to your right name they might use it sometime. Understand? Oh, they don't fool me much."

Maggie was paying no attention, being intent upon the doors. The mere boy relapsed into a period of gloom, during which he exterminated a number of cocktails with a determined air, as if replying defiantly to fate. He occasionally broke forth into sentences composed of invectives joined together in a long chain.

The girl was still staring at the doors. After a time the mere boy began to see cobwebs just in front of his nose. He spurred himself into being agreeable and insisted upon her having a Charlotte Russe and a glass of beer.

"They's gone," he remarked, "they's gone." He looked at her through the smoke-wreaths. "Shay, lil' girl, we mightish well make bes' of it. You ain't such bad-lookin' girl, y' know. Not half bad. Can't come up to Nell, though. No, can't do it! Well, I should shay not! Nell fine-lookin' girl! F-i-n-ine. You look bad longsider her, but by y'self ain't so bad. Have to do, anyhow. Nell gone. O'ny you left. Not half bad, though."

Maggie stood up. "I'm going home," she said.

The mere boy started. "Eh? What? Home!" he cried, struck with amazement. "I beg pardon, did hear say home?"

"I'm going home," she repeated.

"Great heavens! what hav' a struck?" demanded the mere boy of himself, stupefied. In a semi-comatose state he conducted her on board an up-town car, ostentatiously paid her fare, leered kindly at her through the rear window, and fell off the steps.

XV

A forlorn woman went along a lighted avenue. The street was filled with people desperately bound on missions. An endless crowd darted at the elevated station stairs, and the horse-cars were thronged with owners of bundles.

The pace of the forlorn woman was slow. She was apparently searching for some one. She loitered near the doors of saloons and watched men emerge from them. She furtively scanned the faces in the rushing stream of pedestrians. Hurrying men, bent on catching some boat or train, jostled her elbows, failing to notice her, their thoughts fixed on distant dinners.

The forlorn woman had a peculiar face. Her smile was no smile. But when in repose her features had a shadowy look that was like a sardonic grin, as if some one had sketched with cruel forefinger indelible lines about her mouth.

Jimmie came strolling up the avenue. The woman encountered him with an aggrieved air. "Oh, Jimmie, I've been lookin' all over for yehs—" she began.

Jimmie made an impatient gesture and quickened his pace. "Ah, don't bodder me!" he said, with the savageness of a man whose life is pestered.

The woman followed him along the sidewalk in somewhat the manner of a suppliant. "But, Jimmie," she said, "yehs told me yehs—"

Jimmie turned upon her fiercely as if resolved to make a last stand for comfort and peace. "Say, Hattie, don' foller me from one end of deh city teh deh odder. Let up, will yehs! Give me a minute's res', can't yehs? Yehs makes me tired, allus taggin' me. See? Ain' yehs got no sense? Do yehs want people teh get on to me? Go chase yerself."

The woman stepped closer and laid her fingers on his arm. "But, look a' here—"

Jimmie snarled. "Oh, go teh blazes!" He darted into the front door of a convenient saloon and a moment later came out into the shadows that surrounded the side door. On the brilliantly lighted avenue he perceived the forlorn woman dodging about like a scout. Jimmie laughed with an air of relief and went away.

When he returned home he found his mother clamouring. Maggie had returned. She stood shivering beneath the torrent of her mother's wrath.

"Well, I'm damned!" said Jimmie in greeting.

His mother, tottering about the room, pointed a quivering

forefinger. "Look ut her, Jimmie, look ut her. Dere's yer sister, boy. Dere's yer sister. Look ut her! Look ut her!" She screamed at Maggie with scoffing laughter.

The girl stood in the middle of the room. She edged about as if unable to find a place on the floor to put her feet.

"Ha ha, ha!" bellowed the mother. "Dere she stands! Ain't she purty? Look ut her! Ain' she sweet, deh beast? Look ut her! Ha, ha! look ut her!" She lurched forward and put her red and seamed hands upon her daughter's face. She bent down and peered keenly up into the eyes of the girl. "Oh, she's jes dessame as she ever was, ain' she? She's her mudder's putty darlin' yit, ain' she? Look ut her, Jimmie. Come here and look ut her."

The loud, tremendous railing of the mother brought the denizens of the Rum Alley tenement to their doors. Women came in the hallways. Children scurried to and fro.

"What's up? Dat Johnson party on anudder tear?"

"Naw. Young Mag's come home!"

"Git out!"

Through the open doors curious eyes stared in at Maggie. Children ventured into the room and ogled her as if they formed the front row at a theatre. Women, without, bent toward each other and whispered, nodding their heads with airs of profound philosophy.

A baby, overcome with curiosity concerning this object at which all were looking, sidled forward and touched her dress, cautiously, as if investigating a red-hot stove. Its mother's voice rang out like a warning trumpet. She rushed forward and grabbed her child, casting a terrible look of indignation at the girl.

Maggie's mother paced to and fro, addressing the doorful of eyes, expounding like a glib showman. Her voice rang through the building. "Dere she stands," she cried, wheeling suddenly and pointing with dramatic finger. "Dere she stands! Look ut her! Ain' she a dandy? An' she was so good as to come home teh her mudder, she was! Ain' she a beaut'? Ain' she a dandy?"

The jeering cries ended in another burst of shrill laughter.
The girl seemed to awaken. "Jimmie—"
He drew hastily back from her. "Well, now, yer a t'ing, ain'
yeh?" he said, his lips curling in scorn. Radiant virtue sat upon
his brow, and his repelling hands expressed horror of con-
tamination.

Maggie turned and went.

The crowd at the door fell back precipitately. A baby falling
down in front of the door wrenched a scream like that of a
wounded animal from its mother. Another woman sprang forward and picked it up with a chivalrous air, as if rescuing a human being from an oncoming express train.

As the girl passed down through the hall, she went before
open doors framing more eyes strangely microscopic, and sending broad beams of inquisitive light into the darkness of her
path. On the second floor she met the gnarled old woman who
possessed the music-box.

"So," she cried, " 'ere yehs are back again, are yehs? An' dey've
kicked yehs out? Well, come in an' stay wid me t'-night. I ain'
got no moral standin'."

From above came an unceasing babble of tongues, over all
of which rang the mother's derisive laughter.

XVI

Pete did not consider that he had ruined Maggie. If he had
thought that her soul could never smile again, he would have
believed the mother and brother, who were pyrotechnic over
the affair, to be responsible for it. Besides, in his world, souls
did not insist upon being able to smile. "What d' hell?"

He felt a trifle entangled. It distressed him. Revelations and
scenes might bring upon him the wrath of the owner of the
saloon, who insisted upon respectability of an advanced type.
"What do dey wanna raise such a smoke about it fer?" demanded he of himself, disgusted with the attitude of the family.
He saw no necessity that people should lose their equilibrium
merely because their sister or their daughter had stayed away

from home. Searching about in his mind for possible reasons for their conduct, he came upon the conclusion that Maggie's motives were correct, but that the two others wished to snare him. He felt pursued.

The woman whom he had met in the hilarious hall showed a disposition to ridicule him. "A little pale thing with no spirit," she said. "Did you note the expression of her eyes? There was something in them about pumpkin pie and virtue. That is a peculiar way the left corner of her mouth has of twitching, isn't it? Dear, dear, Pete, what are you coming to?"

Pete asserted at once that he never was very much interested in the girl. The woman interrupted him, laughing. "Oh, it's not of the slightest consequence to me, my dear young man. You needn't draw maps for my benefit. Why should I be concerned about it?" But Pete continued with his explanations. If he was laughed at for his tastes in women, he felt obliged to say that they were only temporary or indifferent ones.

The morning after Maggie had departed from home Pete stood behind the bar. He was immaculate in white jacket and apron, and his hair was plastered over his brow with infinite correctness. No customers were in the place. Pete was twisting his napkined fist slowly in a beer-glass, softly whistling to himself, and occasionally holding the object of his attention between his eyes and a few weak beams of sunlight that found their way over the thick screens and into the shaded rooms.

With lingering thoughts of the woman of brilliance and audacity, the bartender raised his head and stared through the varying cracks between the swaying bamboo doors. Suddenly the whistling pucker faded from his lips. He saw Maggie walking slowly past. He gave a great start, fearing for the previously mentioned eminent respectability of the place.

He threw a swift, nervous glance about him, all at once feeling guilty. No one was in the room. He went hastily over to the side door. Opening it and looking out, he perceived Maggie standing, as if undecided, at the corner. She was searching the place with her eyes. As she turned her face toward him, Pete beckoned to her hurriedly, intent upon returning with speed to a position behind the bar, and to the atmosphere of respectability upon which the proprietor insisted.

Maggie came to him, the anxious look disappearing from her face and a smile wreathing her lips. "Oh, Pete—" she began brightly.

The bartender made a violent gesture of impatience. "Oh, say," cried he vehemently. "What d' yeh wanna hang aroun' here fer? Do yer wanna git me inteh trouble?" he demanded with an air of injury.

Astonishment swept over the girl's features. "Why, Pete! yehs tol' me—"

Pete's glance expressed profound irritation. His countenance reddened with the anger of a man whose respectability is being threatened. "Say, yehs makes me tired! See! What d' yeh wanna tag aroun' atter me fer? Yeh'll do me dirt wid' d' ol' man an' dey'll be trouble! If he sees a woman roun' here he'll go crazy an' I'll lose me job! See? Ain' yehs got no sense? Don' be allus bodderin' me. See? Yer brudder came in here an' made trouble an' d' ol' man hadda put up fer it! An' now I'm done! See? I'm done."

The girl's eyes stared into his face. "Pete, don' yeh remem—"

"Oh, go ahn!" interrupted Pete, anticipating.

The girl seemed to have a struggle with herself. She was apparently bewildered and could not find speech. Finally she asked in a low voice, "But where kin I go?"

The question exasperated Pete beyond the powers of endurance. It was a direct attempt to give him some responsibility in a matter that did not concern him. In his indignation he volunteered information. "Oh, go to hell!" cried he. He slammed the door furiously and returned, with an air of relief, to his respectability.

Maggie went away. She wandered aimlessly for several blocks. She stopped once and asked aloud a question of herself: "Who?" A man who was passing near her shoulder humorously took the questioning word as intended for him. "Eh!

What? Who? Nobody! I didn't say anything," he laughingly said, and continued his way.

Soon the girl discovered that if she walked with such apparent aimlessness, some men looked at her with calculating eyes. She quickened her step, frightened. As a protection, she adopted a demeanour of intentness as if going somewhere.

After a time she left rattling avenues and passed between rows of houses with sternness and stolidity stamped upon their features. She hung her head, for she felt their eyes grimly upon her.

Suddenly she came upon a stout gentleman in a silk hat and a chaste black coat, whose decorous row of buttons reached from his chin to his knees. The girl had heard of the grace of God and she decided to approach this man. His beaming, chubby face was a picture of benevolence and kind-heartedness. His eyes shone good will.

But as the girl timidly accosted him he made a convulsive movement and saved his respectability by a vigorous side-step. He did not risk it to save a soul. For how was he to know that there was a soul before him that needed saving?

XVII

Upon a wet evening, several months later, two interminable rows of cars, pulled by slipping horses, jangled along a prominent side street. A dozen cabs, with coat-enshrouded drivers, clattered to and fro. Electric lights, whirring softly, shed a blurred radiance. A flower-dealer, his feet tapping impatiently, his nose and his wares glistening with raindrops, stood behind an array of roses and chrysanthemums. Two or three theatres emptied a crowd upon the stormswept sidewalks. Men pulled their hats over their eyebrows and raised their collars to their ears. Women shrugged impatient shoulders in their warm cloaks and stopped to arrange their skirts for a walk through the storm. People who had been constrained to comparative silence for two hours burst into a roar of conversation, their hearts still kindling from the glowings of the stage.

The sidewalks became tossing seas of umbrellas. Men stepped forth to hail cabs or cars, raising their fingers in varied forms of polite request or imperative demand. An endless procession wended toward elevated stations. An atmosphere of pleasure and prosperity seemed to hang over the throng, born, perhaps, of good clothes and of two hours in a place of forgetfulness.

In the mingled light and gloom of an adjacent park, a handful of wet wanderers, in attitudes of chronic dejection, were scattered among the benches.

A girl of the painted cohorts of the city went along the street. She threw changing glances at men who passed her, giving smiling invitations to those of rural or untaught pattern and usually seeming sedately unconscious of the men with a metropolitan seal upon their faces. Crossing glittering avenues, she went into the throng emerging from the places of forgetfulness. She hurried forward through the crowd as if intent upon reaching a distant home, bending forward in her handsome cloak, daintily lifting her skirts, and picking for her well-shod feet the dryer spots upon the sidewalks.

The restless doors of saloons, clashing to and fro, disclosed animated rows of men before bars and hurrying barkeepers. A concert-hall gave to the street faint sounds of swift, machine-like music, as if a group of phantom musicians were hastening.

A tall young man, smoking a cigarette with a sublime air, strolled near the girl. He had on evening dress, a moustache, a chrysanthemum, and a look of *ennui*, all of which he kept carefully under his eye. Seeing the girl walk on as if such a young man as he was not in existence, he looked back transfixed with interest. He stared glassily for a moment, but gave a slight convulsive start when he discerned that she was neither new, Parisian, nor theatrical. He wheeled about hastily and turned his stare into the air, like a sailor with a searchlight.

A stout gentleman, with pompous and philanthropic whiskers, went stolidly by, the broad of his back sneering at the girl. A belated man in business clothes, and in haste to catch a car, bounced against her shoulder. "Hi, there, Mary, I beg your pardon! Brace up, old girl." He grasped her arm to steady her, and then was away running down the middle of the street.

The girl walked on out of the realm of restaurants and saloons. She passed more glittering avenues and went into darker blocks than those where the crowd travelled.

A young man in light overcoat and Derby hat received a glance shot keenly from the eyes of the girl. He stopped and looked at her, thrusting his hands into his pockets and making a mocking smile curl his lips. "Come, now, old lady," he said, "you don't mean to tell me that you sized me up for a farmer?"

A labouring man marched along with bundles under his arms. To her remarks he replied, "It's a fine evenin', ain't it?"

She smiled squarely into the face of a boy who was hurrying by with his hands buried in his overcoat pockets, his blond locks bobbing on his youthful temples, and a cheery smile of unconcern upon his lips. He turned his head and smiled back at her, waving his hands. "Not this eve—some other eve."

A drunken man, reeling in her pathway, began to roar at her. "I ain' go' no money!" he shouted, in a dismal voice. He lurched on up the street, wailing to himself: "I ain' go' no money. Ba' luck. Ain' go' no more money."

The girl went into gloomy districts near the river, where the tall black factories shut in the street and only occasional broad beams of light fell across the sidewalks from saloons. In front of one of these places, whence came the sound of a violin vigorously scraped, the patter of feet on boards, and the ring of loud laughter, there stood a man with blotched features.

Farther on in the darkness she met a ragged being with shifting, bloodshot eyes and grimy hands.

She went into the blackness of the final block. The shutters of the tall buildings were closed like grim lips. The structures seemed to have eyes that looked over them, beyond them, at other things. Afar off the lights of the avenues glittered as if from an impossible distance. Street-car bells jingled with a sound of merriment.

At the feet of the tall buildings appeared the deathly black hue of the river. Some hidden factory sent up a yellow glare, that lit for a moment the waters lapping oilily against timbers. The varied sounds of life, made joyous by distance and seem-ing unapproachableness, came faintly and died away to a silence.

XVIII

In a partitioned-off section of a saloon sat a man with a half-dozen women, gleefully laughing, hovering about him. The man had arrived at that stage of drunkenness where affection is felt for the universe. "I'm good f'ler, girls," he said, convinc-ingly. "I'm good f'ler. An'body trea's me right, I allus trea's zem right! See?"

The women nodded their heads approvingly. "To be sure," they cried in hearty chorus. "You're the kind of a man we like, Pete. You're outa sight! What yeh goin' to buy this time, dear?"

"An't'ing yehs wants!" said the man in an abandonment of good will. His countenance shone with the true spirit of benev-olence. He was in the proper mood of missionaries. He would have fraternized with obscure Hottentots. And above all he was overwhelmed in tenderness for his friends, who were all illustrious. "An't'ing yehs wants!" repeated he, waving his hands with beneficent recklessness. "I'm good f'ler, girls, an' if an'body trea's me right I— Here," called he through an open door to a waiter, "bring girls drinks. What 'ill yehs have, girls? An't'ing yehs want."

The waiter glanced in with the disgusted look of the man who serves intoxicants for the man who takes too much of them. He nodded his head shortly at the order from each in-dividual, and went.

"W' 're havin' great time," said the man. "I like you girls! Yer right sort! See?" He spoke at length and with feeling con-cerning the excellences of his assembled friends. "Don' try pull man's leg, but have a good time! Dass right! Dass way teh do! Now, if I s'ought yehs tryin' work me fer drinks, wouldn' buy notting! But yer right sort! Yehs know how ter treat a f'ler, an' I stays by yehs till spen' las' cent! Dass right! I'm good f'ler an' I knows when an'body trea's me right!"

Between the times of the arrival and departure of the waiter, the man discoursed to the women on the tender regard he felt for all living things. He laid stress upon the purity of his motives in all dealings with men in the world, and spoke of the fervour of his friendship for those who were amiable. Tears welled slowly from his eyes. His voice quavered when he spoke to his companions.

Once when the waiter was about to depart with an empty tray, the man drew a coin from his pocket and held it forth. "Here," said he, quite magnificently, "here's quar'."

The waiter kept his hands on his tray. "I don't want yer money," he said.

The other put forth the coin with tearful insistence. "Here's quar'!" cried he, "take 't! Yer goo' f'ler an' I wan' yehs take 't!"

"Come, come, now," said the waiter, with the sullen air of a man who is forced into giving advice. "Put yer mon in yer pocket! Yer loaded an' yehs on'y makes a fool of yerself."

As the waiter passed out of the door the man turned pathetically to the women. "He don't know I'm goo' f'ler," cried he, dismally.

"Never you mind, Pete, dear," said the woman of brilliance and audacity, laying her hand with great affection upon his arm. "Never you mind, old boy! We'll stay by you, dear!"

"Dass ri'!" cried the man, his face lighting up at the soothing tones of the woman's voice. "Dass ri'; I'm goo' f'ler, an' w'en any one trea's me ri', I trea's zem ri'! Shee?"

"Sure!" cried the women. "And we're not goin' back on you, old man."

The man turned appealing eyes to the woman. He felt that if he could be convicted of a contemptible action he would die.

"Shay, Nell, I allus trea's yehs shquare, didn' I? I allus been goo' f'ler wi' yehs, ain't I, Nell?"

"Sure you have, Pete," assented the woman. She delivered an oration to her companions. "Yessir, that's a fact. Pete's a square fellah, he is. He never goes back on a friend. He's the right kind an' we stay by him, don't we, girls?"

"Sure!" they exclaimed. Looking lovingly at him they raised their glasses and drank his health.

"Girlsh," said the man, beseechingly, "I allus trea's yehs ri', didn' I? I'm goo' f'ler, ain' I, girlsh?"

"Sure!" again they chorused.

"Well," said he finally, "le's have nozzer drink, zen."

"That's right," hailed a woman, "that's right. Yer no bloomin' jay! Yer spends yer money like a man. Dat's right."

The man pounded the table with his quivering fists. "Yessir," he cried, with deep earnestness, as if some one disputed him. "I'm goo' f'ler, an' w'en any one trea's me ri', I allus trea's—le's have nozzer drink." He began to beat the wood with his glass. "Shay!" howled he, growing suddenly impatient. As the waiter did not then come, the man swelled with wrath. "Shay!" howled he again. The waiter appeared at the door. "Bringsh drinksh," said the man.

The waiter disappeared with the orders.

"Zat f'ler fool!" cried the man. "He insul' me! I'm ge'man! Can' stan' be insul'! I'm goin' lick 'im when comes!"

"No, no!" cried the women, crowding about and trying to subdue him. "He's all right! He didn't mean anything! Let it go! He's a good fellah!"

"Di'n' he insul' me?" asked the man earnestly.

"No," said they. "Of course he didn't! He's all right!"

"Sure he didn' insul' me?" demanded the man, with deep anxiety in his voice.

"No, no! We know him! He's a good fellah. He didn't mean anything."

"Well, zen," said the man resolutely, "I'm go' 'pol'gize!"

When the waiter came, the man struggled to the middle of the floor. "Girlsh shed you insul' me! I shay—lie! I 'pol'gize!"

"All right," said the waiter.

The man sat down. He felt a sleepy but strong desire to straighten things out and have a perfect understanding with everybody. "Nell, I allus trea's yeh shquare, di'n' I? Yeh likes me, don' yehs, Nell? I'm goo' f'ler?"

"Sure!" said the woman.

"Yeh knows I'm stuck on yehs, don' yehs, Nell?"

"Sure!" she repeated carelessly.

Overwhelmed by a spasm of drunken adoration, he drew two or three bills from his pocket and, with the trembling fingers of an offering priest, laid them on the table before the woman. "Yehs knows yehs kin have all I got, 'cause I'm stuck on yehs, Nell, I—I'm stuck on yehs, Nell—buy drinksh—we're havin' grea' time—w'en any one trea's me ri'—I—Nell—we're havin' heluva—time."

Presently he went to sleep with his swollen face fallen forward on his chest.

The women drank and laughed, not heeding the slumbering man in the corner. Finally he lurched forward and fell groaning to the floor.

The women screamed in disgust and drew back their skirts. "Come ahn!" cried one, starting up angrily, "let's get out of here."

The woman of brilliance and audacity stayed behind, taking up the bills and stuffing them into a deep, irregularly shaped pocket. A guttural snore from the recumbent man caused her to turn and look down at him. She laughed. "What a fool!" she said, and went.

The smoke from the lamps settled heavily down in the little compartment, obscuring the way out. The smell of oil, stifling in its intensity, pervaded the air. The wine from an overturned glass dripped softly down upon the blotches on the man's neck.

XIX

In a room a woman sat at a table eating like a fat monk in a picture.

A soiled, unshaven man pushed open the door and entered. "Well," said he, "Mag's dead."

"What?" said the woman, her mouth filled with bread.

"Mag's dead," repeated the man.

"Deh blazes she is!" said the woman. She continued her meal.

When she finished her coffee she began to weep. "I kin remember when her two feet was no bigger dan yer t'umb, and she weared worsted boots," moaned she.

"Well, what a' dat?" said the man.

"I kin remember when she weared worsted boots," she cried.

The neighbours began to gather in the hall, staring in at the weeping woman as if watching the contortions of a dying dog. A dozen women entered and lamented with her. Under their busy hands the room took on that appalling appearance of neatness and order with which death is greeted.

Suddenly the door opened and a woman in a black gown rushed in with outstretched arms. "Ah, poor Mary!" she cried, and tenderly embraced the moaning one. "Ah, what ter'ble affliction is dis!" continued she. Her vocabulary was derived from mission churches. "Me poor Mary, how I feel fer yehs! Ah, what a ter'ble affliction is a disobed'ent chile." Her good, motherly face was wet with tears. She trembled in eagerness to express her sympathy.

The mourner sat with bowed head, rocking her body heavily to and fro, and crying out in a high, strained voice that sounded like a dirge on some forlorn pipe. "I kin remember when she weared worsted boots, an' her two feets was no bigger dan yer t'umb, an' she weared worsted boots, Miss Smith," she cried, raising her streaming eyes.

"Ah, me poor Mary!" sobbed the woman in black. With low, coddling cries, she sank on her knees by the mourner's chair, and put her arms about her. The other women began to groan in different keys.

"Yer poor misguided chil' is gone now, Mary, an' let us hope it's fer deh bes'. Yeh'll fergive her now, Mary, won't yehs, dear, all her disobed'ence? All her t'ankless behaviour to her mudder an' all her badness? She's gone where her ter'ble sins will be judged."

The woman in black raised her face and paused. The inevitable sunlight came streaming in at the window and shed a ghastly cheerfulness upon the faded hues of the room. Two or three of the spectators were sniffling, and one was weeping loudly.

The mourner arose and staggered into the other room. In a moment she emerged with a pair of faded baby shoes held in the hollow of her hand. "I kin remember when she used to wear dem!" cried she. The women burst anew into cries as if they had all been stabbed. The mourner turned to the soiled and unshaven man. "Jimmie, boy, go git yer sister! Go git yer sister an' we'll put deh boots on her feets!"

"Dey won't fit her now, yeh fool," said the man.

"Go git yer sister, Jimmie!" shrieked the woman, confronting him fiercely.

The man swore sullenly. He went over to a corner and slowly began to put on his coat. He took his hat and went out, with a dragging, reluctant step.

The woman in black came forward and again besought the mourner. "Yeh'll fergive her, Mary! Yeh'll fergive yer bad, bad chil'! Her life was a curse an' her days were black, an' yeh'll fergive yer bad girl? She's gone where her sins will be judged."

"She's gone where her sins will be judged!" cried the other women, like a choir at a funeral.

"Deh Lord gives and deh Lord takes away," said the woman in black, raising her eyes to the sunbeams.

"Deh Lord gives and deh Lord takes away," responded the others.

"Yeh'll fergive her, Mary?" pleaded the woman in black.

The mourner essayed to speak, but her voice gave way. She shook her great shoulders frantically, in an agony of grief. The tears seemed to scald her face. Finally her voice came and arose in a scream of pain. "Oh, yes, I'll fergive her! I'll fergive her!"

GEORGE'S MOTHER

I

In the swirling rain that came at dusk the broad avenue
glistened with that deep bluish tint which is so widely condemned when it is put into pictures. There were long rows of
shops, whose fronts shone with full, golden light. Here and
there, from druggists' windows or from the red street-lamps
that indicated the positions of fire-alarm boxes, a flare of uncertain, wavering crimson was thrown upon the wet pavements.

The lights made shadows, in which the buildings loomed
with a new and tremendous massiveness, like castles and for-
tresses. There were endless processions of people, mighty hosts,
with umbrellas waving, banner-like, over them. Horse-cars,
a-glitter with new paint, rumbled in steady array between the
pillars that supported the elevated railroad. The whole street
resounded with the tinkle of bells, the roar of iron-shod wheels
on the cobbles, the ceaseless trample of the hundreds of feet.
Above all, too, could be heard the loud screams of the tiny
newsboys who scurried in all directions. Upon the corners,
standing in from the dripping eaves, were many loungers, descended from the world that used to prostrate itself before
pageantry.

A brown young man went along the avenue. He held a tin
lunch-pail under his arm in a manner that was evidently uncomfortable. He was puffing at a corncob pipe. His shoulders
had a self-reliant poise, and the hang of his arms and the
raised veins of his hands showed him to be a man who worked
with his muscles.

As he passed a street-corner a man in old clothes gave a
shout of surprise and, rushing impetuously forward, grasped
his hand.

"Hello, Kelcey, ol' boy!" cried the man in old clothes. "How's th' boy, anyhow? Where in thunder yeh been fer th' last seventeen years? I'll be hanged if you ain't th' last man I ever expected t' see."

The brown youth put his pail to the ground and grinned. "Well, if it ain't ol' Charley Jones," he said, ecstatically shaking hands. "How are yeh, anyhow? Where yeh been keepin' yerself? I ain't seen yeh fer a year."

"Well, I should say so! Why, th' last time I saw you was up in Handyville!"

"Sure! On Sunday, we—"

"Sure. Out at Bill Sickles's place. Let's go get a drink!"

They made toward a little glass-fronted saloon that sat blinking jovially at the crowds. It engulfed them with a gleeful motion of its two widely smiling lips.

"What'll yeh take, Kelcey?"

"Oh, I guess I'll take a beer."

"Gimme little whisky, John."

The two friends leaned against the bar and looked with enthusiasm upon each other.

"Well, well, I'm thunderin' glad t' see yeh," said Jones.

"Well, I guess," replied Kelcey. "Here's to yeh, ol' man."

"Let 'er go."

They lifted their glasses, glanced fervidly at each other, and drank.

"Yeh ain't changed much, on'y yeh've growed like th' devil," said Jones, reflectively, as he put down his glass. "I'd know yeh anywheres!"

"Certainly yeh would," said Kelcey. "An' I knew you, too, th' minute I saw yeh. Yer changed, though!"

"Yes," admitted Jones with some complacency, "I s'pose I am." He regarded himself in the mirror that multiplied the bottles on the shelf in back of the bar. He should have seen a grinning face with a rather pink nose. His derby was perched carelessly on the back part of his head. Two wisps of hair straggled down over his hollow temples. There was something very worldly and wise about him. Life did not seem to confuse him. Evidently he understood its complications. His hand thrust into his trousers pocket, where he jingled keys, and his hat perched back on his head expressed a young man of vast knowledge. His extensive acquaintance with bartenders aided him materially in this habitual expression of wisdom.

Having finished, he turned to the barkeeper. "John, has any of th' gang been in t'-night yet?"

"No—not yet," said the barkeeper. "Ol' Bleecker was aroun' this afternoon about four. He said if I seen any of th' boys t' tell 'em he'd be up t'-night if he could get away. I saw Connor an' that other fellah goin' down th' avenyeh about an hour ago. I guess they'll be back after a while."

"This is th' hang-out fer a great gang," said Jones, turning to Kelcey. "They're a great crowd, I tell yeh. We own th' place when we get started. Come aroun' some night. Any night, almost. T'-night, b' jiminy. They'll almost all be here, an' I'd like t' interduce yeh. They're a great gang! Gre-e-at!"

"I'd like teh," said Kelcey.

"Well, come ahead, then," cried the other, cordially. "Ye'd like t' know 'em. It's an outa-sight crowd. Come aroun' t'-night!"

"I will if I can."

"Well, yeh ain't got anything t' do, have yeh?" demanded Jones. "Well, come along, then. Yeh might just as well spend yer time with a good crowd a' fellahs. An' it's a great gang. Great! Gre-e-at!"

"Well, I must make fer home now, anyhow," said Kelcey. "It's late as blazes. What'll yeh take this time, ol' man?"

"Gimme little more whisky, John."

"Guess I'll take another beer!"

Jones emptied the whisky into his large mouth and then put the glass upon the bar. "Been in th' city long?" he asked. "Um— well, three years is a good deal fer a slick man. Doin' well? Oh, well, nobody's doin' well these days." He looked down mournfully at his shabby clothes. "Father's dead, ain't 'e? Yeh don't say so? Fell off a scaffoldin', didn't 'e? I heard it somewheres. Mother's livin', of course? I thought she was. Fine ol' lady— fi-i-ne. Well, you're th' last of her boys. Was five of yeh oncet, wasn't there? I knew four m'self. Yes, five! I thought so. An' all gone but you, hey? Well, you'll have t' brace up an' be a comfort t' th' ol' mother. Well, well, well, who would 'a' thought that on'y you'd be left out a' all that mob a' tow-headed kids? Well, well, well, it's a queer world, ain't it?"

A contemplation of this thought made him sad. He sighed, and moodily watched the other sip beer.

"Well, well, it's a queer world—a damn queer world."

"Yes," said Kelcey, "I'm th' on'y one left!" There was an accent of discomfort in his voice. He did not like this dwelling upon a sentiment that was connected with himself.

"How is th' ol' lady, anyhow?" continued Jones. "Th' last time I remember she was as spry as a little ol' cricket, an' was helpeltin' aroun' th' country lecturin' before W.C.T.U.'s an' one thing an' another."

"Oh, she's pretty well," said Kelcey.

"An' out a' five boys you're th' on'y one she's got left? Well, well—have another drink before yeh go."

"Oh, I guess I've had enough."

A wounded expression came into Jones's eyes. "Oh, come on," he said.

"Well, I'll take another beer!"

"Gimme little more whisky, John!"

When they had concluded this ceremony, Jones went with his friend to the door of the saloon. "Good-bye, ol' man," he said genially. His homely features shone with friendliness. "Come aroun', now, sure. T'-night! See? They're a great crowd. Gre-e-at!"

II

A man with a red, mottled face put forth his head from a window and cursed violently. He flung a bottle high across two back yards at a window of the opposite tenement. It broke against the bricks of the house, and the fragments fell crackling upon the stones below. The man shook his fist.

A bare-armed woman, making an array of clothes on a line in one of the yards, glanced casually up at the man and listened to his words. Her eyes followed his to the other tenement. From a distant window a youth with a pipe yelled some comments upon the poor aim. Two children, being in the proper yard, picked up the bits of broken glass and began to fondle them as new toys.

From the window at which the man raged came the sound of an old voice, singing. It quavered and trembled out into the air as if a sound-spirit had a broken wing.

> *"Should I be car-reed tew th' skies*
> *O-on flow'ry be-eds of ee-ease,*
> *While others fought tew win th' prize*
> *An' sailed through blood-ee seas?"*

The man in the opposite window was greatly enraged. He continued to swear.

A little old woman was the owner of the voice. In a fourth-storey room of the red-and-black tenement she was trudging on a journey. In her arms she bore pots and pans, and sometimes a broom and dust-pan. She wielded them like weapons. Their weight seemed to have bended her back and crooked her arms until she walked with difficulty. Often she plunged her hands into water at a sink. She splashed about, the dwindled muscles working to and fro under the loose skin of her arms. She came from the sink streaming and bedraggled as if she had crossed a flooded river.

There was the flurry of a battle in this room. Through the clouded dust or steam one could see the thin figure dealing mighty blows. Always her way seemed beset. Her broom was continually poised, lance-wise, at dust demons. There came clashings and clangings as she strove with her tireless foes.

It was a picture of indomitable courage. And as she went on her way her voice was often raised in a long cry, a strange war-chant, a shout of battle and defiance, that rose and fell in harsh screams, and exasperated the ears of the man with the red, mottled face.

"Should I be car-reed tew th' skies
O-on flow'ry be-eds of ee-ease—"

Finally she halted for a moment. Going to the window, she sat down and mopped her face with her apron. It was a lull, a moment of respite. Still it could be seen that she even then was planning skirmishes, charges, campaigns. She gazed thoughtfully about the room and noted the strength and position of her enemies. She was very alert.

At last she returned to the mantel. "Five o'clock," she murmured, scrutinizing a little swaggering nickel-plated clock.

She looked out at chimneys growing thickly on the roofs. A man at work on one seemed like a bee. In the intricate yards below, vine-like lines had strange leaves of cloth. To her ears there came the howl of the man with the red, mottled face. He was engaged in a furious altercation with the youth who had called attention to his poor aim. They were like animals in a jungle.

In the distance an enormous brewery towered over the other buildings. Great gilt letters advertised a brand of beer. Thick smoke came from funnels and spread near it like vast and powerful wings. The structure seemed a great bird, flying. The letters of the sign made a chain of gold hanging from its neck. The little old woman looked at the brewery. It vaguely interested her, for a moment, as a stupendous affair, a machine of mighty strength.

Presently she sprang from her rest and began to buffet with her shrivelled arms. In a moment the battle was again in full swing. Terrific blows were given and received. There arose the clattering uproar of a new fight. The little intent warrior never hesitated nor faltered. She fought with a strong and relentless will. Beads and lines of perspiration stood upon her forehead.

Three blue plates were leaning in a row on the shelf in back of the stove. The little old woman had seen it done some-where. In front of them swaggered the round nickel-plated clock. Her son had stuck many cigarette pictures in the rim of a looking-glass that hung near. Occasional chromos were tacked upon the yellowed walls of the room. There was one in a gilt frame. It was quite an affair, in reds and greens. They all seemed like trophies.

It began to grow dark. A mist came winding. Rain plashed softly upon the window-sill. A lamp had been lighted in the opposite tenement; the strong orange glare revealed the man with a red, mottled face. He was seated by a table, smoking and reflecting.

The little old woman looked at the clock again. "Quarter a' six."

She had paused for a moment, but she now hurled herself fiercely at the stove that lurked in the gloom, red-eyed, like a dragon. It hissed, and there was renewed clangour of blows. The little old woman dashed to and fro.

III

As it grew toward seven o'clock the little old woman became nervous. She often would drop into a chair and sit staring at the little clock.

"I wonder why he don't come," she continually repeated. There was a small, curious note of despair in her voice. As she sat thinking and staring at the clock the expressions of her face changed swiftly. All manner of emotions flickered in her eyes and about her lips. She was evidently perceiving in her imagination the journey of a loved person. She dreamed for him mishaps and obstacles. Something tremendous and irritating was hindering him from coming to her.

She had lighted an oil lamp. It flooded the room with vivid yellow glare. The table, in its oil-cloth covering, had previously appeared like a bit of bare brown desert. It now was a white garden, growing the fruits of her labour.

"Seven o'clock," she murmured, finally. She was aghast.

Then suddenly she heard a step upon the stair. She sprang up and began to bustle about the room. The little fearful emotions passed at once from her face. She seemed now to be ready to scold.

Young Kelcey entered the room. He gave a sigh of relief, and dropped his pail in a corner. He was evidently greatly wearied by a hard day of toil.

The little old woman hobbled over to him and raised her wrinkled lips. She seemed on the verge of tears and an outburst of reproaches.

"Hello!" he cried, in a voice of cheer. "Been gettin' anxious?"

"Yes," she said, hovering about him. "Where yeh been, George? What made yeh so late? I've been waitin' th' longest while. Don't throw your coat down there. Hang it up behind th' door."

The son put his coat on the proper hook, and then went to splatter water in a tin wash-basin at the sink.

"Well, yeh see, I met Jones—you remember Jones? Ol' Handyville fellah. An' we had t' stop an' talk over ol' times. Jones is quite a boy."

The little old woman's mouth set in a sudden straight line. "Oh, that Jones," she said. "I don't like him."

The youth interrupted a flurry of white towel to give a glance of irritation. "Well, now, what's th' use of talking that way?" he said to her. "What do yeh know 'bout 'im? Ever spoke to 'im in yer life?"

"Well, I don't know as I ever did since he grew up," replied the little old woman. "But I know he ain't th' kind a' man I'd like t' have you go around with. He ain't a good man. I'm sure he ain't. He drinks."

Her son began to laugh. "Th' dickens he does!" He seemed amazed, but not shocked, at this information.

She nodded her head with the air of one who discloses a dreadful thing. "I'm sure of it! Once I saw 'im comin' out a' Simpson's Hotel, up in Handyville, an' he could hardly walk. He drinks! I'm sure he drinks!"

"Holy smoke!" said Kelcey.

They sat down at the table and began to wreck the little white garden. The youth leaned back in his chair, in the manner of a man who is paying for things. His mother bended alertly forward, apparently watching each mouthful. She perched on the edge of her chair, ready to spring to her feet and run to the closet or the stove for anything that he might need. She was as anxious as a young mother with a babe. In the careless and comfortable attitude of the son there was denoted a great deal of dignity.

"Yeh ain't eatin' much t'-night, George?"

"Well, I ain't very hungry, t' tell th' truth."

"Don't yeh like yer supper, dear? Yeh must eat somethin', chile. Yeh mustn't go without."

"Well, I'm eatin' somethin', ain't I?"

He wandered aimlessly through the meal. She sat over behind the little blackened coffee-pot and gazed affectionately upon him.

After a time she began to grow agitated. Her worn fingers were gripped. It could be seen that a great thought was within her. She was about to venture something. She had arrived at a supreme moment. "George," she said suddenly, "come t' prayer-meetin' with me t'-night."

The young man dropped his fork. "Say, you must be crazy," he said, in amazement.

"Yes, dear," she continued, rapidly, in a small pleading voice, "I'd like t' have yeh go with me oncet in a while. Yeh never go with me any more, dear, an' I'd like t' have yeh go. Yeh ain't been anywheres at all with me in th' longest while."

"Well," he said, "well, but what th' blazes—"

"Ah, come on," said the little old woman. She went to him and put her arms about his neck. She began to coax him with caresses.

The young man grinned. "Thunderation!" he said, "what would I do at a prayer-meetin'?"

The mother considered him to be consenting. She did a little antique caper.

"Well, yeh can come an' take care a' yer mother," she cried gleefully. "It's such a long walk every Thursday night alone, an' don't yeh s'pose that when I have such a big, fine, strappin' boy I want 'im t' beau me aroun' some? Ah, I knew ye'd come!"

He smiled for a moment, indulgent of her humour. But presently his face turned a shade of discomfort. "But," he began, protesting.

"Ah, come on!" she continually repeated.

He began to be vexed. He frowned into the air. A vision came to him of dreary blackness arranged in solemn rows. A mere dream of it was depressing.

"But—" he said again. He was obliged to make great search for an argument. Finally he concluded: "But what th' blazes would I do at prayer-meetin'?"

In his ears was the sound of a hymn, made by people who tilted their heads at a prescribed angle of devotion. It would be too apparent that they were all better than he. When he entered they would turn their heads and regard him with suspicion. This would be an enormous aggravation, since he was certain that he was as good as they.

"Well, now, y' see," he said, quite gently, "I don't wanta go, an' it wouldn't do me no good t' go if I didn't wanta go."

His mother's face swiftly changed. She breathed a huge sigh, the counterpart of ones he had heard upon like occasions. She put a tiny black bonnet on her head, and wrapped her figure in an old shawl. She cast a martyr-like glance upon her son and went mournfully away. She resembled a limited funeral procession.

The young man writhed under it to an extent. He kicked moodily at a table-leg. When the sound of her footfalls died away he felt distinctly relieved.

IV

That night, when Kelcey arrived at the little smiling saloon, he found his friend Jones standing before the bar engaged in a violent argument with a stout man.

"Oh, well," this latter person was saying, "you can make a lot of noise, Charley, for a man that never says anything—let's have a drink!"

Jones was waving his arms and delivering splintering blows upon some distant theories. The stout man chuckled fatly and winked at the bartender.

The orator ceased for a moment to say, "Gimme little whisky, John." At the same time he perceived young Kelcey. He sprang forward with a welcoming cry. "Hello, ol' man! didn't much think ye'd come." He led him to the stout man.

"Mr. Bleecker—my friend Mr. Kelcey!"

"How d' yeh do?"

"Mr. Kelcey, I'm happy to meet you, sir; have a drink."

They drew up in line and waited. The busy hands of the bartender made glasses clink. Mr. Bleecker, in a very polite way, broke the waiting silence.

"Never been here before, I believe, have you, Mr. Kelcey?"

The young man felt around for a high-bred reply. "Er— no—I've never had that—er—pleasure," he said.

After a time the strained and wary courtesy of their manners wore away. It became evident to Bleecker that his importance slightly dazzled the young man. He grew warmer. Obviously, the youth was one whose powers of perception were developed. Directly, then, he launched forth into a tale of bygone days, when the world was better. He had known all the great men of that age. He reproduced his conversations with them. There were traces of pride and of mournfulness in his voice. He rejoiced at the glory of the world of dead spirits. He grieved at the youth and flippancy of the present one. He lived with his head in the clouds of the past, and he seemed obliged to talk of what he saw there.

Jones nudged Kelcey ecstatically in the ribs. "You've got th' ol' man started in great shape," he whispered.

Kelcey was proud that the prominent character of the place talked at him, glancing into his eyes for appreciation of fine points.

Presently they left the bar and, going into a little rear room, took seats about a table. A gas-jet with a coloured globe shed a crimson radiance. The polished wood of walls and furniture gleamed with faint rose-coloured reflections. Upon the floor sawdust was thickly sprinkled.

Two other men presently came. By the time Bleecker had told three tales of the grand past, Kelcey was slightly acquainted with everybody.

He admired Bleecker immensely. He developed a brotherly feeling for the others, who were all gentle-spoken. He began to feel that he was passing the happiest evening of his life. His companions were so jovial and good-natured; and everything they did was marked by such courtesy.

For a time the two men who had come in late did not presume to address him directly. They would say: "Jones, won't your friend have so and so, or so and so?" And Bleecker would begin his orations: "Now, Mr. Kelcey, don't you think—"

Presently he began to believe that he was a most remarkably fine fellow, who had at last found his place in a crowd of most remarkably fine fellows.

Jones occasionally breathed comments into his ear.

"I tell yeh, Bleecker's an ol'-timer. He was a husky guy in his day, yeh can bet. He was one a' th' best-known men in N' York oncet. Yeh ought to hear him tell about—"

Kelcey listened intently. He was profoundly interested in these intimate tales of men who had gleamed in the rays of old suns.

"That O'Connor's a damn fine fellah," interjected Jones once, referring to one of the others. "He's one a' th' best fellahs I ever knowed. He's always on th' dead level. An' he's always jest th' same as yeh see him now—good-natured an' grinnin'."

Kelcey nodded. He could well believe it.

When he offered to buy drinks there came a loud volley of protests. "No, no, Mr. Kelcey," cried Bleecker, "no, no. Tonight you are our guest. Some other time—"

"Here," said O'Connor, "it's my turn now."

He called and pounded for the bartender. He then sat with a coin in his hand warily eyeing the others. He was ready to frustrate them if they offered to pay.

After a time Jones began to develop qualities of great eloquence and wit. His companions laughed. "It's the whisky talking now," said Bleecker.

He grew earnest and impassioned. He delivered speeches on various subjects. His lectures were to him very imposing. The force of his words thrilled him. Sometimes he was overcome.

The others agreed with him in all things. Bleecker grew almost tender, and considerately placed words here and there for his use. As Jones became fiercely energetic the others became more docile in agreeing. They soothed him with friendly interjections.

His mode changed directly. He began to sing popular airs with enthusiasm. He congratulated his companions upon being in his society. They were excited by his frenzy. They began to fraternize in jovial fashion. It was understood that they were true and tender spirits. They had come away from a grinding world filled with men who were harsh.

When one of them chose to divulge some place where the world had pierced him, there was a chorus of violent sympathy. They rejoiced at their temporary isolation and safety.

Once a man, completely drunk, stumbled along the floor of the saloon. He opened the door of the little room and made a show of entering. The men sprang instantly to their feet. They were ready to throttle any invader of their island. They elbowed each other in rivalry as to who should take upon himself the brunt of an encounter.

"Oh!" said the drunken individual, swaying on his legs and blinking at the party, "oh! thish private room?"

"That's what it is, Willie," said Jones. "An' you git outa here, er we'll throw yeh out."

"That's what we will," said the others.

"Oh," said the drunken man. He blinked at them aggrievedly for an instant and then went away.

They sat down again. Kelcey felt, in a way, that he would have liked to display his fidelity to the others by whipping the intruder.

The bartender came often. "Gee, you fellas er tanks," he said, in a jocular manner, as he gathered empty glasses and polished the table with his little towel.

Through the exertions of Jones the little room began to grow clamorous. The tobacco smoke eddied about the forms of the men in ropes and wreaths. Near the ceiling there was a thick grey cloud.

Each man explained, in his way, that he was totally out of place in the before-mentioned world. They were possessed of various virtues which were unappreciated by those with whom they were commonly obliged to mingle; they were fitted for a tree-shaded land where everything was peace. Now that five of them had congregated it gave them happiness to speak their inmost thoughts without fear of being misunderstood.

As he drank more beer Kelcey felt his breast expand with manly feeling. He knew that he was capable of sublime things. He wished that some day one of his present companions would come to him for relief. His mind pictured a little scene. In it he was magnificent in his friendship.

He looked upon the beaming faces and knew that if at that instant there should come a time for a great sacrifice he would blissfully make it. He would pass tranquilly into the unknown, or into bankruptcy, amid the ejaculations of his companions upon his many virtues.

They had no bickerings during the evening. If one chose to momentarily assert himself, the others instantly submitted.

They exchanged compliments. Once old Bleecker stared at Jones for a few moments. Suddenly he broke out: "Jones, you're one of the finest fellows I ever knew!" A flush of pleasure went over the other's face, and then he made a modest gesture, the protest of a humble man. "Don't flimflam me, ol' boy," he said, with earnestness. But Bleecker roared that he was serious about it. The two men arose and shook hands emotionally. Jones bunted against the table and knocked off a glass.

Afterward a general hand-shaking was inaugurated. Brotherly sentiments flew about the room. There was an uproar of fraternal feeling.

Jones began to sing. He beat time with precision and dignity. He gazed into the eyes of his companions, trying to call music from their souls. O'Connor joined in heartily, but with another tune. Off in a corner old Bleecker was making a speech.

The bartender came to the door. "Gee, you fellahs er making a row. It's time fer me t' shut up th' front th' place, an' you mugs better sit on yerselves. It's one o'clock."

They began to argue with him. Kelcey, however, sprang to his feet. "One o'clock," he said. "Holy smoke, I mus' be flyin'!"

There came protesting howls from Jones. Bleecker ceased his oration. "My dear boy—" he began. Kelcey searched for his hat. "I've gotta go t' work at seven," he said.

The others watched him with discomfort in their eyes. "Well," said O'Connor, "if one goes we might as well all go." They sadly took their hats and filed out.

The cold air of the street filled Kelcey with vague surprise. It made his head feel hot. As for his legs, they were like willow-twigs.

A few yellow lights blinked. In front of an all-night restaurant a huge red electric lamp hung and sputtered. Horse-car bells jingled far down the street. Overhead a train thundered on the elevated road.

On the sidewalk the men took fervid leave. They clutched

hands with extraordinary force and proclaimed, for the last time, ardent and admiring friendships.

When he arrived at his home Kelcey proceeded with caution. His mother had left a light burning low. He stumbled once in his voyage across the floor. As he paused to listen he heard the sound of little snores coming from her room.

He lay awake for a few moments and thought of the evening. He had a pleasurable consciousness that he had made a good impression upon those fine fellows. He felt that he had spent the most delightful evening of his life.

V

Kelcey was cross in the morning. His mother had been obliged to shake him a great deal, and it had seemed to him a most unjust thing. Also, when he, blinking his eyes, had entered the kitchen, she had said: "Yeh left th' lamp burnin' all night last night, George. How many times must I tell yeh never t' leave th' lamp burnin'?"

He ate the greater part of his breakfast in silence, moodily stirring his coffee and glaring at a remote corner of the room with eyes that felt as if they had been baked. When he moved his eyelids there was a sensation that they were cracking. In his mouth there was a singular taste. It seemed to him that he had been sucking the end of a wooden spoon. Moreover, his temper was rampant within him. It sought something to devour.

Finally he said savagely: "Damn these early hours!"

His mother jumped as if he had flung a missile at her. "Why, George—" she began.

Kelcey broke in again. "Oh, I know all that—but this gettin' up in th' mornin' so early makes me sick. Jest when a man is gettin' his mornin' nap he's gotta get up. I—"

"George, dear," said his mother, "yeh know how I hate yeh t' swear, dear. Now, please don't." She looked beseechingly at him.

He made a swift gesture. "Well, I ain't swearin', am I?" he

demanded. "I was on'y sayin' that this gettin'-up business gives me a pain, wasn't I?"

"Well, yeh know how swearin' hurts me," protested the little old woman. She seemed about to sob. She gazed off retrospectively. She apparently was recalling persons who had never been profane.

"I don't see where yeh ever caught this way a' swearin' out at everything," she continued presently. "Fred, ner John, ner Willie never swore a bit. Ner Tom neither, except when he was real mad."

The son made another gesture. It was directed into the air, as if he saw there a phantom injustice. "Oh, good thunder," he said, with an accent of despair. Thereupon, he relapsed into a mood of silence. He sombrely regarded his plate.

This demeanour speedily reduced his mother to meekness. When she spoke again it was in a conciliatory voice. "George, dear, won't yeh bring some sugar home t'-night?" It could be seen that she was asking for a crown of gold.

Kelcey aroused from his semi-slumber. "Yes, if I kin remember it," he said.

The little old woman arose to stow her son's lunch into the pail. When he had finished his breakfast he stalked for a time about the room in a dignified way. He put on his coat and hat and, taking his lunch-pail, went to the door. There he halted and, without turning his head, stiffly said: "Well, good-bye."

The little old woman saw that she had offended her son. She did not seek an explanation. She was accustomed to these phenomena. She made haste to surrender.

"Ain't yeh goin' t' kiss me good-bye?" she asked in a little woeful voice.

The youth made a pretence of going on, deaf-heartedly. He wore the dignity of an injured monarch.

Then the little old woman called again in forsaken accents: "George—George—ain't yeh goin' t' kiss me good-bye?" When he moved he found that she was hanging to his coat-tails.

He turned eventually with a murmur of a sort of tenderness. "Why, a' course I am," he said. He kissed her. Withal there was an undertone of superiority in his voice, as if he were granting an astonishing suit. She looked at him with reproach and gratitude and affection.

She stood at the head of the stairs and watched his hand sliding along the rail as he went down. Occasionally she could see his arm and part of his shoulder. When he reached the first floor she called to him: "Good-bye!"

The little old woman went back to her work in the kitchen with a frown of perplexity upon her brow. "I wonder what was th' matter with George this mornin'," she mused. "He didn't seem a bit like himself!"

As she trudged to and fro at her labour she began to speculate. She was much worried. She surmised in a vague way that he was a sufferer from a great internal disease. It was something, no doubt, that devoured the kidneys or quietly fed upon the lungs. Later, she imagined a woman, wicked and fair, who had fascinated him and was turning his life into a bitter thing. Her mind created many wondrous influences that were swooping like green dragons at him. They were changing him to a morose man who suffered silently. She longed to discover them, that she might go bravely to the rescue of her heroic son. She knew that he, generous in his pain, would keep it from her. She racked her mind for knowledge.

However, when he came home at night he was extraordinarily blithe. He seemed to be a lad of ten. He capered all about the room. When she was bringing the coffee-pot from the stove to the table he made show of waltzing with her, so that she spilled some of the coffee. She was obliged to scold him.

All through the meal he made jokes. She occasionally was compelled to laugh, despite the fact that she believed that she should not laugh at her own son's jokes. She uttered reproofs at times, but he did not regard them.

"Golly," he said once, "I feel fine as silk. I didn't think I'd get over feelin' bad so quick. It—" He stopped abruptly.

During the evening he sat content. He smoked his pipe and read from an evening paper. She bustled about at her work. She seemed utterly happy with him there, lazily puffing out little clouds of smoke and giving frequent brilliant dissertations upon the news of the day. It seemed to her that she must be a model mother to have such a son, one who came home to her at night and sat contented, in a languor of the muscles after a good day's toil. She pondered upon the science of her management.

The week thereafter, too, she was joyous, for he stayed at home each night of it, and was sunny-tempered. She became convinced that she was a perfect mother, rearing a perfect son. There came often a love-light into her eyes. The wrinkled, yellow face frequently warmed into a smile of the kind that a maiden bestows upon him who to her is first and perhaps last.

VI

The little old woman habitually discouraged all outbursts of youthful vanity on the part of her son. She feared that he would get to think too much of himself, and she knew that nothing could do more harm. Great self-esteem was always passive, she thought, and if he grew to regard his qualities of mind as forming a dazzling constellation, he would tranquilly sit still and not do those wonders she expected of him. So she was constantly on the alert to suppress even a shadow of such a thing. As for him, he ruminated with the savage, vengeful bitterness of a young man, and decided that she did not comprehend him.

But despite her precautions he often saw that she believed him to be the most marvellous young man on the earth. He had only to look at those two eyes that became lighted with a glow from her heart whenever he did some excessively brilliant thing. On these occasions he could see her glance triumphantly at a neighbour, or whoever happened to be present. He grew to plan for these glances. And then he took a vast satisfaction in detecting and appropriating them.

Nevertheless, he could not understand why, directly after a scene of this kind, his mother was liable to call to him to hang his coat on the hook under the mantel, her voice in a key of despair, as if he were negligent and stupid in what was, after all, the only important thing in life.

"If yeh'll only get in the habit of doin' it, it'll be jest as easy as throwin' it down anywheres," she would say to him. "When ye pitch it down anywheres, somebody's got t' pick it up, an' that'll most likely be your poor ol' mother. Yeh can hang it up yerself, if yeh'll on'y think." This was intolerable. He usually went then and hurled his coat savagely at the hook. The correctness of her position was maddening.

It seemed to him that any one who had a son of his glowing attributes should overlook the fact that he seldom hung up his coat. It was impossible to explain this situation to his mother. She was unutterably narrow. He grew sullen.

There came a time, too, when, even in all his mother's tremendous admiration for him, he did not entirely agree with her. He was delighted that she liked his great wit. He spurred himself to new and flashing effort because of this appreciation. But for the greater part he could see that his mother took pride in him in quite a different way from that in which he took pride in himself. She rejoiced at qualities in him that indicated that he was going to become a white and looming king among men. From these she made pictures in which he appeared as a benign personage, blessed by the filled hands of the poor, one whose brain could hold massive thoughts and awe certain men about whom she had read. She was fêted as the mother of this enormous man. These dreams were her solace. She spoke of them to no one, because she knew that, worded, they would be ridiculous. But she dwelt with them, and they shed a radiance of gold upon her long days, her sorry labour. Upon the dead altars of her life she had builded the little fires of hope for another.

He had a complete sympathy for as much as he understood of these thoughts of his mother. They were so wise that he admired her foresight. As for himself, however, most of his dreams were of a nearer time. He had many of the distant future when he would be a man with a cloak of coldness concealing his gentleness and his faults, of whom the men, and more particularly the women, would think with reverence. He agreed with his mother that at that time he would go through what were obstacles to other men like a flung stone. And then he would have power, and he would enjoy having his bounty and his wrath alike fall swiftly upon those below. They would be awed. And above all he would mystify them.

But then his nearer dreams were a multitude. He had begun to look at the great world revolving near to his nose. He had a vast curiosity concerning this city in whose complexities he was buried. It was an impenetrable mystery, this city. It was a blend of many enticing colours. He longed to comprehend it completely, that he might walk understandingly in its greatest marvels, its mightiest march of life, sin. He dreamed of a comprehension whose pay was the admirable attitude of a man of knowledge. He remembered Jones. He could not but admire a man who knew so many bartenders.

VII

An indefinite woman was in all of Kelcey's dreams. As a matter of fact it was not he whom he pictured as wedding her. It was a vision of himself greater, finer, more terrible. It was himself as he expected to be. In scenes which he took mainly from pictures, this vision conducted a courtship, strutting, posing, and lying through a drama which was magnificent from glow of purple. In it he was icy, self-possessed; but she, the dream-girl, was consumed by wild, torrential passion. He went to the length of having her display it before the people. He saw them wonder at his tranquillity. It amazed them infinitely to see him remain cold before the glory of this peerless woman's love. She was to him as beseeching for affection as a pet animal, but still he controlled appearances, and none knew of his deep abiding love. Some day, at the critical romantic time, he was going to divulge it. In these long dreams there were accessories of castle-like houses, wide lands, servants, horses, clothes.

They began somewhere in his childhood. When he ceased to see himself as a stern general pointing a sword at the nervous and abashed horizon, he became this sublime king of a vague woman's heart. Later, when he had read some books, it all achieved clearer expression. He was told in them that there was a goddess in the world whose business it was to wait until he should exchange a glance with her. It became a creed, subtly powerful. It saved discomfort for him and for several women who flitted by him. He used her as a standard.

Often he saw the pathos of her long wait, but his faith did not falter. The world was obliged to turn gold in time. His life was to be fine and heroic, else he would not have been born. He believed that the commonplace lot was the sentence, the doom, of certain people who did not know how to feel. His blood was a tender current of life. He thought that the usual should fall to others whose nerves were of lead. Occasionally he wondered how fate was going to begin making an enormous figure of him; but he had no doubt of the result. A chariot of pink clouds was coming for him. His faith was his reason for existence. Meanwhile he could dream of the indefinite woman and the fragrance of roses that came from her hair.

One day he met Maggie Johnson on the stairs. She had a pail of beer in one hand and a brown-paper parcel under her arm. She glanced at him. He discovered that it would wither his heart to see another man signally successful in the smiles of her. And the glance that she gave him was so indifferent and so unresponsive to the sudden vivid admiration in his own eyes that he immediately concluded that she was magnificent in two ways.

As she came to the landing, the light from a window passed in a silver gleam over the girlish roundness of her cheek. It was a thing that he remembered.

He was silent for the most part at supper that night. He was particularly unkind when he did speak. His mother, observing

him apprehensively, tried in vain to picture the new terrible
catastrophe. She eventually concluded that he did not like the
beef-stew. She put more salt in it.

He saw Maggie quite frequently after the meeting upon the
stairs. He reconstructed his dreams and placed her in the full
glory of that sun. The dream-woman, the goddess, pitched from
her pedestal, lay prostrate, unheeded, save when he brought
her forth to call her insipid and childish in the presence of his
new religion.

He was relatively happy sometimes when Maggie's mother
would get drunk and make terrific uproars. He used then to sit
in the dark and make scenes in which he rescued the girl from
her hideous environment.

He laid clever plans by which he encountered her in the
halls, at the door, on the street. When he succeeded in meeting
her he was always overcome by the thought that the whole
thing was obvious to her. He could feel the shame of it burn
his face and neck. To prove to her that she was mistaken he
would turn away his head or regard her with a granite stare.

After a time he became impatient of the distance between
them. He saw looming princes who would aim to seize her.
Hours of his leisure and certain hours of his labour he spent
in contriving. The shade of this girl was with him continually. With her he builded his grand dramas so that he trod in
clouds, the matters of his daily life obscured and softened by
a mist.

He saw that he need only break down the slight conventional
barriers and she would soon discover his noble character. Sometimes he could see it all in his mind. It was very skilful. But
then his courage flew away at the supreme moment. Perhaps
the whole affair was humorous to her. Perhaps she was watching his mental contortions. She might laugh. He felt that he
would then die or kill her. He could not approach the dread
moment. He sank often from the threshold of knowledge. Directly after these occasions, it was his habit to avoid her to
prove that she was a cipher to him.

He reflected that if he could only get a chance to rescue her from something, the whole tragedy would speedily unwind.

He met a young man in the halls one evening who said to him: "Say, me frien', where d' d' Johnson birds live in heh? I can't fin' me feet in dis bloomin' joint. I been battin' around heh fer a half-hour."

"Two flights up," said Kelcey stonily. He had felt a sudden quiver of his heart. The grandeur of the clothes, the fine worldly air, the experience, the self-reliance, the courage that shone in the countenance of this other young man made him suddenly sink to the depths of woe. He stood listening in the hall, flushing and ashamed of it, until he heard them coming downstairs together. He slunk away then. It would have been a horror to him if she had discovered him there. She might have felt sorry for him.

They were going out to a show, perhaps. That pig of the world in his embroidered cloak was going to dazzle her with splendour. He mused upon how unrighteous it was for other men to dazzle women with splendour.

As he appreciated his handicap he swore with savage, vengeful bitterness. In his home his mother raised her voice in a high key of monotonous irritability. "Hang up yer coat, can't yeh, George?" she cried at him. "I can't go round after yeh all th' time. It's jest as easy t' hang it up as it is t' throw it down that way. Don't yeh ever git tired a' hearing me yell at yeh?"

"Yes," he exploded. In this word he put a profundity of sudden anger. He turned toward his mother a face red, seamed, hard with hate and rage. They stared a moment in silence. Then she turned and staggered toward her room. Her hip struck violently against the corner of the table during this blind passage. A moment later the door closed.

Kelcey sank down in a chair with his legs thrust out straight and his hands deep in his trousers pockets. His chin was forward upon his breast, and his eyes stared before him. There swept over him all the self-pity that comes when the soul is turned back from a road.

VIII

During the next few days Kelcey suffered from his first gloomy conviction that the earth was not grateful to him for his presence upon it. When sharp words were said to him, he interpreted them with what seemed to be a lately acquired insight. He could now perceive that the universe hated him. He sank to the most sublime depths of despair.

One evening of this period he met Jones. The latter rushed upon him with enthusiasm. "Why, yer jest th' man I wanted t' see! I was comin' round t' your place t'-night. Lucky I met yeh! Ol' Bleecker's goin' t' give a blow-out t'-morrah night. Anything yeh want t' drink! All th' boys'll be there, an' everything. He tol' me expressly that he wanted yeh t' be there. Great time! Great! Can yeh come?"

Kelcey grasped the other's hand with fervour. He felt now that there was some solacing friendship in space. "You bet I will, ol' man," he said huskily. "I'd like nothin' better in th' world!"

As he walked home he thought that he was a very grim figure. He was about to taste the delicious revenge of a partial self-destruction. The universe would regret its position when it saw him drunk.

He was a little late in getting to Bleecker's lodging. He was delayed while his mother read aloud a letter from an old uncle, who wrote in one place: "God bless the boy! Bring him up to be the man his father was." Bleecker lived in an old three-storeyed house on a side street. A Jewish tailor lived and worked in the front parlour, and old Bleecker lived in the back parlour. A German, whose family took care of the house, occupied the basement. Another German, with a wife and eight children, rented the dining-room. The two upper floors were inhabited by tailors, dressmakers, a pedlar, and mysterious people who were seldom seen. The door of the little hall bedroom, at the foot of the second flight, was always open, and in there could be seen two bended men who worked at mending opera-glasses. The German woman in the dining-room was not friends with the little dressmaker in the rear room of the third floor, and frequently they yelled the vilest names up and down between the balusters. Each part of the woodwork was scratched and rubbed by the contact of innumerable persons. In one wall there was a long slit with chipped edges, celebrating the time when a man had thrown a hatchet at his wife. In the lower hall there was an eternal woman, with a rag and a pail of suds, who knelt over the worn oil-cloth. Old Bleecker felt that he had quite respectable and high-class apartments. He was glad to invite his friends.

Bleecker met Kelcey in the hall. He wore a collar that was cleaner and higher than his usual one. It changed his appearance greatly. He was now formidably aristocratic. "How are yeh, ol' man?" he shouted. He grasped Kelcey's arm and, babbling jovially, conducted him down the hall and into the ex-parlour.

A group of standing men made vast shadows in the yellow glare of the lamp. They turned their heads as the two entered. "Why, hello, Kelcey, ol' man," Jones exclaimed, coming rapidly forward. "Good fer you! Glad yeh come! Yeh know O'Connor, a' course! An' Schmidt! an' Woods! Then there's Zeusentell! Mr. Zeusentell—my friend Mr. Kelcey! Shake hands—both good fellows, damn-it-all! Then here is—oh, gentlemen, my friend Mr. Kelcey! A good fellow, he is, too. I've known 'im since I was a kid. Come, have a drink!" Everybody was excessively amiable. Kelcey felt that he had social standing. The strangers were cautious and respectful.

"By all means," said old Bleecker, "Mr. Kelcey, have a drink! An' by th' way, gentlemen, while we're about it, let's all have a drink!" There was much laughter. Bleecker was so droll at times.

With mild and polite gesturing they marched up to the table. There were upon it a keg of beer, a long row of whisky-bottles, a little heap of corncob pipes, some bags of tobacco, a box of cigars, and a mighty collection of glasses, cups, and mugs. Old

Bleecker had arranged them so deftly that they resembled a primitive bar. There was considerable scuffling for possession of the cracked cups. Jones politely but vehemently insisted upon drinking from the worst of the assortment. He was quietly opposed by others. Everybody showed that they were awed by Bleecker's lavish hospitality. Their demeanours expressed their admiration at the cost of this entertainment.

Kelcey took his second mug of beer away to a corner and sat down with it. He wished to socially reconnoitre. Over in a corner a man was telling a story in which at intervals he grunted like a pig. A half-dozen men were listening. Two or three others sat alone in isolated places. They looked expectantly bright, ready to burst out cordially if any one should address them. The row of bottles made quaint shadows upon the table, and upon a side-wall the keg of beer created a portentous black figure that reared toward the ceiling, hovering over the room and its inmates with spectral stature. Tobacco smoke lay in lazy cloud-banks overhead.

Jones and O'Connor stayed near the table, occasionally being affable in all directions. Kelcey saw old Bleecker go to them and heard him whisper: "Come, we must git th' thing started. Git th' thing started." Kelcey saw that the host was fearing that all were not having a good time. Jones conferred with O'Connor, and then O'Connor went to the man named Zeusentell. O'Connor evidently proposed something. Zeusentell refused at once. O'Connor beseeched. Zeusentell remained implacable. At last O'Connor broke off his argument and, going to the centre of the room, held up his hand. "Gentlemen," he shouted loudly, "we will now have a recitation by Mr. Zeusentell, entitled 'Patrick Clancy's Pig'!" He then glanced triumphantly at Zeusentell and said: "Come on!" Zeusentell had been twisting and making pantomimic appeals. He said, in a reproachful whisper: "You son of a gun."

The men turned their heads to glance at Zeusentell for a moment, and then burst into a sustained clamour. "Hurray! Let 'er go! Come—give it t' us! Spring it! Spring it! Let it come!"

As Zeusentell made no advances, they appealed personally. "Come, ol' man, let 'er go! Whatter yeh 'fraid of? Let 'er go! Go ahn! Hurry up!"

Zeusentell was protesting with almost frantic modesty. O'Connor took him by the lapel and tried to drag him; but he leaned back, pulling at his coat and shaking his head. "No, no, I don't know it, I tell yeh! I can't! I don't know it! I tell yeh I don't know it! I've forgotten it, I tell yeh! No—no—no—no. Ah, say, look-a-here, le' go me, can't yeh? What's th' matter with yeh? I tell yeh I don't know it!" The men applauded violently. O'Connor did not relent. A little battle was waged until all of a sudden Zeusentell was seen to grow wondrously solemn. A hush fell upon the men. He was about to begin. He paused in the middle of the floor and nervously adjusted his collar and cravat. The audience became grave. " 'Patrick Clancy's Pig,' " announced Zeusentell in a shrill, dry, unnatural tone. And then he began in rapid sing-song:

> *"Patrick Clancy had a pig*
> *Th' pride uv all th' nation,*
> *The half uv him was half as big*
> *As half uv all creation—"*

When he concluded the others looked at each other to convey their appreciation. They then wildly clapped their hands or tinkled their glasses. As Zeusentell went toward his seat a man leaned over and asked: "Can yeh tell me where I kin git that?" He had made a great success. After an enormous pressure he was induced to recite two more tales. Old Bleecker finally led him forward and pledged him in a large drink. He declared that they were the best things he had ever heard.

The efforts of Zeusentell imparted a gaiety to the company. The men, having laughed together, were better acquainted, and there was now a universal topic. Some of the party, too, began to be quite drunk.

The invaluable O'Connor brought forth a man who could play the mouth-organ. The latter, after wiping his instrument upon his coat-sleeve, played all the popular airs. The men's heads swayed to and fro in the clouded smoke. They grinned and beat time with their feet. A valour, barbaric and wild, began to show in their poses and in their faces, red and glistening from perspiration. The conversation resounded in a hoarse roar. The beer would not run rapidly enough for Jones, so he remained behind to tilt the keg. This caused the black shadow on the wall to retreat and advance, sinking mystically to loom forward again with sudden menace, a huge dark figure controlled as by some unknown emotion. The glasses, mugs, and cups travelled swift and regular, catching orange reflections from the lamp-light. Two or three men were grown so careless that they were continually spilling their drinks. Old Bleecker, cackling with pleasure, seized time to glance triumphantly at Jones. His party was going to be a success.

IX

Of a sudden Kelcey felt the buoyant thought that he was having a good time. He was all at once an enthusiast, as if he were at a festival of a religion. He felt that there was something fine and thrilling in this affair isolated from a stern world, from which the laughter arose like incense. He knew that old sentiment of brotherly regard for those about him. He began to converse tenderly with them. He was not sure of his drift of thought, but he knew that he was immensely sympathetic. He rejoiced at their faces, shining red and wrinkled with smiles. He was capable of heroisms.

His pipe irritated him by going out frequently. He was too busy in amiable conversations to attend to it. When he arose to go for a match he discovered that his legs were a trifle uncertain under him. They bended and did not precisely obey his intent. At the table he lit a match and then, in laughing at a joke made near him, forgot to apply it to the bowl of his pipe. He succeeded with the next match after annoying trouble. He swayed so that the match would appear first on one side of the bowl and then on the other. At last he happily got it directly over the tobacco. He had burned his fingers. He inspected them, laughing vaguely.

Jones came and slapped him on the shoulder. "Well, ol' man, let's take a drink fer ol' Handyville's sake!"

Kelcey was deeply affected. He looked at Jones with moist eyes. "I'll go yeh," he said. With an air of profound melancholy, Jones poured out some whisky. They drank reverently. They exchanged a glistening look of tender recollections and then went over to where Bleecker was telling a humorous story to a circle of giggling listeners. The old man sat like a fat, jolly god. "—And just at that moment th' old woman put her head out of th' window an' said: 'Mike, yez lazy divil, fer phwat do yez be slapin' in me new geranium bid?' An' Mike woke up an' said: 'Domn a washwoman thot do niver wash her own bid-clues. Here do I be slapin' in nothin' but dhirt an' wades.'" The men slapped their knees, roaring loudly. They begged him to tell another. A clamour of comment arose concerning the anecdote, so that when old Bleecker began a fresh one nobody was heeding.

It occurred to Jones to sing. Suddenly he burst forth with a ballad that had a rippling waltz movement, and, seizing Kelcey, made a furious attempt to dance. They sprawled over a pair of outstretched legs and pitched headlong. Kelcey fell with a yellow crash. Blinding lights flashed before his vision. But he arose immediately, laughing. He did not feel at all hurt. The pain in his head was rather pleasant.

Old Bleecker, O'Connor, and Jones, who now limped and drew breath through his teeth, were about to lead him with much care and tenderness to the table for another drink, but he laughingly pushed them away and went unassisted. Bleecker told him: "Great Gawd, your head struck hard enough t' break a trunk."

He laughed again, and with a show of steadiness and courage he poured out an extravagant portion of whisky. With cold muscles he put it to his lips and drank it. It chanced that this addition dazed him like a powerful blow. A moment later it affected him with blinding and numbing power. Suddenly unbalanced, he felt the room sway. His blurred sight could only distinguish a tumbled mass of shadow through which the beams from the light ran like swords of flame. The sound of the many voices was to him like the roar of a distant river. Still, he felt that if he could only annul the force of these million winding fingers that gripped his senses, he was capable of most brilliant and entertaining things.

He was at first of the conviction that his feelings were only temporary. He waited for them to pass away, but the mental and physical pause only caused a new reeling and swinging of the room. Chasms with inclined approaches were before him; peaks leaned toward him. And withal he was blind and numb with surprise. He understood vaguely in his stupefaction that it would disgrace him to fall down a chasm.

At last he perceived a shadow, a form, which he knew to be Jones. The adorable Jones, the supremely wise Jones, was walking in this strange land without fear or care, erect and tranquil. Kelcey murmured in admiration and affection, and fell toward his friend. Jones's voice sounded as from the shores of the unknown. "Come, come, ol' man, this will never do. Brace up." It appeared after all that Jones was not wholly wise. "Oh, I'm—all ri', Jones! I'm all ri'! I wan' shing song! Tha' 's all! I wan' shing song!"

Jones was stupid. "Come, now, sit down an' shut up."

It made Kelcey burn with fury. "Jones, le' me alone, I tell yeh! Le' me alone! I wan' shing song er te' story! G'l'm'n, I lovsh girl live down my shtreet. Thash reason 'm drunk—'tis! She—"

Jones seized him and dragged him toward a chair. He heard him laugh. He could not endure these insults from his friend. He felt a blazing desire to strangle his companion. He threw out his hand violently, but Jones grappled him close and he was no more than a dried leaf. He was amazed to find that Jones possessed the strength of twenty horses. He was forced skilfully to the floor.

As he lay he reflected in great astonishment upon Jones's muscle. It was singular that he had never before discovered it. The whole incident had impressed him immensely. An idea struck him that he might denounce Jones for it. It would be a sage thing. There would be a thrilling and dramatic moment in which he would dazzle all the others. But at this moment he was assailed by a mighty desire to sleep. Sombre and soothing clouds of slumber were heavily upon him. He closed his eyes with a sigh that was yet like that of a babe.

When he awoke there was still the battleful clamour of the revel. He half arose with a plan of participating, when O'Connor came and pushed him down again, throwing out his chin in affectionate remonstrance and saying, "Now, now," as to a child.

The change that had come over these men mystified Kelcey in a great degree. He had never seen anything so vastly stupid as their idea of his state. He resolved to prove to them that they were dealing with one whose mind was very clear. He kicked and squirmed in O'Connor's arms, until, with a final wrench, he scrambled to his feet and stood tottering in the middle of the room. He would let them see that he had a strangely lucid grasp of events. "G'l'm'n, I lovsh girl! I ain' drunker'n yeh all are! She—"

He felt them hurl him to a corner of the room and pile chairs and tables upon him until he was buried beneath a stupendous mountain. Far above, as up a mine's shaft, there were voices, lights, and vague figures. He was not hurt physically, but his feelings were unutterably injured. He, the brilliant, the good, the sympathetic, had been thrust fiendishly from the party. They had had the comprehension of red lobsters. It was an unspeakable barbarism. Tears welled piteously from his eyes. He planned long diabolical explanations!

X

At first the grey lights of dawn came timidly into the room, remaining near the windows, afraid to approach certain sinister corners. Finally, mellow streams of sunshine poured in, undraping the shadows to disclose the putrefaction, making pitiless revelation. Kelcey awoke with a groan of undirected misery. He tossed his stiffened arms about his head for a moment, and then, leaning heavily upon his elbow, stared blinking at his environment. The grim truthfulness of the day showed disaster and death. After the tumults of the previous night the interior of this room resembled a decaying battlefield. The air hung heavy and stifling with the odours of tobacco, men's breaths, and beer half filling forgotten glasses. There was ruck of broken tumblers, pipes, bottles, spilled tobacco, cigar-stumps. The chairs and tables were pitched this way and that way, as after some terrible struggle. In the midst of it all lay old Bleecker, stretched upon a couch in deepest sleep, as abandoned in attitude, as motionless, as ghastly, as if it were a corpse that had been flung there.

A knowledge of the thing came gradually into Kelcey's eyes. He looked about him with an expression of utter woe, regret, and loathing. He was compelled to lie down again. A pain above his eyebrows was like that from an iron clamp.

As he lay pondering, his bodily condition created for him a bitter philosophy, and he perceived all the futility of a red existence. He saw his life problems confronting him like granite giants, and he was no longer erect to meet them. He had made a calamitous retrogression in his war. Spectres were to him now as large as clouds.

Inspired by the pitiless ache in his head, he was prepared to reform and live a white life. His stomach informed him that a good man was the only being who was wise. But his perception of his future was hopeless. He was aghast at the prospect of the old routine. It was impossible. He trembled before its exactions.

Turning toward the other way, he saw that the gold portals of vice no longer enticed him. He could not hear the strains of alluring music. The beckoning sirens of drink had been killed by this pain in his head. The desires of his life suddenly lay dead like mullein-stalks. Upon reflection, he saw, therefore, that he was perfectly willing to be virtuous if somebody would come and make it easy for him.

When he stared over at old Bleecker, he felt a sudden contempt and dislike for him. He considered him to be a tottering old beast. It was disgusting to perceive aged men so weak in sin. He dreaded to see him awaken, lest he should be required to be somewhat civil to him.

Kelcey wished for a drink of water. For some time he had dreamed of the liquid, deliciously cool. It was an abstract, uncontained thing that poured upon him and tumbled him, taking away his pain like a kind of surgery. He arose and staggered slowly toward a little sink in a corner of the room. He understood that any rapid movement might cause his head to split.

The little sink was filled with a chaos of broken glass and spilled liquids. A sight of it filled him with horror, but he rinsed a glass with scrupulous care and, filling it, took an enormous drink. The water was an intolerable disappointment. It was insipid and weak to his scorched throat, and not at all cool. He put down the glass with a gesture of despair. His face became fixed in the stony and sullen expression of a man who waits for the recuperative power of morrows.

Old Bleecker awakened. He rolled over and groaned loudly. For a while he thrashed about in a fury of displeasure at his bodily stiffness and pain. Kelcey watched him as he would have watched a death agony. "Good Gawd!" said the old man, "beer an' whisky make th' devil of a mix! Did yeh see th' fight?"

"No," said Kelcey stolidly.

"Why, Zeusentell an' O'Connor had a great old mill. They were scrappin' all over th' place. I thought we were all goin' t' get pulled. Thompson, that fellah over in th' corner, though, he sat down on th' whole business. He was a dandy! He had t' poke Zeusentell! He was a bird! Lord, I wish I had a Manhattan!"

Kelcey remained in bitter silence while old Bleecker dressed.

"Come an' get a cocktail," said the latter briskly. This was part of his aristocracy. He was the only man of them who knew much about cocktails. He perpetually referred to them. "It'll brace yeh right up! Come along! Say, you get full too soon. You oughter wait until later, me boy! You're too speedy!" Kelcey wondered vaguely where his companion had lost his zeal for polished sentences, his iridescent mannerisms.

"Come along," said Bleecker.

Kelcey made a movement of disdain for cocktails, but he followed the other to the street. At the corner they separated. Kelcey attempted a friendly parting smile and then went on up the street. He had to reflect to know that he was erect and using his own muscles in walking. He felt like a man of paper, blown by the winds. Withal, the dust of the avenue was galling to his throat, eyes, and nostrils, and the roar of traffic cracked his head. He was glad, however, to be alone, to be rid of old Bleecker. The sight of him had been as the contemplation of a disease.

His mother was not at home. In his little room he mechanically undressed and bathed his head, arms, and shoulders. When he crawled between the two white sheets he felt a first lifting of his misery. His pillow was soothingly soft. There was an effect that was like the music of tender voices.

When he awoke again his mother was bending over him giving vent to alternate cries of grief and joy. Her hands trembled so that they were useless to her. "Oh, George, George, where have yeh been? What has happened t' yeh? Oh, George, I've been so worried! I didn't sleep a wink all night!"

Kelcey was instantly wide awake. With a moan of suffering he turned his face to the wall before he spoke. "Never mind, mother, I'm all right. Don't fret now! I was knocked down by a truck last night in th' street, an' they took me t' th' hospital; but it's all right now. I got out jest a little while ago. They told me I'd better go home an' rest up."

His mother screamed in pity, horror, joy, and self-reproach for something unknown. She frenziedly demanded the details.

He sighed with unutterable weariness. "Oh—wait—wait—wait," he said, shutting his eyes as from the merciless monotony of a pain. "Wait—wait—please wait. I can't talk now. I want t' rest."

His mother condemned herself with a little cry. She adjusted his pillow, her hands shaking with love and tenderness. "There, there, don't mind, dearie! But yeh can't think how worried I was—an' crazy. I was near frantic. I went down t' th' shop, an' they said they hadn't seen anything a' yeh there. The foreman was awful good t' me. He said he'd come up this afternoon t' see if yeh had come home yet. He tol' me not t' worry. Are yeh sure yer all right? Ain't there anythin' I kin git fer yeh? What did th' doctor say?"

Kelcey's patience was worn. He gestured, and then spoke querulously. "Now—now—mother, it's all right, I tell yeh! All I need is a little rest, an' I'll be as well as ever. But it makes it all th' worse if yeh stand there an' ask me questions an' make me think. Jest leave me alone fer a little while, an' I'll be as well as ever. Can't yeh do that?"

The little old woman puckered her lips funnily. "My, what an old bear th' boy is!" She kissed him blithely. Presently she went out, upon her face a bright and glad smile that must have been a reminiscence of some charming girlhood.

XI

At one time Kelcey had a friend who was struck in the head by the pole of a truck and knocked senseless. He was taken to the hospital, from which he emerged in the morning an astonished man, with rather a dim recollection of the accident. He used to hold an old brier-wood pipe in his teeth in a manner peculiar to himself, and, with a brown derby hat tilted back on his head, recount his strange sensations. Kelcey had always remembered it as a bit of curious history. When his mother cross-examined him in regard to the accident, he told this story with barely a variation. Its truthfulness was incontestable.

At the shop he was welcomed on the following day with

considerable enthusiasm. The foreman had told the story, and there were already jokes created concerning it. Mike O'Donnell, whose wit was famous, had planned a humorous campaign, in which he made charges against Kelcey which were, as a matter of fact, almost the exact truth. Upon hearing it, Kelcey looked at him suddenly from the corners of his eyes, but otherwise remained imperturbable. O'Donnell eventually despaired. "Yez can't goiy that kid! He takes ut all loike mate an' dhrink." Kelcey often told the story, his pipe held in his teeth peculiarly, and his derby tilted back on his head.

He remained at home for several evenings, content to read the papers and talk with his mother. She began to look around for the tremendous reason for it. She suspected that his nearness to death in the recent accident had sobered his senses and made him think of high things. She mused upon it continually. When he sat moodily pondering she watched him. She said to herself that she saw the light breaking in upon his spirit. She felt that it was a very critical period of his existence. She resolved to use all her power and skill to turn his eyes toward the lights in the sky. Accordingly, she addressed him one evening. "Come, go t' prayer-meetin' t'-night with me, will yeh, George?" It sounded more blunt than she intended.

He glanced at her in sudden surprise. "Huh?"

As she repeated her request, her voice quavered. She felt that it was a supreme moment. "Come, go t' prayer-meetin' t'-night, won't yeh?"

He seemed amazed. "Oh, I don't know," he began. He was fumbling in his mind for a reason for refusing. "I don't wanta go. I'm tired as the dickens!" His obedient shoulders sank down languidly. His head mildly drooped.

The little old woman, with a quick perception of her helplessness, felt a motherly rage at her son. It was intolerable that she could not impart motion to him in a chosen direction. The waves of her desires were puny against the rocks of his indolence. She had a great wish to beat him. "I don't know what I'm ever goin' t' do with yeh," she told him, in a choking voice.

"Yeh won't do anything I ask yeh to. Yeh never pay th' least bit a' attention t' what I say. Yeh don't mind me any more than yeh would a fly. Whatever am I goin' t' do with yeh?" She faced him in a battleful way, her eyes blazing with a sombre light of despairing rage.

He looked up at her ironically. "I don't know," he said, with calmness. "What are yeh?" He had traced her emotions and seen her fear of his rebellion. He thrust out his legs in the easy scorn of a rapier-bravo. "What are yeh?"

The little old woman began to weep. They were tears without a shame of grief. She allowed them to run unheeded down her cheeks. As she stared into space her son saw her regarding there the powers and influences that she had held in her younger life. She was in some way acknowledging to fate that she was now but withered grass, with no power but the power to feel the winds. He was smitten with a sudden shame. Besides, in the last few days he had gained quite a character for amiability. He saw something grand in relenting at this point. "Well," he said, trying to remove a sulky quality from his voice, "well, if yer bound t' have me go, I s'pose I'll have t' go."

His mother, with strange, immobile face, went to him and kissed him on the brow. "All right, George!" There was in her wet eyes an emotion which he could not fathom.

She put on her bonnet and shawl, and they went out together. She was unusually silent, and made him wonder why she did not appear gleeful at his coming. He was resentful because she did not display more appreciation of his sacrifice. Several times he thought of halting and refusing to go farther, to see if that would not wring from her some acknowledgment.

In a dark street the little chapel sat humbly between two towering apartment-houses. A red street-lamp stood in front. It threw a marvellous reflection upon the wet pavements. It was like the death-stain of a spirit. Farther up, the brilliant lights of an avenue made a span of gold across the black street. A roar of wheels and a clangour of bells came from this point, interwoven into a sound emblematic of the life of the city. It seemed somehow to affront this solemn and austere little edifice. It suggested an approaching barbaric invasion. The little church, pierced, would die with a fine illimitable scorn for its slayers.

When Kelcey entered with his mother he felt a sudden quaking. His knees shook. It was an awesome place to him. There was a menace in the red padded carpet and the leather doors, studded with little brass tacks that penetrated his soul with their pitiless glances. As for his mother, she had acquired such a new air that he would have been afraid to address her. He felt completely alone and isolated at this formidable time.

There was a man in the vestibule who looked at them blandly. From within came the sound of singing. To Kelcey there was a million voices. He dreaded the terrible moment when the doors should swing back. He wished to recoil, but at that instant the bland man pushed the doors aside, and he followed his mother up the centre aisle of the little chapel. To him there was a riot of lights that made him transparent. The multitudinous pairs of eyes that turned toward him were implacable in their cool valuations.

They had just ceased singing. He who conducted the meeting motioned that the service should wait until the newcomers found seats. The little old woman went slowly on toward the first rows. Occasionally she paused to scrutinize vacant places, but they did not seem to meet her requirements. Kelcey was in agony. He thought the moment of her decision would never come. In his unspeakable haste he walked a little faster than his mother. Once she paused to glance in her calculating way at some seats, and he forged ahead. He halted abruptly and returned, but by that time she had resumed her thoughtful march up the aisle. He could have assassinated her. He felt that everybody must have seen his torture, during which his hands were to him like monstrous swollen hides. He was wild with a rage in which his lips turned slightly livid. He was capable of doing some furious, unholy thing.

When the little old woman at last took a seat, her son sat down beside her slowly and stiffly. He was opposing his strong desire to drop.

When from the mists of his shame and humiliation the scene came before his vision, he was surprised to find that all eyes were not fastened upon his face. The leader of the meeting seemed to be the only one who saw him. He stared gravely, solemnly, regretfully. He was a pale-faced but plump young man in a black coat that buttoned to his chin. It was evident to Kelcey that his mother had spoken of him to the young clergyman, and that the latter was now impressing upon him the sorrow caused by the contemplation of his sin. Kelcey hated the man.

A man seated alone over in a corner began to sing. He closed his eyes and threw back his head. Others, scattered sparsely throughout the innumerable light-wood chairs, joined him as they caught the air. Kelcey heard his mother's frail, squeaking soprano. The chandelier in the centre was the only one lighted, and far at the end of the room one could discern the pulpit swathed in gloom, solemn and mystic as a bier. It was surrounded by vague shapes of darkness on which at times was the glint of brass, or of glass that shone like steel, until one could feel there the presence of the army of the unknown, possessors of the great eternal truths, and silent listeners at this ceremony. High up, the stained-glass windows loomed in leaden array like dull-hued banners, merely catching occasional splashes of dark wine-colour from the lights. Kelcey fell to brooding concerning this indefinable presence which he felt in a church.

One by one people arose and told little tales of their religious faith. Some were tearful, and others calm, emotionless, and convincing. Kelcey listened closely for a time. These people filled him with a great curiosity. He was not familiar with their types.

At last the young clergyman spoke at some length. Kelcey was amazed, because, from the young man's appearance, he

would not have suspected him of being so glib; but the speech
had no effect on Kelcey, excepting to prove to him again that
he was damned.

XII

Kelcey sometimes wondered whether he liked beer. He had
been obliged to cultivate a talent for imbibing it. He was born
with an abhorrence which he had steadily battled until it had
come to pass that he could drink from ten to twenty glasses
of beer without the act of swallowing causing him to shiver.
He understood that drink was an essential to joy, to the cov-
eted position of a man of the world and of the streets. The
saloons contained the mystery of a street for him. When he
knew its saloons he comprehended the street. Drink and its
surroundings were the eyes of a superb green dragon to him.
He followed a fascinating glitter, and the glitter required no
explanation.

Directly after old Bleecker's party he almost reformed. He
was tired and worn from the tumult of it, and he saw it as
one might see a skeleton emerged from a crimson cloak. He
wished then to turn his face away. Gradually, however, he
recovered his mental balance. Then he admitted again by his
point of view that the thing was not so terrible. His headache
had caused him to exaggerate. A drunk was not the blight
which he had once remorsefully named it. On the contrary, it
was a mere unpleasant incident. He resolved, however, to be
more cautious.

When prayer-meeting night came again his mother approached him hopefully. She smiled like one whose request is
already granted. "Well, will yeh go t' prayer-meetin' with me
t'-night again?"

He turned toward her with eloquent suddenness, and then
riveted his eyes upon a corner of the floor. "Well, I guess not,"
he said.

His mother tearfully tried to comprehend his state of mind.
"What has come over yeh?" she said tremblingly. "Yeh never

used t' be this way, George. Yeh never used t' be so cross an' mean t' me—"

"Oh, I ain't cross an' mean t' yeh," he interpolated, exasperated and violent.

"Yes, yeh are, too! I ain't hardly had a decent word from yeh in ever so long. Yer as cross an' as mean as yeh can be. I don't know what t' make of it. It can't be"—there came a look in her eyes that told that she was going to shock and alarm him with her heaviest sentence—"it can't be that yeh've got t' drinkin'."

Kelcey grunted with disgust at the ridiculous thing. "Why, what an old goose yer gettin' t' be!"

She was compelled to laugh a little, as a child laughs between tears at a hurt. She had not been serious. She was only trying to display to him how she regarded his horrifying mental state. "Oh, of course, I didn't mean that, but I think yeh act jest as bad as if yeh did drink. I wish yeh would do better, George!"

She had grown so much less frigid and stern in her censure that Kelcey seized the opportunity to try to make a joke of it. He laughed at her, but she shook her head and continued: "I do wish yeh would do better. I don't know what's t' become a' yeh, George. Yeh don't mind what I say no more 'n if I was th' wind in th' chimbly. Yeh don't care about nothin' 'cept goin' out nights. I can't ever get yeh t' prayer-meetin' ner church; yeh never go out with me anywheres unless yeh can't get out of it; yeh swear an' take on sometimes like everything; yeh never—"

He gestured wrathfully in interruption. "Say, look-a here, can't yeh think a' something I do?"

She ended her oration then in the old way. "An' I don't know what's goin' t' become a' yeh."

She put on her bonnet and shawl and then came and stood near him, expectantly. She imparted to her attitude a subtle threat of unchangeableness. He pretended to be engrossed in his newspaper. The little swaggering clock on the mantel became suddenly evident, ticking with loud monotony. Presently she said, firmly: "Well, are yeh comin'?"

He was reading. "Well, are yeh comin'?"

He threw his paper down, angrily. "Oh, why don't yeh go on an' leave me alone?" he demanded in supreme impatience. "What do yeh wanta pester me fer? Ye'd think there was robbers. Why can't yeh go alone or else stay home? You wanta go, an' I don't wanta go, an' yeh keep all time tryin' t' drag me. Yeh know I don't wanta go." He concluded in a last defiant wounding of her. "What do I care 'bout those ol' bags-a'-wind, anyhow? They gimme a pain!"

His mother turned her face and went from him. He sat staring with a mechanical frown. Presently he went and picked up his newspaper.

Jones told him that night that everybody had had such a good time at old Bleecker's party that they were going to form a club. They waited at the little smiling saloon, and then amid much enthusiasm all signed a membership-roll. Old Bleecker, late that night, was violently elected president. He made speeches of thanks and gratification during the remainder of the meeting. Kelcey went home rejoicing. He felt that at any rate he could have true friends. The dues were a dollar for each week.

He was deeply interested. For a number of evenings he fairly gobbled his supper in order that he might be off to the little smiling saloon to discuss the new organization. All the men were wildly enthusiastic. One night the saloon-keeper announced that he would donate half the rent of quite a large room over his saloon. It was an occasion for great cheering. Kelcey's legs were like whalebone when he tried to go upstairs upon his return home, and the edge of each step was moved curiously forward.

His mother's questions made him snarl. "Oh, nowheres!" At other times he would tell her: "Oh, t' see some friends a' mine! Where d' yeh s'pose?"

Finally, some of the women of the tenement concluded that

the little old mother had a wild son. They came to condole with her. They sat in the kitchen for hours. She told them of his wit, his cleverness, his kind heart.

XIII

At a certain time Kelcey discovered that some young men who stood in the cinders between a brick wall and the pavement, and near the side-door of a corner saloon, knew more about life than other people. They used to lean there smoking and chewing, and comment upon events and persons. They knew the neighbourhood extremely well. They debated upon small typical things that transpired before them, until they had extracted all the information that existence contained. They sometimes inaugurated little fights with foreigners or well-dressed men. It was here that Sapristi Glielmi, the pedlar, stabbed Pete Brady to death, for which he got a life-sentence. Each patron of the saloon was closely scrutinized as he entered the place. Sometimes they used to throng upon the heels of a man and in at the bar assert that he had asked them in to drink. When he objected, they would claim with one voice that it was too deep an insult and gather about to thrash him. When they had caught chance customers and absolute strangers, the barkeeper had remained in stolid neutrality, ready to serve one or seven, but two or three times they had encountered the wrong men. Finally, the proprietor had come out one morning and told them, in the fearless way of his class, that their pastime must cease. "It quits right here! See? Right here! Th' nex' time yeh try t' work it, I come with th' bung-starter, an' th' mugs I miss with it git pulled. See? It quits!" Infrequently, however, men did ask them in to drink.

The policeman of that beat grew dignified and shrewd whenever he approached this corner. Sometimes he stood with his hands behind his back and cautiously conversed with them. It was understood on both sides that it was a good thing to be civil.

In winter this band, a trifle diminished in numbers, huddled in their old coats and stamped little flat places in the snow, their faces turned always toward the changing life in the streets. In the summer they became more lively. Sometimes, then, they walked out to the kerb to look up and down the street. Over in a trampled vacant lot, surrounded by high tenement-houses, there was a sort of den among some boulders. An old truck was made to form a shelter. The small hoodlums of that vicinity all avoided the spot. So many of them had been thrashed upon being caught near it. It was the summer-time lounging place of the band from the corner.

They were all too clever to work. Some of them had worked, but these used their experiences as stores from which to draw tales. They were like veterans with their wars. One lad in particular used to recount how he whipped his employer, the proprietor of a large grain and feed establishment. He described his victim's features and form and clothes with minute exactness. He bragged of his wealth and social position. It had been a proud moment of the lad's life. He was like a savage who had killed a great chief.

Their feeling for contemporaneous life was one of contempt. Their philosophy taught that in a large part the whole thing was idle and a great bore. With fine scorn they sneered at the futility of it. Work was done by men who had not the courage to stand still and let the skies clap together if they willed.

The vast machinery of the popular law indicated to them that there were people in the world who wished to remain quiet. They awaited the moment when they could prove to them that a riotous upheaval, a cloudburst of destruction, would be a delicious thing. They thought of their fingers buried in the lives of these people. They longed dimly for a time when they could run through decorous streets with crash and roar of war, an army of revenge for pleasures long possessed by others, a wild sweeping compensation for their years without crystal and gilt, women and wine. This thought slumbered in them, as the image of Rome might have lain small in the hearts of the barbarians.

Kelcey respected these youths so much that he ordinarily used the other side of the street. He could not go near to them, because if a passer-by minded his own business he was a disdainful prig and had insulted them; if he showed that he was aware of them they were likely to resent his not minding his own business and prod him into a fight if the opportunity were good. Kelcey longed for their acquaintance and friendship, for with it came social safety and ease; they were respected so universally.

Once in another street Fidsey Corcoran was whipped by a short, heavy man. Fidsey picked himself up, and in the fury of defeat hurled pieces of brick at his opponent. The short man dodged with skill, and then pursued Fidsey for over a block. Sometimes he got near enough to punch him. Fidsey raved in maniacal fury. The moment the short man would attempt to resume his own affairs, Fidsey would turn upon him again, tears and blood upon his face, with the lashed rage of a vanquished animal. The short man used to turn about, swear madly, and make little dashes. Fidsey always ran, and then returned as pursuit ceased. The short man apparently wondered if this maniac was ever going to allow him to finish whipping him. He looked helplessly up and down the street. People were there who knew Fidsey, and they remonstrated with him; but he continued to confront the short man, gibbering like a wounded ape, using all the eloquence of the street in his wild oaths.

Finally, the short man was exasperated to black fury. He decided to end the fight. With low snarls, ominous as death, he plunged at Fidsey.

Kelcey happened there then. He grasped the short man's shoulder. He cried out in the peculiar whine of the man who interferes. "Oh, hol' on! Yeh don't wanta hit 'im any more! Yeh've done enough to 'im now! Leave 'im be!"

The short man wrenched and tugged. He turned his face until his teeth were almost at Kelcey's cheek. "Le' go me! Le' go me, you—" The rest of his sentence was screamed curses.

Kelcey's face grew livid from fear, but he somehow managed to keep his grip. Fidsey, with but an instant's pause, plunged into the new fray.

They beat the short man. They forced him against a high board fence, where for a few seconds their blows sounded upon his head in swift thuds. A moment later Fidsey descried a running policeman. He made off, fleet as a shadow. Kelcey noted his going. He ran after him.

Three or four blocks away they halted. Fidsey said: "I'd 'a' licked dat big stiff in 'bout a minute more," and wiped the blood from his eyes.

At the gang's corner, they asked: "Who soaked yeh, Fidsey?" His description was burning. Everybody laughed. "Where is 'e now?" Later they began to question Kelcey. He recited a tale in which he allowed himself to appear prominent and redoubtable. They looked at him then as if they thought he might be quite a man.

Once when the little old woman was going out to buy something for her son's supper, she discovered him standing at the side-door of the saloon engaged intimately with Fidsey and the others. She slunk away, for she understood that it would be a terrible thing to confront him and his pride there with youths who were superior to mothers.

When he arrived home he threw down his hat with a weary sigh, as if he had worked long hours, but she attacked him before he had time to complete the falsehood. He listened to her harangue with a curled lip. In defence he merely made a gesture of supreme exasperation. She never understood the advanced things in life. He felt the hopelessness of ever making her comprehend. His mother was not modern.

XIV

The little old woman arose early and bustled in the preparation of breakfast. At times she looked anxiously at the clock. An hour before her son should leave for work she went to his room and called him in the usual tone of sharpness. "George! George!"

A sleepy growl came to her.

"Come, come, it's time t' git up," she continued. "Come, now, git right up!"

Later she went again to the door. "George, are yeh gittin' up?"

"Huh?"

"Are yeh gittin' up?"

"Yes, I'll git right up!" He had introduced a valour into his voice which she detected to be false. She went to his bedside and took him by the shoulder. "George—George—git up!"

From the mist-lands of sleep he began to protest incoherently. "Oh, le' me be, won' yeh? 'm sleepy!"

She continued to shake him. "Well, it's time t' git up. Come—come—come on, now."

Her voice, shrill with annoyance, pierced his ears in a slender, piping thread of sound. He turned over on the pillow to bury his head in his arms. When he expostulated, his tones came half smothered. "Oh, le' me be, can't yeh? There's plenty a' time! Jest fer ten minutes! 'm sleepy!"

She was implacable. "No, yeh must git up now! Yeh ain't got more'n time enough t' eat yer breakfast an' git t' work."

Eventually he arose, sullen and grumbling. Later he came to his breakfast, blinking his dry eyelids, his stiffened features set in a mechanical scowl.

Each morning his mother went to his room, and fought a battle to arouse him. She was like a soldier. Despite his pleadings, his threats, she remained at her post, imperturbable and unyielding. These affairs assumed large proportions in his life. Sometimes he grew beside himself with a bland, unformulated wrath. The whole thing was a consummate imposition. He felt that he was being cheated of his sleep. It was an injustice to compel him to arise morning after morning with bitter regularity, before the sleep-gods had at all loosened their grasp. He hated that unknown force which directed his life.

One morning he swore a tangled mass of oaths, aimed into the air, as if the injustice poised there. His mother flinched at first; then her mouth set in the little straight line. She saw that the momentous occasion had come. It was the time of the critical battle. She turned upon him valorously. "Stop your swearin', George Kelcey. I won't have yeh talk so before me! I won't have it! Stop this minute! Not another word! Do yeh think I'll allow yeh t' swear b'fore me like that? Not another word! I won't have it! I declare I won't have it another minute!"

At first her projected words had slid from his mind as if striking against ice, but at last he heeded her. His face grew sour with passion and misery. He spoke in tones dark with dislike. "Th' 'ell yeh won't! Whatter yeh goin' t' do 'bout it?" Then, as if he considered that he had not been sufficiently impressive, he arose and slowly walked over to her. Having arrived at point-blank range he spoke again. "Whatter yeh goin' t' do 'bout it?" He regarded her then with an unaltering scowl, albeit his mien was as dark and cowering as that of a condemned criminal.

She threw out her hands in the gesture of an impotent one. He was acknowledged victor. He took his hat and slowly left her.

For three days they lived in silence. He brooded upon his mother's agony and felt a singular joy in it. As opportunity offered, he did little despicable things. He was going to make her abject. He was now uncontrolled, ungoverned; he wished to be an emperor. Her suffering was all a sort of compensation for his own dire pains.

She went about with a grey, impassive face. It was as if she had survived a massacre in which all that she loved had been torn from her by the brutality of savages.

One evening at six he entered and stood looking at his mother as she peeled potatoes. She had hearkened to his coming listlessly, without emotion, and at his entrance she did not raise her eyes.

"Well, I'm fired," he said suddenly.

It seemed to be the final blow. Her body gave a convulsive movement in the chair. When she finally lifted her eyes, horror possessed her face. Her under jaw had fallen. "Fired? Outa work? Why—George?" He went over to the window and stood with his back to her. He could feel her grey stare upon him.

"Yep! Fired!"

At last she said: "Well, whatter yeh goin' t' do?"

He tapped the pane with his fingernail. He answered in a tone made hoarse and unnatural by an assumption of gay carelessness: "Oh, nothin'!"

She began, then, her first weeping. "Oh—George—George— George—"

He looked at her scowling. "Ah, whatter yeh givin' us? Is this all I git when I come home f'm bein' fired? Anybody 'ud think it was my fault. I couldn't help it."

She continued to sob in a dull, shaking way. In the pose of her head there was an expression of her conviction that comprehension of her pain was impossible to the universe. He paused for a moment, and then, with his usual tactics, went out, slamming the door. A pale flood of sunlight, imperturbable at its vocation, streamed upon the little old woman, bowed with pain, forlorn in her chair.

XV

Kelcey was standing on the corner next day when three little boys came running. Two halted some distance away, and the other came forward. He halted before Kelcey, and spoke importantly.

"Hey, your ol' woman's sick."

"What?"

"Your ol' woman's sick."

"Git out!"

"She is, too!"

"Who tol' yeh?"

"Mis' Callahan. She said fer me t' run an' tell yeh. Dey want yeh."

A swift dread struck Kelcey. Like flashes of light little scenes from the past shot through his brain. He had thoughts of a vengeance from the clouds. As he glanced about him the familiar view assumed a meaning that was ominous and dark. There was prophecy of disaster in the street, the buildings, the sky, the people. Something tragic and terrible in the air was known to his nervous, quivering nostrils. He spoke to the little boy in a tone that quavered. "All right!"

Behind him he felt the sudden contemplative pause of his companions of the gang. They were watching him. As he went rapidly up the street he knew that they had come out to the middle of the walk and were staring after him. He was glad that they could not see his face, his trembling lips, his eyes wavering in fear. He stopped at the door of his home and stared at the panel as if he saw written thereon a word. A moment later he entered. His eyes comprehended the room in a frightened glance.

His mother sat gazing out at the opposite walls and windows. She was leaning her head upon the back of the chair. Her face was overspread with a singular pallor, but the glance of her eyes was strong, and the set of her lips was tranquil.

He felt an unspeakable thrill of thanksgiving at seeing her seated there calmly. "Why, mother, they said yeh was sick," he cried, going toward her impetuously. "What's th' matter?"

She smiled at him. "Oh, it ain't nothin'! I on'y got kinda dizzy, that's all." Her voice was sober and had the ring of vitality in it.

He noted her commonplace air. There was no alarm or pain in her tones, but the misgivings of the street, the prophetic twinges of his nerves, made him still hesitate. "Well—are you sure it ain't? They scared me 'bout t' death."

"No, it ain't anything, on'y some sorta dizzy feelin'. I fell down b'hind th' stove. Missis Callahan, she came an' picked me up. I must 'a' laid there fer quite a while. Th' doctor said he guessed I'd be all right in a couple a' hours. I don't feel nothin'!"

Kelcey heaved a great sigh of relief. "Lord, I was scared!" He began to beam joyously, since he was escaped from his fright. "Why, I couldn't think what had happened," he told her.

"Well, it ain't nothin'," she said.

He stood about awkwardly, keeping his eyes fastened upon her in a sort of surprise, as if he had expected to discover that she had vanished. The reaction from his panic was a thrill of delicious contentment. He took a chair and sat down near her, but presently he jumped up to ask: "There ain't nothin' I can git fer yeh, is ther?" He looked at her eagerly. In his eyes shone love and joy. If it were not for the shame of it, he would have called her endearing names.

"No, ther ain't nothin'," she answered. Presently she continued, in a conversational way: "Yeh ain't found no work yit, have yeh?"

The shadow of his past fell upon him then, and he became suddenly morose. At last he spoke in a sentence that was a vow, a declaration of change. "No, I ain't, but I'm goin' t' hunt fer it hard, you bet."

She understood from his tone that he was making peace with her. She smiled at him gladly. "Yer a good boy, George!" A radiance from the stars lit her face.

Presently she asked: "D' yeh think yer old boss would take yeh on ag'in if I went t' see him?"

"No," said Kelcey at once. "It wouldn't do no good! They got all th' men they want. There ain't no room there. It wouldn't do no good." He ceased to beam for a moment as he thought of certain disclosures. "I'm goin' t' try to git work everywheres. I'm goin' t' make a wild break t' git a job, an' if there's one anywheres I'll git it."

She smiled at him again. "That's right, George!"

When it came supper-time he dragged her in her chair over

to the table and then scurried to and fro to prepare a meal for her. She laughed gleefully at him. He was awkward and densely ignorant. He exaggerated his helplessness sometimes until she was obliged to lean back in her chair to laugh. Afterward they sat by the window. Her hand rested upon his hair.

XVI

When Kelcey went to borrow money from old Bleecker, Jones, and the others, he discovered that he was below them in social position. Old Bleecker said gloomily that he did not see how he could loan money at that time. When Jones asked him to have a drink, his tone was careless. O'Connor recited at length some bewildering financial troubles of his own. In them all he saw that something had been reversed. They remained silent upon many occasions when they might have grunted in sympathy for him.

As he passed along the street near his home he perceived Fidsey Corcoran and another of the gang. They made eloquent signs. "Are yeh wid us?"

He stopped and looked at them. "What's wrong with yeh?"

"Are yeh wid us er not?" demanded Fidsey. "New barkeep'! Big can! We got it over in d' lot. Big can, I tell yeh." He drew a picture in the air, so to speak, with his enthusiastic fingers.

Kelcey turned dejectedly homeward. "Oh, I guess not, this roun'."

"What's d' matter wi'che?" said Fidsey. "Yer gittin' t' be a reg'lar Willie! Come ahn, I tell yeh! Youse gits one smoke at d' can b'cause yeh b'longs t' d' gang, an' yeh don't wanta give it up widout er scrap! See? Some udder john'll git yer smoke. Come ahn!"

When they arrived at the place among the boulders in the vacant lot, one of the band had a huge and battered tin pail tilted afar up. His throat worked convulsively. He was watched keenly and anxiously by five or six others. Their eyes followed carefully each fraction of distance that the pail was lifted. They were very silent.

Fidsey burst out violently as he perceived what was in progress. "Heh, Tim, yeh big sojer, le' go d' can! Whatta yeh t'ink? Wees er in dis! Le' go dat!"

He who was drinking made several angry protesting contortions of his throat. Then he put down the pail and swore. "Who's a big sojer? I ain't gittin' more'n me own smoke! Yer too bloomin' swift! Ye'd t'ink yeh was d' on'y mug what owned dis can! Close yer face while I gits me smoke!"

He took breath for a moment and then returned the pail to its tilted position. Fidsey went to him and worried and clamoured. He interfered so seriously with the action of drinking that the other was obliged to release the pail again for fear of choking.

Fidsey grabbed it and glanced swiftly at the contents. "Dere! Dat's what I was hollerin' at! Look-ut d' beer! Not 'nough t' wet yer t'roat! Yehs can't have nottin' on d' level wid youse damn' tanks! Youse was a reg'lar rese'voiy, Tim Connigan! Look what yeh lef' us! Ah, say, youse was a dandy! Whatta yeh t'ink we ah? Willies? Don' we want no smoke? Say, look-ut dat can! It's drier'n hell! Whatta yeh t'ink?"

Tim glanced in at the beer. Then he said: "Well, d' mug what come b'fore me, he on'y lef' me dat much. Blue Billie, he done d' swallerin'! I on'y had a tas'e!"

Blue Billie, from his seat near, called out in wrathful protest: "Yeh lie, Tim. I never had more'n a mouf-full!" An inspiration evidently came to him then, for his countenance suddenly brightened, and, arising, he went toward the pail. "I ain't had me reg'lar smoke yit! Guess I come in ahead a' Fidsey, don't I?"

Fidsey, with a sardonic smile, swung the pail behind him. "I guess nit! Not dis minnet! Youse hadger smoke. If yeh ain't, yeh don't git none. See?"

Blue Billie confronted Fidsey determinedly. "D' 'ell I don't!"

"Nit," said Fidsey.

Billie sat down again.

Fidsey drank his portion. Then he manœuvred skilfully before the crowd until Kelcey and the other youth took their shares. "Youse er a mob a' tanks," he told the gang. "Nobody 'ud git nottin' if dey wasn't on t' yehs!"

Blue Billie's soul had been smouldering in hate against Fidsey. "Ah, shut up! Youse ain't gotta take care a' dose two mugs, dough. Youse hadger smoke, ain't yeh? Den yer t'rough. G' home!"

"Well, I hate t' see er bloke use 'imself fer a tank," said Fidsey. "But youse don't wanta go jollyin' 'round 'bout d' can, Blue, er youse'll git done."

"Who'll do me?" demanded Blue Billie, casting his eye about him.

"Kel will," said Fidsey bravely.

"D' 'ell he will!"

"Dat's what he will!"

Blue Billie made the gesture of a warrior. "He never saw d' day a' his life dat he could do me little finger. If 'e says much t' me, I'll push 'is face all over d' lot."

Fidsey called to Kelcey. "Say, Kel, hear what dis mug is chewin'?"

Kelcey was apparently deep in other matters. His back was half turned.

Blue Billie spoke to Fidsey in a battleful voice. "Did 'e ever say 'e could do me?"

Fidsey said: "Soitenly 'e did. Youse is dead easy, 'e says. He says he kin punch holes in you, Blue!"

"When did 'e say it?"

"Oh—any time. Youse is a cinch, Kel says."

Blue Billie walked over to Kelcey. The others of the band followed him, exchanging joyful glances.

"Did youse say yeh could do me?"

Kelcey slowly turned, but he kept his eyes upon the ground. He heard Fidsey darting among the others, telling of his prowess, preparing them for the downfall of Blue Billie. He stood heavily on one foot and moved his hands nervously. Finally he said, in a low growl: "Well, what if I did?"

The sentence sent a happy thrill through the band. It was the formidable question. Blue Billie braced himself. Upon him came the responsibility of the next step. The gang fell back a little upon all sides. They looked expectantly at Blue Billie.

He walked forward with a deliberate step until his face was close to Kelcey.

"Well, if you did," he said, with a snarl between his teeth, "I'm goin' t' t'ump d' life outa yeh right heh!"

A little boy, wild of eye and puffing, came down the slope as from an explosion. He burst out in a rapid treble: "Is dat Kelcey feller here? Say, yeh ol' woman's sick again. Dey want yeh! Yehs better run! She's awful sick!"

The gang turned with loud growls. "Ah, git outa here!" Fidsey threw a stone at the little boy and chased him a short distance, but he continued to clamour: "Youse better come, Kelcey feller! She's awful sick! She was hollerin'! Dey been lookin' fer yeh over 'n hour!" In his eagerness he returned part way, regardless of Fidsey.

Kelcey had moved away from Blue Billie. He said: "I guess I'd better go." They howled at him. "Well," he continued, "I can't—I don't wanta—I don't wanta leave me mother be—she—"

His words were drowned in the chorus of their derision. "Well, look-a-here," he would begin, and at each time their cries and screams ascended. They dragged at Blue Billie. "Go fer 'im, Blue! Slug 'im! Go ahn!"

Kelcey went slowly away while they were urging Blue Billie to do a decisive thing. Billie stood fuming and blustering and explaining himself. When Kelcey had achieved a considerable distance from him, he stepped forward a few paces and hurled a terrible oath. Kelcey looked back darkly.

XVII

When he entered the chamber of death, he was brooding over the recent encounter and devising extravagant revenges upon Blue Billie and the others.

The little old woman was stretched upon her bed. Her face and hands were of the hue of the blankets. Her hair, seemingly of a new and wondrous greyness, hung over her temples in whips and tangles. She was sickeningly motionless, save for her eyes, which rolled and swayed in maniacal glances.

A young doctor had just been administering medicine. "There," he said, with a great satisfaction, "I guess that'll do her good!" As he went briskly toward the door he met Kelcey. "Oh," he said. "Son?"

Kelcey had that in his throat which was like fur. When he forced his voice, the words came first low and then high, as if they had broken through something. "Will she—will she—"

The doctor glanced back at the bed. She was watching them as she would have watched ghouls, and muttering.

"Can't tell," he said. "She's a wonderful woman! Got more vitality than you and I together! Can't tell! May—may not! Good-day! Back in two hours."

In the kitchen Mrs. Callahan was feverishly dusting the furniture, polishing this and that. She arranged everything in decorous rows. She was preparing for the coming of death. She looked at the floor as if she longed to scrub it.

The doctor paused to speak in an undertone to her, glancing at the bed. When he departed she laboured with a renewed speed.

Kelcey approached his mother. From a little distance he called to her. "Mother—mother—" He proceeded with caution lest this mystic being upon the bed should clutch at him.

"Mother—mother—don't yeh know me?" He put forth apprehensive, shaking fingers and touched her hand.

There were two brilliant steel-coloured points upon her eyeballs. She was staring off at something sinister.

Suddenly she turned to her son in a wild babbling appeal. "Help me! Help me! Oh, help me! I see them coming."

Kelcey called to her as to a distant place. "Mother! Mother!" She looked at him, and then there began within her a struggle to reach him with her mind. She fought with some implacable power whose fingers were in her brain. She called to Kelcey in stammering, incoherent cries for help.

Then she again looked away. "Ah, there they come! There they come! Ah, look—look—loo—" She arose to a sitting posture without the use of her arms.

Kelcey felt himself being choked. When her voice pealed forth in a scream he saw crimson curtains moving before his eyes. "Mother—oh, mother—there's nothin'—there's nothin'—"

She was at a kitchen door with a dish-cloth in her hand. Within there had just been a clatter of crockery. Down through the trees of the orchard she could see a man in a field plough-ing. "Bill—o-o-oh, Bill—have yeh seen Georgie? Is he out there with you? Georgie! Georgie! Come right here this minnet! Right—this—minnet!"

She began to talk to some people in the room. "I want t' know what yeh want here! I want yeh t' git out! I don't want yeh here! I don't feel good t'-day, an' I don't want yeh here! I don't feel good t'-day! I want yeh t' git out!" Her voice be-came peevish. "Go away! Go away! Go away!"

Kelcey lay in a chair. His nerveless arms allowed his fingers to sweep the floor. He became so that he could not hear the chatter from the bed, but he was always conscious of the tick-ing of the little clock out on the kitchen shelf.

When he aroused, the pale-faced but plump young clergy-man was before him.

"My poor lad!" began this latter.

The little old woman lay still with her eyes closed. On the table at the head of the bed was a glass containing a water-like medicine. The reflected lights made a silver star on its side. The two men sat side by side, waiting. Out in the kitchen Mrs. Callahan had taken a chair by the stove and was waiting.

Kelcey began to stare at the wall-paper. The pattern was clusters of brown roses. He felt them like hideous crabs crawl-ing upon his brain.

Through the doorway he saw the oil-cloth covering of the table catching a glimmer from the warm afternoon sun. The window disclosed a fair, soft sky, like blue enamel, and a fringe of chimneys and roofs, resplendent here and there. An endless roar, the eternal trample of the marching city, came mingled with vague cries. At intervals the woman out by the stove moved restlessly and coughed.

Over the transom from the hallway came two voices.

"Johnnie!"

"Wot!"

"You come right here t' me! I want yehs t' go t' d' store fer me!"

"Ah, ma, send Sally!"

"No, I will not! You come right here!"

"All right, in a minnet!"

"Johnnie!"

"In a minnet, I tell yeh!"

"Johnnie—" There was the sound of a heavy tread, and later a boy squealed. Suddenly the clergyman started to his feet. He rushed forward and peered. The little old woman was dead.

HOWELLS FEARS REALISTS MUST WAIT [1]

☼ ☼ ☼

Fears Realists Must Wait

AN INTERESTING TALK WITH
WILLIAM DEAN HOWELLS

The Eminent Novelist Still Holds a Firm
Faith in Realism, but Confesses a Doubt if Its Day
Has Yet Come—He Has Observed a Change in the
Literary Pulse of the Country Within the Last Few
Months—A Reactionary Wave.

[Copyright, 1894, by L. S. McClure, Limited.]

William Dean Howells leaned his cheek upon the two outstretched fingers of his right hand and gazed thoughtfully at
the window—the panes black from the night without, although
studded once or twice with little electric stars far up on the
west side of the Park. He was looking at something which his
memory had just brought to him.

"I have a little scheme," he at last said, slowly. "I saw a young
girl out in a little Ohio town once—she was the daughter of the
carpetwoman there—that is to say, her mother made ragcarpets
and rugs for the villagers. And this girl had the most wonderful instinct in manner and dress. Her people were of the lowest
of the low in a way and yet this girl was a lady. It used to completely amaze me—to think how this girl could grow there in
that squalor. She was as chic as chic could be, and yet the
money spent and the education was nothing—nothing at all.
Where she procured her fine taste you could not imagine. It

---

[1] Reprinted verbatim from the *New York Times*, Sunday, October 28,
1894.

was deeply interesting to me—it overturned so many of my rooted social dogmas. It was the impossible, appearing suddenly. And then there was another in Cambridge—a wonderful type. I have come upon them occasionally here and there. I intend to write something of the kind if I can. I have thought of a good title, too, I think—a name of a flower—'The Ragged Lady.' "

"I suppose this is a long way off," said the other man reflectively. "I am anxious to hear what you say in 'The Story of a Play.' Do you raise your voice toward reforming the abuses that are popularly supposed to hide in the manager's office for use upon the struggling artistic playwright and others? Do you recite the manager's divine misapprehension of art?"

"No, I do not," said Mr. Howells.

"Why?" said the other man.

"Well, in the first place, the manager is a man of business. He preserves himself. I suppose he judges not against art, but between art and act. He looks at art through the crowds."

"I don't like reformatory novels anyhow," said the other man.

"And in the second place," continued Mr. Howells, "it does no good to go at things hammer and tongs in this obvious way. I believe that every novel should have an intention. A man should mean something when he writes. Ah, this writing merely to amuse people—why, it seems to me altogether vulgar. A man may as well blacken his face and go out and dance on the street for pennies. The author is a sort of trained bear, if you accept certain standards. If literary men are to be the public fools, let us at any rate have it clearly understood, so that those of us who feel differently can take measures. But, on the other hand, a novel should never preach and berate and storm. It does no good. As a matter of fact, a book of that kind is ineffably tiresome. People don't like to have their lives half cudgeled out in that manner, especially in these days, when a man, likely enough, only reaches for a book when he wishes to be fanned, so to speak, after the heat of the daily struggle. When a writer desires to preach in an obvious way he should an-

nounce his intention—let him cry out then that he is in the pulpit. But it is the business of the novel—"

"Ah!" said the other man.

"It is the business of the novel to picture the daily life in the
most exact terms possible, with an absolute and clear sense of
proportion. That is the important matter—the proportion. As a
usual thing, I think, people have absolutely no sense of proportion. Their noses are tight against life, you see. They perceive
mountains where there are no mountains, but frequently a
great peak appears no larger than a rat trap. An artist sees a
dog down the street—well, his eye instantly relates the dog to
its surroundings. The dog is proportioned to the buildings and
the trees. Whereas, many people can conceive of that dog's tail
resting upon a hill top."

"You have often said that the novel is a perspective," observed the other man.

"A perspective, certainly. It is a perspective made for the
benefit of people who have no true use of their eyes. The novel,
in its real meaning, adjusts the proportions. It preserves the
balances. It is in this way that lessons are to be taught and re-
forms to be won. When people are introduced to each other
they will see the resemblances, and won't want to fight so
badly."

"I suppose that when a man tries to write 'what the people
want'—when he tries to reflect the popular desire, it is a bad
quarter of an hour for the laws of proportion."

"Do you recall any of the hosts of stories that began in love
and ended a little further on. Those stories used to represent
life to the people, and I believe they do now to a large class.
Life began when the hero saw a certain girl, and it ended
abruptly when he married her. Love and courtship was not an
incident, a part of life—it was the whole of it. All else was of no
value. Men of that religion must have felt very stupid when
they were engaged at anything but courtship. Do you see the
false proportion? Do you see the dog with his tail upon the hill-
top? Somebody touched the universal heart with the fascinat-

ing theme—the relation of man to maid—and, for many years, it was as if no other relation could be recognized in fiction. Here and there an author raised his voice, but not loudly. I like to see the novelists treating some of the other important things of life—the relation of mother and son, of husband and wife, in fact all those things that we live in continually. The other can be but fragmentary."

"I suppose there must be two or three new literary people just back of the horizon somewhere," said the other man. "Books upon these lines that you speak of are what might be called unpopular. Do you think them to be a profitable investment?"

"From my point of view it is the right—it is sure to be a profitable investment. After that it is a question of perseverance, courage. A writer of skill cannot be defeated because he remains true to his conscience. It is a long, serious conflict sometimes, but he must win, if he does not falter. Lowell said to me one time: 'After all, the barriers are very thin. They are paper. If a man has his conscience and one or two friends who can help him, it becomes very simple at last.'"

"Mr. Howells," said the other man, suddenly, "have you observed a change in the literary pulse of the country within the last four months? Last Winter, for instance, it seemed that realism was about to capture things, but then recently I have thought that I saw coming a sort of counter wave, a flood of the other—a reaction, in fact. Trivial, temporary, perhaps, but a reaction, certainly."

Mr. Howells dropped his hand in a gesture of emphatic assent. "What you say is true. I have seen it coming. . . . I suppose we shall have to wait."

STEPHEN CRANE.[2]

---

[2] Discovered by George Arms, this article was reprinted in *Americana* for April 1943.

PART II [A]

War Tales

THE RED BADGE OF COURAGE

INTRODUCTION

The *Red Badge of Courage* was the first non-romantic novel of the Civil War to attain widespread popularity. Appearing at a time when the war was still treated primarily as the subject for romance, it turned the tide of the prevailing convention and established a new if not unprecedented one. It was boomed by reviewers as the most realistic war novel that had ever been written, and so, next to Ambrose Bierce, who despised "realism" (but not in his own war tales), Crane won a reputation greater than any other American as a realistic writer on war. Both Bierce and J. W. De Forest (in his *Miss Ravenel's Conversion*) had presented war from as unromantic a view as Crane, yet De Forest was never recognized and Bierce's war tales caused "scarcely a ripple" in 1892. The American public, fed up with Civil War memoirs and novels, had escaped into the romantic world of George du Maurier's *Trilby*, yet that same public in 1895 took to *The Red Badge of Courage*. In England, because the public there was at a greater distance from war (though at the same time, in another sense, closer to it), Crane's book was read with much more detachment, read not alone for its "realism" but also for purely literary reasons—its craftsmanship. What excited Edward Garnett in his *Academy* "Appreciation" of 1898 was solely Crane's artistry.

The Red Badge of Courage is a literary exercise in language, in the patterning of words and the counterpointing of themes and tropes and colors. It was realism that Crane himself aimed at, a photographic copy of reality, and his *Red Badge* has always been read as just that and nothing more. Shakespeare's play *I Henry IV* appears to be no more than a history play, a realistic reproduction of life; *Huckleberry Finn* is simply the biography of a boy, a record of his adventures. Beneath their surface drama, however, lies a concealed meaning. No work of art is what it appears to be. Crane's *Red Badge* is far more than a fictional account of the Civil War.

The Red Badge is realistic enough, said the New York *World*, "to set the blood tingling in the veins of a veteran." "This young man," said Bierce, "has the power to feel. He knows nothing of war, yet he is drenched in blood. Most beginners who deal with this subject spatter themselves merely with ink." A British general, praising the book in the *Illustrated London News* for 1896 as "quite the finest thing in that line that has ever been done," shrewdly observed that "the intuitions of the boy who has never seen war are worth far more than the experiences of any writer . . . even though he may have been in the thick of the fiercest battle." Bierce, the experienced soldier, would have agreed. It is ironical that Bierce, who was wounded in battle, used his war experience only for imaginative constructs and sardonic fantasies of it, whereas Crane, without any experience of war, created a much greater illusion of reality. So great was the illusion that the *Saturday Review* and other British periodicals took it for granted that the author of *The Red Badge* had seen actual warfare. "Certainly, if his book were altogether a work of imagination unbased on personal experience, his realism would be nothing short of a miracle." The blood of angry veterans tingled, but it was for quite different reasons. Crane's book was an insult to his country's honor, said General A. C. McClurg. It's "a vicious satire upon American soldiers. The hero is without a spark of soldierly ambition. No thrill of patriotic devotion ever moves his breast. There is no evidence of drill, none of discipline." In copies returned to Brentano's bookshop (according to Beer) other veterans scribbled such marginal notes of indignation as "insulting," "unpatriotic," and "damned nonsense."

Neither the question of personal experience nor the test of realism is relevant to any critical judgment of *The Red Badge of Courage*. (Verifying Crane's picture of warfare as the real thing can be done only by those who have experienced warfare, and trenches are not very handy for the critic.) Fidelity to life does not establish any work *as* a work of art; to equate life with art is to confuse their absolute boundaries. Truth in art consists not in the artist's fidelity to the observed facts of the actual world; it consists rather in the artist's fidelity to the *felt* truth of his vision. It is *there,* as Conrad intimated, that the honor of the artist lies—in fidelity to every part of the patterned whole. *The Open Boat* is a work of art not because it is a slice out of life, which explains only its source and its verisimilitude, but because it is an imaginative re-creation of life possessing a pattern of significance. Henry Fleming is composed not of flesh and blood, much as he may seem so to some readers; he is, of course, composed of words—solely of words patterned to evoke an *illusion* of reality.

Yet what Crane wrote still passes—even for Hemingway— as "real war literature." Modern realism, according to all the critics, was initiated by Stephen Crane. That is approximately true enough, but, like every other pronouncement about him, not quite accurate. To say that Crane "anticipated" modern realism "by thirty or forty years" is to ignore De Forest, whose work appeared more than a quarter of a century before *The Red Badge.* The fact of this matter is that neither Crane nor Bierce rendered the actualities of recruits under fire with anything like the graphic realism of De Forest. Crane did not write our first realistic war novel—our literary historians are mistaken. Nor did Crane write, as some critics have said, our first ironic novel. Neither *Maggie* nor *The Red Badge,* but Mark Twain's *Huckleberry Finn,* deserves that claim. Beer makes no mention of De Forest and he is mistaken about the Civil War's leaving "almost nothing printed that the literate peasants and clerks who fought would recognize as the truth of their acts." That is precisely what they got in *Miss Ravenel's Conversion* in 1867, or again in Colonel Wilbur F. Hinman's *Corporal Si Klegg and His "Pard"* twenty years later—and eight years before *The Red Badge.* De Forest's realism, though William Dean

Howells spread the word, remained unnoticed for over fifty years. Crane captured the field, and the banner Realism has floated above him ever since.

"Most of my prose writings have been toward the goal partially described by that misunderstood and abused word, realism." Yet Crane is, in essence, no realist.

If Crane is a realist, then what label is left for De Forest's *Conversion* or, among later war novels, Henri Barbusse's *Under Fire*? Beside De Forest's *First Time under Fire* and his *Conversion*, Crane's imagined account of the battlefield appears somewhat synthetic and even theatrical.

In the centre of this mass of suffering stood several operating tables, each burdened by a grievously wounded man and surrounded by surgeons and their assistants. Underneath were great pools of clotted blood, amidst which lay amputated fingers, hands, arms, feet and legs, only a little more ghastly in color than the faces of those who waited their turn on the table. The surgeons, who never ceased their awful labor, were daubed with blood to the elbows and a smell of blood drenched the stifling air, overpowering even the pungent odor of chloroform. The place resounded with groans, notwithstanding that the most of the injured men who retained their senses exhibited the heroic endurance so common on the battle-field. One man, whose leg was amputated close to his body, uttered an inarticulate jabber of broken screams, and rolled, or rather bounced from side to side on a pile of loose cotton, with such violence that two hospital attendants were fully occupied in holding him. Another shot through the body, lay speechless and dying, but quivering from head to foot with a prolonged though probably unconscious agony. He continued to shudder thus for half an hour, when he gave one superhuman throe, and then lay quiet for ever.[1]

The photographic realism of De Forest, of Tolstoy in *Sebastopol* and Zola in *La Débâcle*, Crane can be said to have approached only in some few scattered passages of *The Red Badge*. Of the two most frequently quoted examples of Crane's

---

[1] *Miss Ravenel's Conversion from Secession to Loyalty,* edited by Gordon Haight (Harper & Brothers, 1939), p. 258.

realism, one is the detail of the dead soldier leaning against a tree with sodden eyes staring as from a dead fish. That looks merely realistic, but the dead man is a symbol. The other is this picture of a corpse encountered in battle:

> Once the line encountered the body of a dead soldier. He lay upon his back staring at the sky. He was dressed in an awkward suit of yellowish brown.

Here again the realistic detail is not realism for realism's sake: it is used as basis for a symbol. It is realistic detail not for the sake of realism, but for the sake of symbolic purpose. To the youth, the dead soldier is burdened with meaning—"and it was as if fate had betrayed the soldier." The youth identifies himself with the corpse: he too is betrayed. By the technique of transferred epithet Crane converts the realistic image into a symbol of psychic kinship. The rebel lies dead—the Rebel Death. It is the Youth who is invulnerable!

> The ranks opened covertly to avoid the corpse. The *invulnerable* dead man forced a way for himself. The youth looked keenly at the ashen face.

The first part of the image contributes themes of betrayal and death, and the final part contributes still another theme—the motif of change and mobility, which is one of the main recurrent themes of the whole book. Barbusse's *Under Fire* (1917), influenced by Crane, paints the very same picture. It is the same except for the immobility of the corpse:

> As soon as our pushing and jolted file emerges, two men close to me are hit . . . the one with a sharp cry, and the other silently, as a felled ox. Another disappears with the caper of a lunatic, as if he had been snatched away. Instinctively we close up as we hustle forward—always forward—and the wound in our line closes of its own accord. The adjutant stops, raises his sword, lets it fall, and drops to his knees. His kneeling body slopes backward in jerks, his helmet drops on his heels, and he remains there, bareheaded,

face to the sky. Hurriedly the rush of the rank has split open to respect his immobility.[2]

But you have only to compare it with Crane's picture to see the difference. Barbusse's details convey neither theme, symbolic intent, nor painterly design. They are facts in black and white. He evokes emotions, but they are not the same emotions or effects a painter like Crane evokes. The difference is that Crane's realistic detail is used metaphorically.

2

In style and method Crane had no predecessors, but in viewing war from the vantage point of the unromantic and commonplace conscript he was following the line set down by Walt Whitman, whose *Specimen Days* is our first modern approach to the subject.[3] Whitman's prediction that "the real war will never get in the-books" was belied by De Forest (as Alexander Cowie points out). *Harper's Weekly* in 1900, remarking on Crane's originality, said that his *Red Badge* is not quite as original a contribution to "the literature of fighting as many took it to be, and as it would have been had Tolstoy never written *Sebastopol*." *Sebastopol* and *War and Peace* are realistic accounts of the tragedy of the rank and file in the Napoleonic and Crimean wars, and Zola's *Débâcle* describes war from the point of view of the ignorant private. Crane was also anticipated by Colonel Wilbur F. Hinman's *Corporal Si Klegg and His "Pard,"* a fictionalized diary of the everyday life of the civilian soldier in the American Civil War.

In contemporary reviews Crane's book was everywhere rated above Zola and recognized as standing alone, unique among all war novels—or all except Tolstoy's *Sebastopol*. The *Saturday Review* (January 11, 1896) thought Zola "far inferior" and rated Crane's novel above or as equal to the war pictures of Tolstoy, Mérimée, and Kipling. And the claim made by almost all

---

[2] *Under Fire* (E. P. Dutton & Co., 1917), p. 256.
[3] See V. S. Pritchett: *The Living Novel* (1946), pp. 166 ff.

critics since then is that Tolstoy's *Sebastopol* exerted a powerful
influence on the conception of *The Red Badge,* some critics
arguing that but for Tolstoy it would never have been written.
Yet no palpable debts can be established. Tolstoy was the
writer Crane most admired: "I think Tolstoy greater than any
other novelist because he is a greater artist. His morality is
simply that of Christ." (Quoted in Curtis Brown's *Contacts,*
1935.) Howells also admired Tolstoy, but nowhere in his writings, nor in Crane's so far as I can discover, is Tolstoy to be
detected. One critic locates the whole source of Crane's irony
in Tolstoy on the supposition that Crane must have derived his
ironic outlook from him because Howells is not ironic. But the
label *irony* does not stick to Tolstoy, and furthermore there is
more difficulty in supposing that Crane learned from Tolstoy
"how an ironic mind takes expression in literary art" than there
is in supposing that he learned it from Mark Twain, who influenced Crane in a number of ways and works. Twain is a
true ironist. Not only Crane's irony but his social outlook, his
sympathy with the underprivileged, bears close kinship to
Twain's.

Other source-hunters have thought of Stendhal's battle
scenes as Crane's model for *The Red Badge,* but the fact is
that Crane never read *La Chartreuse de Parma* and was an-
gered when told that he had. He wrote *The Red Badge* on the
dare of a friend to do better than Zola, whose *Débâcle* Crane
dipped into some time before writing his novel but never finished. It is ironical that his own book was called "tiresome" in
the *Academy* review of 1896, too boring for its readers to get
to the end of it; it is ironical because "tiresome" was Crane's own
favorite epithet whenever he was asked to read Zola and Tolstoy and Henry James. They bored him. He disliked Zola's
statistical realism and he disliked Tolstoy's panoramic method.
He found *Peace and War* (as he called it) tiresome: "He could
have done the whole business in one third the time and made it
just as wonderful. It goes on and on like Texas." *Anna Karenina*
was "too long," and Tolstoy stopped to preach.

But I confess [Crane wrote about Tolstoy in a letter of 1897] that the conclusions of some of his novels, and the lectures he sticks in, leave me feeling that he regards his genius as the means to an end. I happen to be a preacher's son, but that heredity does not preclude —in me—a liking for sermons unmixed with other material. . . . *I mean that I like my art straight.*

Flaubert's *Salammbô* he resented too. Even his own *Red Badge* he criticized for the same reason—it was too long.

Crane confessed that he had read the French realists, but it is probable that he absorbed them only through translations and from Henry James's criticism of the French novelists. Essentially uneducated, he was not a bookish man. "His reading was miscellaneous, desultory, and unguided.[4] In general he disliked the writers of his time whom it was the fashion to like —including Stevenson." He judged literature and people by the criterion of sincerity and, hating the literary dandy, he detested Stevenson—the very man he himself most nearly resembled. Both are mannered writers, addicted to the word, stylists *par excellence;* both, limited in range, write on similar fields of experience and out of childhood reminiscences. And each personality stirred up the legend of the artist. Both men were nomadic, magnetic, charming, and chivalrous, plagued by ill-health; and they resembled each other not only in temperaments but in picturesque exteriors—each wore, as it were, the same absurd mustache.

The whole question of influences on Crane is very difficult to answer. It is debatable whether Crane took over anything from his French and Russian readings. Most of these so-called influences are in fact (I think) nothing more than parallelisms. It is true that the formula for his short stories parallels the Flaubert-Maupassant-Turgenyev formulas (as Ford Madox Ford points out), but this much Crane could just as readily have taken

---

[4] From Vincent Starrett's introduction to Ames W. Williams's *Bibliography* (1948), p. 10. The contrary view is expressed by Ford Madox Ford and by Thomas Beer, who remarks that Crane "was yet a man of letters." In this matter I share Starrett's judgment.

from Ambrose Bierce. In form and theme or subject Bierce's
affinities with Maupassant are the same as Crane's. Bierce's *An
Occurrence at Owl Creek Bridge* and Crane's *The Upturned
Face* have the same structural design as Maupassant's bitter
war story *La Mère sauvage*. They have the form of a single
mood; they are patterned upon an ironic contrast; they turn
upon a central paradox. Bierce casts his stories at a distance
from ordinary life and romanticizes life by employing melodramatic movie-thriller plots, but (like Crane) he invests his
war pictures with a conviction of visual reality. Their short
stories are alike in form, in subject (children and the untried
soldier), in theme (conscience and courage), in the use of
chance or coincidence, and, with different emphasis, in tone
and emotional tension. Not only in their fiction but also in their
parable poetry there is a very close kinship between Bierce and
Crane.

Crane's originality had its ancestry in his readings—the Bible,
Bierce, Kipling, Poe, Twain, Tolstoy, and others—and in what
he inherited from experiences on the diamond and on the
gridiron. As Shakespeare's *Tempest* had its source in tavern
talk about a shipwreck off the Bermudas, so Crane's *Red Badge*
had its source in conversations with veterans of the Civil War:
the reminiscences of his brother William, who was an expert in
the strategy of Chancellorsville, and the tactical accounts of
battle which Crane got from General Van Petten, his teacher
at the Hudson River Institute, at Claverack, New York, where
Crane was schooled and drilled. As Harvey Wickham, his col-
league there, later reported: "that touch of personal experience
so essential to the birth of a great idea must have come to
Crane through his connection with Claverack's student battalion. Its four straggling companies were in fact the nucleus
of that 'blue demonstration,' the very heart of his subsequent
conception of an army." [5] Crane studied, furthermore, some of
the contemporary accounts of the Civil War—the four volumes

---

[5] In "Stephen Crane at College," *American Mercury*, 7 (March 1926),
291–7.

of *Battles and Leaders of the Civil War,* which were written almost exclusively by veterans, Harper's *History,* Winslow Homer's drawings, and Mathew Brady's remarkable photographs. But, above all these sources, he drew chiefly from Colonel Hinman's *Si Klegg* (1887), particularly for the conception of the new recruit who develops into a veteran. Colonel Hinman's book was, I think, almost certainly Crane's primary literary source.[6]

Corwin Linson, the artist who did illustrations for some of Crane's stories (*The Reluctant Voyagers,* for one), wrote reminiscences of these bohemian days when Crane used to spend his time at Linson's studio (winter of 1892–3) "rummaging through old periodicals, poring over the Civil War articles." [7] Melville swallowed whole libraries to write *Moby Dick;* Crane studied to write his *Red Badge.* But we are still left wondering where he learned *how* to write. The answer to that question is given, I believe, in Hemingway's remark: "I learned to write looking at paintings at the Luxembourg Museum in Paris."

Crane knew Albert Pinkham Ryder personally; he knew not only Ryder's paintings, but some of Monet's, Winslow Homer's, and Frederic Remington's drawings, and he had Brady's poignant photographs to brood over, Coffin's illustrations to *Si Klegg,* and the apprenticeship paintings of Linson and of Crane's fellow lodgers at the Art Students' League, where he lived during the period when he was composing his own impressionistic paintings: *Maggie* and *The Red Badge.* Two recent critics contend that Crane borrowed nothing of his technique from paintings, and here again it is difficult to establish proof of positive influence. I do not think the influence of the studio on Crane can be denied. The critically relevant point, however, is that there is a close parallelism between Crane's impression-

---

[6] For a collation of parallel passages, episodes, and details, in *Si Klegg* and *The Red Badge,* see H. T. Webster's article in *American Literature* for November 1939.

[7] "Little Stories of 'Steve' Crane," *Saturday Evening Post,* April 11, 1903, pp. 19–20.

istic prose and impressionistic painting. This much can be established: Crane adumbrated the French post-impressionist painters. "Impressionism was his faith," says R. G. Vosburgh in his reminiscences of Crane. As H. G. Wells concluded, "there is Whistler even more than there is Tolstoy in *The Red Badge of Courage*."

3

Crane's style is prose pointillism. It is composed of disconnected images, which coalesce like the blobs of color in French impressionist paintings, every word-group having a cross-reference relationship, every seemingly disconnected detail having interrelationship to the configurated whole. The intensity of a Crane work is owing to this patterned coalescence of disconnected things, everything at once fluid and precise. A striking analogy is established between Crane's use of colors and the method employed by the impressionists and the neo-impressionists or divisionists, and it is as if he had known about their theory of contrasts and had composed his own prose paintings by the same principle. Their principle, as one writer defines it, is this: "Each plane of shade creates around itself a sort of aura of light, and each luminous plane creates around itself a zone of shade. In a similar way a coloured area communicates its 'complementary' to the neighbouring colour, or heightens it if it is 'complementary.'" [8] In almost every battle scene in *The Red Badge of Courage* the perspective is blurred by smoke or by the darkness of night. Here is one example of the former contrast: namely, dark masses circled by light; and of the latter contrast: namely, a luminous spot circled by darkness. (The former contrast is created in the first sentence of Crane's description, and the latter contrast in the second.)

The clouds were tinged an earthlike yellow in the sunrays and in the shadow were a sorry blue. The flag was sometimes eaten and lost in this mass of vapor, but more often it projected, sun-touched, resplendent. [Page 267.]

[8] Cited in *Painting in France: 1895–1949*, by G. di San Lazzaro (1949), p. 28 n.

Crane's perspectives, almost without exception, are fashioned by contrasts—black masses juxtaposed against brightness, colored light set against gray mists. At dawn the army glows with a purple hue, and "In the eastern sky there was a yellow patch like a rug laid for the feet of the coming sun; and against it, *black and pattern-like,* loomed the gigantic figure of the colonel on a gigantic horse" (page 239). Black is juxtaposed against yellow (page 241) or against red (pages 243, 307). Smoke wreathes around a square of white light and a patch of yellow shade (pages 228, 333). Smoke dimly outlines a distance filled with *blue* uniforms, a *green* sward, and a *sapphire* sky (page 359). Further examples of color-contrast, particularly white versus black, occur throughout *The Open Boat,* and blue is used symbolically in *The Blue Hotel.* Crane had an extraordinary predilection for blue, which Hamlin Garland took to be the sign manual of the impressionists. It seems likely that Crane read Garland's *Crumbling Idols* (1894), but in any case he wrote a novel about an impressionistic painter—the hero of *The Third Violet.* And in one of his sketches he wrote:

The flash of the impression was like light, and for this instant it illumined all the dark recesses of one's remotest idea of sacrilege, ghastly and wanton. I bring this to you merely as an effect, *an effect of mental light and shade,* if you like; something done in thought *similar to that which the French impressionists do in colour;* something meaningless and at the same time overwhelming, crushing, monstrous.[9]

Crane paints with words "exactly" as the French impressionists paint with pigments: both use pure colors and contrasts of colors. Black clouds or dark smoke or masses of mist and vapor are surrounded by a luminous zone; or, conversely, specks of prismatic color are enclosed by a zone of shade. Shifting gray mists open out before the splendor of the sunrays (page 312). Or, conversely, billowing smoke is "filled with horizontal flashes" (page 257): "the mist of smoke [is] gashed by the little

---

[9] *Work,* IX, 245-6.

knives of fire" (page 360). Inside the surrounding darkness the
waters of the river appear wine-tinted, and campfires "shining
upon the moving masses of troops, brought forth here and
there sudden gleams of silver and gold. Upon the other shore
a dark and mysterious range of hills was curved against the
sky" (page 246; the same scene is duplicated on page 310).
Cleared atmospheres, unimpeded vision of perspective, are
rarely delineated; and where they occur the precision of vision
is equated, symbolically, with revelation or spiritual insight.
One instance of this symbolic use of color appears on page 248.
Dark mists and vapors represent the haze of Henry's unen-
lightened mind ("He, the enlightened man who looks afar in
the dark, had fled because of his superior perceptions and
knowledge"). Darkness and smoke serve as symbols of con-
cealment and deception, vapors masking the light of truth.
Sunlight and changing colors signify spiritual insight and rebirth (as on page 226). Henry is a color-bearer, but it is not until he recognizes the truth of his self-deception that the youth
keeps "the bright colors to the front." In the celebrated impression of the red sun "pasted in the sky like a wafer" Crane is at
once an impressionist painter and a symbolic artist.

Theme and style in *The Red Badge of Courage* are organ-
ically conceived, the theme of change conjoined with the fluid
style by which it is evoked. The style, calculated to create impressions of confused motion and change, is deliberately disconnected and apparently disordered. Fluidity and change
characterize the whole book. Crane interjects disjointed details,
one non-sequitur melting into another. Scenes and objects are
felt as blurred; they appear under a haze or vapor or cloud. Yet
everything has relationship and is manipulated into contra-
puntal patterns of color and cross-references of meaning.

4

"The interesting thing," Crane said to a fellow war-correspondent above the din of riflefire in Cuba, "is the mental attitude of

the men." And on an earlier occasion when discussing war memoirs with Corwin Linson, he said: "I wonder that some of these fellows don't tell how they *felt* in those scraps. They spout enough of what they *did,* but they're as emotionless as rocks." It is the same in *The Red Badge,* seeing the imagined battle-field from the angle of psychological insight, and it is this psychological realism that separates Crane from the realism of Zola, Tolstoy, and Barbusse. His technique—his word-painting —differentiates him from all other "realists." Writing from England to his American editor about the reception of *The Red Badge,* Crane said that "the big reviews here praise it for just what I intended it to be, a psychological portrayal of fear."

No critic has ever made any other interpretation but this one. It is the standard reading of all Crane's writings, the reading of fear into everything he wrote, and for this misleading diagnosis Thomas Beer is almost solely responsible. It is his Handbook of Fear that accounts for the neglect of all critics to attempt any other reading. Beer's thesis is that all the works from the first story to the last dissect fear, and that as they deal exclusively with fear, *so* fear was the motivating passion of Crane's life. "That newspaper feller was a nervy man," said the cook of the ill-fated *Commodore.* "*He didn't seem to know what fear was.*" Yet in his art there is fear, little more than that, and in *The Blue Hotel*—so the *Literary History of the United States* tells us—the premonition of the Swede is nothing "but the manifestation of Crane's own intense fear."

This equation of his works with his life, however seemingly plausible, is critically fallacious, and the resulting reading is a grossly oversimplified one. To say that *The Red Badge* is a study of fear is an interpretation as shallow as to say that it is no more than a narrative of the Civil War. Reduction of the enigma of Crane's life and works to the Œdipus complex is (according to John Berryman) certainly not literary criticism. Berryman is himself in agreement with this principle: "Psychological inquiry is certainly not literary criticism, and can reasonably begin only after full account has been taken of literary questions" (Preface to *Stephen Crane,* page xiii). Unconscious compulsions explain perhaps the tensions in Crane's life, but no psychological inquiry can explain what tensions in the works establish them as works of art. Their meanings as art reside in textural and structural tensions, not in purely personal ones. Nothing could be further from the intrinsic meaning of the works as literature. No Crane work depends for our understanding of it upon knowledge of Crane's personal plight. Pathological or sociological inquiry into causes and sources cannot answer the question of critical inquiry: why is Crane an artist *in* his writings? That question has yet to be answered. Nor can such inquiry establish grounds for estimating his achievement. In order to revaluate Crane's art and achievement what must be established first of all is a critical reading of his works.

Critics of American writers from Mark Twain to F. Scott Fitzgerald have concerned themselves almost exclusively with literary works as biographers, historians, sociologists, or psychoanalysts, probing the works for what they disclose about the personality of the author. As Lionel Trilling recently remarked: "We have all too many American writers who live for us only because they can be so neatly 'placed,' whose life in literature consists of their being influences or precursors, or of being symbols of intellectual tendencies, which is to say that their life is not in literature at all but in the history of culture." We know from Mark Twain's critics what the social conditions were for which—or against which—he labored as writer, and we now know all about the personal history of F. Scott Fitzgerald; but we have yet to be shown—This Side of Biography—what makes *The Great Gatsby* and *Huckleberry Finn* works of art. Although Crane has been dead half a century, no critical study of him has yet been made. Analysis of his works is nonexistent. Probably no American author, unless it is Mark Twain, stands today in more imperative need of critical revaluation.

That Crane is incapable of architectonics has been the critical consensus for over half a century: "his work is a mass of fragments"; "he can only string together a series of loosely

cohering incidents"; *The Red Badge of Courage* is not constructed—it is "not a sustained narrative, but a sequence of
extraordinary tableaux" (*Book Buyer*, July 1896). That Crane
lacks the great artist's arrangement of complex effects, as Edward Garnett pointed out in his 1898 appraisal of Crane, is
certainly true. We look to Conrad and Henry James for "exquisite grouping of devices"; Crane's figure in the carpet is a
much simpler one. What it consists in is the very thing Garnett
failed to detect—a schemework of striking contrasts, alternations of contradictory moods. Crane once defined a novel as a
"succession of sharply-outlined pictures, which pass before the
reader like a panorama, leaving each its definite impression."
His own novel, nonetheless, is not simply a succession of pictures. It is a sustained structural whole. Every Crane critic
concurs in this mistaken notion that *The Red Badge of Courage* is nothing more than "a series of episodic scenes," but not
one critic has yet undertaken an analysis of Crane's work to
see *how* the sequence of tableaux is constructed.

Crane in his best works is a symbolic artist. Joseph Hergesheimer, whose edition of *The Red Badge* appeared in 1925
as Volume I of the collected *Work*, recognized that for Crane
it was not a story he had to tell, but rather a literary exercise of
some sort. Hergesheimer did not go into the meaning of the
book, but he saw what Crane was up to. Nowhere else in the
whole body of Crane criticism is there a hint that Crane was
writing with symbolic intention. The exceptions occur in one
of Conrad's tributes to Crane, where he mentions the word
symbolism, and in two or three contemporary reviews. The
New York *Bookman* reduced *The Red Badge* to a mere alle-
gory: "The young soldier, starting out to face his first trial by
fire, may be either an individual or man universal; the battle
may be either the Battle of the Wilderness or the Battle of Life."
The *Bookman* did not like the book because it employed a
double meaning—"always a dangerous and usually fatal method
in literature." The *Critic* for November 1895 said that the book
is a true book—true in two senses: "true to life, whether it be

taken as a literal transcript of a soldier's experiences in his
first battle, or (as some have fancied) a great parable of the
inner battle which every man must fight." The *Critic* was not
convinced about that fancied idea, but the London *Bookman*
two months later said simply, without any misgivings: "*The
youth's mind is a battleground too.*" The *Spectator* for June 27,
1896 struck off a singularly penetrating observation in pointing
out that Henry's encounter with the wounded soldiers is his
salvation. "He got back with them to the body of the regiment,
and the sight of his comrades, notably the heroic death of one
of them, made a beginning of the end of his egoism." As the
Critic keenly noted, Crane's metaphors and similes "are not
strung on for effect, but living and actual as Homer's." What
the perceptive *Critic* was first to detect has gone unnoticed for
the past fifty-five years: namely, that Crane's metaphors are
employed purposefully—for theme or for structural pattern.

5

NOTES TOWARD AN ANALYSIS OF
The Red Badge of Courage

Ernest Hemingway's remark that *The Red Badge of Courage*
"is all as much one piece as a great poem is" is doubly revelatory because it defines not only Crane's novel but Hemingway's
own *Farewell to Arms. A Farewell to Arms* is an inverted *Red
Badge of Courage*: the one deals with disenchantment and
withdrawal, the other with quest and triumph. Hemingway's
novel starts, as it were, where Crane's left off: Frederic Henry,
the already maimed hero, is the idealistic Henry Fleming
turned cynic. It is significant that both are without father and
are virtually nameless. Crane's hero is always just "the youth,"
and it is not until halfway through the book (on the last page
of Chapter xi) that the youth discloses what his name is, and
then, ashamed because he has fled the battlefield, he utters
his name only to himself. Hemingway's hero has for surname
a given name. Both heroes undergo change and insight through

wounds, but in opposite directions. Where Crane's Henry progresses upward toward manhood and moral triumph, Hemingway's Henry descends toward moral and spiritual degeneration. In both novels the education of the hero ends as it began: in self-deception. Frederic Henry renounces war, society, and the "comforting stench" of comrades and makes a "separate peace." But his farewell to arms is as illusory as Henry Fleming's farewell to vain ideals and compromising illusions. Both heroes are deluded, the one believing he can turn his back upon the battle of life, the other believing that he has triumphed in facing up to it shorn of all romantic notions.

Both novels are ritualistic, mythic, symbolic. The dominant symbolism is religious. Henry Fleming's forest chapel transposes into the mountain sanctuary of the lovers in *A Farewell to Arms*. As in *The House of the Seven Gables* and *Huckleberry Finn*, the alternating episodes of *Farewell* and *The Red Badge* concern withdrawal and return, the quest for self-identity, and insight or recognition through wound or suffering. The central theme of *Farewell*—everyone has to "get down off the mountains"—harks back through *The Red Badge* to *Huckleberry Finn*. And Twain's "You Can't Pray a Lie," the leitmotiv of deception in *Huckleberry Finn*, vibrates through both *The Red Badge* and *A Farewell to Arms*.

Like Henry Fleming, Frederic Henry has romantic illusions about war. The opening scene of the novel delineates this "picturesque front." The army is on the move:

Troops went by the house and down the road and the dust they raised powdered the leaves of the trees. The trunks of the trees too were dusty and the leaves fell early that year and we saw the troops marching along the road and the dust rising and leaves, stirred by the breeze, falling and the soldiers marching and afterward the road bare and white except for the leaves.

Hemingway begins his novel exactly as Crane begins his: the opening picture manifests motifs of change and deception. On the first page of *The Red Badge of Courage* the army is about

to move. The landscape changes "from brown to green," and
the river—"swiftly moving" in Hemingway's scene—here is purl-
ing "at the army's feet." As the falling leaves in Hemingway's
picture symbolize an event that has not yet occurred—the death
of Catherine—so the "retiring fogs" in Crane's opening sentence
anticipate Henry's mental awakening: "The cold passed reluctantly from the earth, and the retiring fogs revealed an army
stretched out on the hills, resting." They are the fogs of Henry's
own mind, and not until they are dispersed ("reluctantly") can
Henry establish warm identity with life.

The Red Badge of Courage probes a state of mind under the
incessant pinpricks and bombardments of life. The theme is
that man's salvation lies in change, in spiritual growth. It is
only by immersion in the flux of experience that man becomes
disciplined and develops in character, conscience, or soul. Potentialities for change are at their greatest in battle—a battle
represents life at its most intense flux. Crane's book is not about
the combat of armies; it is about the self-combat of a youth
who fears and stubbornly resists change, and the actual battle
is symbolic of this spiritual warfare against change and growth.
Henry Fleming recognizes the necessity for change and development, but wars against it. But man must lose his soul in order
to save it. The youth develops into the veteran: "So it came to
pass . . . his soul changed." Significantly enough, in stating
what the book is about Crane intones Biblical phrasing.

The book begins with the army immobilized—with restless
men waiting for orders to move—and, because the army has
done nothing, with Henry disillusioned by his first days as a
recruit. In the first picture we get of Henry, he is lying on his
army cot—resting on an idea. Or, rather, he is wrestling with the
personal problem it poses. The idea is a third-hand rumor that
tomorrow, at last, the army will go into action. When the tall
soldier first announced it, he waved a shirt that he had just
washed in a muddy brook, waved it in bannerlike fashion to
summon the men around the flag of his colorful rumor. It was
a call to the colors—he shook it out and spread it about for the

men to admire. But Jim Conklin's prophecy of hope meets with disbelief. "It's a lie!" shouts the loud soldier. "I don't believe the derned old army's ever going to move." No disciples rally around the red and gold flag of the herald. The skeptical soldiers think the tall soldier is telling just a tall tale; a furious altercation ensues. Meanwhile Henry in his hut engages in a spiritual debate with himself; whether to believe or disbelieve the word of his friend, whom he has known since childhood. It is the gospel truth, but Henry is one of the doubting apostles.

The opening scene thus sets going the structural pattern of the whole book. Hope and faith (paragraphs 1–3) shift to despair or disbelief (4–7). The counter movement of opposition begins in paragraph 4, in the small detail of the Negro teamster who stops his dancing, when the men desert him to wrangle over Jim Conklin's rumor. "He sat mournfully down." This image of motion and change (the motion ceasing and the joy turning to gloom) presents the dominant leitmotiv and the form of the whole book in miniature. (Another striking instance of emblematic form occurs in Chapter vi, where Crane pictures a terror-stricken lad who throws down his gun and runs: "A lad whose face had borne an expression of exalted courage, the majesty of he who dares give his life, was, at an instant, smitten abject.") In Chapter i the opening prologue ends in a coda (paragraph 7) with theme and anti-theme interjoined. It is the picture of the corporal. His uncertainties (whether to repair his house) and his shifting attitudes of trust and distrust (whether the army is going to move) parallel the skeptical outlook of the wrangling men. The same anti-theme of distrust is dramatized in the episode that follows this coda, and every subsequent episode in the sequence is designed similarly by one contrast pattern or another.

Change and motion begin the book. The army, which lies resting on the hills, is first revealed to us by "the retiring fogs," and as the weather changes, the landscape changes, the brown hills turning to a new green. As nature stirs, the army stirs too. Nature and man are in psychic affinity; even the weather changes as though in sympathetic accord with man's plight. In the final scene it is raining, but the leaden rain clouds shine with "a golden ray" as though to reflect Henry's own bright serenity, his own tranquillity of mind. But now at the beginning, and throughout the book, Henry's mind is in a "tumult of agony and despair." This psychological tumult began when Henry heard the church bell announce the gospel truth that a great battle had been fought. Noise begins the whole mental melee. The clanging church bell and then the noise disorder his mind by stirring up legendary visions of heroic selfhood. The noisy world that first colored his mind with myths now clamors to Henry to become absorbed into the solidarity of self-forgetful comradeship, but Henry resists this challenge of the "mysterious fraternity born of the smoke and danger of death," and withdraws again and again from the din of the affray to indulge in self-contemplative moods and magic reveries. The walls of the forest insulate him from the noise of battle. In seeking retreat to absolve his shame and guilt, Henry, renouncing manhood, is "seeking dark and intricate places." It is as though he were seeking return to the womb. Nature, that "woman with a deep aversion to tragedy," is Mother Nature, and the human equation for the forest is of course Henry's own mother. Henry's flight from the forest sanctuary represents his momentary rejection of womblike innocence; periodically he rejects Mother Nature with her sheltering arms and her "religion of peace," and his flight from Mother Nature is symbolic of his initiation into the truth of the world he must measure up to. He is the deceived youth, for death lurks even in the forest sanctuary. In the pond a gleaming fish is killed by one of the forest creatures, and in the forest Henry meets a rotted corpse, a man whose eyes stare like a dead fish, with ants scurrying over the face. The treachery of this forest retreat, where nothing is as it seems, symbolizes the treachery of ideals —the illusions by which we are all betrayed.

Henry's mind is in constant flux. Henry's self-combat is symbolized by the conflict among the men and between the armies, their altercation being a duplication of his own. Like the regiment that marches and countermarches over the same ground, so Henry's mind traverses the same ideas over and over again. As the cheery-voiced soldier says about the battle, "It's th' most mixed up dern thing I ever see." Mental commotion, confusion, and change are externalized in the "mighty altercation" of men and guns and nature herself. Everything becomes activated, *even the dead.* That corpse Henry meets on the battlefield, "the *invulnerable* dead man," cannot stay still—he "*forced*' a way for himself" through the ranks. And guns throb too, "restless guns." Back and forth the stage scenery shifts from dreams to "jolted dreams" and grim fact. Henry's illusions collapse, dreams pinpricked by reality.

Thoughout the whole book *withdrawals* alternate with *engagements,* with scenes of entanglement and tumult, but the same nightmarish atmosphere of upheaval disorder pervades both the inner and the outer realms. The paradox is that when Henry becomes activated in the "vast blue demonstration" and is thereby reduced to anonymity he is most a man, and, conversely, when he affects self-dramatizing picture-postcard poses of himself as hero he is least a man and not at all heroic. He is then innocent as a child. When disengaged from the external tumult, Henry's mind recollects domestic scenes. Pictures of childhood and nursery imagery of babes recur at almost every interval of withdrawal. Childhood innocence and withdrawal are thus equated. The nursery limerick that the wounded soldiers sing as they retreat from the battlefront is at once a travesty of their own plight and a mockery of Henry's mythical innocence.

> *Sing a song 'a vic'try,*
> *A pocketful 'a bullets,*
> *Five an' twenty dead men*
> *Baked in a—pie.*

Everything goes awry; nothing turns out as Henry had expected. Battles turn out to be "an immense and terrible ma-

chine to him" (the awful machinery is also his own mind). At
his battle task Henry, we are told, "was like a carpenter who
has made many boxes, making still another box, only there
was furious haste in his movements." Henry, "frustrated by
hateful circumstances," pictures himself as boxed in by fate, by
the regiment, and by the "iron laws of tradition and law on
four sides. He was in a moving box." And furthermore there
are those purely theoretical boxes by which he is shut in from
reality—his romantic dreams, legendary visions of heroic selfhood, illusions that the vainglorious machinery of his own mind
has manufactured.

The youth who had envisioned himself in Homeric poses,
the legendary hero of a Greek-like struggle, has his pretty illusion shattered as soon as he announces his enlistment to his
mother. "I've knet yeh eight pair of socks, Henry. . . ." His
mother is busy peeling potatoes, and, madonna-like, she kneels
among the parings. They are the scraps of his romantic dreams.
The youthful private imagines armies to be monsters, "redoubtable dragons," but then he sees the real thing—the colonel who
strokes his mustache and shouts over his shoulder: "Don't forget that box of cigars!"

Spiritual change is Henry Fleming's red badge. *His red badge
is his conscience reborn and purified.* Whereas Jim Conklin's
red badge of courage is the literal one, the wound of which he
dies, Henry's is the psychological badge, the wound of conscience. Internal wounds are more painful than external ones.
It is fitting that Henry should receive a head wound, a bump
that jolts him with a severe headache. But what "salve" is there
to ease the pain of his internal wound of dishonor? That is
Henry's "headache"! It is the ache of his conscience that he has
been honored by the regiment he has dishonored. Just as Jim
runs into the fields to hide his true wound from Henry, so Henry
runs into the fields to hide his false wound, his false badge of
courage, from the tattered man who asks him where he is
wounded. "It might be inside mostly, an' them plays thunder.
Where is it located?" The men, so Henry feels, are perpetually

probing his guilt-wound, "ever upraising the ghost of shame on the stick of their curiosity." The unmistakable implication here is of a flag, and the actual flag that Henry carries in battle is the symbol of his conscience. Conscience is also symbolized by the forest, the cathedral-forest where Henry retreats to nurse his guilt-wound and be consoled by the benedictions that nature sympathetically bestows upon him. Here in this forest chapel there is a churchlike silence as insects bow their beaks while Henry bows his head in shame; they make a "devotional pause" while the trees chant a soft hymn to comfort him. But Henry is troubled; he cannot "conciliate the forest." Nor can he conciliate the flag. The flag registers the commotion of his mind, and it registers the restless movements of the nervous regiment—it flutters when the men expect battle. And when the regiment runs from battle, the flag sinks down "as if dying. Its motion as it fell was a gesture of despair." Henry dishonors the flag not when he flees from battle but when he flees from himself, and he redeems it when he redeems his conscience.

Redemption begins in confession, in absolution—in a change of heart. Henry's plight is identical with the Reverend Mr. Dimmesdale's plight in Hawthorne's psychological novel *The Scarlet Letter*. The mythology of the scarlet letter is much the same as that of the red badge: each is the emblem of moral guilt and salvation. The red badge is the scarlet letter of dishonor transferred from the bosom of Hester, the social outcast, to the mind of Henry Fleming, the "mental outcast." Henry's wounded conscience is not healed until he confesses the truth to himself and opens his eyes to new ways; not until he strips his enemy heart of "the brass and bombast of his earlier gospels," the vainglorious illusions he had fabricated into a cloak of pride and self-vindication, not until he puts on new garments of humility and loving-kindness for his fellow men. Redemption begins in humility—Henry's example is the loud soldier who becomes the humble soldier. The loud soldier admits the folly of his former ways. Henry's spiritual

change is a prolonged process, but it is signalized in moments
when he loses his soul in the flux of things; then he coura-
geously deserts himself instead of his fellow men; then, fear-
lessly plunging into battle, charging the enemy like "a pagan
who defends his religion," he becomes swept up in a delirium
of selflessness and feels himself "capable of profound sacrifices." The brave new Henry, "new bearer of the colors," tri-
umphs over the former one. The enemy flag is wrenched from
the hands of "the rival color bearer," the symbol of Henry's
own other self, and as this rival color-bearer dies, Henry is
"reborn."

Henry's regeneration is brought about by the death of Jim
Conklin, his friend since childhood. He goes under various
names. He is sometimes called the spectral soldier (his face is
a pasty gray) and sometimes the tall soldier (he is taller than
all the other men), but there are unmistakable hints—in such
descriptive details about him as his wound in the side, his torn
body and his gory hand, and even in the initials of his name,
Jim Conklin—that he is intended to represent Jesus Christ. We
are told that there is "a resemblance in him to a devotee of
a mad religion," and among his followers the doomed man
stirs up "thoughts of a solemn ceremony." When he dies, the
heavens signify his death—the red sun bleeds with the passion
of his wounds:

The red sun was pasted in the sky like a wafer.

This grotesque image, the most notorious metaphor in American literature, has been much debated and roundly damned by
all Crane critics (excepting Conrad, Willa Cather, and Hergesheimer, who admired it, but failed to explain why), ridiculed
as downright bad writing—a false, melodramatic nonfunctional
figure. It is, in fact, the key to the symbolism of the whole
novel, particularly the religious symbolism that radiates out-
wards from Jim Conklin. Like any image, it has to be related
to the structure of meaning in which it functions; when lifted
out of its context it is bound to seem artificial and irrelevant or,
on the other hand, merely "a superb piece of imagery." I do

not think it can be doubted that Crane intended to suggest here the sacrificial death celebrated in communion.

Henry and the tattered soldier consecrate the death of the spectral soldier in "a solemn ceremony." Henry partakes of the sacramental blood and body of Christ, and the process of his spiritual rebirth begins at the moment when the wafer-like sun appears in the sky. It is a symbol of salvation through death. Henry, we are made to feel, recognizes in the lifeless sun his own lifeless conscience, his dead and as yet unregenerated selfhood or conscience, and that is why he blasphemes against it. His moral salvation and triumph are prepared for by this ritual of purification and religious devotion and, at the very start of the book, by the ritual of absolution that Jim Conklin performs in the opening scene (pages 226–7). It was the tall soldier who first "developed virtues" and showed the boys how to cleanse a flag. The way is to wash it in the muddy river. Only by experiencing life, the muddy river, can the soul be cleansed. In *The Open Boat* it is the black sea, and the whiteness of the waves as they pace to and fro in the moonlight signifies the spiritual purification that the men win from their contest against the terrible water. The ritual of domestic comforts bestowed upon the saved men by the people on the shore, "all the remedies sacred to their minds," is a shallow thing, devoid of spiritual value. The sea offers the only true remedy, though it costs a "terrible grace." The way—as Stein said in Conrad's *Lord Jim*—is to immerse oneself in the destructive element!

Kurtz, in Conrad's *Heart of Darkness*, washed his soul in the Congo, and Marlow, because he had become a part of Kurtz, redeemed the heart of darkness by the same token. Conrad, like Crane, had himself experienced his own theme, but Crane was the first to produce a work based on it. Crane's influence on Conrad is apparent in *Lord Jim*. Both *Lord Jim* and *The Red Badge of Courage* variously exploit the same thematic contrast of ideals versus realities. In terms of religious symbolism they have further affinities. When Lord Jim goes to his death, there is an awful sunset. Conrad's enormous sun—"The sky over Patusan was blood-red, immense, streaming like an open vein"—recalls Crane's symbolic red sun "pasted in the sky like a wafer." [1]

6

THE ORIGINAL MANUSCRIPTS OF THE RED BADGE OF COURAGE

Writing from Hartwood to Willis Hawkins, Crane's closest friend, Crane added a postscript to his letter of January 27, 1896: "I am expressing you the original ms of the Red Badge. Thought maybe you'd like it." Crane sent Hawkins, in fact, two drafts: the final handwritten one and part of an earlier draft written on the back sides of the same leaves. The existence of these manuscripts remained until very recently unknown or was denied. They exist in a bound notebook with the front cover stamped in gold lettering—The *Red Badge of Courage / Stephen Crane*. Manuscripts of nineteenth-century American authors are by now something of a rarity. These Crane holographs, of inestimable literary value both to the scholar and to the critic, are certainly important discoveries. In this new edition of *The Red Badge* about two thousand words that were expunged from the final handwritten manuscript are restored to the printed version of the First American Edition (1895), and several passages that were canceled in the manuscripts during the process of revision are reproduced here in footnotes to the text for the first time [2] (new passages are indicated in the text by the use of square brackets).

---

[1] Portions of this Introduction first appeared in the Introduction to the Modern Library edition of *The Red Badge of Courage*, copyright 1951 by Random House, Inc., and used here by courtesy of Random House, Inc.

Other portions of this Introduction first appeared in an essay entitled "Stephen Crane: A Revaluation," which appeared in *Critiques and Essays on Modern Fiction: 1920–1951*, edited by John Aldridge, copyright 1952 by Ronald Press, and used here by courtesy of Ronald Press.

[2] The new passages from the final handwritten version were first reproduced in John T. Winterich's Folio Society edition, published in London late in 1951. The manuscript is not accurately reproduced in that edition, however; nor is it accurately described.

Crane, in sending his friend the original manuscript of *The Red Badge,* was paying off old debts; Hawkins had done him many good turns. That Hawkins—himself a writer, editor of *Brains,* and a member of a literary club—was cognizant of Crane's genius from the start is evidenced by the fact that he preserved Crane's letters and even the paper cardtable cover used in one of their several games of poker. Crane had doodled on it while keeping score and, like Stephen Daedalus in Joyce's *Portrait of the Artist,* he had scribbled his name over and over again: "Stephen Crane, Chauncey Depew, Stephen Crane, Chauncey Depew, Stephen Crane, Stephen Crane." It looks as though Crane was in desperate need of winning that poker game! I suppose that is why he had Chauncey Depew on his mind. Crane needed money. Now, it was certainly not Crane but Hawkins who took precautions to preserve the manuscript of *The Red Badge* by having it bound into a notebook. What Crane sent him consisted of loose sheets. (The only notebook—other than scrapbooks of reviews—that Crane kept was a pocket-sized secretary notebook in which he jotted down literary notes, scraps of conversation, and first drafts of sketches and articles.)

On looking into the notebook of *The Red Badge* one dis-covers that the script of an earlier version appears *upside down* on the left hand leaves of the bound notebook. These two ver-sions may be described as the Short Version (short because only one third of it is extant) and the Long Version, the final handwritten draft. Manuscript LV consists of 176 pages, folio, numbered 193 owing to the author's alterations. Manuscript SV appears *on verso* of 56 of the 176 pages of the final hand-written draft. They are written on blue-lined paper having a one-inch red-lined margin at the side of each sheet. (Each sheet measures $12\frac{11}{16}$ by $7\frac{1}{2}$ inches.) What Crane used was legal-cap paper, the same kind of paper he used for writing his first batch of poems (the batch he brought to Hamlin Gar-land) and for writing at least two of his short stories, *The Snake* and *The Holler Tree*.[3] But in writing the final handwritten draft of *The Red Badge* he ran out of paper and used the clean back sides of sheets used for the earlier draft. He used fifty-six pages of the earlier draft. And that is why the bound notebook contains two versions.

The reason Crane used legal-cap paper is that he got it free from his brother—William was an attorney. One conjectures that the reason the final draft was not written on fresh sheets entirely is that he wrote it, not at William's house, but at Frederic Gordon's studio in New York City; Crane was then living in a little room near by.

In transcribing Manuscript LV Crane used the clean back sides of fifty-six leaves of Manuscript SV, and as he transcribed he added new matter. After finishing this enlarged draft he then cut it down, canceling many passages in order to speed up the pace of the narrative. He crossed out by downward wavy pencil-strokes the used pages of his earlier draft so as to avoid possible confusion with his new and final copy. (There can be no question that Manuscript LV was transcribed from Manuscript SV, this earlier draft being used for copying and revising the other.)

Before sending the loose sheets to Hawkins, Crane had removed fifteen pages of Manuscript LV.[4] The only portions of the

---

[3] The paper used for writing these stories measures 12⅜ by 7⅞ inches; there are 25 blue lines per page, and the red-lined margin on each sheet is 1½ inches from the edge of the sheet.

[4] Four of these missing leaves belonged to Chapter iv (pages 41–4 LV). Five of the leaves that Manuscript LV lacks contained canceled pages. Page 126, not found in the manuscript, must have been a canceled page, as part of the preceding page 125 is canceled. Page 125 contains the ending of Chapter xiv, and then following this uncanceled part there is a canceled passage. Similarly the last half of page 85 is canceled, and no doubt the four leaves for pages 86–9 were canceled pages. It is probably for this reason that they were removed from the manuscript. But it is difficult to account for the fact that the last part of Chapter iv was removed from the manuscript and never replaced there.
Two pages of the expunged Chapter xii of the final handwritten manuscript, pp. 98 and 102, are—I find now—in the possession of the

printed version (that is, the first American edition) which are *not* found in the final handwritten draft are (1) the final image of Chapter xxiv and (2) the last half of Chapter iv beginning with the paragraph: "The din in front swelled to a tremendous chorus." One part of this last half of Chapter iv, however, remains in Manuscript SV. It appears on page 36 in Crane's pagination of the earlier draft. (Page 36 SV appears on verso of page 127 LV.)

The earlier draft, Manuscript SV, is a portion of a running narrative. One of the interesting discoveries about it is that one of its pages, page 3 by Crane's pagination, does not belong to the war story. It is a page from an unpublished short story with the scene a Parisian boudoir and the action depicting a certain Monsieur Gustave in search of his wife, Marie. Evidently this page happened to get itself stacked in with the loose sheets of the manuscript of the war story—namely, Manuscript SV. The stack was then turned upside down, and the final handwritten copy of *The Red Badge* was made on the clean back sides of the stacked sheets. But the sheets of Manuscript SV were not stacked in consecutive order and consquently they do not appear in consecutive order in the bound notebook. Two pages of this early draft have been reported to be among the papers of Cora Crane. This early draft lacks page 1, the opening page of the novel, and since this opening page of the novel was likely to be more prized than later pages, it is probably one of the two pages that Crane gave Cora. The other (if I may speculate) is probably the missing page 3. What happened to the rest of this manuscript? It is not unlikely that the large portion of Manuscript SV which is not represented in the notebook of *The Red Badge,* as well as the fifteen pages removed from Manuscript LV, still exists.[5]

Houghton Library. Their discovery corrects the conjecture on p. 204. These two pages are evidently the same pages reported to have been among Cora Crane's papers.

[5] Manuscript SV contains only one complete chapter, Chapter vi (pages 46–52 by Crane's pagination of SV). Two other chapters are almost complete, vii and xi lacking only one page each.

In revising the final handwritten draft Crane's tendency was toward the gradual elimination of all unnecessary words, paragraphs, and in one instance an entire chapter. One part of this expunged chapter, Chapter xii, is found on three pages of the earlier draft. After Crane copied it into the final draft he removed six pages from Manuscript LV and then renumbered his chapter headings, Chapter xiii being renumbered xii and several subsequent chapters renumbered accordingly.[6] The excision of this Chapter xii from the final draft speeds up the pace of the narrative. In this excised chapter Henry philosophizes, but his philosophizing is not created here as a felt experience. It is all too flatly out there on the page. Though most of the early draft has the appearance of being a transcription, as it contains very few instances of corrected phrases, the procedure of composition in several passages seems more characteristic of the mind inventing rather than of the mind merely copying. One striking instance occurs toward the end of Manuscript SV (page 76). The signs of original composition that I think are evidenced here are the false starts, the unfinished and uncorrected syntax and sense, and the noticeable uncertainties of intention: "And with heavy [satire *canceled*] humor [*written above the canceled word*], he thought of how nature must smile when she the men come running. They regarding [ador ardor *crossed out with one stroke of the pen*] war-fire and courage as holy things and did not see that nature . . ." (Similar examples occur at the beginning of Manuscript SV—on pages 10, 13, and 49.)

Was there a still earlier draft? All the evidence—including Crane's own account—contradicts any supposition that Manu-

---

[6] The portion of Chapter xii appearing in Manuscript SV is reproduced here for the first time, in a footnote to the text. The fact that Chapter xii consisted of six pages is that Manuscript LV, into which it was copied, lacks six pages after page 97 (where Chapter xi ends). Crane did not trouble to renumber all his chapter headings. He failed to renumber Chapter xvii, which should be xvi, and likewise he failed to renumber subsequent chapters. In Manuscript LV, consequently, the final chapter, which in fact is Chapter xxiv, is designated as Chapter xxv.

script SV might be the original first-draft. The existence of an earlier draft is supported by the testimony of Hamlin Garland and other friends of Crane who saw *a* manuscript of the war novel. One friend says that it was written "on the paper the meat came home in" (home for Stephen being his brothers' houses) and another says that it was written "in nine days with a soft lead-pencil on pulpy copy paper, such as every reporter in the land uses quires of every day." Now the Short Version Manuscript is not written in soft lead-pencil on pulpy copy-paper, nor on meat-wrapping paper, and therefore this is not the manuscript that Louis Senger and Karl Harriman (however contradictory their accounts) claim to have seen. (Harriman's story appeared in the *New Hope*, October 1934.)

The birth notice (as Beer calls it) of *The Red Badge of Courage* is a note to Mrs. Armstrong dated April 2: "I have spent ten nights writing a story of the war on my own responsibility but I am not sure that my facts are real and the books won't tell me what I want to know so I must do it all over again, I guess." It took some research to evolve the background for his war story, and he had read Civil War periodicals and pored over Winslow Homer's drawings and Mathew Brady's photographs. What he had failed to find in the periodicals at Corwin Linson's studio and in the books that Mrs. Armstrong had lent him he had to find within himself, in his own emotions, and that is why his picture of war is stamped with unprecedented psychological realism. Not sure, however, that his facts were "real," he took a trip this summer to Virginia to talk with veterans in Fredericksburg and other towns. He spent this summer reworking and enlarging his first draft (Beer, page 284). This second draft is Manuscript SV, written at Edmund Crane's house some time after June. He had struck off that first draft at one blow, this much of it coming to him "intuitively"; but he kept repolishing it for over a year, and it was probably these revisions he was referring to when he said that writing *The Red Badge* had cost him "an effort born of pain—

despair almost; and I believe that this made it a better piece
of literature than it otherwise would have been."

Crane wrote with astonishing facility. He did a draft of
Maggie "in two days before Christmas" (1891), and he wrote
about a dozen or more poems (*The Black Riders* poems) in
three days; he finished *The Monster* (probably not the first
draft, however) in one week; he clipped off *The Third Violet*
at the pace of twenty-five pages a week; and he wrote many
of his short stories and sketches in the same incandescent state
—in one night, sometimes doing them in an hour. When Corwin
Linson, the artist who illustrated some of Crane's sketches,
called at Crane's room one morning, he discovered him "feverishly writing. He waved me to a seat, and soon handed me the
first pages of a story. 'Been at it most of the night, and it's
nearly finished.'" Short stories, he told another friend, "are
the easiest things to write" (Herbert P. Williams in the *Illustrated American*, July 18, 1896). He wasn't sure *The Third
Violet* was any good, he wrote Hawkins. "It is easy work. I can
finish a chapter each day" (letter of November 1895). Night
was when he did most of his writing. One morning he tossed
Linson the manuscript of *The Men in the Storm*: "He had been
out all night at it, out in the storm in line with the hungry men,
studying them; then inside, writing it." [7]

Written in Crane's round and almost perpendicular script,
the manuscripts of *The Red Badge* are remarkably clean and
neat, without any smudged fingerprints (except on one or two
pages) or creased markings such as would indicate their having once been used for printer's copy. They show no signs of
having been handled much or carried about rolled or folded.
Crane's handwriting is always very legible. On seeing the
manuscript of an essay that Crane wrote at the Delta Upsilon
house at Syracuse, one of his fraternity brothers expressed surprise to find such legibility in a newspaper reporter, and Crane

---

[7] Corwin Knapp Linson: "Little Stories of 'Steve' Crane," *Saturday
Evening Post*, April 11, 1903, pp. 19–20.

explained that from the outset "he had kept in mind the compositor, whose earnings depended upon the amount he could set, and this in turn upon the time it took to read the copy." [8] Another friend, R. G. Vosburgh, reports: "In revising his work he would rewrite a whole sheet when a correction was necessary rather than make an erasure, if only to change one word." [9] The notebook of *The Red Badge* contains several sheets that are blank except for a single sentence or but part of one, Crane discarding these first attempts to make a second start. The first drafts he jotted down in his stenographer's notebook, the little pocket notebook he carried about with him; and the manuscripts of two stories written on legal-cap paper— *The Snake* and *The Holler Tree*—are written in a steady flow of invention without pause and almost without correction of more than a phrase.

Conrad describes how Crane during one of his prolonged creative spurts would go on writing whole chapters with no revisions other than a few words. He would "sit down before a blank sheet of paper, dip his pen, write the first line at once, and go on without haste and without pause for a couple of hours." His manuscripts would show "no more than half a dozen erasures—mostly single words—in the whole lot. It seemed to me always a perfect miracle in the way of mastery over material and expression" (Introduction to Beer's *Stephen Crane*). It is no wonder that Corwin Linson was awed by Crane's genius and felt in his presence "a power mysterious and unaccountable." Garland was amazed to see Crane "drawing off" poems spontaneously and "all without blot or erasure. Every letter stood out like the writing of a bank bill. . . . He wrote steadily in beautifully clear script with perfect alignment and spacing, precisely as if he were copying something

---

[8] Frank W. Noxon: "The Real Stephen Crane," *Step Ladder,* 14 (January 1928), 4–9.

[9] "The Darkest Hour in the Life of Stephen Crane," *Book Lover,* 2 (Summer 1901), 338–9. Reprinted from the *Criterion,* 1 (February 1901), 26–7.

already written and before his eyes." [1] The second draft of
The Red Badge, Manuscript SV, contains only a dozen instances of crossed-out word or phrase in the first twenty-three
pages and not more than thirty corrections in the entire fifty-
six sheets.

Garland, reconstructing Crane's explanation of how his
poems came to him, says that it was "an entirely automatic,
sub-conscious process . . . it was evident that his composition
(even to the process of punctuation) went on beneath consciousness, and that setting his poems down was for him a kind
of transcribing as from a printed page. He told me that the
first pages of *The Red Badge of Courage* came to him in just
that way, every word in place, every comma, every period
fixed" (in *Yale Review*, April 1914). "Here," said Howells as
he introduced Crane to some guests, "Here is a writer who has
sprung into life fully armed."

This legend of Crane as the purely inspirational writer is
propped up by Beer's claim that Crane "would not rewrite"
and that once his work appeared in print he would not revise.
Crane insisted that revisions were "dishonest" to his readers,
and Garland held the same notion. But Beer is wholly mistaken. Crane several times rewrote *The Red Badge*, *Maggie*,
George's Mother; and he restored large portions of *The Red
Badge*—including the last three chapters—after its first publication in truncated newspaper form. Beer failed to look into the
newspaper version ("He restored only a few paragraphs of *The
Red Badge* for its final form," page 377). It first appeared in
the *Philadelphia Press* serially from December 3 to 8, 1894,
and then all in one page of the *New York Press* on December 9.

It began as a potboiler (so he told Louis Senger and again
the *Book Buyer* when he was interviewed there in 1896), and
his motive for tackling the job was a wager made during the
heat of an argument with Acton Davies (in the studio of Wil-

---

[1] "Stephen Crane as I Knew Him," *Yale Review*, 3 (April 1914),
494–506. A later variant account appears in Garland's *Roadside Meetings*
(1930).

liam Dallgren) over Zola's *La Débâcle*. Crane declared that
though he had never seen even a sham battle, he could write a
better book. "I deliberately started in to do a pot-boiler," he
told Senger, "something that would take the boarding-school
element—you know the kind. Well, I got interested in the thing
in spite of myself, and I couldn't, I couldn't! I *had* to do it my
own way." What ended as a work of art began as no more than
a potboiler short story for a newspaper. By a curious coincidence the first draft was written in a studio (Corwin Linson's)
and the last draft in another studio (Frederic Gordon's), and
furthermore the dare to try his hand at a war novel took place
in a studio (William Dallgren's). But when he wrote the first
draft of *The Red Badge* in March 1893, he had already worked
out the idea for it—"not so much on paper as in his own mind.
He spoke frequently of its hero as 'growing.' 'He's getting to
be quite a character now,' he said one day. . . . The character was as clear and vital to him, in his mind, as a living person could have been; and it was such a conception and development of him that made him, when Stephen finally got him
upon paper, appear so marvelously real." What Willis Johnson here reports must have taken place during the winter of
1892–3; the point is that Crane had been brooding over his
conception for many months before he undertook to write it.[2]
Writing *The Red Badge* wasn't, therefore, the spontaneous, un-
premeditated creative spurt that Crane experienced in writing
his poems. Crane's saying that he wrote it "intuitively" means,
among other things, that he wrote it without effort—this first
draft.

"I write what is in me," Crane remarked during the banquet
given in his honor by the Philistine Society (1895), "and it will
be enough to follow with obedience the promptings of that

---

[2] Johnson's "*At this time* he was also greatly engaged with *The Red
Badge of Courage*" is indefinite; but figured against his references to
Maggie, Johnson apparently is recalling events of 1892. Johnson's ac-
count is not cited by Beer and Berryman. It appeared in the *Literary
Digest International Book Review*, April 1926.

inspiration, if it be worthy of so dignified a name" (quoted from the *Bookman,* February 1896). Conrad describes Crane as a writer "who in his art (as indeed in his private life) was the least 'contriving' of men." But he concedes that *The Red Badge* was "contrived" (Introduction to *Stephen Crane*). In *A Personal Record* Conrad speaks of Crane's "unsophisticated inspiration," but in Crane's art surely what is "inspired" is what is "contrived." There are no grounds for thinking that Crane was any more "inspirational" than other artists. He brooded over his germinal ideas the same as Brahms and Yeats and Conrad. After the germinal idea, as he explained to Herbert P. Williams, "Then comes a longing for you don't know what; sorrow, too, and heart-hunger." Whatever he begins with "is immaterial; but once written, it determines the rest of the book."

Now, *The Red Badge* was created just that way. As each part progressed he discovered his next move—"never knowing the end, but forcing himself to follow 'that fearful logical conclusion'" (Herbert P. Williams in the *Illustrated American,* July 18, 1896). All his daring phrases and metaphors "were studied out with much care, and after they had been trimmed and turned and changed to final form," as R. G. Vosburgh testifies, "he would repeat them aloud and dwell on them lovingly." He did the same with *Maggie*—showing the manuscript to his fraternity brothers after he had blocked out the plot, "putting it in various lights and constructions, and then asking which was more effective." Crane is no different from other artists. All artists deliberate their inventions and calculate their effects. That is what the word *artist* means. "Every incident and phase of character in *The Red Badge* was discussed fully and completely before being incorporated in the story" (in *Book Lover,* Summer 1901). Vosburgh, himself an artist, speaks with the authority of creative and critical insight: "almost every impression was preconceived." *This point has critical importance.*

What I have been leading up to is the fact that Crane, having brooded over his hero, Henry Fleming, started off the writing of his war novel not with a character but with a metaphor. When he first put his conception down on paper a metaphor cut across his preconceived plan. *Inspiration*, to define it, is just that. It is what surprises the preconceived plan. And then the whole ground plans alters itself accordingly. What was this metaphor?

Hamlin Garland, recording (in the *Yale Review* for April 1914) his astonishment upon first looking into the manuscript that Crane brought him in Harlem "one clear winter's day" (1893), remembered a metaphor appearing in the first page of this draft. "The first sentence fairly took me captive. It described a vast army in camp on one side of the river, confronting with its thousands of eyes a similar monster on the opposite bank." The metaphor that Garland identifies as a "monster" does not exist in the final handwritten manuscript, nor in the earlier draft used for the final version, and no such creature exists in the text of the printed version. In the opening scene of the novel, however, there are imaginative grounds for Garland's apocryphal monster: the two opposing armies glare at each other *implicitly* like beasts, and beast imagery—recurrent throughout the novel—is prepared for here in this implied one. What Crane knew about the psychology of opposing armies he got from the gridiron: "The psychology is the same. The opposing team is an enemy tribe."

Garland's monster made its appearance only in Crane's first rapid draft, the draft he wrote in ten nights. According to Berryman, "Whether anyone ever saw this story is unknown" (page 66). But Garland saw it, and the proof is found not in Garland's *Roadside Meetings* (1930) but in "Stephen Crane as I Knew Him," which appeared in 1914. These two accounts of Crane's visits differ considerably. The fact is that Crane brought Garland first the manuscript of *The Red Badge* and then, "after a week or two of absence," the manuscript of the poems. In *Roadside Meetings*, however, the sequence of these visits is reversed, and furthermore the identity of manuscripts of *The Red Badge* is obscured by the omission here of a single sentence. This sentence solves the mystery. Crane (as Beer suggested) made two visits to Garland: first in the spring of 1893 with the original draft, and then a year later with the typescript copy. "The prodigious opening sentence which so impressed me on that memorable day *disappeared entirely from his copy* [that is, the typescript copy that Crane brought him a year later] and the printed book lacked many other of the most notable pages of the original manuscript." Beer says that Crane "restored only a few paragraphs of *The Red Badge* for its final form, so an opening description of the two armies as watchful beasts which so pleased Mr. Garland is forever lost" (page 377). What this statement indicates, apart from its telling us that Beer neglected to study the newspaper serial version, is that Beer never saw the notebook manuscripts of *The Red Badge*. Whether Garland ever saw them cannot be ascertained, but they are not the manuscripts he describes in his variant accounts of what Crane brought him in the spring of 1893. In *Roadside Meetings* he added to his earlier account the fact that the manuscript "had, however, no name at this time." And in his *Yale Review* account he says it was "a fat roll of a manuscript sagging the side pocket of his long, shabby gray ulster," and Crane handed it over to his friend with seeming reluctance.

The manuscript that Crane brought Garland, then, is evidently the same manuscript that he brought Irving Bacheller the next year. Bacheller and his wife took turns reading it aloud to each other one night. It was not Manuscript SV nor Manuscript LV that Bacheller then handled, as these manuscripts are not soiled and show no signs of having been rolled or folded. The manuscript that Bacheller describes in *Coming up the Road* (1928) and in *From Stories of Memory* (1938) was "a bulky manuscript," "slightly worn," "a bit soiled from much handling. It had not been typed. It was in the clearly legible and rather handsome script of the author." Crane mentioned modestly, with no sign of "hopeful enthusiasm," that

Howells and Garland had read it and he asked for Bacheller's
frank opinion whether he accepted the manuscript for publication by the Bacheller-Johnson syndicate or not. Bacheller
says that at least two magazines had declined it. (One was
Leslie's Weekly.) It is difficult to unscramble the chronology
of the manuscripts and composition of *The Red Badge* because
so many facts about it are contradictory or nonexistent. Neither
Beer nor Berryman documents his account, and each uses only
a portion of the available data.[3] If one could only buttress

[3] Berryman does not attempt a chronological account of the composition of *The Red Badge* (the notebook manuscripts were not available
to him), but what he says about it is filled with errors. I have in my
possession a copy of one of Thomas Beer's letters stating that Crane's remark to Garland: "I'd trade my entire future for twenty-three dollars in
cash," was made in the spring of 1893. Berryman quotes Crane's remark
on p. 83 and immediately follows it with the statement that "McClure
was delaying, McClure would delay for months." Berryman intends this
as occurring in 1894. But it was made in March or in April 1893, when
Crane first visited Garland. The crucial evidence that Berryman neglected
to study is Garland's essay in the *Yale Review* of 1914; he drew solely
upon Garland's *Roadside Meetings* (1930). It would appear—from Berryman's version—that Crane visited Garland with the manuscript of *The
Red Badge* only once, with the typescript copy in 1894. Berryman errs
furthermore in misdating the occasion when Crane drew off his poems
as February 1894. It occurred the year before. He has it that Crane suddenly started writing poems just after sending *The Red Badge* to the
typist in February 1894, but he also has it that Crane *first* brought Garland these poems and *then* he brought him *The Red Badge* manuscript
(that is, the typescript). This contradicts Crane's own account: "I wrote
the things in February of 1893." It also runs counter to Garland's account in the *Yale Review*. The sequence was just the reverse. And furthermore it runs counter to Beer's statements—the few he makes—about
these visits to Garland. Berryman misdates the occasion of Crane's poetic
ghost, the visitation of the poetic medium that Crane drew upon in
Garland's presence, only because 1894 would appear to be the logical
date according to Garland's version in *Roadside Meetings* (1930). The
variant version in the *Yale Review* (1914) would have set Berryman
straight furthermore about Garland's recollection of a monster appearing on the first page of the manuscript Crane brought him. That mon-
ster-image existed in the first draft, which Garland saw in the spring of
1893. Garland was not inventing its existence, nor is it (as Berryman
says, p. 76) that Garland "misremembered it" from other Crane short
stories.

opinions with evidence! It is no wonder that Thomas Beer, in order to dig out facts for his biography of Crane, hired a detective. On what date did Crane see Irving Bacheller? Why did he take him the original draft of *The Red Badge* instead of the typescript? And so on. I have not unriddled these enigmas, but here meanwhile is a first attempt:

In February 1894 Crane sent his manuscript of *The Red Badge* to a professional typist, and then ransomed one half of it and called on Garland, whereupon Garland asked him: "Where's the rest of it?"

> —In hock.—
> —To whom?—
> —Typewriter.—
> —How much do you owe him or her?—
> —Fifteen dollars.—

And that is how Crane got back the rest of the manuscript from the typist; Garland lent him the fifteen dollars on condition that he would bring him the other half the next day. " 'I'll do it,' " said Crane—"as if he were joining me in some heroic enterprise, and away he went in high spirits." A certain mystery attaches to this episode, also; for a letter that must have been written at this time reveals that Crane applied to a fellow journalist for the money to pay the typist—the bill was thirty dollars. This letter was first printed in the *Bookman* for May 1912 and is here reproduced for the first time.

Dear Dicon:

Beg, borrow or steal fifteen dollars. —— like the Red Badge and want to make a contract for it. It's in pawn at the typewriter's for fifteen.

Thine,
Steve

The unnamed publisher was apparently McClure (judging by the *Bookman*'s story about this letter). Crane showed him the first half of the typescript, evidently immediately after visiting Garland with it, "and the book was practically accepted, on condition that the remaining chapters were up to the same standard." When Crane got back the rest of the typescript from Garland he submitted it to McClure. Either now or later this year he submitted the original draft to Irving Bacheller. On February 24, 1894 Crane wrote to Holmes Bassett: "I have just sold another book and my friends think it is pretty good and that some publisher ought to bring it out when it has been shown as a serial. It is a war-story and the syndicate people think that several papers could use it." If Beer is correct, it was on February 24—the same morning that Crane wrote to Bassett—that Bacheller bought for ninety dollars *The Red Badge* for serialization in the newspapers. Crane's words "syndicate people" would seem to describe more likely the Bacheller-Johnson syndicate than McClure's monthly magazine. What actually happened will probably never be established beyond dispute, but in the absence of facts one speculates that Crane, desperate by now, might very well have approached two publishers at the same time—Bacheller with the original draft and McClure with the typescript. That version would explain why Crane brought Bacheller the original pulp-paper draft, the soiled and untyped manuscript, instead of the final handwritten manuscript. The final handwritten manuscript was at the typist's office—in hock. The original draft presumably was virtually the narrative as we know it, though shorter no doubt than Manuscript SV. (An estimate of the length of Manuscript SV can be made from the fact that one of its pages is numbered 149.) The typescript no longer exists; presumably it was destroyed at the printer's. More than one typescript probably circulated, Bacheller using one for the newspaper publication of *The Red Badge*.

McClure was a Beast about the war novel and that has been the thing that put me in one of the ditches. He kept it for six months until I was nearly mad. Oh, yes, he was going to use it, but finally I took it to Bacheller's. They use it in January in shortened form.[4]

---

[4] Letter to Garland, November 15, 1894.

Bacheller brought it out sooner than Crane expected. When it appeared in December, Crane sent Ripley Hitchcock, editor at Appleton's, the clippings of this newspaper version (on December 18), and Hitchcock bought the war novel this same month—for book publication the next year—on the basis of this serialized shortened form—18,000 words of the complete draft. Here, Crane wrote to Hitchcock, "is the war story in its syndicate form—that is to say, much smaller & to my mind much worse than its original form." One wonders why Crane did not send Hitchcock the typescript.

It would take another Keats to describe my excitement on first looking into Crane's handwritten manuscripts of *The Red Badge*. The new planets that swam into my ken brightened up my theory of the whole symbolic system and reinforced the interpretation I had already made.[5]

Many of the passages that Crane expunged from the typescript or canceled in the manuscripts during the process of revision contribute additional symbolic overtones, reinforce the dominant patterns of imagery and meaning; they help toward illuminating what the book is really all about. Their omission is therefore a distinct loss not only to the imaginative scheme of relationships but also to the directional line of the author's concealed intention. A few of these expunged passages are furthermore a loss to the picturesqueness of the style. *The Red Badge*, according to my reading of it, is loaded with Biblical allusions and religious symbolism. In one of the passages appearing in the final handwritten manuscript but not in the printed version of Chapter i, Henry Fleming receives a Bible from his mother.

Don't fergit to send yer socks to me the minute they git holes in 'em, and *here's a little bible I want yeh to take along with yeh, Henry*. I don't presume yeh'll be a-setting reading it all day long,

---

[5] I have left my analysis of *The Red Badge* here mainly as I originally wrote it.

child, ner nothin' like that. Many a time, yeh'll fergit yeh got it, I don't doubt. But there'll be many a time, too, Henry, when yeh'll be wanting advice, boy, and all like that, and there'll be nobody round, perhaps, to tell yeh things. Then if yeh take it out, boy, yeh'll find wisdom in it—wisdom in it, Henry—with little or no searching.

Perhaps Crane felt that this passage revealed too much of his hidden ground plan to appear this early and deleted it for that reason from the typescript copy of the final handwritten manuscript. Crane's theory (misquoting Emerson) was that "There should be a long logic beneath the story, but it should be carefully kept out of sight."

The same tendency to keep things hidden, oblique, and enigmatic is disclosed in other canceled or excised passages. For example, the original title for the novel: *Private Fleming / His various battles*, not only names the hero but hints that his battles are psychological as well as physical ones. Crane's revised and final title is far more enigmatic: *The Red Badge of Courage / an Episode of the American Civil War*. This last part of the title is straightforward, matter-of-fact; but the first part indicates a symbol.

This final title was unquestionably an added second thought. (It is written in darker ink and with far more pressure on the pen than used in writing the original title *and* the opening pages of the manuscript, the first title and the first page being done at the same time.) Now, the source of the final title (as Mr. Winterich notices) was a sentence that Crane struck off in Chapter ix: "He wished that he, too, had a wound, a little [warm *canceled*] red badge of courage." The first title is crossed out by wavy slanting pencil-lines, and across the left margin at the top of the page there is the word *Cap* appearing in pencil—and by another hand. Evidently it was written there by the typist or by the editor; printer's copy or typescript was made from this final handwritten draft.

Two further points relating to Crane's revision of the title are also characteristic of his process of revision. The hero's name is concealed not only in the final title but throughout

Manuscript LV, from the first page of the final manuscript to the last (with but few exceptions). To cite one instance where the hero's name is not crossed out, "What's the matter, Flem?" appears in the printed version as "What's the matter, Henry?" Crane intended anonymity for his soldiers except on occasions when they are addressing one another. Secondly, the final title announces and initiates the motif of color, which is recurrent throughout the book. The *Spectator,* reviewing *The Red Badge of Courage* on June 27, 1896, said that the book carried "an infelicitous title by the way." And Ripley Hitchcock, editor at Appleton's, anticipated that criticism and asked Crane to shorten the title. And so Crane, writing to Hitchcock from New Orleans on March 8, 1895, suggested that the word *red* be cut from the title: "That would shorten it." But so concerned was Crane with color that in one instance in the manuscript he used the word *color,* absent-mindedly, in place of *collar!* (In the phrase "long troughs of liquid mud" appearing in the printed version of the opening page of the novel, the word *long,* in the manuscript, was originally followed by the word *red.*) The use of the word *Red* in the final title, as Frank Noxon reports, "was part of a program. After the book appeared he and I had somewhere a talk about color in literature. He told me that a passage in Goethe analyzed the effect which the several colors have upon the human mind. Upon Crane this had made a profound impression and he utilized the idea to produce his effects" (in *Step Ladder,* January 1928).

The most interesting discovery in Manuscript LV is that the ending of the novel underwent several changes. Crane first intended the novel to end with the words: "oaths and walking sticks," which are the last words in the paragraph beginning "It rained."

It rained. The procession of weary soldiers became a bedraggled train, despondent and muttering, marching with churning effort in a trough of liquid brown mud under a low, wretched sky. Yet the youth smiled, for he saw that the world was a world for him, though many discovered it to be made of oaths and walking sticks.

The words "The End" are written after this paragraph. On second thought Crane added fifty-five words to the paragraph. He crossed out the phrases "walking sticks" and "The End" and wrote in this second ending:

walking sticks. He had rid himself of the red sickness of battle. The sultry nightmare was in the past. He had been an animal blistered and sweating in the heat and pain of war. He turned now with a lover's thirst to images of tranquil skies, fresh meadows, cool brooks —an existence of soft and eternal peace.

That this ending represents a second intention and was added at some later time, not during the period of original composition, is evidenced by the use of a new pen for writing it. (Most of Crane's revisions in Manuscript LV were made after the whole draft had been finished, the evidence for this being the dark ink and the comparatively heavy pen pressure used when crossing out and writing in the first and second variant. Revisions made during original composition are quite infrequent.)

Compared with the first ending, this second one is the less effective of the two. Crane realized this himself and therefore added a third ending. It consists of a single image:

Over the river a golden ray of sun came through the hosts of leaden rain clouds.

This third ending does not appear in the manuscript. The proof that it was Crane himself who inserted it in the typescript is that this final ending recapitulates one of the dominant contrast-patterns of the book: the despair-hope contrast mood initiated by the opening scene of Chapter i. The mood of hope and faith evoked by this opening scene (paragraphs 1–3) shifts to despair and disbelief (paragraphs 4–7), and this same alternation of mood patterns every tableau in the whole sequence and is epitomized in the final sun-through-rainclouds image. That fact alone suffices, I think, to discredit Winterich's supposition that this third ending "bears the unmistakable spoor of the editor—an editor not too happily inspired." Who but the artist himself could possibly possess the requisite insight for inventing this double-mood image by which the ending of the book reconstructs its very beginning? That Crane consciously designed the book with this device and burden is revealed in a passage canceled in Manuscript LV: "*Again* the youth was in despair." It would seem reasonable to assume then, since this final ending must have been the invention of the author, that most of the other alterations made in the typescript were similarly the rewrite work of the author, though it certainly was the editor who corrected Crane's innumerable errors in grammar, syntax, punctuation, and spelling.[6]

Winterich, in his Introduction to the Folio Society edition of *The Red Badge*, goes on to say that "The 'rain clouds' ending sounds like a concession to the send-the-audience-home-feeling-good school. But let us all feel good ourselves—there are not many novels in which the reader is offered a choice of three endings." But the reader is not offered any choice, and in fact no choice is possible. The final ending is built on the two preceding ones, and each of these prepares for the one that follows it. The "sun-through-rainclouds" image gives an ironic twist to the flat sentimental "images of tranquil skies, fresh meadows, cool brooks—an existence of eternal peace." Henry has not attained eternal peace, and though the sun shines, it pierces "hosts of leaden rain clouds." It is interesting to notice that Hemingway's hero in *A Farewell to Arms* also makes his "separate peace"—that too an illusion not unlike Henry Fleming's. From the start Henry Fleming recognizes the necessity for change of heart but wars against it, and at the end he is the same Henry Fleming. He has undergone no change, no real spiritual development. In an excised passage

---

[6] Conrad designated the third from the last paragraph of the printed version as the ending of the actual *action* of the narrative: "He had been to touch the great death, and found that, after all, it was but the great death. He was a man."

appearing in Chapter xii of the Short Version Manuscript Crane's ironic method presents the mocked hero as *"a-blaze with desire to change.* He saw himself, a sun-lit figure upon a peak, pointing with true and *unchangeable* gesture. 'There!' And all men could see and no man would falter." His self-contradiction is summed up in this single turnabout.

It is certainly not by chance that this theme of change begins the book and ends it. The altered mood of the soldiers in the opening scene is accompanied by a change in the weather, and this initial image of the book is paralleled in the concluding images of Chapter xxiv. Both *The Red Badge of Courage* and *A Farewell to Arms* close with the same image that their opening scenes prepared for. In both it is an image of fog or rain. In *A Farewell* the terminal word of the book is *rain,* and throughout the story rain is associated with motifs of death and deception. In the paragraph that Crane first intended as the ending of *The Red Badge,* rain reappears. Rain associated with the despondent mood of the soldiers here returns us to the beginning image of Chapter i: "The cold passed . . . and the retiring fogs . . ." In both novels the weather and the terrain *act* as protagonists, and all weather and terrain images— sun and rain or fog, river, and so on—carry symbolic significance.

In the ending Crane first intended for his novel the image of "oaths and walking sticks" echoes an image canceled from Chapter xx in the final handwritten draft. This is the canceled passage: "The youth noted that the lieutenant held his sword in the manner of a walking-stick." (Crane first wrote the word *cane* for *sword.*) The lieutenant leans on his sword as though in need of a cane or walking-stick to support him. Henry, at the end of the book, smiles *although* it is raining and the soldiers are despondent. He smiles because the world, so he now thinks, was made for him. He has no need for walking-sticks— that is, creeds—to support him. "Yet the youth smiled, for he saw that the world was a world for him, though many discovered it to be made of oaths and walking sticks." In a passage expunged from the printed version this telltale image appears in the manuscript: "The imperturbable sun shines on insult and worship." *Insult* equates with *oaths,* and *worship* equates with *walking sticks.* Men insult with oaths the very creed they worship; they curse their walking-sticks—that which props them. Crane's example is Henry Fleming.

Fleming, when Jim Conklin dies, curses the red sun pasted in the sky "like a wafer." Nature, we are told, "had given him a sign." Henry blasphemes against this emblem of his faith, the wafer-like red sun. The manuscripts provide two variants of this final image for Chapter ix. In the earlier draft Crane wrote: "The fierce red sun was pasted in the sky like a fierce wafer." The first *fierce* was then canceled, and in the final handwritten draft the image remained thus: "The red sun was pasted in the sky like a fierce wafer." The emphatic *fierce* personifies the sun as the Divinity, a wrathful Jehovah. This central and crucial episode of the story is echoed in the "oaths and walking sticks" image of that paragraph which Crane first intended as the final one for Chapter xxiv, and again in the already quoted excised image: "The imperturbable sun shines on insult and worship." That the sun is indifferent to the blasphemy of the youth is underscored in another image new to the printed text: "But the sky would forget." In contrast with Henry's blasphemy against the sun, there was a soldier who "swore *by* the sun"—in a passage canceled in the manuscript. The wafer-like sun, the object of insult and worship, signifies the sacrificial death of *the* Son.

Religious symbolism toolmarks the whole book. Collaborative evidence for this interpretation is found in several passages canceled in the manuscripts or expunged from the printed version. In Chapter iv Henry Fleming—in an excised passage—vaingloriously regards himself as "the chosen of some gods. By fearful and wonderful roads he was to be led to a crown." Henry, in the cant phrase for it, thinks he is a little tin Christ. In a passage appearing only in the Short Version Manuscript, Crane wrote in mockery of his hero: "He had a feeling that he was the coming prophet of a world reconstruction." (Crane wrote first the word *social* and then canceled it and added the variant *world*.) Another image revelatory of the author's schemework of Biblical "parallelisms" occurs in an excised passage in Manuscript LV: Henry in his blind egotism remembers the words of the "insane lieutenant," words that praised his battle grit, and he reflects: "It was a little coronation." It looks as though Henry had read the Bible his mother gave him!

The Red Badge of Courage begins with a metaphor (implied in the printed version, explicitly present in the original draft), strikes off near its center another metaphor ("The red sun was pasted in the sky like a fierce wafer"), and ends with a metaphor. There can be no question that this book was constructed by an artist.

THE RED BADGE OF COURAGE
AN EPISODE OF THE AMERICAN CIVIL WAR

BY STEPHEN CRANE *

* In Manuscript LV the original title appears as *Private Fleming/His various battles./By Stephen Crane.* This first title is crossed out and the new title added above it at the top of the page in Crane's script but with a different pen. Whether the original title was copied from the earlier draft cannot be ascertained since Manuscript SV lacks the first page.

FOOTNOTES

The present text of The Red Badge of Courage *makes no attempt to provide a definitive scholarly edition. Such an edition would entail a reconstruction of all the textual variants in manuscripts and printed version. (It would include also the first published text, the newspaper version, as well as consideration of the nonexistent typescript and the conjectured first draft.) While such a study falls outside the aim and scope of this anthology, I once entertained the notion of attempting it, and I have selected these footnotes from that first attempt. For the purpose of this edition I have selected only the critically interesting variations existing between manuscripts and printed version. (The printed version is the First American Edition, hereafter coded as FAE. The final handwritten manuscript is indicated by the symbol LV, and the earlier draft by the symbol SV.)*

These footnotes reproduce passages crossed out by the author in Manuscript SV, the earlier draft, and canceled passages in Manuscript LV, the final handwritten version. These passages appear here for the first time. My annotations collate and criticize these and other variants having critical relevancy for the student and general reader toward an interpretation of the meaning of the novel and the evolution of its composition and style.

Italicized words in the footnotes represent editorial comment. Words or phrases not italicized represent matter quoted from printed text or manuscripts.

Uncanceled passages in Manuscript LV are here restored to the text and indicated by the use of square brackets [ ].

CHAPTER I [1]

THE COLD passed reluctantly from the earth, and the retiring fogs revealed an army stretched out on the hills, resting. As the landscape changed from brown to green, the army awakened, and began to tremble with eagerness at the noise of rumors. It cast its eyes upon the roads, which were growing from long troughs [2] of liquid mud to proper thoroughfares. A river, amber-tinted in the shadow of its banks, purled at the army's feet; and at night, when the stream had become of a sorrowful blackness, one could see across it [3] the red, eyelike gleam of hostile camp-fires set in the low brows of distant hills.

Once a certain tall soldier [4] developed virtues and went

---

[1] The text of *The Red Badge of Courage* is that of the First American Edition (1895). In instances of differences between Manuscript LV and the First American Edition I have kept the latter version when the variant does not alter the meaning (e.g., *thoughts* in LV and *thought* in FAE; *doomed* in LV and *damned* in FAE); when the LV variant consists of a new word or passage I have inserted the new matter in the text and indicated it there by the use of square brackets; when the FAE variant is obviously a misprint or a misconstruction of the author's intention, I have replaced it with the original word or phrase appearing in the final handwritten manuscript (e.g., *bunk* in LV restored for *bank* in FAE; *fiends* in LV restored for *friends* in FAE); in some instances where both LV and FAE are obviously incorrect (e.g., *was* in LV and in FAE should be *were*), no alteration has been made.

[2] *LV:* long red troughs/red *canceled*

[3] *LV:* see, across

[4] *LV:* Jim Conklin *canceled. Throughout Manuscript LV names of characters are crossed out. Exceptions occur in Chapters xiii and xiv. Here and in a few subsequent instances name alterations do not appear in the manuscript. They were evidently made in the typescript. Cancellations of names were made after the entire draft of Manuscript LV had been finished, the evidence for this fact being the dark ink and heavy pen pressure used for these and for almost all other revisions. In Chapter xiii the word* Fleming *is canceled in pencil. Unquestionably, anonymity was a second thought. These name alterations frequently involved several revisions. For instance in Chapter i the phrase* another private loudly (*para-*

resolutely to wash a shirt. He came flying back from a brook waving his garment bannerlike. He was swelled with a tale he had heard from a reliable friend, who had heard it from a truthful cavalryman, who had heard it from his trustworthy brother, one of the orderlies at division headquarters. He adopted the important air of a herald in red and gold.

"We're goin' t' move t' morrah—sure," he said pompously to a group in the company street. "We're goin' 'way up the river, cut across, an' come around in behint 'em."

To his attentive audience he drew a loud and elaborate plan of a very brilliant campaign. When he had finished, the blue-clothed men scattered into small arguing groups between the rows of squat brown huts. A negro teamster who had been dancing upon a cracker box with the hilarious encouragement of twoscore soldiers was deserted. He sat mournfully down. Smoke drifted lazily from a multitude of quaint chimneys.

"It's a lie! that's all it is—a thunderin' lie!" said another private loudly. His smooth face was flushed, and his hands were thrust sulkily into his trousers' pockets. He took the matter as an affront to him. "I don't believe the derned old army's ever going to move. We're set. I've got ready to move eight times in the last two weeks, and we ain't moved yet."

The tall soldier felt called upon to defend the truth of a rumor he himself had introduced. He and the loud one came near to fighting over it.

A corporal began to swear before the assemblage. He had just put a costly board floor in his house, he said. During the early spring he had refrained from adding extensively to the comfort of his environment because he had felt that the army might start on the march at any moment. Of late, however, he had been impressed that they were in a sort of eternal camp.

Many of the men engaged in a spirited debate. One outlined in a peculiarly lucid manner all the plans of the commanding

---

graph 5) was the fourth variant. The first variant young Wilson *was crossed out; in the second variant,* another soldier, *the word* soldier *was canceled;* private *was written in; and finally* loudly *was added.*

general. He was opposed by men who advocated that there were other plans of campaign. They clamored at each other, numbers making futile bids for the popular attention. Meanwhile, the soldier who had fetched the rumor bustled about with much importance. He was continually assailed by questions.

"What's up, Jim?"

"Th' army's goin' t' move."

"Ah, what yeh talkin' about? How yeh know it is?"

"Well, yeh kin b'lieve me er not, jest as yeh like. I don't care a hang. [I tell yeh what I know an' yeh kin take it er leave it. Suit yourselves. It don't make no difference t' me.]"

There was much food for thought in the manner in which he replied. He came near to convincing them by disdaining to produce proofs. They grew much excited over it.

There was a youthful private who listened with eager ears to the words of the tall soldier and to the varied comments of his comrades. After receiving a fill of discussions concerning marches and attacks, he went to his hut and crawled through an intricate hole that served it as a door. He wished to be alone with some new thoughts that had lately come to him.

He lay down on a wide bunk [5] that stretched across the end of the room. In the other end, cracker boxes were made to serve as furniture. They were grouped about the fireplace. A picture from an illustrated weekly was upon the log walls, and three rifles were paralleled on pegs. Equipments hung on handy projections, and some tin dishes lay upon a small pile of firewood. A folded tent was serving as a roof. The sunlight, without, beating upon it, made it glow a light yellow shade. A small window shot an oblique square of whiter light upon the cluttered floor. The smoke from the fire at times neglected the clay chimney and wreathed into the room, and this flimsy chimney of clay and sticks made endless threats to set ablaze the whole establishment.

---

[5] *FAE has:* bank. *This misprint occurs in all Appleton editions until 1900. (Cf. Williams's* Bibliography, *1948, p. 20.)*

The youth was in a little trance of astonishment. So they were at last going to fight. On the morrow, perhaps, there would be a battle, and he would be in it. For a time he was obliged to labor to make himself believe. He could not accept with assurance an omen that he was about to mingle in one of those great affairs of the earth.

He had, of course, dreamed of battles all his life—of vague and bloody conflicts that had thrilled him with their sweep and fire. In visions he had seen himself in many struggles. He had imagined peoples secure in the shadow of his eagle-eyed prowess. But awake he had regarded battles as crimson blotches on the pages of the past. He had put them as things of the bygone with his thought-images of heavy crowns and high castles. There was a portion of the world's history which he had regarded as the time of wars, but it, he thought, had been long gone over the horizon and had disappeared forever.

From his home his youthful eyes had looked upon the war in his own country with distrust. It must be some sort of a play affair. He had long despaired of witnessing a Greeklike struggle. Such would be no more, he had said. Men were better, or more timid. Secular and religious education had effaced the throat-grappling instinct, or else firm finance held in check the passions.

He had burned several times to enlist. Tales of great movements shook the land. They might not be distinctly Homeric, but there seemed to be much glory in them. He had read of marches, sieges, conflicts, and he had longed to see it all. His busy mind had drawn for him large pictures extravagant in color, lurid with breathless deeds.

But his mother had discouraged him. She had affected to look with some contempt upon the quality of his war ardor and patriotism. She could calmly seat herself and with no apparent difficulty give him many hundreds of reasons why he was of vastly more importance on the farm than on the field of battle. She had had certain ways of expression that told him that her statements on the subject came from a deep conviction. Moreover, on her side, was his belief that her ethical motive in the argument was impregnable.

At last, however, he had made firm rebellion against this yellow light thrown upon the color of his ambitions. The newspapers, the gossip of the village, his own picturings, had aroused him to an uncheckable degree. They were in truth fighting finely down there. Almost every day the newspapers printed accounts of a decisive victory.

One night, as he lay in bed, the winds had carried to him the clangoring of the church bell as some enthusiast jerked the rope frantically to tell the twisted news of a great battle. This voice of the people rejoicing in the night had made him shiver in a prolonged ecstasy of excitement. Later, he had gone down to his mother's room and had spoken thus: "Ma, I'm going to enlist."

"Henry, don't you be a fool," his mother had replied. She had then covered her face with the quilt. There was an end to the matter for that night.

Nevertheless, the next morning he had gone to a town that was near his mother's farm and had enlisted in a company that was forming there. When he had returned home his mother was milking the brindle cow. Four others stood waiting. "Ma, I've enlisted," he had said to her diffidently. There was a short silence. "The Lord's will be done, Henry," she had finally replied, and had then continued to milk the brindle cow.

When he had stood in the doorway with his soldier's clothes on his back, and with the light of excitement and expectancy in his eyes almost defeating the glow of regret for the home bonds, he had seen two tears leaving their trails on his mother's scarred cheeks.

Still, she had disappointed him by saying nothing whatever about returning with his shield or on it. He had privately primed himself for a beautiful scene. He had prepared certain sentences which he thought could be used with touching effect. But her words destroyed his plans. She had doggedly peeled potatoes and addressed him as follows: "You watch out, Henry, an' take good care of yerself in this here fighting business— you watch out, an' take good care of yerself. Don't go a-thinkin' you can lick the hull rebel army at the start, because yeh can't. Yer jest one little feller amongst a hull lot of others, and yeh've got to keep quiet an' do what they tell yeh. I know how you are, Henry.

"I've knet yeh eight pair of socks, Henry, and I've put in all yer best shirts, because I want my boy to be jest as warm and comf'able as anybody in the army. Whenever they get holes in 'em, I want yeh to send 'em right-away back to me, so's I kin dern 'em.

"An' allus be careful an' choose yer comp'ny. There's lots of bad men in the army, Henry. The army makes 'em wild, and they like nothing better than the job of leading off a young feller like you, as ain't never been away from home much and has allus had a mother, an' a-learning 'em to drink and swear. Keep clear of them folks, Henry. I don't want yeh to ever do anything, Henry, that yeh would be 'shamed to let me know about. Jest think as if I was a-watchin' yeh. If yeh keep that in yer mind allus, I guess yeh'll come out about right.

["Young fellers in the army get awful careless in their ways, Henry. They're away f'm home and they don't have nobody to look after 'em. I'm 'feared fer yeh about that. Yeh ain't never been used to doing for yerself. So yeh must keep writing to me how yer clothes are lasting.]

"Yeh must allus remember yer father, too, child, an' remember he never drunk a drop of licker in his life, and seldom swore a cross oath.

"I don't know what else to tell yeh, Henry, excepting that yeh must never do no shirking, child, on my account. If so be a time comes when yeh have to be kilt or do a mean thing, why, Henry, don't think of anything 'cept what's right, because there's many a woman has to bear up 'ginst sech things these times, and the Lord'll take keer of us all. [Don't fergit to send yer socks to me the minute they git holes in 'em, and here's a little bible I want yeh to take along with yeh, Henry. I don't presume yeh'll be a-setting reading it all day long, child, ner nothin' like that. Many a time, yeh'll fergit yeh got it, I don't doubt. But there'll be many a time, too, Henry, when yeh'll be wanting advice, boy, and all like that, and there'll be no-body round, perhaps, to tell yeh things. Then if yeh take it out, boy, yeh'll find wisdom in it—wisdom in it, Henry—with little or no searching.] Don't forget about the socks and the shirts, child; and I've put a cup of blackberry jam with yer bundle, because I know yeh like it above all things. Good-by, Henry. Watch out, and be a good boy."

He had, of course, been impatient under the ordeal of this speech. It had not been quite what he expected, and he had borne it with an air of irritation. He departed feeling vague relief.

Still, when he had looked back from the gate, he had seen his mother kneeling among the potato parings. Her brown face, upraised, was stained with tears, and her spare form was quiv-ering. He bowed his head and went on, feeling suddenly ashamed of his purposes.

From his home he had gone to the seminary to bid adieu to many schoolmates. They had thronged about him with wonder and admiration. He had felt the gulf now between them and had swelled with calm pride. He and some of his fellows who had donned blue were quite overwhelmed with privileges for all of one afternoon, and it had been a very delicious thing. They had strutted.

A certain light-haired girl had made vivacious fun at his martial spirit, but there was another and darker girl whom he had gazed at steadfastly, and he thought she grew demure and sad at sight of his blue and brass. As he had walked down the path between the rows of oaks, he had turned his head and detected her at a window watching his departure. As he perceived her, she had immediately begun to stare up through the high tree branches at the sky. He had seen a good deal of flurry and haste in her movement as she changed her attitude. He often thought of it.

On the way to Washington his spirit had soared. The regiment was fed and caressed at station after station until the youth had believed that he must be a hero. There was a lavish expenditure of bread and cold meats, coffee, and pickles and cheese. As he basked in the smiles of the girls and was patted and complimented by the old men, he had felt growing within him the strength to do mighty deeds of arms.

After complicated journeyings with many pauses, there had come months of monotonous life in a camp. He had had the belief that real war was a series of death struggles with small time in between for sleep and meals; but since his regiment had come to the field the army had done little but sit still and try to keep warm.

He was brought then gradually back to his old ideas. Greeklike struggles would be no more. Men were better, or more timid. Secular and religious education had effaced the throat-grappling instinct, or else firm finance held in check the passions.

He had grown to regard himself merely as a part of a vast blue demonstration. His province was to look out, as far as he could, for his personal comfort. For recreation he could twiddle his thumbs and speculate on the thoughts which must agitate the minds of the generals. Also, he was drilled and drilled and reviewed, and drilled and drilled and reviewed.

The only foes he had seen were some pickets along the river bank. They were a sun-tanned, philosophical lot, who sometimes shot reflectively at the blue pickets. When reproached for this afterward, they usually expressed sorrow, and swore by their gods that the guns had exploded without their permission. The youth, on guard duty one night, conversed across the stream with one of them. He was a slightly ragged man, who spat skillfully between his shoes and possessed a great fund of bland and infantile assurance. The youth liked him personally.

"Yank," the other had informed him, "yer a right dum good feller." This sentiment, floating to him upon the still air, had made him temporarily regret war.

Various veterans had told him tales. Some talked of gray, bewhiskered hordes who were advancing with relentless curses and chewing tobacco with unspeakable valor; tremendous bodies of fierce soldiery who were sweeping along like the Huns. Others spoke of tattered and eternally hungry men who fired despondent powders. "They'll charge through hell's fire an' brimstone t' git a holt on a haversack, an' sech stomachs ain't a-lastin' long," he was told. From the stories, the youth imagined the red, live bones sticking out through slits in the faded uniforms.

Still, he could not put a whole faith in veterans' tales, for recruits were their prey. They talked much of smoke, fire, and blood, but he could not tell how much might be lies. They persistently yelled, "Fresh fish!" at him, and were in no wise to be trusted.

However, he perceived now that it did not greatly matter what kind of soldiers he was going to fight, so long as they fought, which fact no one disputed. There was a more serious problem. He lay in his bunk pondering upon it. He tried to mathematically prove to himself that he would not run from a battle.

Previously he had never felt obliged to wrestle too seriously with this question. In his life he had taken certain things for granted, never challenging his belief in ultimate success, and bothering little about means and roads. But here he was confronted with a thing of moment. It had suddenly appeared to him that perhaps in a battle he might run. He was forced to admit that as far as war was concerned he knew nothing of himself.

A sufficient time before he would have allowed the problem to kick its heels at the outer portals of his mind, but now he felt compelled to give serious attention to it.

A little panic-fear grew in his mind. As his imagination went forward to a fight, he saw hideous possibilities. He contemplated the lurking menaces of the future, and failed in an effort to see himself standing stoutly in the midst of them. He recalled his visions of broken-bladed glory, but in the shadow of the impending tumult he suspected them to be impossible pictures.

He sprang from the bunk and began to pace nervously to and fro. "Good Lord, what's th' matter with me?" he said aloud.

He felt that in this crisis his laws of life were useless. Whatever he had learned of himself was here of no avail. He was an unknown quantity. He saw that he would again be obliged to experiment as he had in early youth. He must accumulate information of himself, and meanwhile he resolved to remain close upon his guard lest those qualities of which he knew nothing should everlastingly disgrace him. "Good Lord!" he repeated in dismay.

After a time the tall soldier slid dexterously through the hole. The loud private followed. They were wrangling.

"That's all right," said the tall soldier as he entered. He waved his hand expressively. "You can believe me or not, jest as you like. All you got to do is to sit down and wait as quiet as you can. Then pretty soon you'll find out I was right."

His comrade grunted stubbornly. For a moment he seemed to be searching for a formidable reply. Finally he said: "Well, you don't know everything in the world, do you?"

"Didn't say I knew everything in the world," retorted the other sharply. He began to stow various articles snugly into his knapsack.

The youth, pausing in his nervous walk, looked down at the busy figure. "Going to be a battle, sure, is there, Jim?" he asked.

"Of course there is," replied the tall soldier. "Of course there is. You jest wait 'til to-morrow, and you'll see one of the biggest battles ever was. You jest wait."

"Thunder!" said the youth.

"Oh, you'll see fighting this time, my boy, what'll be regular out-and-out fighting," added the tall soldier, with the air of a man who is about to exhibit a battle for the benefit of his friends.

"Huh!" said the loud one from a corner.

"Well," remarked the youth, "like as not this story'll turn out jest like them others did."

"Not much it won't," replied the tall soldier, exasperated. "Not much it won't. Didn't the cavalry all start this morning?" He glared about him. No one denied his statement. "The cavalry started this morning," he continued. "They say there ain't hardly any cavalry left in camp. They're going to Richmond, or some place, while we fight all the Johnnies. It's some dodge like that. The regiment's got orders, too. A feller what seen 'em go to headquarters told me a little while ago. And they're raising blazes all over camp—anybody can see that."

"Shucks!" said the loud one.

The youth remained silent for a time. At last he spoke to the tall soldier. "Jim!"

"What?"

"How do you think the reg'ment 'll do?"

"Oh, they'll fight all right, I guess, after they once get into it," said the other with cold judgment. He made a fine use of the third person. "There's been heaps of fun poked at 'em because they're new, of course, and all that; but they'll fight all right, I guess."

"Think any of the boys 'll run?" persisted the youth.

"Oh, there may be a few of 'em run, but there's them kind in every regiment, 'specially when they first goes under fire," said the other in a tolerant way. "Of course it might happen that the hull kit-and-boodle might start and run, if some big fighting came first-off, and then again they might stay and fight like fun. But you can't bet on nothing. Of course they ain't never been under fire yet, and it ain't likely they'll lick the hull rebel army all-to-oncet the first time; but I think they'll fight better than some, if worse than others. That's the way I figger. They call the reg'ment 'Fresh fish' and everything; but the boys come of good stock, and most of 'em 'll fight like sin after they oncet git shootin'," he added, with a mighty emphasis on the last four words.

"Oh, you think you know—" began the loud soldier with scorn.

The other turned savagely upon him. They had a rapid altercation, in which they fastened upon each other various strange epithets.

The youth at last interrupted them. "Did you ever think you might run yourself, Jim?" he asked. On concluding the sentence he laughed as if he had meant to aim a joke. The loud soldier also giggled.

The tall private waved his hand. "Well," said he profoundly, "I've thought it might get too hot for Jim Conklin in some of them scrimmages, and if a whole lot of boys started and run, why, I s'pose I'd start and run. And if I once started to run, I'd run like the devil, and no mistake. But if everybody was a-standing and a-fighting, why, I'd stand and fight. Be jiminey, I would. I'll bet on it."

"Huh!" said the loud one.

The youth of this tale felt gratitude for these words of his comrade. He had feared that all of the untried men possessed a great and correct confidence. He now was in a measure reassured.

CHAPTER II

The next morning the youth discovered that his tall comrade had been the fast-flying messenger of a mistake. There was much scoffing at the latter by those who had yesterday been firm adherents of his views, and there was even a little sneering by men who had never believed the rumor. The tall one fought with a man from Chatfield Corners and beat him severely.

The youth felt, however, that his problem was in no wise lifted from him. There was, on the contrary, an irritating prolongation. The tale had created in him a great concern for himself. Now, with the newborn question in his mind, he was compelled to sink back into his old place as part of a blue demonstration.

For days he made ceaseless calculations, but they were all wondrously unsatisfactory. He found that he could establish nothing. He finally concluded that the only way to prove himself was to go into the blaze, and then figuratively to watch his legs to discover their merits and faults. He reluctantly admitted that he could not sit still and with a mental slate and pencil derive an answer. To gain it, he must have blaze, blood, and danger, even as a chemist requires this, that, and the other. So he fretted for an opportunity.

Meanwhile he continually tried to measure himself by his comrades. The tall soldier, for one, gave him some assurance. This man's serene unconcern dealt him a measure of confidence, for he had known him since childhood, and from his intimate knowledge he did not see how he could be capable of anything that was beyond him, the youth. Still, he thought that his comrade might be mistaken about himself. Or, on the other hand, he might be a man heretofore doomed to peace and obscurity, but, in reality, made to shine in war.

The youth would have liked to have discovered another who suspected himself. A sympathetic comparison of mental notes would have been a joy to him.

He occasionally tried to fathom a comrade with seductive sentences. He looked about to find men in the proper mood. All attempts failed to bring forth any statement which looked in any way like a confession to those doubts which he privately acknowledged in himself. He was afraid to make an open declaration of his concern, because he dreaded to place some unscrupulous confidant upon the high plane of the unconfessed from which elevation he could be derided.

In regard to his companions his mind wavered between two opinions, according to his mood. Sometimes he inclined to believing them all heroes. In fact, he usually admitted in secret the superior development of the higher qualities in others. He could conceive of men going very insignificantly about the world bearing a load of courage unseen, and, although he had known many of his comrades through boyhood, he began to fear that his judgment of them had been blind. Then, in other moments, he flouted these theories, and assured himself that his fellows were all privately wondering and quaking.

His emotions made him feel strange in the presence of men who talked excitedly of a prospective battle as of a drama they were about to witness, with nothing but eagerness and curiosity apparent in their faces. It was often that he suspected them to be liars.

He did not pass such thoughts without severe condemnation of himself. He dinned reproaches at times. He was convicted by himself of many shameful crimes against the gods of traditions.

In his great anxiety his heart was continually clamoring at what he considered the intolerable slowness of the generals. They seemed content to perch tranquilly on the river bank, and leave him bowed down by the weight of a great problem. He wanted it settled forthwith. He could not long bear such a load, he said. Sometimes his anger at the commanders reached an acute stage, and he grumbled about the camp like a veteran.

One morning, however, he found himself in the ranks of his prepared regiment. The men were whispering speculations and recounting the old rumors. In the gloom before the break of the day their uniforms glowed a deep purple hue. From across the river the red eyes were still peering. In the eastern sky there was a yellow patch like a rug laid for the feet of the coming sun; and against it, black and patternlike, loomed the gigantic figure of the colonel on a gigantic horse.

From off in the darkness came the trampling of feet. The youth could occasionally see dark shadows that moved like monsters. The regiment stood at rest for what seemed a long

time. The youth grew impatient. It was unendurable the way
these affairs were managed. He wondered how long they were
to be kept waiting.

As he looked all about him and pondered upon the mystic
gloom, he began to believe that at any moment the ominous
distance might be aflare, and the rolling crashes of an engagement come to his ears. Staring once at the red eyes across the
river, he conceived them to be growing larger, as the orbs of a
row of dragons advancing. He turned toward the colonel and
saw him lift his gigantic arm and calmly stroke his mustache.

At last he heard from along the road at the foot of the hill
the clatter of a horse's galloping hoofs. It must be the coming
of orders. He bent forward, scarce breathing. The exciting
clickety-click, as it grew louder and louder, seemed to be beating upon his soul. Presently a horseman with jangling equipment drew rein before the colonel of the regiment. The two
held a short, sharp-worded conversation. The men in the foremost ranks craned their necks.

As the horseman wheeled his animal and galloped away he
turned to shout over his shoulder, "Don't forget that box of
cigars!" The colonel mumbled in reply. The youth wondered
what a box of cigars had to do with war.

A moment later the regiment went swinging off into the darkness. It was now like one of those moving monsters wending
with many feet. The air was heavy, and cold with dew. A mass
of wet grass, marched upon, rustled like silk.

There was an occasional flash and glimmer of steel from the
backs of all these huge crawling reptiles. From the road came
creakings and grumblings as some surly guns were dragged
away.

The men stumbled along still muttering speculations. There
was a subdued debate. Once a man fell down, and as he reached
for his rifle a comrade, unseeing, trod upon his hand. He of the
injured fingers swore bitterly and aloud. A low, low, tittering
laugh went among his fellows.

Presently they passed into a roadway and marched forward

with easy strides. A dark regiment moved before them, and from behind also came the tinkle of equipments on the bodies of marching men.

The rushing yellow of the developing day went on behind their backs. When the sunrays at last struck full and mellowingly upon the earth, the youth saw that the landscape was streaked with two long, thin, black columns which disappeared on the brow of a hill in front and rearward vanished in a wood. They were like two serpents crawling from the cavern of the night.

The river was not in view. The tall soldier burst into praises of what he thought to be his powers of perception. ["I told you so, didn't I?"] [1]

Some of the tall one's companions cried with emphasis that they, too, had evolved the same thing, and they congratulated themselves upon it. But there were others who said that the tall one's plan was not the true one at all. They persisted with other theories. There was a vigorous discussion.

The youth took no part in them. As he walked along in careless line he was engaged with his own eternal debate. He could not hinder himself from dwelling upon it. He was despondent and sullen, and threw shifting glances about him. He looked ahead, often expecting to hear from the advance the rattle of firing.

But the long serpents crawled slowly from hill to hill without bluster of smoke. A dun-colored cloud of dust floated away to the right. The sky overhead was of a fairy blue.

The youth studied the faces of his companions, ever on the watch to detect kindred emotions. He suffered disappointment. Some ardor of the air which was causing the veteran commands to move with glee—almost with song—had infected the new regiment. The men began to speak of victory as of a thing they knew. Also, the tall soldier received his vindication. They were certainly going to come around in behind the enemy. They

---

[1] *LV:* We're going up th' river, cut across, an' come around behint 'em *canceled.*

expressed commiseration for that part of the army which had been left upon the river bank, felicitating themselves upon being a part of a blasting host.

The youth, considering himself as separated from the others, was saddened by the blithe and merry speeches that went from rank to rank. The company wags all made their best endeavors. The regiment tramped to the tune of laughter.

The blatant soldier [2] often convulsed whole files by his biting sarcasms aimed at the tall one.

And it was not long before all the men seemed to forget their mission. Whole brigades grinned in unison, and regiments laughed.

A rather fat soldier attempted to pilfer a horse from a dooryard. He planned to load his knapsack upon it. He was escaping with his prize when a young girl rushed from the house and grabbed the animal's mane. There followed a wrangle. The young girl, with pink cheeks and shining eyes, stood like a dauntless statue.

The observant regiment, standing at rest in the roadway, whooped at once, and entered whole-souled upon the side of the maiden. The men became so engrossed in this affair that they entirely ceased to remember their own large war. They jeered the piratical private, and called attention to various defects in his personal appearance; and they were wildly enthusiastic in support of the young girl.[3]

To her, from some distance, came bold advice. "Hit him with a stick."

There were crows and catcalls showered upon him when he retreated without the horse. The regiment rejoiced at his downfall. Loud and vociferous congratulations were showered upon the maiden, who stood panting and regarding the troops with defiance.

---

[2] *LV has:* The loud soldier.

[3] *In LV a canceled passage:*

"Gin' it to 'em, Mary, 'gin' it to 'em."

"Don't let 'em steal yer horse."

"Gin' him thunder."

At nightfall the column broke into regimental pieces, and the fragments went into the fields to camp. Tents sprang up like strange plants. Camp fires, like red, peculiar blossoms, dotted the night.

The youth kept from intercourse with his companions as much as circumstances would allow him. In the evening he wandered a few paces into the gloom. From this little distance the many fires, with the black forms of men passing to and fro before the crimson rays, made weird and satanic effects.

He lay down in the grass. The blades pressed tenderly against his cheek. The moon had been lighted and was hung in a treetop. The liquid stillness of the night enveloping him made him feel vast pity for himself. There was a caress in the soft winds; and the whole mood of the darkness, he thought, was one of sympathy for himself in his distress.

He wished, without reserve, that he was at home again making the endless rounds from the house to the barn, from the barn to the fields, from the fields to the barn, from the barn to the house. He remembered he had often cursed the brindle cow and her mates, and had sometimes flung milking stools. But, from his present point of view, there was a halo of happiness about each of their heads, and he would have sacrificed all the brass buttons on the continent to have been enabled to return to them. He told himself that he was not formed for a soldier. And he mused seriously upon the radical differences between himself and those men who were dodging implike around the fires.

As he mused thus he heard the rustle of grass, and, upon turning his head, discovered the loud soldier. He called out, "Oh, Wilson!"

The latter approached and looked down. "Why, hello, Henry; is it you? What you doing here?"

"Oh, thinking," said the youth.

The other sat down and carefully lighted his pipe. "You're getting blue, my boy. You're looking thundering peeked. What the dickens is wrong with you?"

"Oh, nothing," said the youth.

The loud soldier launched then into the subject of the antici‑ pated fight. "Oh, we've got 'em now!" As he spoke his boyish face was wreathed in a gleeful smile, and his voice had an ex‑ ultant ring. "We've got 'em now. At last, by the eternal thun‑ ders, we'll lick 'em good!"

"If the truth was known," he added, more soberly, "*they've* licked *us* about every clip up to now; but this time—this time— we'll lick 'em good!"

"I thought you was objecting to this march a little while ago," said the youth coldly.

"Oh, it wasn't that," explained the other. "I don't mind march‑ ing, if there's going to be fighting at the end of it. What I hate is this getting moved here and moved there, with no good com‑ ing of it, as far as I can see, excepting sore feet and damned short rations."

"Well, Jim Conklin says we'll get a plenty of fighting this time."

"He's right for once, I guess, though I can't see how it come. This time we're in for a big battle, and we've got the best end of it, certain sure. Gee rod! how we will thump 'em!"

He arose and began to pace to and fro excitedly. The thrill of his enthusiasm made him walk with an elastic step. He was sprightly, vigorous, fiery in his belief in success. He looked into the future with clear, proud eye, and he swore with the air of an old soldier.

The youth watched him for a moment in silence. When he finally spoke his voice was as bitter as dregs. "Oh, you're go‑ ing to do great things, I s'pose!"

The loud soldier blew a thoughtful cloud of smoke from his pipe. "Oh, I don't know," he remarked with dignity; "I don't know. I s'pose I'll do as well as the rest. I'm going to try like thunder." He evidently complimented himself upon the mod‑ esty of this statement.

"How do you know you won't run when the time comes?" asked the youth.

"Run?" said the loud one; "run?—of course not!" He laughed.

"Well," continued the youth, "lots of good-a-'nough men have thought they was going to do great things before the fight, but when the time come they skedaddled."

"Oh, that's all true, I s'pose," replied the other; "but I'm not going to skedaddle. The man that bets on my running will lose his money, that's all." He nodded confidently.

"Oh, shucks!" said the youth. "You ain't the bravest man in the world, are you?"

"No, I ain't," exclaimed the loud soldier [4] indignantly; "and I didn't say I was the bravest man in the world, neither. I said I was going to do my share of fighting—that's what I said. And I am, too. Who are you, anyhow? You talk as if you thought you was Napoleon Bonaparte." He glared at the youth for a moment, and then strode away.

The youth called in a savage voice after his comrade: "Well, you needn't git mad about it!" But the other continued on his way and made no reply.

He felt alone in space when his injured comrade had disappeared. His failure to discover any mite of resemblance in their view points made him more miserable than before. No one seemed to be wrestling with such a terrific personal problem. He was a mental outcast.

He went slowly to his tent and stretched himself on a blanket by the side of the snoring tall soldier. In the darkness he saw visions of a thousand-tongued fear that would babble at his back and cause him to flee, while others were going coolly about their country's business. He admitted that he would not be able to cope with this monster. He felt that every nerve in his body would be an ear to hear the voices, while other men would remain stolid and deaf.

And as he sweated with the pain of these thoughts, he could hear low, serene sentences. "I'll bid five." "Make it six." "Seven." "Seven goes."

---

[4] *LV has:* the blatant soldier.

He stared at the red, shivering reflection of a fire on the white wall of his tent until, exhausted and ill from the monotony of his suffering, he fell asleep.

CHAPTER III

When another night came the columns, changed to purple streaks, filed across two pontoon bridges. A glaring fire wine-tinted the waters of the river. Its rays, shining upon the moving masses of troops, brought forth here and there sudden gleams of silver or gold. Upon the other shore a dark and mysterious range of hills was curved against the sky. The insect voices of the night sang solemnly.

After this crossing the youth assured himself that at any moment they might be suddenly and fearfully assaulted from the caves of the lowering woods. He kept his eyes watchfully upon the darkness.

But his regiment went unmolested to a camping place, and its soldiers slept the brave sleep of wearied men. In the morning they were routed out with early energy, and hustled along a narrow road that led deep into the forest.

It was during this rapid march that the regiment lost many of the marks of a new command.

The men had begun to count the miles upon their fingers, and they grew tired. "Sore feet an' damned short rations, that's all," said the loud soldier. There was [1] perspiration and grumblings. After a time they began to shed their knapsacks. Some tossed them unconcernedly down; others hid them carefully, asserting their plans to return for them at some convenient time. Men extricated themselves from thick shirts. Presently few carried anything but their necessary clothing, blankets, haversacks, canteens, and arms and ammunition. ["Yuh kin now eat, drink, sleep and shoot," said the tall soldier to the youth. "That's all you need. What do you want to do—carry a hotel?"] [2]

---

[1] *Same in LV.*

[2] *FAE has:* "You can now eat and shoot," said the tall soldier to the youth. "That's all you want to do."

There was sudden change from the ponderous infantry of theory to the light and speedy infantry of practice. The regiment, relieved of a burden, received a new impetus. But there was much loss of valuable knapsacks, and, on the whole, very good shirts.

But the regiment was not yet veteranlike in appearance. Veteran regiments in the army were likely to be very small aggregations of men. Once, when the command had first come to the field, some perambulating veterans, noting the length of their column, had accosted them thus: "Hey, fellers, what brigade is that?" And when the men had replied that they formed a regiment and not a brigade, the older soldiers had laughed, and said, "O Gawd!"

Also, there was too great a similarity in the hats. The hats of a regiment should properly represent the history of headgear for a period of years. And, moreover, there were no letters of faded gold speaking from the colors. They were new and beautiful, and the color bearer habitually oiled the pole.

Presently the army again sat down to think. The odor of the peaceful pines was in the men's nostrils. The sound of monotonous axe blows rang through the forest, and the insects, nodding upon their perches, crooned like old women. The youth returned to his theory of a blue demonstration.

One gray dawn, however, he was kicked in the leg by the tall soldier, and then, before he was entirely awake, he found himself running down a wood road in the midst of men who were panting from the first effects of speed. His canteen banged rhythmically upon his thigh, and his haversack bobbed softly. His musket bounced a trifle from his shoulder at each stride and made his cap feel uncertain upon his head.

He could hear the men whisper jerky sentences: "Say—what's all this—about?" "What th' thunder—we—skedaddlin' this way fer?" "Billie—keep off m' feet. Yeh run—like a cow." And the loud soldier's shrill voice could be heard: "What th' devil they in sich a hurry for?"

The youth thought the damp fog of early morning moved

from the rush of a great body of troops. From the distance came a sudden spatter of firing.

He was bewildered. As he ran with his comrades he strenuously tried to think, but all he knew was that if he fell down those coming behind would tread upon him. All his faculties seemed to be needed to guide him over and past obstructions. He felt carried along by a mob.

The sun spread disclosing rays, and, one by one, regiments burst into view like armed men just born of the earth. The youth perceived that the time had come. He was about to be measured. For a moment he felt in the face of his great trial like a babe, and the flesh over his heart seemed very thin. He seized time to look about him calculatingly.

But he instantly saw that it would be impossible for him to escape from the regiment. It inclosed him. And there were iron laws of tradition and law on four sides. He was in a moving box.

As he perceived this fact it occurred to him that he had never wished to come to the war. He had not enlisted of his free will. He had been dragged by the merciless government. And now they were taking him out to be slaughtered.

The regiment slid down a bank and wallowed across a little stream. The mournful current moved slowly on, and from the water, shaded black, some white bubble eyes looked at the men.

As they climbed the hill on the farther side artillery began to boom. Here the youth forgot many things as he felt a sudden impulse of curiosity. He scrambled up the bank with a speed that could not be exceeded by a bloodthirsty man.

He expected a battle scene.

There were some little fields girted and squeezed by a forest. Spread over the grass and in among the tree trunks, he could see knots and waving lines of skirmishers who were running hither and thither and firing at the landscape. A dark battle line lay upon a sunstruck clearing that gleamed orange color. A flag fluttered.

Other regiments floundered up the bank. The brigade was formed in line of battle, and after a pause started slowly through the woods in the rear of the receding skirmishers, who were continally melting into the scene to appear again farther on. They were always busy as bees, deeply absorbed in their little combats.

The youth tried to observe everything. He did not use care to avoid trees and branches, and his forgotten feet were constantly knocking against stones or getting entangled in briers. He was aware that these battalions with their commotions were woven red and startling into the gentle fabric of softened greens and browns. It looked to be a wrong place for a battle field.

The skirmishers in advance fascinated him. Their shots into thickets and at distant and prominent trees spoke to him of tragedies—hidden, mysterious, solemn.

Once the line encountered the body of a dead soldier. He lay upon his back staring at the sky. He was dressed in an awkward suit of yellowish brown. The youth could see that the soles of his shoes had been worn to the thinness of writing paper, and from a great rent in one the dead foot projected piteously. And it was as if fate had betrayed the soldier. In death it exposed to his enemies that poverty which in life he had perhaps concealed from his friends.

The ranks opened covertly to avoid the corpse. The invulnerable dead man forced a way for himself. The youth looked keenly at the ashen face. The wind raised the tawny beard. It moved as if a hand were stroking it. He vaguely desired to walk around and around the body and stare; the impulse of the living to try to read in dead eyes the answer to the Question.

During the march the ardor which the youth had acquired when out of view of the field rapidly faded to nothing. His curiosity was quite easily satisfied. If an intense scene had caught him with its wild swing as he came to the top of the bank, he might have gone roaring on. This advance upon Nature was too calm. He had opportunity to reflect. He had time in which to wonder about himself and to attempt to probe his sensations.

Absurd ideas took hold upon him. He thought that he did not relish the landscape. It threatened him. A coldness swept over his back, and it is true that his trousers felt to him that they were no fit for his legs at all.

A house standing placidly in distant fields had to him an ominous look. The shadows of the woods were formidable. He was certain that in this vista there lurked fierce-eyed hosts. The swift thought came to him that the generals did not know what they were about. It was all a trap. Suddenly those close forests would bristle with rifle barrels. Ironlike brigades would appear in the rear. They were all going to be sacrificed. The generals were stupids. The enemy would presently swallow the whole command. He glared about him, expecting to see the stealthy approach of his death.

He thought that he must break from the ranks and harangue his comrades. They must not all be killed like pigs; and he was sure it would come to pass unless they were informed of these dangers. The generals were idiots to send them marching into a regular pen. There was but one pair of eyes in the corps. He would step forth and make a speech. Shrill and passionate words came to his lips.

The line, broken into moving fragments by the ground, went calmly on through fields and woods. The youth looked at the men nearest him, and saw, for the most part, expressions of deep interest, as if they were investigating something that had fascinated them. One or two stepped with overvaliant airs as if they were already plunged into war. Others walked as upon thin ice. The greater part of the untested men appeared quiet and absorbed. They were going to look at war, the red animal— war, the blood-swollen god. And they were deeply engrossed in this march.

As he looked the youth gripped his outcry at his throat. He saw that even if the men were tottering with fear they would laugh at his warning. They would jeer him, and, if practicable, pelt him with missiles. Admitting that he might be wrong, a frenzied declamation of the kind would turn him into a worm.

He assumed, then, the demeanor of one who knows that he is doomed alone to unwritten responsibilities. He lagged, with tragic glances at the sky.

He was surprised presently by the young lieutenant of his company, who began heartily to beat him with a sword, calling out in a loud and insolent voice: "Come, young man, get up into ranks there. No skulking 'll do here." He mended his pace with suitable haste. And he hated the lieutenant, who had no appreciation of fine minds. He was a mere brute.

After a time the brigade was halted in the cathedral light of a forest. The busy skirmishers were still popping. Through the aisles of the wood could be seen the floating smoke from their rifles. Sometimes it went up in little balls, white and compact.

During this halt many men in the regiment began erecting tiny hills in front of them. They used stones, sticks, earth, and anything they thought might turn a bullet. Some built comparatively large ones, while others seemed content with little ones.

This procedure caused a discussion among the men. Some wished to fight like duelists, believing it to be correct to stand erect and be, from their feet to their foreheads, a mark. They said they scorned the devices of the cautious. But the others scoffed in reply, and pointed to the veterans on the flanks who were digging at the ground like terriers. In a short time there was quite a barricade along the regimental fronts. Directly, however, they were ordered to withdraw from that place.

This astounded the youth. He forgot his stewing over the advance movement. "Well, then, what did they march us out here for?" he demanded of the tall soldier. The latter with calm faith began a heavy explanation, although he had been compelled to leave a little protection of stones and dirt to which he had devoted much care and skill.

When the regiment was aligned in another position each man's regard for his safety caused another line of small intrenchments. They ate their noon meal behind a third one. They were moved from this one also. They were marched from place to place with apparent aimlessness.

The youth had been taught that a man became another thing in a battle. He saw his salvation in such a change. Hence this waiting was an ordeal to him. He was in a fever of impatience. He considered that there was denoted a lack of purpose on the part of the generals. He began to complain to the tall soldier. "I can't stand this much longer," he cried. "I don't see what good it does to make us wear out our legs for nothin'." He wished to return to camp, knowing that this affair was a blue demonstration; or else to go into a battle and discover that he had been a fool in his doubts, and was, in truth, a man of traditional courage. The strain of present circumstances he felt to be intolerable.

The philosophical tall soldier measured a sandwich of cracker and pork and swallowed it in a nonchalant manner. "Oh, I suppose we must go reconnoitering around the country jest to keep 'em from getting too close, or to develop 'em, or something."

"Huh!" said the loud soldier.

"Well," cried the youth, still fidgeting, "I'd rather do anything 'most than go tramping 'round the country all day doing no good to nobody and jest tiring ourselves out."

"So would I," said the loud soldier. "It ain't right. I tell you if anybody with any sense was a-runnin' this army it—"

"Oh, shut up!" roared the tall private. "You little fool. You little damn' cuss. You ain't had that there coat and them pants on for six months, and yet you talk as if—"

"Well, I wanta do some fighting anyway," interrupted the other. "I didn't come here to walk. I could 'ave walked to home —'round and 'round the barn, if I jest wanted to walk."

The tall one, red-faced, swallowed another sandwich as if taking poison in despair.

But gradually, as he chewed, his face became again quiet and contented. He could not rage in fierce argument in the presence of such sandwiches. During his meals he always wore an air of blissful contemplation of the food he had swallowed. His spirit seemed then to be communing with the viands.

He accepted new environment and circumstance with great coolness, eating from his haversack at every opportunity. On the march he went along with the stride of a hunter, objecting to neither gait nor distance. And he had not raised his voice when he had been ordered away from three little protective piles of earth and stone, each of which had been an engineering feat worthy of being made sacred to the name of his grandmother.

In the afternoon the regiment went out over the same ground it had taken in the morning. The landscape then ceased to threaten the youth. He had been close to it and become familiar with it.

When, however, they began to pass into a new region, his fears of stupidity and incompetence reassailed him, but this time he doggedly let them babble. He was occupied with his problem, and in his desperation he concluded that the stupidity did not greatly matter.

Once he thought he had concluded that it would be better to get killed directly and end his troubles. Regarding death thus out of the corner of his eye, he conceived it to be nothing but rest, and he was filled with a momentary astonishment that he should have made an extraordinary commotion over the mere matter of getting killed. He would die; he would go to some place where he would be understood. It was useless to expect appreciation of his profound and fine senses from such men as the lieutenant. He must look to the grave for comprehension.

The [unceasing] skirmish fire increased to a long clattering sound. With it was mingled far-away cheering. A battery spoke.

Directly the youth would see the skirmishers running. They were pursued by the sound of musketry fire. After a time the hot, dangerous flashes of the rifles were visible. Smoke clouds went slowly and insolently across the fields like observant phantoms. The din became crescendo, like the roar of an on-coming train.

A brigade ahead of them and on the right went into action with a rending roar. It was as if it had exploded. And there-after it lay stretched in the distance behind a long gray wall, that one was obliged to look twice at to make sure that it was smoke.

The youth, forgetting his neat plan of getting killed, gazed spell bound. His eyes grew wide and busy with the action of the scene. His mouth was a little ways open.

Of a sudden he felt a heavy and sad hand laid upon his shoulder. Awakening from his trance of observation he turned and beheld the loud soldier.

"It's my first and last battle, old boy," said the latter, with intense gloom. He was quite pale and his girlish lip was trem-bling.

"Eh?" murmured the youth in great astonishment.

"It's my first and last battle, old boy," continued the loud sol-dier. "Something tells me—"

"What?"

"I'm a gone coon this first time and—and I w-want you to take these here things—to—my—folks." He ended in a quavering sob of pity for himself. He handed the youth a little packet done up in a yellow envelope.

"Why, what the devil—" began the youth again.

But the other gave him a glance as from the depths of a tomb, and raised his limp hand in a prophetic manner and turned away.

CHAPTER IV

The brigade was halted in the fringe of a grove. The men crouched among the trees and pointed their restless guns out at the fields. They tried to look beyond the smoke.

Out of this haze they could see running men. Some shouted information and gestured as they hurried.

The men of the new regiment watched and listened eagerly,

while their tongues ran on in gossip of the battle. They mouthed rumors that had flown like birds out of the unknown.

"They say Perry [1] has been driven in with big loss."

"Yes, Carrott went t' th' hospital. He said he was sick. That smart lieutenant is commanding 'G' Company. Th' boys say they won't be under Carrott no more if they all have t' desert. They allus knew he was a—" [2]

"Hannises' batt'ry is took."

"It ain't either. I saw Hannises' batt'ry off on th' left not more'n fifteen minutes ago."

"Well—"

"Th' general, he ses he is goin' t' take th' hull cammand of th' 304th [3] when we go inteh action, an' then he ses we'll do sech fightin' as never another one reg'ment done." [4]

"They say we're catchin' it over on th' left. They say th' enemy driv' our line inteh a devil of a swamp an' took Hannises' batt'ry."

"No sech thing. Hannises' batt'ry was 'long here 'bout a minute ago."

"That young Hasbrouck, he makes a good off'cer. He ain't afraid 'a nothin'."

"I met one of th' 148th Maine boys an' he ses his brigade fit th' hull rebel army fer four hours over on th' turnpike road an' killed about five thousand of 'em. He ses one more sech fight as that an' th' war 'll be over."

---

[1] *LV: Perrett canceled.*

[2] *In LV a canceled passage:* "Dern this bein' in reserve, anyhouse. I didnt come here to be in reserve. I—"

[3] *This 304th regiment is purely imaginary. There was, however, a 34th New York Volunteers under General John Bullock Van Petten, subsequently professor of history and elocution at Claverack Academy, where Crane went to school.*

[4] *In LV a canceled passage:*
"Th' boys of th' 47th, they took a hull string of rifle-pits."
"It wasn't th' 47th [at all *canceled*]. It was th' 99th Vermont."
"There haint nobody took no rifle-pits. Th' 47th driv a lot a Johnnies from behint a fence."
"Well—"

"Bill wasn't scared either. No, sir! It wasn't that. Bill ain't a-gittin' scared easy. He was jest mad, that's what he was. When that feller trod on his hand, he up an' sed that he was willin' t' give his hand t' his country, but he be dumbed if he was goin' t' have every dumb bushwacker [5] in th' kentry walkin' 'round on it. So he went t' th' hospital disregardless of th' fight. Three fingers was crunched. Th' dern doctor wanted t' amputate 'm, an' Bill, he raised a heluva row, I hear. He's a funny feller."

["Hear that what the ol' colonel ses, boys. He ses he'll shoot th' first man what'll turn an' run."

"He'd better try it. I'd like t' see him shoot at *me*."

"He wants t' look fer his *own* self. *He* don't wanta go 'round talkin' big."

"They say Perry's division's a-givin' 'em thunder."

"Ed Williams over in Company A, he ses the rebs 'll all drop their guns an' run an' holler if we onct give 'em one good lickin'."

"Oh, thunder, Ed Williams, what does he know? Ever since he got shot at on picket he's been runnin' th' war."

"Well, he—"

"Hear th' news, boys? Corkright's crushed th' hull rebel right an' captured two hull divisions. We'll be back in winter quarters by a short cut t'-morrah."

"I tell yeh I've been all over that there kentry where th' rebel right is an' it's th' nastiest part th' rebel line. It's all mussed up with hills an' little damn creeks. I'll bet m' shirt Corkright never harmed 'em down there."

"Well he's a fighter an' if they could be licked, he'd lick 'em."]

The din in front swelled to a tremendous chorus. The youth and his fellows were frozen to silence. They could see a flag that tossed in the smoke angrily. Near it were the blurred and agitated forms of troops. There came a turbulent stream of

---

[5] bushwacker—*an unenlisted combatant, a Confederate guerrilla.*

men across the fields. A battery changing position at a frantic gallop scattered the stragglers right and left.[6]

A shell screaming like a storm banshee went over the huddled heads of the reserves. It landed in the grove, and exploding redly flung the brown earth. There was a little shower of pine needles.

Bullets began to whistle among the branches and nip at the trees. Twigs and leaves came sailing down. It was as if a thousand axes, wee and invisible, were being wielded. Many of the men were constantly dodging and ducking their heads.

The lieutenant of the youth's company was shot in the hand. He began to swear so wondrously that a nervous laugh went along the regimental line. The officer's profanity sounded conventional. It relieved the tightened senses of the new men. It was as if he had hit his fingers with a tack hammer at home.

He held the wounded member carefully away from his side so that the blood would not drip upon his trousers.

The captain of the company, tucking his sword under his arm, produced a handkerchief and began to bind with it the lieutenant's wound. And they disputed as to how the binding should be done.

The battle flag in the distance jerked about madly. It seemed to be struggling to free itself from an agony. The billowing smoke was filled with horizontal flashes.

Men running swiftly emerged from it. They grew in numbers until it was seen that the whole command was fleeing. The flag suddenly sank down as if dying. Its motion as it fell was a gesture of despair.

Wild yells came from behind the walls of smoke. A sketch in gray and red dissolved into a moblike body of men who galloped like wild horses.

The veteran regiments on the right and left of the 304th im-

---

[6] *This paragraph and subsequent ones are missing from Chapter iv of Manuscript LV. The matter appearing in the text, however, apparently follows the earlier draft, Manuscript SV, in so far as can be judged by the single passage belonging to Chapter iv extant in SV, namely page 36 (in Crane's pagination of SV).*

mediately began to jeer. With the passionate song of the bullets and the banshee shrieks of shells were mingled loud catcalls and bits of facetious advice concerning places of safety.

But the new regiment was breathless with horror. "Gawd! Saunders's got crushed!" whispered the man at the youth's elbow. They shrank back and crouched as if compelled to await a flood.

The youth shot a swift glance along the blue ranks of the regiment. The profiles were motionless, carven; and afterward he remembered that the color sergeant was standing with his legs apart, as if he expected to be pushed to the ground.

The following throng went whirling around the flank. Here and there were officers carried along on the stream like exasperated chips. They were striking about them with their swords and with their left fists, punching every head they could reach. They cursed like highwaymen.

A mounted officer displayed the furious anger of a spoiled child. He raged with his head, his arms, and his legs.

Another, the commander of the brigade, was galloping about bawling. His hat was gone and his clothes were awry. He resembled a man who has come from bed to go to a fire. The hoofs of his horse often threatened the heads of the running men, but they scampered with singular fortune. In this rush they were apparently all deaf and blind. They heeded not the largest and longest of the oaths that were thrown at them from all directions.

Frequently over this tumult could be heard the grim jokes of the critical veterans; but the retreating men apparently were not even conscious of the presence of an audience.

The battle reflection that shone for an instant in the faces on the mad current made the youth feel that forceful hands from heaven would not have been able to have held him in place if he could have got intelligent control of his legs.

There was an appalling imprint upon these faces. The struggle in the smoke had pictured an exaggeration of itself on the bleached cheeks and in the eyes wild with one desire.

The sight of this stampede exerted a floodlike force that seemed able to drag sticks and stones and men from the ground. They of the reserves had to hold on. They grew pale and firm, and red and quaking.

The youth achieved one little thought in the midst of this chaos. The composite monster which had caused the other troops to flee had not then appeared. He resolved to get a view of it, and then, he thought he might very likely run better than the best of them.

CHAPTER V

There were moments of waiting. The youth thought of the village street at home before the arrival of the circus parade on a day in the spring. He remembered how he had stood, a small, thrillful boy, prepared to follow the dingy lady upon the white horse, or the band in its faded chariot. He saw the yellow road, the lines of expectant people, and the sober houses. He particularly remembered an old fellow who used to sit upon a cracker box in front of the store and feign to despise such exhibitions. A thousand details of color and form surged in his mind. The old fellow upon the cracker box appeared in middle prominence.

Some one cried, "Here they come!"

There was rustling and muttering among the men. They displayed a feverish desire to have every possible cartridge ready to their hands. The boxes were pulled around into various positions, and adjusted with great care. It was as if seven hundred new bonnets were being tried on.

The tall soldier, having prepared his rifle, produced a red handkerchief of some kind. He was engaged in knitting it about his throat with exquisite attention to its position, when the cry was repeated up and down the line in a muffled roar of sound.

"Here they come! Here they come!" Gun locks clicked.

Across the smoke-infested fields came a brown swarm of running men who were giving shrill yells. They came on, stooping and swinging their rifles at all angles. A flag, tilted forward, sped near the front.

As he caught sight of them the youth was momentarily startled by a thought that perhaps his gun was not loaded. He stood trying to rally his faltering intellect so that he might recollect the moment when he had loaded, but he could not.

A hatless general pulled his dripping horse to a stand near the colonel of the 304th. He shook his fist in the other's face. "You've got to hold 'em back!" he shouted, savagely; "you've got to hold 'em back!"

In his agitation the colonel began to stammer. "A-all r-right, General, all right, by Gawd! We-we'll do our—we-we'll d-d-do —do our best, General." The general made a passionate gesture and galloped away. The colonel, perchance to relieve his feelings, began to scold like a wet parrot. The youth, turning swiftly to make sure that the rear was unmolested, saw the commander regarding his men in a highly resentful manner, as if he regretted above everything his association with them.

The man at the youth's elbow was mumbling, as if to himself: "Oh, we're in for it now! oh, we're in for it now!"

The captain of the company had been pacing excitedly to and fro in the rear. He coaxed in schoolmistress fashion, as to a congregation of boys with primers. His talk was an endless repetition. "Reserve your fire, boys—don't shoot till I tell you— save your fire—wait till they get close up—don't be damned fools—"

Perspiration streamed down the youth's face, which was soiled like that of a weeping urchin. He frequently, with a nervous movement, wiped his eyes with his coat sleeve. His mouth was still a little ways open.

He got the one glance at the foe-swarming field in front of him, and instantly ceased to debate the question of his piece being loaded. Before he was ready to begin—before he had announced to himself that he was about to fight—he threw the obedient, well-balanced rifle into position and fired a first wild shot. Directly he was working at his weapon like an automatic affair.

He suddenly lost concern for himself, and forgot to look at a menacing fate. He became not a man but a member. He felt that something of which he was a part—a regiment, an army, a cause, or a country—was in a crisis. He was welded into a common personality which was dominated by a single desire. For some moments he could not flee no more than a little finger can commit a revolution from a hand.

If he had thought the regiment was about to be annihilated perhaps he could have amputated himself from it. But its noise gave him assurance. The regiment was like a firework that, once ignited, proceeds superior to circumstances until its blazing vitality fades. It wheezed and banged with a mighty power. He pictured the ground before it as strewn with the discomfited.

There was a consciousness always of the presence of his comrades about him. He felt the subtle battle brotherhood more potent even than the cause for which they were fighting. It was a mysterious fraternity born of the smoke and danger of death.

He was at a task. He was like a carpenter who has made many boxes, making still another box, only there was furious haste in his movements. He, in his thought,[1] was careering off in other places, even as the carpenter who as he works whistles and thinks of his friend or his enemy, his home or a saloon. And these jolted dreams were never perfect to him afterward, but remained a mass of blurred shapes.

Presently he began to feel the effects of the war atmosphere—a blistering sweat, a sensation that his eyeballs were about to crack like hot stones. A burning roar filled his ears.

Following this came a red rage. He developed the acute exasperation of a pestered animal, a well-meaning cow worried by dogs. He had a mad feeling against his rifle, which could only be used against one life at a time. He wished to rush for-

---

[1] *LV:* thoughts.

ward and strangle with his fingers. He craved a power that
would enable him to make a world-sweeping gesture and brush
all back. His impotency appeared to him, and made his rage
into that of a driven beast.

Buried in the smoke of many rifles his anger was directed not
so much against men whom he knew were rushing toward him
as against the swirling battle phantoms which were choking
him, stuffing their smoke robes down his parched throat. He
fought frantically for respite for his senses, for air, as a babe
being smothered attacks the deadly blankets.

There was a blare of heated rage mingled with a certain expression of intentness on all faces. Many of the men were
making low-toned noises with their mouths, and these subdued
cheers, snarls, imprecations, prayers, made a wild, barbaric
song that went as an undercurrent of sound, strange and chant-
like with the resounding chords of the war march. The man at
the youth's elbow was babbling. In it there was something soft
and tender like the monologue of a babe. The tall soldier was
swearing in a loud voice. From his lips came a black procession
of curious oaths. Of a sudden another broke out in a querulous
way like a man who has mislaid his hat. "Well, why don't
they support us? Why don't they send supports? Do they
think—"

The youth in his battle sleep heard this as one who dozes
hears.

There was a singular absence of heroic poses. The men bending and surging in their haste and rage were in every impossible
attitude. The steel ramrods clanked and clanged with incessant
din as the men pounded them furiously into the hot rifle barrels.
The flaps of the cartridge boxes were all unfastened, and
bobbed idiotically with each movement. The rifles, once loaded,
were jerked to the shoulder and fired without apparent aim into
the smoke or at one of the blurred and shifting forms which
upon the field before the regiment had been growing larger
and larger like puppets under a magician's hand.

The officers, at their intervals, rearward, neglected to stand in picturesque attitudes. They were bobbing to and fro roaring directions and encouragements. The dimensions of their howls were extraordinary. They expended their lungs with prodigal wills. And often they nearly stood upon their heads in their anxiety to observe the enemy on the other side of the tumbling smoke.

The lieutenant of the youth's company had encountered a soldier who had fled screaming at the first volley of his comrades. Behind the lines these two were acting a little isolated scene. The man was blubbering and staring with sheeplike eyes at the lieutenant, who had seized him by the collar and was pommeling him. He drove him back into the ranks with many blows. The soldier went mechanically, dully, with his animal-like eyes upon the officer. Perhaps there was to him a divinity expressed in the voice of the other—stern, hard, with no reflection of fear in it. He tried to reload his gun, but his shaking hands prevented. The lieutenant was obliged to assist him.

The men dropped here and there like bundles. The captain of the youth's company had been killed in an early part of the action. His body lay stretched out in the position of a tired man resting, but upon his face there was an astonished and sorrowful look, as if he thought some friend had done him an ill turn. The babbling man was grazed by a shot that made the blood stream widely down his face. He clapped both hands to his head. "Oh!" he said, and ran. Another grunted suddenly as if he had been struck by a club in the stomach. He sat down and gazed ruefully. In his eyes there was mute, indefinite reproach. Farther up the line a man, standing behind a tree, had had his knee joint splintered by a ball. Immediately he had dropped his rifle and gripped the tree with both arms. And there he remained, clinging desperately and crying for assistance that he might withdraw his hold upon the tree.

At last an exultant yell went along the quivering line. The firing dwindled from an uproar to a last vindictive popping. As the smoke slowly eddied away, the youth saw that the charge had been repulsed. The enemy were scattered into reluctant groups. He saw a man climb to the top of the fence, straddle the rail, and fire a parting shot. The waves had receded, leaving bits of dark *débris* upon the ground.

Some in the regiment began to whoop frenziedly. Many were silent. Apparently they were trying to contemplate themselves.

After the fever had left his veins, the youth thought that at last he was going to suffocate. He became aware of the foul atmosphere in which he had been struggling. He was grimy and dripping like a laborer in a foundry. He grasped his canteen and took a long swallow of the warmed water.

A sentence with variations went up and down the line. "Well, we've helt 'em back. We've helt 'em back; derned if we haven't." The men said it blissfully, leering at each other with dirty smiles.

The youth turned to look behind him and off to the right and off to the left. He experienced the joy of a man who at last finds leisure in which to look about him.

Under foot there were a few ghastly forms motionless. They lay twisted in fantastic contortions. Arms were bent and heads were turned in incredible ways. It seemed that the dead men must have fallen from some great height to get into such positions. They looked to be dumped out upon the ground from the sky.

From a position in the rear of the grove a battery was throwing shells over it. The flash of the guns startled the youth at first. He thought they were aimed directly at him. Through the trees he watched the black figures of the gunners as they worked swiftly and intently. Their labor seemed a complicated thing. He wondered how they could remember its formula in the midst of confusion.

The guns squatted in a row like savage chiefs. They argued with abrupt violence. It was a grim pow-wow. Their busy servants ran hither and thither.

A small procession of wounded men were going drearily

toward the rear. It was a flow of blood from the torn body of the brigade.

To the right and to the left were the dark lines of other troops. Far in front he thought he could see lighter masses protruding in points from the forest. They were suggestive of unnumbered thousands.

Once he saw a tiny battery go dashing along the line of the horizon. The tiny riders were beating the tiny horses.

From a sloping hill came the sound of cheerings and clashes. Smoke welled slowly through the leaves.

Batteries were speaking with thunderous oratorical effort. Here and there were flags, the red in the stripes dominating. They splashed bits of warm color upon the dark lines of troops.

The youth felt the old thrill at the sight of the emblem. They were like beautiful birds strangely undaunted in a storm.

As he listened to the din from the hillside, to a deep pulsating thunder that came from afar to the left, and to the lesser clamors which came from many directions, it occurred to him that they were fighting, too, over there, and over there, and over there. Heretofore he had supposed that all the battle was directly under his nose.

As he gazed around him the youth felt a flash of astonishment at the blue, pure sky and the sun gleamings on the trees and fields. It was surprising that Nature had gone tranquilly on with her golden process in the midst of so much devilment.

CHAPTER VI

The youth awakened slowly. He came gradually back to a position from which he could regard himself. For moments he had been scrutinizing his person in a dazed way as if he had never before seen himself. Then he picked up his cap from the ground. He wriggled in his jacket to make a more comfortable fit, and kneeling relaced his shoe. He thoughtfully mopped his reeking features.

So it was all over at last! The supreme trial had been passed. The red, formidable difficulties of war had been vanquished.

He went into an ecstasy of self-satisfaction. He had the most delightful sensations of his life. Standing as if apart from himself, he viewed that last scene. He perceived that the man who had fought thus was magnificent.

He felt that he was a fine fellow. He saw himself even with those ideals which he had considered as far beyond him. He smiled in deep gratification.

Upon his fellows he beamed tenderness and good will. "Gee! ain't it hot, hey?" he said affably to a man who was polishing his streaming face with his coat sleeves.

"You bet!" said the other, grinning sociably. "I never seen sech dumb hotness." He sprawled out luxuriously on the ground. "Gee, yes! An' I hope we don't have no more fightin' till a week from Monday."

There were some handshakings and deep speeches with men whose features were familiar, but with whom the youth now felt the bonds of tied hearts. He helped a cursing comrade to bind up a wound of the shin.

But, of a sudden, cries of amazement broke out along the ranks of the new regiment. "Here they come ag'in! Here they come ag'in!" The man who had sprawled upon the ground started up and said, "Gosh!"

The youth turned quick eyes upon the field. He discerned forms begin to swell in masses out of a distant wood. He again saw the tilted flag speeding forward.

The shells, which had ceased to trouble the regiment for a time, came swirling again, and exploded in the grass or among the leaves of the trees. They looked to be strange war flowers bursting into fierce bloom.

The men groaned. The luster faded from their eyes. Their smudged countenances now expressed a profound dejection. They moved their stiffened bodies slowly, and watched in sullen mood the frantic approach of the enemy. The slaves toiling in the temple of this god began to feel rebellion at his harsh tasks.

They fretted and complained each to each. "Oh, say, this is

too much of a good thing! Why can't somebody send us supports?"

"We ain't never goin' to stand this second banging. I didn't come here to fight the hull damn' rebel army."

There was one who raised a doleful cry. "I wish Bill Smithers had trod on my hand, insteader me treddin' on his'n." The sore joints of the regiment creaked as it painfully floundered into position to repulse.

The youth stared. Surely, he thought, this impossible thing was not about to happen. He waited as if he expected the enemy to suddenly stop, apologize, and retire bowing. It was all a mistake.

But the firing began somewhere on the regimental line and ripped along in both directions. The level sheets of flame developed great clouds of smoke that tumbled and tossed in the mild wind near the ground for a moment, and then rolled through the ranks as through a gate. The clouds were tinged an earthlike yellow in the sunrays and in the shadow were a sorry blue. The flag was sometimes eaten and lost in this mass of vapor, but more often it projected, sun-touched, resplendent.

Into the youth's eyes there came a look that one can see in the orbs of a jaded horse. His neck was quivering with nervous weakness and the muscles of his arms felt numb and bloodless. His hands, too, seemed large and awkward as if he was wearing invisible mittens. And there was a great uncertainty about his knee joints.

The words that comrades had uttered previous to the firing began to recur to him. "Oh, say, this is too much of a good thing! What do they take us for—why don't they send supports? I didn't come here to fight the hull damned rebel army."

He began to exaggerate the endurance, the skill, and the valor of those who were coming. Himself reeling from exhaustion, he was astonished beyond measure at such persistency. They must be machines of steel. It was very gloomy struggling against such affairs, wound up perhaps to fight until sundown.

He slowly lifted his rifle and catching a glimpse of the thick·

spread field he blazed at a cantering cluster. He stopped then and began to peer as best he could through the smoke. He caught changing views of the ground covered with men who were all running like pursued imps, and yelling.[1]

To the youth it was an onslaught of redoubtable dragons. He became like the man who lost his legs at the approach of the red and green monster. He waited in a sort of a horrified, listening attitude. He seemed to shut his eyes and wait to be gobbled.

A man near him who up to this time had been working feverishly at his rifle suddenly stopped and ran with howls. A lad whose face had borne an expression of exalted courage, the majesty of he who dares give his life, was, at an instant, smitten abject. He blanched like one who has come to the edge of a cliff at midnight and is suddenly made aware. There was a revelation. He, too, threw down his gun and fled. There was no shame in his face. He ran like a rabbit.

Others began to scamper away through the smoke. The youth turned his head, shaken from his trance by this movement as if the regiment was leaving him behind. He saw the few fleeting forms.

He yelled then with fright and swung about. For a moment, in the great clamor, he was like a proverbial chicken. He lost the direction of safety. Destruction threatened him from all points.

Directly he began to speed toward the rear in great leaps. His rifle and cap were gone. His unbuttoned coat bulged in the wind. The flap of his cartridge box bobbed wildly, and his canteen, by its slender cord, swung out behind. On his face was all the horror of those things which he imagined.

The lieutenant sprang forward bawling. The youth saw his features wrathfully red, and saw him make a dab with his sword. His one thought of the incident was that the lieutenant

---

[1] *In LV a canceled passage:* It seemed that this swift swarming crowd, crying savagely, would surely break the brittle line of new men in blue.

was a peculiar creature to feel interested in such matters upon this occasion.

He ran like a blind man. Two or three times he fell down. Once he knocked his shoulder so heavily against a tree that he went headlong.

Since he had turned his back upon the fight his fears had been wondrously magnified. Death about to thrust him between the shoulder blades was far more dreadful than death about to smite him between the eyes. When he thought of it later, he conceived the impression that it is better to view the appalling than to be merely within hearing. The noises of the battle were like stones; he believed himself liable to be crushed.

As he ran on he mingled with others. He dimly saw men on his right and on his left, and he heard footsteps behind him. He thought that all the regiment was fleeing, pursued by these ominous crashes.

In his flight the sound of these following footsteps gave him his one meager relief. He felt vaguely that death must make a first choice of the men who were nearest; the initial morsels for the dragons would be then those who were following him. So he displayed the zeal of an insane sprinter in his purpose to keep them in the rear. There was a race.

As he, leading, went across a little field, he found himself in a region of shells. They hurtled over his head with long wild screams. As he listened he imagined them to have rows of cruel teeth that grinned at him. Once one lit before him and the livid lightning of the explosion effectually barred the way in his chosen direction. He groveled on the ground and then springing up went careering off through some bushes.

He experienced a thrill of amazement when he came within view of a battery in action. The men there seemed to be in conventional moods, altogether unaware of the impending annihilation. The battery was disputing with a distant antagonist and the gunners were wrapped in admiration of their shooting. They were continually bending in coaxing postures over the guns. They seemed to be patting them on the back and encouraging them with words. The guns, stolid and undaunted, spoke with dogged valor.

The precise gunners were coolly enthusiastic. They lifted their eyes every chance to the smoke-wreathed hillock from whence the hostile battery addressed them. The youth pitied them as he ran. Methodical idiots! Machinelike fools! The refined joy of planting shells in the midst of the other battery's formation would appear a little thing when the infantry came swooping out of the woods.

The face of a youthful rider, who was jerking his frantic horse with an abandon of temper he might display in a placid barnyard, was impressed deeply upon his mind. He knew that he looked upon a man who would presently be dead.

Too, he felt a pity for the guns, standing, six good comrades, in a bold row.

He saw a brigade going to the relief of its pestered fellows. He scrambled upon a wee hill and watched it sweeping finely, keeping formation in difficult places. The blue of the line was crusted with steel color, and the brilliant flags projected. Officers were shouting.

This sight also filled him with wonder. The brigade was hurrying briskly to be gulped into the infernal mouths of the war god. What manner of men were they, anyhow? Ah, it was some wondrous breed! Or else they didn't comprehend—the fools.

A furious order caused commotion in the artillery. An officer on a bounding horse made maniacal motions with his arms. The teams went swinging up from the rear, the guns were whirled about, and the battery scampered away. The cannon with their noses poked slantingly at the ground grunted and grumbled like stout men, brave but with objections to hurry.

The youth went on, moderating his pace since he had left the place of noises.

Later he came upon a general of division seated upon a horse that pricked its ears in an interested way at the battle. There was a great gleaming of yellow and patent leather about the saddle and bridle. The quiet man astride looked mouse-colored upon such a splendid charger.

A jingling staff was galloping hither and thither. Sometimes the general was surrounded by horsemen and at other times he was quite alone. He looked to be much harassed. He had the appearance of a business man whose market is swinging up and down.

The youth went slinking around this spot. He went as near as he dared trying to overhear words. Perhaps the general, unable to comprehend chaos, might call upon him for information. And he could tell him. He knew all concerning it. Of a surety the force was in a fix, and any fool could see that if they did not retreat while they had opportunity—why—

He felt that he would like to thrash the general, or at least approach and tell him in plain words exactly what he thought him to be. It was criminal to stay calmly in one spot and make no effort to stay destruction. He loitered in a fever of eagerness for the division commander to apply to him.

As he warily moved about, he heard the general call out irritably: "Tompkins, go over an' see Taylor, an' tell him not t' be in such an all-fired hurry; tell him t' halt his brigade in th' edge of th' woods; tell him t' detach a reg'ment—say I think th' center 'll break if we don't help it out some; tell him t' hurry up."

A slim youth on a fine chestnut horse caught these swift words from the mouth of his superior. He made his horse bound into a gallop almost from a walk in his haste to go upon his mission. There was a cloud of dust.

A moment later the youth saw the general bounce excitedly in his saddle.

"Yes, by heavens, they have!" The officer leaned forward. His face was aflame with excitement. "Yes, by heavens, they've held 'im! They've held 'im!"

He began to blithely roar at his staff: "We'll wallop 'im now. We'll wallop 'im now. We've got 'em sure." He turned suddenly upon an aid: "Here—you—Jones—quick—ride after Tompkins—

see Taylor—tell him t' go in—everlastingly—like blazes—anything."

As another officer sped his horse after the first messenger, the general beamed upon the earth like a sun. In his eyes was a desire to chant a pæan. He kept repeating, "They've held 'em, by heavens!"

His excitement made his horse plunge, and he merrily kicked and swore at it. He held a little carnival of joy on horseback.

CHAPTER VII

The youth cringed as if discovered in a crime. By heavens, they had won after all! The imbecile line had remained and become victors. He could hear cheering.

He lifted himself upon his toes and looked in the direction of the fight. A yellow fog lay wallowing on the treetops. From beneath it came the clatter of musketry. Hoarse cries told of an advance.

He turned away amazed and angry. He felt that he had been wronged.

He had fled, he told himself, because annihilation approached. He had done a good part in saving himself, who was a little piece of the army. He had considered the time, he said, to be one in which it was the duty of every little piece to rescue itself if possible. Later the officers could fit the little pieces together again, and make a battle front. If none of the little pieces were wise enough to save themselves from the flurry of death at such a time, why, then, where would be the army? It was all plain that he had proceeded according to very correct and commendable rules. His actions had been sagacious things. They had been full of strategy. They were the work of a master's legs.

Thoughts of his comrades came to him. The brittle blue line had withstood the blows and won. He grew bitter over it. It seemed that the blind ignorance and stupidity of those little pieces had betrayed him. He had been overturned and crushed by their lack of sense in holding the position, when intelligent deliberation would have convinced them that it was impossible. He, the enlightened man who looks afar in the dark, had fled because of his superior perceptions and knowledge. He felt a great anger against his comrades. He knew it could be proved that they had been fools.

He wondered what they would remark when later he appeared in camp. His mind heard howls of derision. Their destiny would not enable them to understand his sharper point of view.

He began to pity himself acutely. He was ill used. He was trodden beneath the feet of an iron injustice. He had proceeded with wisdom and from the most righteous motives under heaven's blue only to be frustrated by hateful circumstances.

A dull, animal-like rebellion against his fellows, war in the abstract, and fate grew within him. He shambled along with bowed head, his brain in a tumult of agony and despair. When he looked loweringly up, quivering at each sound, his eyes had the expression of those of a criminal who thinks his guilt and his punishment great, and knows that he can find no words; [who, through his suffering, thinks that he peers into the core of things and sees that the judgment of man is thistledown in wind].

He went from the fields into a thick woods, as if resolved to bury himself. He wished to get out of hearing of the crackling shots which were to him like voices.

The ground was cluttered with vines and bushes, and the trees grew close and spread out like bouquets. He was obliged to force his way with much noise. The creepers, catching against his legs, cried out harshly as their sprays were torn from the barks of trees. The swishing saplings tried to make known his presence to the world. He could not conciliate the forest. As he made his way, it was always calling out protesta- tions. When he separated embraces of trees and vines the disturbed foliages waved their arms and turned their face leaves toward him. He dreaded lest these noisy motions and cries should bring men to look at him. So he went far, seeking dark and intricate places.

After a time the sound of musketry grew faint and the cannon boomed in the distance. The sun, suddenly apparent, blazed among the trees. The insects were making rhythmical noises. They seemed to be grinding their teeth in unison. A woodpecker stuck his impudent head around the side of a tree. A bird flew on lighthearted wing.

Off was the rumble of death. It seemed now that Nature had no ears.

This landscape gave him assurance. A fair field holding life. It was the religion of peace. It would die if its timid eyes were compelled to see blood. He conceived Nature to be a woman with a deep aversion to tragedy.

He threw a pine cone at a jovial squirrel, and he ran with chattering fear. High in a treetop he stopped, and, poking his head cautiously from behind a branch, looked down with an air of trepidation.

The youth felt triumphant at this exhibition. There was the law, he said. Nature had given him a sign. The squirrel, immediately upon recognizing danger, had taken to his legs without ado. He did not stand stolidly baring his furry belly to the missile, and die with an upward glance at the sympathetic heavens. On the contrary, he had fled as fast as his legs could carry him; and he was but an ordinary squirrel, too—doubtless no philosopher of his race.[1] The youth wended, feeling that Nature was of his mind. She re-enforced his argument with proofs that lived where the sun shone.

Once he found himself almost into a swamp. He was obliged to walk upon bog tufts and watch his feet to keep from the oily mire. Pausing at one time to look about him he saw, out at some black water, a small animal pounce in and emerge directly with a gleaming fish.

---

[1] *In LV a canceled passage:* else he would have been likely to have defied their traditions instead of obeying them with rare promptitude.

The youth went again into the deep thickets. The brushed branches made a noise that drowned the sounds of cannon. He walked on, going from obscurity into promises of a greater obscurity.

At length he reached a place where the high, arching boughs made a chapel. He softly pushed the green doors aside and entered. Pine needles were a gentle brown carpet. There was a religious half light.

Near the threshold he stopped, horror-stricken at the sight of a thing.

He was being looked at by a dead man who was seated with his back against a columnlike tree. The corpse was dressed in a uniform that once had been blue, but was now faded to a melancholy shade of green. The eyes, staring at the youth, had changed to the dull hue to be seen on the side of a dead fish. The mouth was open. Its red had changed to an appalling yellow. Over the gray skin of the face ran little ants. One was trundling some sort of a bundle along the upper lip.

The youth gave a shriek as he confronted the thing. He was for moments turned to stone before it. He remained staring into the liquid-looking eyes. The dead man and the living man exchanged a long look. Then the youth cautiously put one hand behind him and brought it against a tree. Leaning upon this he retreated, step by step, with his face still toward the thing. He feared that if he turned his back the body might spring up and stealthily pursue him.

The branches, pushing against him, threatened to throw him over upon it. His unguided feet, too, caught aggravatingly in brambles; and with it all he received a subtle suggestion to touch the corpse. As he thought of his hand upon it he shuddered profoundly.

At last he burst the bonds which had fastened him to the spot and fled, unheeding the underbrush. He was pursued by a sight of the black ants swarming greedily upon the gray face and venturing horribly near to the eyes.

After a time he paused, and, breathless and panting, listened.

He imagined some strange voice would come from the dead throat and squawk after him in horrible menaces.

The trees about the portals of the chapel moved soughingly in a soft wind. A sad silence was upon the little guarding edifice.[2]

CHAPTER VIII

The trees began softly to sing a hymn of twilight. The sun sank until slanted bronze rays struck the forest. There was a lull in the noises of insects as if they had bowed their beaks and were making a devotional pause. There was silence save for the chanted chorus of the trees.

Then, upon this stillness, there suddenly broke a tremendous clangor of sounds. A crimson roar came from the distance.

The youth stopped. He was transfixed by this terrific medley of all noises. It was as if worlds were being rended. There was the ripping sound of musketry and the breaking crash of the artillery.

His mind flew in all directions. He conceived the two armies to be at each other panther fashion. He listened for a time. Then he began to run in the direction of the battle. He saw that it was an ironical thing for him to be running thus toward that which he had been at such pains to avoid. But he said, in substance, to himself that if the earth and the moon were about to clash, many persons would doubtless plan to get upon the roofs to witness the collision.

As he ran, he became aware that the forest had stopped its

---

² *In LV a canceled passage:*
Again the youth was in despair. Nature no longer condoled with him. There was nothing, then, after all, in that demonstration she gave—the frightened squirrel fleeing aloft from the missile. He thought as he remembered the small animal capturing the fish and the greedy ants feeding upon the flesh of the dead soldier, that there was given another law which far-over-topped it—all life existing upon death, eating ravenously, stuffing itself with the hopes of the dead. And nature's processes were obliged to hurry *unfinished passage on page 65 LV; page 67 is missing, and page 66 is renumbered 67 (in Crane's pagination of LV).*

music, as if at last becoming capable of hearing the foreign sounds. The trees hushed and stood motionless. Everything seemed to be listening to the crackle and clatter and ear-shaking thunder. The chorus pealed over the still earth.

It suddenly occurred to the youth that the fight in which he had been was, after all, but perfunctory popping. In the hearing of this present din he was doubtful if he had seen real battle scenes. This uproar explained a celestial battle; it was tumbling hordes a-struggle in the air.

Reflecting, he saw a sort of a humor in the point of view of himself and his fellows during the late encounter. They had taken themselves and the enemy very seriously and had imagined that they were deciding the war. Individuals must have supposed that they were cutting the letters of their names deep into everlasting tablets of brass, or enshrining their reputations forever in the hearts of their countrymen, while, as to fact, the affair would appear in printed reports under a meek and immaterial title. But he saw that it was good, else, he said, in battle every one would surely run save forlorn hopes and their ilk.

He went rapidly on. He wished to come to the edge of the forest that he might peer out.

As he hastened, there passed through his mind pictures of stupendous conflicts. His accumulated thought upon such subjects was used to form scenes. The noise was as the voice of an eloquent being, describing.

Sometimes the brambles formed chains and tried to hold him back. Trees, confronting him, stretched out their arms and forbade him to pass. After its previous hostility this new resistance of the forest filled him with a fine bitterness. It seemed that Nature could not be quite ready to kill him.

But he obstinately took roundabout ways, and presently he was where he could see long gray walls of vapor where lay battle lines. The voices of cannon shook him. The musketry sounded in long irregular surges that played havoc with his ears. He stood regardant for a moment. His eyes had an awe-struck expression. He gawked in the direction of the fight.

Presently he proceeded again on his forward way. The battle was like the grinding of an immense and terrible machine to him. Its complexities and powers, its grim processes, fascinated him. He must go close and see it produce corpses.

He came to a fence and clambered over it. On the far side, the ground was littered with clothes and guns. A newspaper, folded up, lay in the dirt. A dead soldier was stretched with his face hidden in his arm. Farther off there was a group of four or five corpses keeping mournful company. A hot sun had blazed upon the spot.

In this place the youth felt that he was an invader. This forgotten part of the battle ground was owned by the dead men, and he hurried, in the vague apprehension that one of the swollen forms would rise and tell him to begone.

He came finally to a road from which he could see in the distance dark and agitated bodies of troops, smoke-fringed. In the lane was a blood-stained crowd streaming to the rear. The wounded men were cursing, groaning, and wailing. In the air, always, was a mighty swell of sound that it seemed could sway the earth. With the courageous words of the artillery and the spiteful sentences of the musketry mingled red cheers. And from this region of noises came the steady current of the maimed.

One of the wounded men had a shoeful of blood. He hopped like a schoolboy in a game. He was laughing hysterically.

One was swearing [1] that he had been shot in the arm through the commanding general's mismanagement of the army. One was marching with an air imitative of some sublime drum major. Upon his features was an unholy mixture of merriment and agony. As he marched he sang a bit of doggerel in a high and quavering voice:

---

[1] *LV:* One swore by the sun *canceled. Henry Fleming blasphemes against the sun when Jim Conklin dies, at the end of Chapter ix.*

> *"Sing a song 'a vic'try,*
> *A pocketful 'a bullets,*
> *Five an' twenty dead men*
> *Baked in a—pie."*

Parts of the procession limped and staggered to this tune.

Another had the gray seal of death already upon his face. His lips were curled in hard lines and his teeth were clinched. His hands were bloody from where he had pressed them upon his wound. He seemed to be awaiting the moment when he should pitch headlong. He stalked like the specter of a soldier, his eyes burning with the power of a stare into the unknown.

There were some who proceeded sullenly, full of anger at their wounds, and ready to turn upon anything as an obscure cause.

An officer was carried along by two privates. He was peevish. "Don't joggle so, Johnson, yeh fool," he cried. "Think m' leg is made of iron? If yeh can't carry me decent, put me down an' let some one else do it."

He bellowed at the tottering crowd who blocked the quick march of his bearers. "Say, make way there, can't yeh? Make way, dickens take it all."

They sulkily parted and went to the roadsides. As he was carried past they made pert remarks to him. When he raged in reply and threatened them, they told him to be damned.

The shoulder of one of the tramping bearers knocked heavily against the spectral soldier who was staring into the unknown.

The youth joined this crowd and marched along with it. The torn bodies expressed the awful machinery in which the men had been entangled.

Orderlies and couriers occasionally broke through the throng in the roadway, scattering wounded men right and left, galloping on followed by howls. The melancholy march was continually disturbed by the messengers, and sometimes by bustling batteries that came swinging and thumping down upon them, the officers shouting orders to clear the way.

There was a tattered man, fouled with dust, blood and

powder stain from hair to shoes, who trudged quietly at
the youth's side. He was listening with eagerness and much
humility to the lurid descriptions of a bearded sergeant. His
lean features wore an expression of awe and admiration. He
was like a listener in a country store to wondrous tales told
among the sugar barrels. He eyed the story-teller with unspeakable wonder. His mouth was agape in yokel fashion.

The sergeant, taking note of this, gave pause to his elaborate
history while he administered a sardonic comment. "Be keer-
ful, honey, you'll be a-ketchin' flies," he said.

The tattered man shrank back abashed.

After a time he began to sidle near to the youth, and in a
different way try to make him a friend. His voice was gentle
as a girl's voice and his eyes were pleading. The youth saw
with surprise that the soldier had two wounds, one in the
head, bound with a blood-soaked rag, and the other in the
arm, making that member dangle like a broken bough.

After they had walked together for some time the tattered
man mustered sufficient courage to speak. "Was pretty good
fight, wa'n't it?" he timidly said. The youth, deep in thought,
glanced up at the bloody and grim figure with its lamblike
eyes. "What?"

"Was pretty good fight, wa'n't it?"

"Yes," said the youth shortly. He quickened his pace.

But the other hobbled industriously after him. There was
an air of apology in his manner, but he evidently thought that
he needed only to talk for a time, and the youth would perceive
that he was a good fellow.

"Was pretty good fight, wa'n't it?" he began in a small voice,
and then he achieved the fortitude to continue. "Dern me if
I ever see fellers fight so. Laws, how they did fight! I knowed
th' boys 'd like when they onct got square at it. Th' boys ain't
had no fair chanct up t' now, but this time they showed what
they was. I knowed it 'd turn out this way. Yeh can't lick them
boys. No, sir! They're fighters, they be."

He breathed a deep breath of humble admiration. He had

looked at the youth for encouragement several times. He received none, but gradually he seemed to get absorbed in his subject.

"I was talkin' 'cross pickets with a boy from Georgie, onct, an' that boy, he ses, 'Your fellers 'll all run like hell when they onct hearn a gun,' he ses. 'Mebbe they will,' I ses, 'but I don't b'lieve none of it,' I ses; 'an' b'jiminey,' I ses back t' 'um, 'mebbe your fellers 'll all run like hell when they onct hearn a gun,' I ses. He larfed. Well, they didn't run t'-day, did they, hey? No, sir! They fit, an' fit, an' fit."

His homely face was suffused with a light of love for the army which was to him all things beautiful and powerful.

After a time he turned to the youth, "Where yeh hit, ol' boy?" he asked in a brotherly tone.

The youth felt instant panic at this question, although at first its full import was not borne in upon him.

"What?" he asked.

"Where yeh hit?" [2] repeated the tattered man.

"Why," began the youth, "I—I—that is—why—I—"

He turned away suddenly and slid through the crowd. His brow was heavily flushed, and his fingers were picking nervously at one of his buttons. He bent his head and fastened his eyes studiously upon the button as if it were a little problem.

The tattered man looked after him in astonishment.

CHAPTER IX

The youth fell back in the procession until the tattered soldier was not in sight. Then he started to walk on with the others.

But he was amid wounds. The mob of men was bleeding. Because of the tattered soldier's question he now felt that his

[2] *In Newspaper Version this question was incorrectly phrased and the meaning thereby changed: "Were you hit, old boy?" This alteration was undoubtedly the rewrite work of an editor. "The Red Badge" in its Newspaper Version appeared in the "Philadelphia Press" on December 3–8 and in the "New York Times" on December 9, 1894, serialized there in condensed form.*

shame could be viewed. He was continually casting sidelong glances to see if the men were contemplating the letters of guilt he felt burned into his brow.

At times he regarded the wounded soldiers in an envious way. He conceived persons with torn bodies to be peculiarly happy. He wished that he, too, had a wound, a [little] red badge of courage.[1]

The spectral soldier was at his side like a stalking reproach. The man's eyes were still fixed in a stare into the unknown. His gray, appalling face had attracted attention in the crowd, and men, slowing to his dreary pace, were walking with him. They were discussing his plight, questioning him and giving him advice. In a dogged way he repelled them, signing to them to go on and leave him alone. The shadows of his face were deepening and his tight lips seemed holding in check the moan of great despair. There could be seen a certain stiffness in the movements of his body, as if he were taking infinite care not to arouse the passion of his wounds. As he went on, he seemed always looking for a place, like one who goes to choose a grave.

Something in the gesture of the man as he waved the bloody and pitying soldiers away made the youth start as if bitten. He yelled in horror. Tottering forward he laid a quivering hand upon the man's arm. As the latter slowly turned his waxlike features toward him, the youth screamed:

"Gawd! Jim Conklin!"[2]

The tall soldier made a little commonplace smile. "Hello, Henry," he said.

The youth swayed on his legs and glared strangely. He stuttered and stammered. "Oh, Jim—oh, Jim—oh, Jim—"

---

[1] *LV has:* a little warm red badge of courage *with the word* warm *canceled. It was this phrase that suggested the final title of the novel. The original title was:* Private Fleming/His various battles. *Manuscript SV contains a page that is blank except for this much of the title:* Private Fleming./His various *with the next letter unfinished but indicating an intended* b.

[2] *Henry's exclamation suggests an identification of Jim Conklin with God.* See also page 286: " 'God!' said the tattered soldier."

The tall soldier held out his gory hand. There was a curious red and black combination of new blood and old blood upon it. "Where yeh been, Henry?" he asked. He continued in a monotonous voice, "I thought mebbe yeh got keeled over. There's been thunder t' pay t'-day. I was worryin' about it a good deal."

The youth still lamented. "Oh, Jim—oh, Jim—oh, Jim—"

"Yeh know," said the tall soldier, "I was out there." He made a careful gesture. "An', Lord, what a circus! An', b'jiminey, I got shot—I got shot. Yes, b'jiminey, I got shot." He reiterated this fact in a bewildered way, as if he did not know how it came about.

The youth put forth anxious arms to assist him, but the tall soldier went firmly on as if propelled. Since the youth's arrival as a guardian for his friend, the other wounded men had ceased to display much interest. They occupied themselves again in dragging their own tragedies toward the rear.

Suddenly, as the two friends marched on, the tall soldier seemed to be overcome by a terror. His face turned to a semblance of gray paste. He clutched the youth's arm and looked all about him, as if dreading to be overheard. Then he began to speak in a shaking whisper:

"I tell yeh what I'm 'fraid of, Henry—I'll tell yeh what I'm 'fraid of. I'm 'fraid I'll fall down—an' then yeh know—them damned artillery wagons—they like as not 'll run over me. That's what I'm 'fraid of—"

The youth cried out to him hysterically: "I'll take care of yeh, Jim! I'll take care of yeh! I swear t' Gawd I will!"

"Sure—will yeh, Henry?" the tall soldier beseeched.

"Yes—yes—I tell yeh—I'll take care of yeh, Jim!" protested the youth. He could not speak accurately because of the gulpings in his throat.

But the tall soldier continued to beg in a lowly way. He now hung babelike to the youth's arm. His eyes rolled in the wildness of his terror. "I was allus a good friend t' yeh, wa'n't I, Henry? I've allus been a pretty good feller, ain't I? An' it ain't much t' ask, is it? Jest t' pull me along outer th' road? I'd do it fer you, wouldn't I, Henry?"

He paused in piteous anxiety to await his friend's reply.

The youth had reached an anguish where the sobs scorched him. He strove to express his loyalty, but he could only make fantastic gestures.

However, the tall soldier seemed suddenly to forget all those fears. He became again the grim, stalking specter of a soldier. He went stonily forward. The youth wished his friend to lean upon him, but the other always shook his head and strangely protested. "No—no—no—leave me be—leave me be—"

His look was fixed again upon the unknown. He moved with mysterious purpose, and all of the youth's offers he brushed aside. "No—no—leave me be—leave me be—"

The youth had to follow.

Presently the latter heard a voice talking softly near his shoulders. Turning he saw that it belonged to the tattered soldier. "Ye'd better take 'im outa th' road, pardner. There's a batt'ry comin' helitywhoop down th' road an' he'll git runned over. He's a goner anyhow in about five minutes—yeh kin see that. Ye'd better take 'im outa th' road. Where th' blazes does he git his stren'th from?"

"Lord knows!" cried the youth. He was shaking his hands helplessly.

He ran forward presently and grasped the tall soldier by the arm. "Jim! Jim!" he coaxed, "come with me."

The tall soldier weakly tried to wrench himself free. "Huh," he said vacantly. He stared at the youth for a moment. At last he spoke as if dimly comprehending. "Oh! Inteh th' fields? Oh!"

He started blindly through the grass.

The youth turned once to look at the lashing riders and jouncing guns of the battery. He was startled from this view by a shrill outcry from the tattered man.

"Gawd! He's runnin'!"

Turning his head swiftly, the youth saw his friend running in a staggering and stumbling way toward a little clump of bushes. His heart seemed to wrench itself almost free from his body at this sight. He made a noise of pain. He and the tattered man began a pursuit. There was a singular race.

When he overtook the tall soldier he began to plead with all the words he could find. "Jim—Jim—what are you doing—what makes you do this way—you'll hurt yerself."

The same purpose was in the tall soldier's face. He protested in a dulled way, keeping his eyes fastened on the mystic place of his intentions. "No—no—don't tech me—leave me be—leave me be—"

The youth, aghast and filled with wonder at the tall soldier, began quaveringly to question him. "Where yeh goin', Jim? What you thinking about? Where you going? Tell me, won't you, Jim?"

The tall soldier faced about as upon relentless pursuers. In his eyes there was a great appeal. "Leave me be, can't yeh? Leave me be fer a minnit."

The youth recoiled. "Why, Jim," he said, in a dazed way, "what's the matter with you?"

The tall soldier turned and, lurching dangerously, went on. The youth and the tattered soldier followed, sneaking as if whipped, feeling unable to face the stricken man if he should again confront them. They began to have thoughts of a solemn ceremony. There was something ritelike in these movements of the doomed soldier. And there was a resemblance in him to a devotee [3] of a mad religion, blood-sucking, muscle-wrenching, bone-crushing. [They could not understand]; they were awed and afraid. They hung back lest he have at command a dreadful weapon.

At last, they saw him stop and stand motionless. Hastening up, they perceived that his face wore an expression telling that he had at last found the place for which he had struggled. His spare figure was erect; his bloody hands were quietly at his side. He was waiting with patience for something that he

---

[3] *LV:* priest *canceled.*

had come to meet. He was at the rendezvous. They paused and stood, expectant.

There was a silence.

Finally, the chest of the doomed soldier began to heave with a strained motion. It increased in violence until it was as if an animal was within and was kicking and tumbling furiously to be free.

This spectacle of gradual strangulation made the youth writhe, and once as his friend rolled his eyes, he saw something in them that made him sink wailing to the ground. He raised his voice in a last supreme call.

"Jim—Jim—Jim—"

The tall soldier opened his lips and spoke. He made a gesture. "Leave me be—don't tech me—leave me be—"

There was another silence while he waited.

Suddenly, his form stiffened and straightened. Then it was shaken by a prolonged ague. He stared into space. To the two watchers there was a curious and profound dignity in the firm lines of his awful face.

He was invaded by a creeping strangeness that slowly enveloped him. For a moment the tremor of his legs caused him to dance a sort of hideous hornpipe. His arms beat wildly about his head in expression of implike enthusiasm.

His tall figure stretched itself to its full height. There was a slight rending sound. Then it began to swing forward, slow and straight, in the manner of a falling tree. A swift muscular contortion made the left shoulder strike the ground first.

The body seemed to bounce a little way from the earth. "God!" said the tattered soldier.

The youth had watched, spellbound, this ceremony at the place of meeting. His face had been twisted into an expression of every agony he had imagined for his friend.

He now sprang to his feet and, going closer, gazed upon the pastelike face. The mouth was opened and the teeth showed in a laugh.

As the flap of the blue jacket fell away from the body, he

could see that the side looked as if it had been chewed by wolves.

The youth turned, with sudden, livid rage, toward the battlefield. He shook his fist. He seemed about to deliver a philippic.

"Hell—"

The red sun was pasted in the sky like a [fierce] wafer.[4]

CHAPTER X

The tattered man stood musing.

"Well, he was reg'lar jim-dandy fer nerve, wa'n't he," said he finally in a little awestruck voice. "A reg'lar jim-dandy." He thoughtfully poked one of the docile hands with his foot. "I wonner where he got 'is stren'th from? I never seen a man do like that before. It was a funny thing. Well, he was a reg'lar jim-dandy."

The youth desired to screech out his grief. He was stabbed, but his tongue lay dead in the tomb of his mouth. He threw himself again upon the ground and began to brood.

The tattered man stood musing.

"Look-a-here, pardner," he said, after a time. He regarded the corpse as he spoke. "He's up an' gone, ain't 'e, an' we might as well begin t' look out fer ol' number one. This here thing is all over. He's up an' gone, ain't 'e? An' he's all right here. Nobody won't bother 'im. An' I must say I ain't enjoying any great health m'self these days."

The youth, awakened by the tattered soldier's tone, looked quickly up. He saw that he was swinging uncertainly on his legs and that his face had turned to a shade of blue.

"Good Lord!" he cried, "you ain't goin' t'—not you, too."

The tattered man waved his hand. "Nary die," he said. "All I want is some pea soup an' a good bed. Some pea soup," he repeated dreamfully.

---

[4] SV: The [fierce *canceled*] red sun was pasted in the sky like a fierce wafer. *The repeated word* fierce *in the SV variant underscores the fact that Crane intended the sun to personify the wrathful gods of Henry's insult and worship.*

The youth arose from the ground. "I wonder where he came from. I left him over there." He pointed. "And now I find 'im here. And he was coming from over there, too." He indicated a new direction. They both turned toward the body as if to ask of it a question.

"Well," at length spoke the tattered man, "there ain't no use in our stayin' here an' tryin' t' ask him anything."

The youth nodded an assent wearily. They both turned to gaze for a moment at the corpse.

The youth murmured something.

"Well, he was a jim-dandy, wa'n't 'e?" said the tattered man as if in response.

They turned their backs upon it and started away. For a time they stole softly, treading with their toes. It remained laughing there in the grass.

"I'm commencin' t' feel pretty bad," said the tattered man, suddenly breaking one of his little silences. "I'm commencin' t' feel pretty damn' bad."

The youth groaned. "O Lord!" He wondered if he was to be the tortured witness of another grim encounter.

But his companion waved his hand reassuringly. "Oh, I'm not goin' t' die yit! There too much dependin' on me fer me t' die yit. No, sir! Nary die! I *can't!* Ye'd oughta see th' swad a' chil'ren I've got, an' all like that."

The youth glancing at his companion could see by the shadow of a smile that he was making some kind of fun.

As they plodded on the tattered soldier continued to talk. "Besides, if I died, I wouldn't die th' way that feller did. That was th' funniest thing. I'd jest flop down, I would. I never seen a feller die th' way that feller did.

"Yeh know Tom Jamison, he lives next door t' me up home. He's a nice feller, he is, an' we was allus good friends. Smart, too. Smart as a steel trap. Well, when we was a-fightin' this afternoon, all-of-a-sudden he begin t' rip up an' cuss an' beller at me. 'Yer shot, yeh blamed infernal [tooty-tooty-tooty-too]!' —he swore horrible—he ses t' me. I put up m' hand t' m' head an' when I looked at m' fingers, I seen, sure 'nough, I was shot. I give a holler an' begin t' run, but b'fore I could git away another one hit me in th' arm an' whirl' me clean 'round. I got skeared when they was all a-shootin' b'hind me an' I run t' beat all, but I cotch it pretty bad. I've an idee I'd a' been fightin' yit, if t'was n't fer Tom Jamison."

Then he made a calm announcement: "There's two of 'em—little ones—but they're beginnin' t' have fun with me now. I don't b'lieve I kin walk much furder."

They went slowly on in silence. "Yeh look pretty peek-ed yerself," said the tattered man at last. "I bet yeh 've got a worser one than yeh think. Ye'd better take keer of yer hurt. It don't do t' let sech things go. It might be inside mostly, an' them plays thunder. Where is it located?" But he continued his harangue without waiting for a reply. "I see' a feller git hit plum in th' head when my reg'ment was a-standin' at ease onct. An' everybody yelled out to 'im: Hurt, John? Are yeh hurt much? 'No,' ses he. He looked kinder surprised, an' he went on tellin' 'em how he felt. He sed he didn't feel nothin'. But, by dad, th' first thing that feller knowed he was dead. Yes, he was dead—stone dead. So, yeh wanta watch out. Yeh might have some queer kind 'a hurt yerself. Yeh can't never tell. Where is your'n located?"

The youth had been wriggling since the introduction of this topic. He now gave a cry of exasperation and made a furious motion with his hand. "Oh, don't bother me!" he said. He was enraged against the tattered man, and could have strangled him. His companions seemed ever to play intolerable parts. They were ever upraising the ghost of shame on the stick of their curiosity. He turned toward the tattered man as one at bay. "Now, don't bother me," he repeated with desperate menace.

"Well, Lord knows I don't wanta bother anybody," said the other. There was a little accent of despair in his voice as he replied, "Lord knows I've gota 'nough m' own t' tend to."

The youth, who had been holding a bitter debate with himself and casting glances of hatred and contempt at the tattered man, here spoke in a hard voice. "Good-by," he said.

The tattered man looked at him in gaping amazement. "Why—why, pardner, where yeh goin'?" he asked unsteadily. The youth looking at him, could see that he, too, like that other one, was beginning to act dumb and animal-like. His thoughts seemed to be floundering about in his head. "Now—now—look—a—here, you Tom Jamison—now—I won't have this—this here won't do. Where—where yeh goin'?"

The youth pointed vaguely. "Over there," he replied.

"Well, now look—a—here—now," said the tattered man, rambling on in idiot fashion. His head was hanging forward and his words were slurred. "This thing won't do, now, Tom Jamison. It won't do. I know yeh, yeh pigheaded devil. Yeh wanta go trompin' off with a bad hurt. It ain't right—now—Tom Jamison—it ain't. Yeh wanta leave me take keer of yeh, Tom Jamison. It ain't—right—it ain't—fer yeh t' go—trompin' off—with a bad hurt—it ain't—ain't—ain't right—it ain't."

In reply the youth climbed a fence and started away. He could hear the tattered man bleating plaintively.

Once he faced about angrily. "What?"

"Look—a—here, now, Tom Jamison—now—it ain't——"

The youth went on. Turning at a distance he saw the tattered man wandering about helplessly in the field.

He now thought that he wished he was dead. He believed that he envied those men whose bodies lay strewn over the grass of the fields and on the fallen leaves of the forest.

The simple questions of the tattered man had been knife thrusts to him. They asserted a society that probes pitilessly at secrets until all is apparent. His late companion's chance persistency made him feel that he could not keep his crime concealed in his bosom. It was sure to be brought plain by one of those arrows which cloud the air and are constantly pricking, discovering, proclaiming those things which are willed to be forever hidden. He admitted that he could not defend himself against this agency. It was not within the power of vigilance.[1]

---

[1] *In LV, a canceled passage:*

Promptly, then, his old rebellious feelings returned. He thought the powers of fate had combined to heap misfortune upon him. He was an innocent victim.

He rebelled against the source of things, according to a law perchance, that the most powerful shall recieve the most blame.

War, he said bitterly to the sky, was a make-shift created because ordinary processes could not furnish deaths enough. Man had been born wary of the grey skeleton and had expended much of his intellect in erecting whatever safe-guards were possible, so that he had long been rather strongly intrenched behind the mass of his inventions. He kept an [calm *canceled*] eye on his bath-tub, his fire-engine, his life-boat, and compelled *unfinished.*

This passage appears on page 85 of Manuscript LV. Pages 86–9 are missing from the manuscript. (Chapter xi begins on page 90, which is renumbered in Crane's hand as 86.)

This passage in its original version was considerably longer. Here is the original passage as it appears in Manuscript SV:

Promptly, his old rebellious feelings returned. He thought the powers of fate had combined to heap misfortune upon him. He was a victim.

He rebelled against the source of things, according to his law that the most powerful should recieve the most blame.

War, he said bitterly to the sky, was a make-shift created because ordinary processes didn't furnish deaths enough. To seduce her victims, nature had to formulate a beautiful excuse. She made glory. This made the men willing, anxious, in haste, to come and be killed.

And, with heavy [satire *canceled*] humor, he thought of how nature must smile when she the men come running. They regarding [ador ardor, *canceled*] war-fire and courage as holy things and did not see that nature had placed them in hearts because virtuous indignation would not last through a black struggle. Men would grow tired of it. They would go home.

They must be inspired by some sentiment that they could call sacred and enshrine in their heart, something that would cause them to regard slaughter as fine and go at it cheerfully; something that could [out shadow all the *canceled*] destroy all the bindings of loves and places that tie men's hearts. She made glory.

From his pinnacle of wisdom, he regarded the armies as large collection of dupes. Nature's dupes, who were killing each other to carry out some great scheme of life. They were under the impression that they were fighting for principles and honor and homes and various things.

CHAPTER XI

He became aware that the furnace roar of the battle was grow-ing louder. Great brown clouds had floated to the still heights of air before him. The noise, too, was approaching. The woods filtered men and the fields became dotted.

As he rounded a hillock, he perceived that the roadway was now a crying mass of wagons, teams, and men. From the heav-ing tangle issued exhortations, commands, imprecations. Fear was sweeping it all along. The cracking whips bit and horses plunged and tugged. The white-topped wagons strained and stumbled in their exertions like fat sheep.

The youth felt comforted in a measure by this sight. They were all retreating. Perhaps, then, he was not so bad after all. He seated himself and watched the terror-stricken wagons. They fled like soft, ungainly animals. All the roarers and lash-ers served to help him to magnify the dangers and horrors of the engagement that he might try to prove to himself that the thing with which men could charge him was in truth a sym-metrical act. There was an amount of pleasure to him in watch-ing the wild march of this vindication.

Presently the calm head of a forward-going column of in-

Well, to be sure; they were.

Nature was miraculously skilful in concocting excuses, he thought, with a heavy, theatrical contempt. It could deck a hideous creature [decked *canceled*] in enticing apparel [*this sentence added between the lines*]. When he saw how [they *canceled*] she [had cozened him out of his home, *canceled*], as a women beckons, had cozened him out of his home and hoodwinked him into wielding a rifle, he went into a rage.

He turned in tupenny fury upon the high, tranquil sky. He would have like to have splashed it with a derisive paint.

And he was bitter that among all men, he should be the only one sufficiently wise to understand these things.

Crane's procedure of composition evidenced in the fourth paragraph bears the appearance of being not a transcription but original writing. On page 76 SV, Crane, having finished Chapter x there, figured out how many words he had so far written. (His figures appear in two columns.) At this point in Manuscript SV he had written 39,035 words. The pages on which the above passage is written are crossed out by downward wavy pencil-lines made after this draft had been used for the LV copy.

fantry appeared in the road. It came swiftly on. Avoiding the obstructions gave it the sinuous movement of a serpent. The men at the head butted mules with their musket stocks. They prodded teamsters indifferent to all howls. The men forced their way through parts of the dense mass by strength. The blunt head of the column pushed. The raving teamsters swore many strange oaths.

The commands to make way had the ring of a great importance in them. The men were going forward to the heart of the din. They were to confront the eager rush of the enemy. They felt the pride of their onward movement when the remainder of the army seemed trying to dribble down this road. They tumbled teams about with a fine feeling that it was no matter so long as their column got to the front in time. This importance made their faces grave and stern. And the backs of the officers were very rigid.

As the youth looked at them the black weight of his woe returned to him. He felt that he was regarding a procession of chosen beings. The separation was as great to him as if they had marched with weapons of flame and banners of sunlight. He could never be like them. He could have wept in his longings.

He searched about in his mind for an adequate malediction for the indefinite cause, the thing upon which men turn the words of final blame. It—whatever it was—was responsible for him, he said. There lay the fault.

The haste of the column to reach the battle seemed to the forlorn young man to be something much finer than stout fighting. Heroes, he thought, could find excuses in that long seething lane. They could retire with perfect self-respect and make excuses to the stars.

He wondered what those men had eaten that they could be in such haste to force their way to grim chances of death. As he watched his envy grew until he thought that he wished to change lives with one of them. He would have liked to have used a tremendous force, he said, throw off himself and become a better. Swift pictures of himself, apart, yet in himself, came to him—a blue desperate figure leading lurid charges with one knee forward and a broken blade high—a blue, determined figure standing before a crimson and steel assault, getting calmly killed on a high place before the eyes of all. He thought of the magnificent pathos of his dead body.

These thoughts uplifted him. He felt the quiver of war desire. In his ears, he heard the ring of victory. He knew the frenzy of a rapid successful charge. The music of the trampling feet, the sharp voices, the clanking arms of the column near him made him soar on the red wings of war. For a few moments he was sublime.

He thought that he was about to start for the front. Indeed, he saw a picture of himself, dust-stained, haggard, panting, flying to the front at the proper moment to seize and throttle the dark, leering witch of calamity.

Then the difficulties of the thing began to drag at him. He hesitated, balancing awkwardly on one foot.

He had no rifle; he could not fight with his hands, said he resentfully to his plan. Well, rifles could be had for the picking. They were extraordinarily profuse.

Also, he continued, it would be a miracle if he found his regiment. Well, he could fight with any regiment.

He started forward slowly. He stepped as if he expected to tread upon some explosive thing. Doubts and he were struggling.

He would truly be a worm if any of his comrades should see him returning thus, the marks of his flight upon him. There was a reply that the intent fighters did not care for what happened rearward saving that no hostile bayonets appeared there. In the battle-blur his face would in a way be hidden, like the face of a cowled man.

But then he said that his tireless fate would bring forth, when the strife lulled for a moment, a man to ask of him an explanation. In imagination he felt the scrutiny of his companions as he painfully labored through some lies.

Eventually, his courage expended itself upon these objections. The debates drained him of his fire.

He was not cast down by this defeat of his plan, for, upon studying the affair carefully, he could not but admit that the objections were very formidable.

Furthermore, various ailments had begun to cry out. In their presence he could not persist in flying high with the wings of war; they rendered it almost impossible for him to see himself in a heroic light. He tumbled headlong.

He discovered that he had a scorching thirst. His face was so dry and grimy that he thought he could feel his skin crackle. Each bone of his body had an ache in it, and seemingly threatened to break with each movement. His feet were like two sores. Also, his body was calling for food. It was more powerful than a direct hunger. There was a dull, weight like feeling in his stomach, and, when he tried to walk, his head swayed and he tottered. He could not see with distinctness. Small patches of green mist floated before his vision.

While he had been tossed by many emotions, he had not been aware of ailments. Now they beset him and made clamor. As he was at last compelled to pay attention to them, his capacity for self-hate was multiplied. In despair, he declared that he was not like those others. He now conceded it to be impossible that he should ever become a hero. He was a craven loon. Those pictures of glory were piteous things. He groaned from his heart and went staggering off.

A certain mothlike quality within him kept him in the vicinity of the battle. He had a great desire to see, and to get news. He wished to know who was winning.

He told himself that, despite his unprecedented suffering, he had never lost his greed for a victory, yet, he said, in a half-apologetic manner to his conscience, he could not but know that a defeat for the army this time might mean many favorable things for him. The blows of the enemy would splinter regiments into fragments. Thus, many men of courage, he considered, would be obliged to desert the colors and scurry like chickens. He would appear as one of them. They would be sullen brothers in distress, and he could then easily believe he had not run any farther or faster than they. And if he himself could believe in his virtuous perfection, he conceived that there would be small trouble in convincing all others.

He said, as if in excuse for this hope, that previously the army had encountered great defeats and in a few months had shaken off all blood and tradition of them, emerging as bright and valiant as a new one; thrusting out of sight the memory of disaster, and appearing with the valor and confidence of unconquered legions. The shrilling voices of the people at home would pipe dismally for a time, but various generals were usually compelled to listen to these ditties. He of course felt no compunctions for proposing a general as a sacrifice. He could not tell who the chosen for the barbs might be, so he could center no direct sympathy upon him. The people were afar and he did not conceive public opinion to be accurate at long range. It was quite probable they would hit the wrong man who, after he had recovered from his amazement would perhaps spend the rest of his days in writing replies to the songs of his alleged failure. It would be very unfortunate, no doubt, but in this case a general was of no consequence to the youth.

In a defeat there would be a roundabout vindication of himself. He thought it would prove, in a manner, that he had fled early because of his superior powers of perception. A serious prophet upon predicting a flood should be the first man to climb a tree. This would demonstrate that he was indeed a seer.

A moral vindication was regarded by the youth as a very important thing. Without salve, he could not, he thought, wear the sore badge of his dishonor through life. With his heart continually assuring him that he was despicable, he could not exist without making it, through his actions, apparent to all men.

If the army had gone gloriously on he would be lost. If the

din meant that now his army's flags were tilted forward he
was a condemned wretch. He would be compelled to doom
himself to isolation. If the men were advancing, their indifferent feet were trampling upon his chances for a successful life.

As these thoughts went rapidly through his mind, he turned
upon them and tried to thrust them away. He denounced himself as a villain. He said that he was the most unutterably
selfish man in existence. His mind pictured the soldiers who
would place their defiant bodies before the spear of the yelling battle fiend, and as he saw their dripping corpses on an
imagined field, he said that he was their murderer.

Again he thought that he wished he was dead. He believed
that he envied a corpse. Thinking of the slain, he achieved a
great contempt for some of them, as if they were guilty for
thus becoming lifeless. They might have been killed by lucky
chances, he said, before they had had opportunities to flee or
before they had been really tested. Yet they would receive laurels from tradition. He cried out bitterly that their crowns were
stolen and their robes of glorious memories were shams. However, he still said that it was a great pity he was not as they.

A defeat of the army had suggested itself to him as a means
of escape from the consequences of his fall. He considered,
now, however, that it was useless to think of such a possibility.
His education had been that success for that mighty blue machine was certain; that it would make victories as a contrivance
turns out buttons. He presently discarded all his speculations
in the other direction. He returned to the creed of soldiers.

When he perceived again that it was not possible for the
army to be defeated, he tried to bethink him of a fine tale
which he could take back to his regiment, and with it turn
the expected shafts of derision.

But, as he mortally feared these shafts, it became impossible
for him to invent a tale he felt he could trust. He experimented
with many schemes, but threw them aside one by one as flimsy.
He was quick to see vulnerable places in them all.

Furthermore, he was much afraid that some arrow of scorn

might lay him mentally low before he could raise his protecting tale.

He imagined the whole regiment saying: "Where's Henry Fleming? He run, didn't 'e? Oh, my!" [1] He recalled various persons who would be quite sure to leave him no peace about it. They would doubtless question him with sneers, and laugh at his stammering hesitation. In the next engagement they would try to keep watch of him to discover when he would run.

Wherever he went in camp, he would encounter insolent and lingeringly cruel stares. As he imagined himself passing near a crowd of comrades, he could hear some one say, "There he goes!"

Then, as if the heads were moved by one muscle, all the faces were turned toward him with wide, derisive grins. He seemed to hear some one make a humorous remark in a low tone. At it the others all crowed and cackled. He was a slang phrase.

CHAPTER XII [1]

The column that had butted stoutly at the obstacles in the roadway was barely out of the youth's sight before he saw dark waves of men come sweeping out of the woods and down through the fields. He knew at once that the steel fibers had been washed from their hearts. They were bursting from their coats and their equipments as from entanglements. They charged down upon him like terrified buffaloes.

---

[1] *Here is the first occasion that finds the hero naming himself, and, significantly, his full name has not yet been uttered by anyone else.*

[1] *Chapter xii was originally intended to be Chapter xiii and is so numbered in Manuscript LV. Then Crane expunged an entire chapter, the original Chapter xii, and he renumbered Chapter xiii as xii. In Manuscript SV part of this original Chapter xii is extant. Here are the three extant pages:*

It was always clear to Fleming that he was entirely different from other men, that he had been cast in a unique mold. Also, he regarded his sufferings as peculiar and unprecedented. No man ever achieved such misery. There was a melancholy grandeur in the isolation of his experiences. He saw that he was a speck raising his [tiny can-

Behind them blue smoke curled and clouded above the tree-tops, and through the thickets he could sometimes see a distant pink glare. The voices of the cannon were clamoring in interminable chorus.

---

celed] minute arms against all possible forces and fates which were swelling down upon him like storms. He could derive some consolation from viewing the sublimity of the odds.

But, as he went on, he began to feel that, after all, [his rebellion, nature perhaps had not concentrated herself against him, or, at least, that *unfinished and canceled*] nature would not blame him for his rebellion. He still distinctly felt that he was arrayed against the universe but he began to believe that there was no malice agitating [his *canceled*] the vast breasts of his [*added above the line*] space-filling foes.

It was merely law.

Nature had provided her creations with various defenses and ways to escape that they might fight or flee, and she had limited dangers in powers of attack and pursuit, that the things might resist or hide with a security proportionate to their strength and wisdom. It was all the same old philosophy. He could not omit a small grunt of satisfaction as he saw with what brilliancy he had reasoned it all out.

He now said that, if, as he supposed his life was being relentlessly pursued, it was not his duty to bow to the inevitable. On the contrary, it was his business to kick and scratch and bite like a child in the hands of a parent. And he would be saved according to the importance of his strength. His egotism made him feel [safe *canceled*] secure for a time from the iron hands.

It being in his mind that he had solved those matters, he eagerly applied his [laws *canceled*] findings to the incident of his own flight from the battle. It was not a fault; it was a law. It was—

But he saw that when he had made a vindicating structure of great principles, it was the calm toes of tradition that kicked it all down about his ears. He immediately antagonized then this devotion to the by-gone; this universal [worship *canceled*] adoration of the past. From the bitter pinnacle of his wisdom he saw that mankind not only worshipped the gods of the ashes but that the gods of the ashes were worshipped because they were the gods of the ashes.

[He had a feeling that he was the coming prophet for a social reconstruction. Far down in his being, in the hidden, untouched currents of his soul, there was born he saw born a voice. *Canceled passage*]

He percieved [with bitterness *canceled*] with anger the present state of affairs in [his *canceled*] it's bearing upon his case.

And he resolved to reform it all.

He had then a feeling that he was the growing prophet of a

The youth was horrorstricken. He stared in agony and amazement. He forgot that he was engaged in combating the universe. He threw aside his mental pamphlets on the philosophy of the retreated and rules for the guidance of the doomed.[2] [He lost concern for himself.]

The fight was lost. The dragons were coming with invincible strides. The army, helpless in the matted thickets and blinded by the overhanging night, was going to be swallowed. War, the red animal, war, the blood-swollen god, would have bloated fill.

Within him something bade to cry out. He had the impulse to make a rallying speech, to sing a battle hymn, but he could only get his tongue to call into the air: "Why—why—what—what's th' matter?"

Soon he was in the midst of them. They were leaping and scampering all about him. Their blanched faces shone in the dusk. They seemed, for the most part, to be very burly men.

---

world-reconstruction. Far down in the pure depths of his being, among the hidden, untouched currents of his soul, he saw born a voice. He concieved a new world, modelled by the pain of his life, in which no old shadows fell darkening upon the temple of thought. And there were many personal advantages in it.

He thought for a time of piercing orations starting multitudes and of books wrung from his heart. In the gloom of his misery, his eyesight proclaimed that mankind were bowing to wrong and ridiculous idols. He said that if some all-powerful joker should take them away in the night, [mankind would *canceled*] and leave only manufactured shadows falling upon the bended heads, mankind would go on counting the hollow beads of their progress until the shriveling of the fingers. He was a-blaze with desire to change. He saw himself, a sun-lit figure upon a peak, pointing with true and unchangeable gesture. "There!" And all men could see and no man would falter.

Gradually the idea grew upon him that the cattle which cluttered the earth, would, in their ignorance and calm faith in the next day, blunder stolidly on and he would be beating his fists against the brass of accepted things. A remarkable facility for abuse came to him then and in supreme disgust and rage, he railed. To him there was something terrible and awesome in these words spoken from his heart to his heart. He was very tragic.

[2] *FAE:* damned.

The youth turned from one to another of them as they galloped along. His incoherent questions were lost. They were heedless of his appeals. They did not seem to see him.

They sometimes gabbled insanely. One huge man was asking of the sky: "Say, where de plank road? Where de plank road!" It was as if he had lost a child. He wept in his pain and dismay.

Presently, men were running hither and thither in all ways. The artillery booming, forward, rearward, and on the flanks made jumble of ideas of direction. Landmarks had vanished into the gathered gloom. The youth began to imagine that he had got into the center of the tremendous quarrel, and he could perceive no way out of it. From the mouths of the fleeing men came a thousand wild questions, but no one made answers.

The youth, after rushing about and throwing interrogations at the heedless bands of retreating infantry, finally clutched a man by the arm. They swung around face to face.

"Why—why—" stammered the youth struggling with his balking tongue.

The man screamed: "Let go me! Let go me!" His face was livid and his eyes were rolling uncontrolled. He was heaving and panting. He still grasped his rifle, perhaps having forgotten to release his hold upon it. He tugged frantically, and the youth being compelled to lean forward was dragged several paces.

"Let go me! Let go me!"

"Why—why—" stuttered the youth.

"Well, then!" bawled the man in a lurid rage. He adroitly and fiercely swung his rifle. It crushed upon the youth's head. The man ran on.

The youth's fingers had turned to paste upon the other's arm. The energy was smitten from his muscles. He saw the flaming wings of lightning flash before his vision. There was a deafening rumble of thunder within his head.

Suddenly his legs seemed to die. He sank writhing to the

ground. He tried to arise. In his efforts against the numbing pain he was like a man wrestling with a creature of the air.

There was a sinister struggle.

Sometimes he would achieve a position half erect, battle with the air for a moment, and then fall again, grabbing at the grass. His face was of a clammy pallor. Deep groans were wrenched from him.

At last, with a twisting movement, he got upon his hands and knees, and from thence, like a babe trying to walk, to his feet. Pressing his hands to his temples he went lurching over the grass.

He fought an intense battle with his body. His dulled senses wished him to swoon and he opposed them stubbornly, his mind portraying unknown dangers and mutilations if he should fall upon the field. He went tall soldier fashion.[3] He imagined secluded spots where he could fall and be unmolested. To search for one he strove against the tide of his pain.

Once he put his hand to the top of his head and timidly touched the wound. The scratching pain of the contact made him draw a long breath through his clinched teeth. His fingers were dabbled with blood. He regarded them with a fixed stare.

Around him he could hear the grumble of jolted cannon as the scurrying horses were lashed toward the front. Once, a young officer on a besplashed charger nearly ran him down. He turned and watched the mass of guns, men, and horses sweeping in a wide curve toward a gap in a fence. The officer was making excited motions with a gauntleted hand. The guns followed the teams with an air of unwillingness, of being dragged by the heels.

Some officers of the scattered infantry were cursing and railing like fishwives. Their scolding voices could be heard above the din. Into the unspeakable jumble in the roadway rode a squadron of cavalry. The faded yellow of their facings shone bravely. There was a mighty altercation.

---

[3] *LV:* went forward, Conklin-fashion *canceled.*

The artillery were assembling as if for a conference.

The blue haze of evening was upon the field. The lines of forest were long purple shadows. One cloud lay along the western sky partly smothering the red.

As the youth left the scene behind him, he heard the guns suddenly roar out. He imagined them shaking in black rage. They belched and howled like brass devils guarding a gate. The soft air was filled with the tremendous remonstrance. With it came the shattering peal of opposing infantry. Turning to look behind him, he could see sheets of orange light illumine the shadowy distance. There were subtle and sudden lightnings in the far air. At times he thought he could see heaving masses of men.

He hurried on in the dusk. The day had faded until he could barely distinguish place for his feet. The purple darkness was filled with men who lectured and jabbered. Sometimes he could see them gesticulating against the blue and somber sky. There seemed to be a great ruck of men and munitions spread about in the forest and in the fields.

The little narrow roadway now lay lifeless. There were overturned wagons like sun-dried bowlders. The bed of the former torrent was choked with the bodies of horses and splintered parts of war machines.

It had come to pass that his wound pained him but little. He was afraid to move rapidly, however, for a dread of disturbing it. He held his head very still and took many precautions against stumbling. He was filled with anxiety, and his face was pinched and drawn in anticipation of the pain of any sudden mistake of his feet in the gloom.

His thoughts, as he walked, fixed intently upon his hurt. There was a cool, liquid feeling about it and he imagined blood moving slowly down under his hair. His head seemed swollen to a size that made him think his neck to be inadequate.

The new silence of his wound made much worriment. The little blistering voices of pain that had called out from his scalp were, he thought, definite in their expression of danger. By them he believed that he could measure his plight. But when they remained ominously silent he became frightened and imagined terrible fingers that clutched into his brain.

Amid it he began to reflect upon various incidents and conditions of the past. He bethought him of certain meals his mother had cooked at home, in which those dishes of which he was particularly fond had occupied prominent positions. He saw the spread table. The pine walls of the kitchen were glowing in the warm light from the stove. Too, he remembered how he and his companions used to go from the schoolhouse to the bank of a shaded pool. He saw his clothes in disorderly array upon the grass of the bank. He felt the swash of the fragrant water upon his body. The leaves of the overhanging maple rustled with melody in the wind of youthful summer.

He was overcome presently by a dragging weariness. His head hung forward and his shoulders were stooped as if he were bearing a great bundle. His feet shuffled along the ground.

He held continuous arguments as to whether he should lie down and sleep at some near spot, or force himself on until he reached a certain haven. He often tried to dismiss the question, but his body persisted in rebellion and his senses nagged at him like pampered babies.

At last he heard a cheery voice near his shoulder: [4] "Yeh seem t' be in a pretty bad way, boy?"

The youth did not look up, but he assented with thick tongue. "Uh!"

The owner of the cheery voice took him firmly by the arm.

---

[4] *The man with the cheery voice whose face is not noticed by the youth was in real life an unknown farmer who happened to befriend Crane while he trudged homeward one night to Hartwood. This is the only incident in "The Red Badge of Courage" that draws upon personal experience. Yet nothing more remains here from the original incident than a cheery voice. A mood is here created; Henry's despondent state of mind is altered by the cheery voice. From the personal experience Crane distilled this much, nothing more.*

"Well," he said, with a round laugh, "I'm goin' your way. Th' hull gang is goin' your way. An' I guess I kin give yeh a lift." They began to walk like a drunken man and his friend.

As they went along, the man questioned the youth and assisted him with the replies like one manipulating the mind of a child. Sometimes he interjected anecdotes. "What reg'ment do yeh b'long teh? Eh? What's that? Th' 304th N' York? Why, what corps is that in? Oh, it is? Why, I thought they wasn't engaged t'-day—they're 'way over in th' center. Oh, they was, eh? Well, pretty nearly everybody got their share 'a fightin' t'-day. By dad, I give myself up fer dead any number 'a times. There was shootin' here an' shootin' there, an' hollerin' here an' hollerin' there, in th' damn' darkness, until I couldn't tell t' save m' soul which side I was on. Sometimes I thought I was sure 'nough from Ohier, an' other times I could a' swore I was from th' bitter end of Florida. It was th' most mixed up dern thing I ever see. An' these here hull woods is a reg'lar mess. It'll be a miracle if we find our reg'ments t'-night. Pretty soon, though, we'll meet a-plenty of guards an' provost-guards, an' one thing an' another. Ho! there they go with an off'cer, I guess. Look at his hand a-draggin'. He's got all th' war he wants, I bet. He won't be talkin' so big about his reputation an' all when they go t' sawin' off his leg. Poor feller! My brother's got whiskers jest like that. How did yeh git 'way over here, anyhow? Your reg'ment is a long way from here, ain't it? Well, I guess we can find it. Yeh know there was a boy killed in my comp'ny t'-day that I thought th' world an' all of. Jack was a nice feller. By ginger, it hurt like thunder t' see ol' Jack jest git knocked flat. We was a-standin' purty peaceable fer a spell, 'though there was men runnin' ev'ry way all 'round us, an' while we was a-standin' like that, 'long come a big fat feller. He began t' peck at Jack's elbow, an' he ses: 'Say, where 's th' road t' th' river?' An' Jack, he never paid no attention, an' th' feller kept on a-peckin' at his elbow an' sayin': 'Say, where's th' road t' th' river?' Jack was a-lookin' ahead all th' time tryin' t' see th'

Johnnies comin' through th' woods, an' he never paid no attention t' this big fat feller fer a long time, but at last he turned 'round an' he ses: 'Ah, go t' hell an' find th' road t' th' river!' An' jest then a shot slapped him bang on th' side th' head. He was a sergeant, too. Them was his last words. Thunder, I wish we was sure 'a findin' our reg'ments t'-night. It's goin' t' be long huntin'. But I guess we kin do it."

In the search that followed, the man of the cheery voice seemed to the youth to possess a wand of a magic kind. He threaded the mazes of the tangled forest with a strange fortune. In encounters with guards and patrols he displayed the keenness of a detective and the valor of a gamin. Obstacles fell before him and became of assistance. The youth, with his chin still on his breast, stood woodenly by while his companion beat ways and means out of sullen things.

The forest seemed a vast hive of men buzzing about in frantic circles, but the cheery man conducted the youth without mistakes, until at last he began to chuckle with glee and self-satisfaction. "Ah, there yeh are! See that fire?"

The youth nodded stupidly.

"Well, there's where your reg'ment is. An' now, good-by, ol' boy, good luck t' yeh."

A warm and strong hand clasped the youth's languid fingers for an instant, and then he heard a cheerful and audacious whistling as the man strode away. As he who had so befriended him was thus passing out of his life, it suddenly occurred to the youth that he had not once seen his face.

CHAPTER XIII

The youth went slowly toward the fire indicated by his departed friend. As he reeled, he bethought him of the welcome his comrades would give him. He had a conviction that he would soon feel in his sore heart the barbed missiles of ridicule. He had no strength to invent a tale; he would be a soft target.

He made vague plans to go off into the deeper darkness

and hide, but they were all destroyed by the voices of exhaustion and pain from his body. His ailments, clamoring, forced him to seek the place of food and rest, at whatever cost.

He swung unsteadily toward the fire. He could see the forms of men throwing black shadows in the red light, and as he went nearer it became known to him in some way that the ground was strewn with sleeping men.

Of a sudden he confronted a black and monstrous figure. A rifle barrel caught some glinting beams. "Halt! halt!" He was dismayed for a moment, but he presently thought that he recognized the nervous voice. As he stood tottering before the rifle barrel, he called out: "Why, hello, Wilson, you—you here?"

The rifle was lowered to a position of caution and the loud soldier came slowly forward. He peered into the youth's face. "That you, Henry?"

"Yes it's—it's me."

"Well, well, ol' boy," said the other, "by ginger, I'm glad t' see yeh! I give yeh up fer a goner. I thought yeh was dead sure enough." There was husky emotion in his voice.

The youth found that now he could barely stand upon his feet. There was a sudden sinking of his forces. He thought he must hasten to produce his tale to protect him from the missiles already at the lips of his redoubtable comrades. So, staggering before the loud soldier, he began: "Yes, yes. I've—I've had an awful time. I've been all over. Way over on th' right. Ter'ble fightin' over there. I had an awful time. I got separated from th' reg'ment. Over on th' right, I got shot. In th' head. I never see sech fightin.' Awful time. I don't see how I could a' got separated from th' reg'ment. I got shot, too."

His friend had stepped forward quickly. "What? Got shot? Why didn't yeh say so first? Poor ol' boy, we must—hol' on a minnit; what am I doin.' I'll call Simpson."

Another figure at that moment loomed in the gloom. They could see that it was the corporal. "Who yeh talkin' to, Wilson?" he demanded. His voice was anger-toned. "Who yeh talkin' to? Yeh th' derndest sentinel—why—hello, Henry, you here? Why, I thought you was dead four hours ago! [1] Great Jerusalem, they keep turnin' up every ten minutes or so! We thought we'd lost forty-two men by straight count, but if they keep on a-comin' this way, we'll git th' comp'ny all back by mornin' yit. Where was yeh?"

"Over on th' right. I got separated"—began the youth with considerable glibness.

But his friend had interrupted hastily. "Yes, an' he got shot in th' head an' he's in a fix, an' we must see t' him right away." He rested his rifle in the hollow of his left arm and his right around the youth's shoulder.

"Gee, it must hurt like thunder!" he said.

The youth leaned heavily upon his friend. "Yes, it hurts—hurts a good deal," he replied. There was a faltering in his voice.

"Oh," said the corporal. He linked his arm in the youth's and drew him forward. "Come on, Henry, I'll take keer 'a yeh."

As they went on together the loud private called out after them: "Put 'im t' sleep in my blanket, Simpson. An'—hol' on a minnit—here's my canteen. It's full 'a coffee. Look at his head by th' fire an' see how it looks. Maybe it's a pretty bad un. When I git relieved in a couple 'a minnits, I'll be over an' see t' him."

The youth's senses were so deadened that his friend's voice sounded from afar and he could scarcely feel the pressure of the corporal's arm. He submitted passively to the latter's directing strength. His head was in the old manner hanging forward upon his breast. His knees wobbled.

The corporal led him into the glare of the fire. "Now, Henry," he said, "let's have look at yer ol' head."

The youth sat down obediently and the corporal, laying aside his rifle, began to fumble in the bushy hair of his comrade. He was obliged to turn the other's head so that the full

---

[1] *This question recalls the question asked of Huck by Jim in "Huckleberry Finn." In both books there is the same motif of death and rebirth.*

flush of the fire light would beam upon it. He puckered his mouth with a critical air. He drew back his lips and whistled through his teeth when his fingers came in contact with the splashed blood and the rare wound.

"Ah, here we are!" he said. He awkwardly made further investigations. "Jest as I thought," he added, presently. "Yeh've been grazed by a ball. It's raised a queer lump jest as if some feller had lammed yeh on th' head with a club. It stopped a-bleedin' long time ago. Th' most about it is that in th' mornin' yeh'll feel that a number ten hat wouldn't fit yeh. An' your head 'll be all het up an' feel as dry as burnt pork. An' yeh may git a lot 'a other sicknesses, too, by mornin'. Yeh can't never tell. Still, I don't much think so. It's jest a damn' good belt on th' head, an' nothin' more. Now, you jest sit here an' don't move, while I go rout out th' relief. Then I'll send Wilson t' take keer 'a yeh."

The corporal went away. The youth remained on the ground like a parcel. He stared with a vacant look into the fire.

After a time he aroused, for some part, and the things about him began to take form. He saw that the ground in the deep shadows was cluttered with men, sprawling in every conceivable posture. Glancing narrowly into the more distant darkness, he caught occasional glimpses of visages that loomed pallid and ghostly, lit with a phosphorescent glow. These faces expressed in their lines the deep stupor of the tired soldiers. They made them appear like men drunk with wine. This bit of forest might have appeared to an ethereal wanderer as a scene of the result of some frightful debauch.

On the other side of the fire the youth observed an officer asleep, seated bolt upright, with his back against a tree. There was something perilous in his position. Badgered by dreams, perhaps, he swayed with little bounces and starts, like an old, toddy-stricken [2] grandfather in a chimney corner. Dust and stains were upon his face. His lower jaw hung down as if

---

[2] *LV:* a tired, old *canceled.*

lacking strength to assume its normal position. He was the picture of an exhausted soldier after a feast of war.

He had evidently gone to sleep with his sword in his arms. These two had slumbered in an embrace, but the weapon had been allowed in time to fall unheeded to the ground. The brass-mounted hilt lay in contact with some parts of the fire.

Within the gleam of rose and orange light from the burning sticks were other soldiers, snoring and heaving, or lying death-like in slumber. A few pairs of legs were stuck forth, rigid and straight. The shoes displayed the mud or dust of marches and bits of rounded trousers, protruding from the blankets, showed rents and tears from hurried pitchings through the dense brambles.

The fire crackled musically. From it swelled light smoke. Overhead the foliage moved softly. The leaves, with their faces turned toward the blaze, were colored shifting hues of silver, often edged with red. Far off to the right, through a window in the forest, could be seen a handful of stars lying, like glittering pebbles, on the black level of the night.

Occasionally, in this low-arched hall, a soldier would arouse and turn his body to a new position, the experience of his sleep having taught him of uneven and objectionable places upon the ground under him. Or, perhaps, he would lift himself to a sitting posture, blink at the fire for an unintelligent moment, throw a swift glance at his prostrate companion, and then cuddle down again with a grunt of sleepy content.

The youth sat in a forlorn heap until his friend, the loud young soldier,[3] came, swinging two canteens by their light strings. "Well, now, Henry, ol' boy," said the latter, "we'll have yeh fixed up in jest about a minnit."

He had the bustling ways of an amateur nurse. He fussed around the fire and stirred the sticks to brilliant exertions. He made his patient drink largely from the canteen that contained the coffee. It was to the youth a delicious draught. He tilted his head afar back and held the canteen long to his lips. The

---

[3] *FAE omits the punctuation.*

cool mixture went caressingly down his blistered throat. Having finished, he sighed with comfortable delight.

The loud young soldier watched his comrade with an air of satisfaction. He later produced an extensive handkerchief from his pocket. He folded it into a manner of bandage and soused water from the other canteen upon the middle of it. This crude arrangement he bound over the youth's head, tying the ends in a queer knot at the back of the neck.

"There," he said, moving off and surveying his deed, "yeh look like th' devil, but I bet yeh feel better."

The youth contemplated his friend with grateful eyes. Upon his aching and swelling head the cold cloth was like a tender woman's hand.

"Yeh don't holler ner say nothin'," remarked his friend approvingly. "I know I'm a blacksmith at takin' keer 'a sick folks, an' yeh never squeaked. Yer a good un, Henry. Most 'a men would a' been in th' hospital long ago. A shot in th' head ain't foolin' business."

The youth made no reply, but began to fumble with the buttons of his jacket.

"Well, come, now," continued his friend, "come on. I must put yeh t' bed an' see that yeh git a good night's rest."

The other got carefully erect, and the loud young soldier led him among the sleeping forms lying in groups and rows. Presently he stooped and picked up his blankets. He spread the rubber one upon the ground and placed the woolen one about the youth's shoulders.

"There now," he said, "lie down an' git some sleep."

The youth, with his manner of doglike obedience, got carefully down like a crone stooping. He stretched out with a murmur of relief and comfort. The ground felt like the softest couch.

But of a sudden he ejaculated: "Hol' on a minnit! Where you goin' t' sleep?"

His friend waved his hand impatiently. "Right down there by yeh."

"Well, but hol' on a minnit," continued the youth. "What yeh goin' t' sleep in? I've got your—"

The loud young soldier snarled: "Shet up an' go on t' sleep. Don't be makin' a damn' fool 'a yerself," he said severely.

After the reproof the youth said no more. An exquisite drowsiness had spread through him. The warm comfort of the blanket enveloped him and made a gentle languor. His head fell forward on his crooked arm and his weighted lids went slowly down over his eyes. Hearing a splatter of musketry from the distance, he wondered indifferently if those men sometimes slept. He gave a long sigh, snuggled down into his blanket, and in a moment was like his comrades.

CHAPTER XIV

When the youth awoke it seemed to him that he had been asleep for a thousand years, and he felt sure that he opened his eyes upon an unexpected world. Gray mists were slowly shifting before the first efforts of the sun-rays. An impending splendor could be seen in the eastern sky. An icy dew had chilled his face, and immediately upon arousing he curled farther down into his blankets. He stared for a while at the leaves overhead, moving in a heraldic wind of the day.[1]

The distance was splintering and blaring with the noise of fighting. There was in the sound an expression of a deadly persistency, as if it had not begun and was not to cease.

About him were the rows and groups of men that he had dimly seen the previous night. They were getting a last draught of sleep before the awakening. The gaunt, careworn features and dusty figures were made plain by this quaint light at the dawning, but it dressed the skin of the men in corpselike hues and made the tangled limbs appear pulseless and dead. The youth started up with a little cry when his eyes first swept over this motionless mass of men, thick-spread upon the ground,

---

[1] *In LV a canceled passage:* He heard the voice of a fire crackling briskly in the cold air, and turning his head listlessly he saw Wilson [and busily pottering about a small blaze. Many other figures *unfinished*].

pallid, and in strange postures. His disordered mind interpreted the hall of the forest as a charnel place. He believed for an instant that he was in the house of the dead, and he did not dare to move lest these corpses start up, squalling and squawking. In a second, however, he achieved his proper mind. He swore a complicated oath at himself. He saw that this somber picture was not a fact of the present, but a mere prophecy.

He heard then the noise of a fire crackling briskly in the cold air, and, turning his head, he saw his friend pottering busily about a small blaze. A few other figures moved in the fog, and he heard the hard cracking of axe blows.

Suddenly there was a hollow rumble of drums. A distant bugle sang faintly. Similar sounds, varying in strength, came from near and far over the forest. The bugles called to each other like brazen gamecocks. The near thunder of the regimental drums rolled.

The body of men in the woods rustled. There was a general uplifting of heads. A murmuring of voices broke upon the air. In it there was much bass of grumbling oaths. Strange gods were addressed in condemnation of the early hours necessary to correct war. An officer's peremptory tenor rang out and quickened the stiffened movement of the men. The tangled limbs unraveled. The corpse-hued faces were hidden behind fists that twisted slowly in the eye sockets. [It was the soldier's bath.]

The youth sat up and gave vent to an enormous yawn. "Thunder!" he remarked petulantly. He rubbed his eyes, and then putting up his hand felt carefully of the bandage over his wound. His friend, perceiving him to be awake, came from the fire. "Well, Henry, ol' man, how do yeh feel this mornin'?" he demanded.

The youth yawned again. Then he puckered his mouth to a little pucker. His head, in truth, felt precisely like a melon, and there was an unpleasant sensation at his stomach.

"Oh, Lord, I feel pretty bad," he said.

"Thunder!" exclaimed the other. "I hoped ye'd feel all right this mornin'. Let's see th' bandage—I guess it's slipped." He began to tinker at the wound in rather a clumsy way until the youth exploded.

"Gosh-dern it!" he said in sharp irritation; "you're the hangdest man I ever saw! You wear muffs on your hands. Why in good thunderation can't you be more easy? I'd rather you'd stand off an' throw guns at it. Now, go slow, an' don't act as if you was nailing down carpet."

He glared with insolent command at his friend, but the latter answered soothingly. "Well, well, come now, an' git some grub," he said. "Then, maybe, yeh'll feel better."

At the fireside the loud young soldier watched over his comrade's wants with tenderness and care. He was very busy marshaling the little black vagabonds of tin cups and pouring into them the streaming, iron colored mixture from a small and sooty tin pail. He had some fresh meat, which he roasted hurriedly upon a stick. He sat down then and contemplated the youth's appetite with glee.

The youth took note of a remarkable change in his comrade since those days of camp life upon the river bank. He seemed no more to be continually regarding the proportions of his personal prowess. He was not furious at small words that pricked his conceits. He was no more a loud young soldier. There was about him now a fine reliance. He showed a quiet belief in his purposes and his abilities. And this inward confidence evidently enabled him to be indifferent to little words of other men aimed at him.

The youth reflected. He had been used to regarding his comrade as a blatant child with an audacity grown from his inexperience, thoughtless, headstrong, jealous, and filled with a tinsel courage. A swaggering babe accustomed to strut in his own dooryard. The youth wondered where had been born these new eyes; when his comrade had made the great discovery that there were many men who would refuse to be subjected by him. Apparently, the other had now climbed a peak of wisdom from which he could perceive himself as a very wee thing. And the youth saw that ever after it would be easier to live in his friend's neighborhood.

His comrade balanced his ebony coffee-cup on his knee. "Well, Henry," he said, "what d'yeh think th' chances are? D'yeh think we'll wallop 'em?"

The youth considered for a moment. "Day-b'fore-yesterday," he finally replied, with boldness, "you would 'a' bet you'd lick the hull kit-an'-boodle all by yourself."

His friend looked a trifle amazed. "Would I?" he asked. He pondered. "Well, perhaps I would," he decided at last. He stared humbly at the fire.

The youth was quite disconcerted at this surprising reception of his remarks. "Oh, no, you wouldn't either," he said, hastily trying to retrace.

But the other made a deprecating gesture. "Oh, yeh needn't mind, Henry," he said. "I believe I was a pretty big fool in those days." He spoke as after a lapse of years.

There was a little pause.

"All th' officers say we've got th' rebs in a pretty tight box," said the friend, clearing his throat in a commonplace way. "They all seem t' think we've got 'em jest where we want 'em."

"I don't know about that," the youth replied. "What I seen over on th' right makes me think it was th' other way about. From where I was, it looked as if we was gettin' a good poundin' yestirday."

"D'yeh think so?" inquired the friend. "I thought we handled 'em pretty rough yestirday."

"Not a bit," said the youth. "Why, lord, man, you didn't see nothing of the fight. Why!" Then a sudden thought came to him. "Oh! Jim Conklin's dead."

His friend started. "What? Is he? Jim Conklin?"

The youth spoke slowly. "Yes. He's dead. Shot in th' side."

"Yeh don't say so. Jim Conklin . . . poor cuss!"

All about them were other small fires surrounded by men with their little black utensils. From one of these near came sudden sharp voices in a row. It appeared that two light-footed soldiers had been teasing a huge, bearded man, causing him to spill coffee upon his blue knees. The man had gone into a rage and had sworn comprehensively. Stung by his language, his tormentors had immediately bristled at him with a great show of resenting unjust oaths. Possibly there was going to be a fight.

The friend arose and went over to them, making pacific motions with his arms. "Oh, here, now, boys, what's th' use?" he said. "We'll be at th' rebs in less'n an hour. What's th' good fightin' 'mong ourselves?"

One of the light-footed soldiers turned upon him red-faced and violent. "Yeh needn't come around here with yer preachin'. I s'pose yeh don't approve 'a fightin' since Charley Morgan licked yeh; but I don't see what business this here is 'a yours or anybody else."

"Well, it ain't," said the friend mildly. "Still I hate t' see—"

That was a tangled argument.

"Well, he—," said the two, indicating their opponent with accusative forefingers.

The huge soldier was quite purple with rage. He pointed at the two soldiers with his great hand, extended clawlike. "Well, they—"

But during this argumentative time the desire to deal blows seemed to pass, although they said much to each other. Finally the friend returned to his old seat. In a short while the three antagonists could be seen together in an amiable bunch.

"Jimmie Rogers ses I'll have t' fight him after th' battle t'-day," announced the friend as he again seated himself. "He ses he don't allow no interferin' in his business. I hate t' see th' boys fightin' 'mong themselves."

The youth laughed. "Yer changed a good bit. Yeh ain't at all like yeh was. I remember when you an' that Irish feller—" He stopped and laughed again.

"No, I didn't use t' be that way," said his friend thoughtfully. "That's true 'nough."

"Well, I didn't mean—" began the youth.

The friend made another deprecatory gesture. "Oh, yeh needn't mind, Henry."

There was another little pause.

"Th' reg'ment lost over half th' men yestirday," remarked the the friend eventually. "I thought a course they was all dead, but, laws, they kep' a-comin' back last night until it seems, after all, we didn't lose but a few. They'd been scattered all over, wanderin' around in th' woods, fightin' with other reg'-ments, an' everything. Jest like you done."

"So?" said the youth.[2]

---

[2] *Manuscript LV contains a long canceled passage appearing on page 125 and crossed out in pencil. Page 126 is missing. Page 127 (in Crane's pagination) is renumbered 126; it is the opening page of Chapter xv. The unfinished and canceled passage on page 125 LV begins after the phrase:* the youth. *This phrase constitutes an alteration made in the typescript since the word* Fleming *appears uncanceled in the manuscript. Here is the canceled page:*

He went into a brown mood. He thought with deep contempt of all his grapplings and tuggings with fate and the universe. It now was evident that a large proportion of the men of the regiment had been, if they choose, [open to *canceled*] capable of the same quan-tity of condemnation of the world and could as righteously have taken arms against everything. He laughed.

He now rejoiced in a view of what he took to be the universal resemblance. He decided that he was not as he had supposed, a unique man. There were many in his type. And he had believed that he was suffering new agonies and feeling new wrongs. On the contrary, they were old, all of them, they were born perhaps with the first life.

These thoughts took the element of grandeur from his experi-ences. Since many had had them there could be nothing fine about them. They were now ridiculous.

However, he [considered *canceled*] yet considered himself to be below the standard of traditional man-hood. He felt abashed [in the *canceled*] when confronting [the *canceled*] memories of some men he had seen. [There *canceled*.]

These thoughts did not appear in his attitude. He now considered the fact of his having fled, as being buried. He was returned to his comrades and unimpeached. So despite the little shadow of his sin upon his mind, he felt his self-respect growing strong within him. His pride had almost recovered it's balance and was about *unfinished.*

CHAPTER XV

The regiment was standing at order arms at the side of a lane, waiting for the command to march, when suddenly the youth remembered the little packet enwrapped in a faded yellow envelope which the loud young soldier with lugubrious words had intrusted to him. It made him start. He uttered an exclamation and turned toward his comrade.

"Wilson!"

"What?"

His friend, at his side in the ranks, was thoughtfully staring down the road. From some cause his expression was at that moment very meek. The youth, regarding him with sidelong glances, felt impelled to change his purpose. "Oh, nothing," he said.

His friend turned his head in some surprise. "Why, what was yeh goin' t' say?"

"Oh, nothing," repeated the youth.

He resolved not to deal the little blow. It was sufficient that the fact made him glad. It was not necessary to knock his friend on the head with the misguided packet.

He had been possessed of much fear of his friend, for he saw how easily questionings could make holes in his feelings. Lately, he had assured himself that the altered comrade would not tantalize him with a persistent curiosity, but he felt certain that during the first period of leisure his friend would ask him to relate his adventures of the previous day.

He now rejoiced in the possession of a small weapon with which he could prostrate his comrade at the first signs of a cross-examination. He was master. It would now be he who could laugh and shoot the shafts of derision.

The friend had, in a weak hour, spoken with sobs of his own death. He had delivered a melancholy oration previous to his funeral, and had doubtless in the packet of letters, presented various keepsakes to relatives. But he had not died, and thus he had delivered himself into the hands of the youth.

The latter felt immensely superior to his friend, but he inclined to condescension. He adopted toward him an air of patronizing good humor.

His self-pride was now entirely restored. In the shade of its flourishing growth he stood with braced and self-confident legs, and since nothing could now be discovered he did not shrink from an encounter with the eyes of judges, and allowed no thoughts of his own to keep him from an attitude of manfulness. He had performed his mistakes in the dark, so he was still a man.

Indeed, when he remembered his fortunes of yesterday, and looked at them from a distance he began to see something fine there. He had license to be pompous and veteranlike.

His panting agonies of the past he put out of his sight. [The long tirades against nature he now believed to be foolish compositions born of his condition. He did not altogether repudiate them because he did not remember all that he had said. He was inclined to regard his past rebellions with an indulgent smile. They were all right in their hour, perhaps.]

In the present, he declared to himself that it was only the doomed and the damned who roared with sincerity at circumstance. Few but they ever did it. A man with a full stomach and the respect of his fellows had no business to scold about anything he might think to be wrong in the ways of the universe, or even with the ways of society. Let the unfortunates rail; the others may play marbles.

[Since he was comfortable and contented, he had no desire to set things straight. Indeed, he no more contended that they were not straight. How could they be crooked when he was restored to a requisite amount of happiness. There was a slowly developeing conviction that in all his red speeches he had been ridiculously mistaken. Nature was a fine thing moving with a magnificent justice. The world was fair and wide and glorious. The sky was kind, and smiled tenderly, full of encouragement, upon him.

Some poets now received his scorn. Yesterday, in his misery, he had thought of certain persons who had written. Their re-membered words, broken and detached, had come piece-meal to him. For these people he had then felt a glowing, brotherly regard. They had wandered in paths of pain and they had made pictures of the black landscape that others might enjoy it with them. He had, at that time, been sure that their wise, contem-plating spirits had been in sympathy with him, had shed tears from the clouds. He had walked alone, but there had been pity, made before a reason for it.

But he was now, in a measure, a successful man and he could no longer tolerate in himself a spirit of fellowship for poets. He abandoned them. Their songs about black landscapes were of no importance to him since his new eyes said that his landscape was not black. People who called landscapes black were idiots.

He achieved a mighty scorn for such a snivelling race.

He felt that he was the child of the powers. Through the peace of his heart, he saw the earth to be a garden in which grew no weeds of agony. Or, perhaps, if there did grow a few, it was in obscure corners where no one was obliged to en-counter them unless a ridiculous search was made. And, at any rate, they were tiny ones.

He returned to his old belief in the ultimate, astounding suc-cess of his life. He, as usual, did not trouble about processes. It was ordained, because he was a fine creation. He saw plainly that he was the chosen of some gods. By fearful and wonderful roads he was to be led to a crown. He was, of course, satisfied that he deserved it.] [1]

---

[1] *This is the longest passage among additions new to the text. It is also the one that is least effective and functional. It contains, however, one sentence that throws considerable light on the author's intention:* By fearful and wonderful roads he was to be led to a crown. *Henry, the mocked hero, has his ironic contrast in Jim Conklin. Crane counterpoints the one against the other. Crane's irony here is echoed in Chapter xxiv, in a passage reproduced here but not in the printed version (see page 366, line 27). The praise Henry received from the insane lieutenant seems to him—*It was a little coronation.

He did not give a great deal of thought to these battles that lay directly before him. It was not essential that he should plan his ways in regard to them. He had been taught that many obligations of a life were easily avoided. The lessons of yesterday had been that retribution was a laggard and blind. With these facts before him he did not deem it necessary that he should become feverish over the possibilities of the ensuing twenty-four hours. He could leave much to chance. Besides, a faith in himself had secretly blossomed. There was a little flower of confidence growing within him. He was now a man of experience. He had been out among the dragons, he said, and he assured himself that they were not so hideous as he had imagined them. Also, they were inaccurate; they did not sting with precision. A stout heart often defied, and defying, escaped.

And, furthermore, how could they kill him who was the chosen of gods and doomed to greatness?

He remembered how some of the men had run from the battle. As he recalled their terror-struck faces he felt a scorn for them. They had surely been more fleet and more wild than was absolutely necessary. They were weak mortals. As for himself, he had fled with discretion and dignity.

He was aroused from this reverie by his friend, who, having hitched about nervously and blinked at the trees for a time, suddenly coughed in an introductory way, and spoke.

"Fleming!"

"What?"

The friend put his hand up to his mouth and coughed again. He fidgeted in his jacket.

"Well," he gulped, at last, "I guess yeh might as well give me back them letters." Dark, prickling blood had flushed into his cheeks and brow.

"All right, Wilson," said the youth. He loosened two buttons of his coat, thrust in his hand, and brought forth the packet. As he extended it to his friend the latter's face was turned from him.

He had been slow in the act of producing the packet because during it he had been trying to invent a remarkable comment upon the affair. He could conjure nothing of sufficient point. He was compelled to allow his friend to escape unmolested with his packet. And for this he took unto himself considerable credit. It was a generous thing.

His friend at his side seemed suffering great shame. As he contemplated him, the youth felt his heart grow more strong and stout. He had never been compelled to blush in such manner for his acts; he was an individual of extraordinary virtues.

He reflected, with condescending pity: "Too bad! Too bad! The poor devil, it makes him feel tough!"

After this incident, and as he reviewed the battle pictures he had seen, he felt quite competent to return home and make the hearts of the people glow with stories of war. He could see himself in a room of warm tints telling tales to listeners. He could exhibit laurels. They were insignificant; still, in a district where laurels were infrequent, they might shine.

He saw his gaping audience picturing him as the central figure in blazing scenes. And he imagined the consternation and the ejaculations of his mother and the young lady at the seminary as they drank his recitals. Their vague feminine formula for beloved ones doing brave deeds on the field of battle without risk of life would be destroyed.

CHAPTER XVI

A sputtering of musketry was always to be heard. Later, the cannon had entered the dispute. In the fog-filled air their voices made a thudding sound. The reverberations were continued. This part of the world led a strange, battleful existence.

The youth's regiment was marched to relieve a command that had lain long in some damp trenches. The men took positions behind a curving line of rifle pits that had been turned up, like a large furrow, along the line of woods. Before them was a level stretch, peopled with short, deformed stumps. From the woods beyond came the dull popping of the skirmishers and pickets, firing in the fog. From the right came the noise of a terrific fracas.

The men cuddled behind the small embankment and sat in easy attitudes awaiting their turn. Many had their backs to the firing. The youth's friend lay down, buried his face in his arms, and almost instantly, it seemed, he was in a deep sleep.

The youth leaned his breast against the brown dirt and peered over at the woods and up and down the line. Curtains of trees interfered with his ways of vision. He could see the low line of trenches but for a short distance. A few idle flags were perched on the dirt hills. Behind them were rows of dark bodies with a few heads sticking curiously over the top.

Always the noise of skirmishers came from the woods on the front and left, and the din on the right had grown to frightful proportions. The guns were roaring without an instant's pause for breath. It seemed that the cannon had come from all parts and were engaged in a stupendous wrangle. It became impossible to make a sentence heard.

The youth wished to launch a joke—a quotation from newspapers.[1] He desired to say, "All quiet on the Rappahannock," but the guns refused to permit even a comment upon their uproar. He never successfully concluded the sentence. But at last the guns stopped, and among the men in the rifle pits rumors again flew, like birds, but they were now for the most part black creatures who flapped their wings drearily near to the ground and refused to rise on any wings of hope. The men's faces grew doleful from the interpreting of omens. Tales of hesitation and uncertainty on the part of those high in place and responsibility came to their ears. Stories of disaster were borne into their minds with many proofs. This din of musketry on the right, growing like a released genie of sound, expressed and emphasized the army's plight.

The men were disheartened and began to mutter. They made gestures expressive of the sentence: "Ah, what more can we

---

[1] *Namely, "All quiet along the Potomac," which was common among newspapers during the Civil War. Crane's variant is satiric.*

do?" And it could always be seen that they were bewildered by the alleged news and could not fully comprehend a defeat.

Before the gray mists had been totally obliterated by the sun-rays, the regiment was marching in a spread column that was retiring carefully through the woods. The disordered, hurrying lines of the enemy could sometimes be seen down through the groves and little fields. They were yelling, shrill and exultant.

At this sight the youth forgot many personal matters and became greatly enraged. He exploded in loud sentences. "B'jimi-ney, we're generaled by a lot 'a lunkheads."

"More than one feller has said that t'-day," observed a man.

His friend, recently aroused, was still very drowsy. He looked behind him until his mind took in the meaning of the movement. Then he sighed. "Oh, well, I s'pose we got licked," he remarked sadly.

The youth had a thought that it would not be handsome for him to freely condemn other men. He made an attempt to restrain himself, but the words upon his tongue were too bitter. He presently began a long and intricate denunciation of the commander of the forces.

"Mebbe, it wa'n't all his fault—not all together. He did th' best he knowed. It's our luck t' git licked often," said his friend in a weary tone. He was trudging along with stooped shoulders and shifting eyes like a man who has been caned and kicked.

"Well, don't we fight like the devil? Don't we do all that men can?" demanded the youth loudly.

He was secretly dumbfounded at this sentiment when it came from his lips. For a moment his face lost its valor and he looked guiltily about him. But no one questioned his right to deal in such words, and presently he recovered his air of courage. He went on to repeat a statement he had heard going from group to group at the camp that morning. "The brigadier said he never saw a new reg'ment fight the way we fought yestir-day, didn't he? And we didn't do better than many another reg'ment, did we? Well, then, you can't say it's th' army's fault, can you?"

In his reply, the friend's voice was stern. " 'A course not," he said. "No man dare say we don't fight like th' devil. No man will ever dare say it. Th' boys fight like hell-roosters. But still—still, we don't have no luck."

"Well, then, if we fight like the devil an' don't ever whip, it must be the general's fault," said the youth grandly and decisively. "And I don't see any sense in fighting and fighting and fighting, yet always losing through some derned old lunkhead of a general."

A sarcastic man who was tramping at the youth's side, then spoke lazily. "Mebbe yeh think yeh fit th' hull battle yestirday, Fleming," he remarked.

The speech pierced the youth. Inwardly he was reduced to an abject pulp by these chance words. His legs quaked privately. He cast a frightened glance at the sarcastic man.

"Why, no," he hastened to say in a conciliating voice, "I don't think I fought the whole battle yesterday."

But the other seemed innocent of any deeper meaning. Apparently, he had no information. It was merely his habit. "Oh!" he replied in the same tone of calm derision.

The youth, nevertheless, felt a threat. His mind shrank from going near to the danger, and thereafter he was silent. The significance of the sarcastic man's words took from him all loud moods that would make him appear prominent. He became suddenly a modest person.

There was low-toned talk among the troops. The officers were impatient and snappy, their countenances clouded with the tales of misfortune. The troops, sifting through the forest, were sullen. In the youth's company once a man's laugh rang out. A dozen soldiers turned their faces quickly toward him and frowned with vague displeasure.

The noise of firing dogged their footsteps. Sometimes, it seemed to be driven a little way, but it always returned again with increased insolence. The men muttered and cursed, throwing black looks in its direction.

In a clear space the troops were at last halted. Regiments and brigades, broken and detached through their encounters with thickets, grew together again and lines were faced toward the pursuing bark of the enemy's infantry.

This noise, following like the yellings of eager, metallic hounds, increased to a loud and joyous burst, and then, as the sun went serenely up the sky, throwing illuminating rays into the gloomy thickets, it broke forth into prolonged pealings. The woods began to crackle as if afire.

"Whoop-a-dadee," said a man, "here we are! Everybody fightin'. Blood an' destruction."

"I was willin' t' bet they'd attack as soon as th' sun got fairly up," savagely asserted the lieutenant who commanded the youth's company. He jerked without mercy at his little mustache. He strode to and fro with dark dignity in the rear of his men, who were lying down behind whatever protection they had collected.

A battery had trundled into position in the rear and was thoughtfully shelling the distance. The regiment, unmolested as yet, awaited the moment when the gray shadows of the woods before them should be slashed by the lines of flame. There was much growling and swearing.

"Good Gawd," the youth grumbled, "we're always being chased around like rats! It makes me sick. Nobody seems to know where we go or why we go. We just get fired around from pillar to post and get licked here and get licked there, and nobody knows what it's done for. It makes a man feel like a damn' kitten in a bag. Now, I'd like to know what the eternal thunders we was marched into these woods for anyhow, unless it was to give the rebs a regular pot shot at us. We came in here and got our legs all tangled up in these cussed briers, and then we begin to fight and the rebs had an easy time of it. Don't tell me it's just luck! I know better. It's this derned old—"

The friend seemed jaded, but he interrupted his comrade with a voice of calm confidence. "It'll turn out all right in th' end," he said.

"Oh, the devil it will! You always talk like a dog-hanged parson. Don't tell me! I know—"

At this time there was an interposition by the savage-minded lieutenant, who was obliged to vent some of his inward dissatisfaction upon his men. "You boys shut right up! There no need 'a your wastin' your breath in long-winded arguments about this an' that an' th' other. You've been jawin' like a lot 'a old hens. All you've got t' do is to fight, an' you'll get plenty 'a that t' do in about ten minutes. Less talkin' an' more fightin' is what's best for you boys. I never saw sech gabbling jackasses."

He paused, ready to pounce upon any man who might have the temerity to reply. No words being said, he resumed his dignified pacing.

"There's too much chin music an' too little fightin' in this war, anyhow," he said to them, turning his head for a final remark.

The day had grown more white, until the sun shed his full radiance upon the thronged forest. A sort of a gust of battle came sweeping toward that part of the line where lay the youth's regiment. The front shifted a trifle to meet it squarely. There was a wait. In this part of the field there passed slowly the intense moments that precede the tempest.

A single rifle flashed in a thicket before the regiment. In an instant it was joined by many others. There was a mighty song of clashes and crashes that went sweeping through the woods. The guns in the rear, aroused and enraged by shells that had been thrown burrlike at them, suddenly involved themselves in a hideous altercation with another band of guns. The battle roar settled to a rolling thunder, which was a single, long explosion.

In the regiment there was a peculiar kind of hesitation denoted in the attitudes of the men. They were worn, exhausted, having slept but little and labored much. They rolled their eyes toward the advancing battle as they stood awaiting the shock. Some shrank and flinched. They stood as men tied to stakes.

CHAPTER XVII

This advance of the enemy had seemed to the youth like a ruthless hunting.[1] He began to fume with rage and exasperation. He beat his foot upon the ground, and scowled with hate at the swirling smoke that was approaching like a phantom flood. There was a maddening quality in this seeming resolution of the foe to give him no rest, to give him no time to sit down and think. Yesterday he had fought and had fled rapidly. There had been many adventures. For to-day he felt that he had earned opportunities for contemplative respose. He could have enjoyed portraying to uninitiated listeners various scenes at which he had been a witness or ably discussing the processes of war with other proved men. Too it was important that he should have time for physical recuperation. He was sore and stiff from his experiences. He had received his fill of all exertions, and he wished to rest.

But those other men seemed never to grow weary; they were fighting with their old speed. He had a wild hate for the relentless foe. Yesterday, when he had imagined the universe to be against him, he had hated it, little gods and big gods; to-day he hated the army of the foe with the same great hatred. He was not going to be badgered of his life, like a kitten chased by boys, he said. It was not well to drive men into final corners; at those moments they could all develop teeth and claws.

He leaned and spoke into his friend's ear. He menaced the woods with a gesture. "If they keep on chasing us, by Gawd, they'd better watch out. Can't stand *too* much."

The friend twisted his head and made a calm reply. "If they keep on a-chasin' us they'll drive us all inteh th' river."

The youth cried out savagely at this statement. He crouched

---

[1] *A variant of this first sentence appears on a sheet in Manuscript LV unnumbered and blank except for these words:* As Fleming had watched this approach of the enemy which had seemed to him like a ru *unfinished, rewritten and revised on page 140 of Manuscript LV. The extra sheet represents Crane's first attempt at Chapter xvii.*

behind a little tree, with his eyes burning hatefully and his teeth set in a curlike snarl. The awkward bandage was still about his head, and upon it, over his wound, there was a spot of dry blood. His hair was wondrously tousled, and some straggling, moving locks hung over the cloth of the bandage down toward his forehead. His jacket and shirt were open at the throat, and exposed his young bronzed neck. There could be seen spasmodic gulpings at his throat.

His fingers twined nervously about his rifle. He wished that it was an engine of annihilating power. He felt that he and his companions were being taunted and derided from sincere convictions that they were poor and puny. His knowledge of his inability to take vengeance for it made his rage into a dark and stormy specter, that possessed him and made him dream of abominable cruelties. The tormentors were flies sucking insolently at his blood, and he thought that he would have given his life for a revenge of seeing their faces in pitiful plights.

The winds of battle had swept all about the regiment, until the one rifle, instantly followed by others, flashed in its front. A moment later the regiment roared forth its sudden and valiant retort. A dense wall of smoke settled slowly down. It was furiously slit and slashed by the knifelike fire from the rifles.

To the youth the fighters resembled animals tossed for a death struggle into a dark pit. There was a sensation that he and his fellows, at bay, were pushing back, always pushing fierce onslaughts of creatures who were slippery. Their beams of crimson seemed to get no purchase upon the bodies of their foes; the latter seemed to evade them with ease, and come through, between, around, and about with unopposed skill.

When, in a dream, it occurred to the youth that his rifle was an impotent stick, he lost sense of everything but his hate, his desire to smash into pulp the glittering smile of victory which he could feel upon the faces of his enemies.

The blue smoke-swallowed line curled and writhed like a snake stepped upon. It swung its ends to and fro in an agony of fear and rage.

The youth was not conscious that he was erect upon his feet. He did not know the direction of the ground. Indeed, once he even lost the habit of balance and fell heavily. He was up again immediately. One thought went through the chaos of his brain at the time. He wondered if he had fallen because he had been shot. But the suspicion flew away at once. He did not think more of it.

He had taken up a first position behind the little tree, with a direct determination to hold it against the world. He had not deemed it possible that his army could that day succeed, and from this he felt the ability to fight harder. But the throng had surged in all ways, until he lost directions and locations, save that he knew where lay the enemy.

The flames bit him, and the hot smoke broiled his skin. His rifle barrel grew so hot that ordinarily he could not have borne it upon his palms; but he kept on stuffing cartridges into it, and pounding them with his clanking, bending ramrod. If he aimed at some changing form through the smoke, he pulled his trigger with a fierce grunt, as if he were dealing a blow of the fist with all his strength.

When the enemy seemed falling back before him and his fellows, he went instantly forward, like a dog who, seeing his foes lagging, turns and insists upon being pursued. And when he was compelled to retire again, he did it slowly, sullenly, taking steps of wrathful despair.

Once he, in his intent hate, was almost alone, and was firing, when all those near him had ceased. He was so engrossed in his occupation that he was not aware of a lull.

He was recalled by a hoarse laugh and a sentence that came to his ears in a voice of contempt and amazement. "Yeh infernal fool, don't yeh know enough t' quit when there ain't anything t' shoot at? Good Gawd!"

He turned then and, pausing with his rifle thrown half into position, looked at the blue line of his comrades. During this moment of leisure they seemed all to be engaged in staring with astonishment at him. They had become spectators. Turning to the front again he saw, under the lifted smoke, a deserted ground.

He looked bewildered for a moment. Then there appeared upon the glazed vacancy of his eyes a diamond point of intelligence. "Oh," he said, comprehending.

He returned to his comrades and threw himself upon the ground. He sprawled like a man who had been thrashed. His flesh seemed strangely on fire, and the sounds of the battle continued in his ears. He groped blindly for his canteen.

The lieutenant was crowing. He seemed drunk with fighting. He called out to the youth: "By heavens, if I had ten thousand wild cats like you I could tear th' stomach outa this war in less'n a week!" He puffed out his chest with large dignity as he said it.

Some of the men muttered and looked at the youth in awestruck ways. It was plain that as he had gone on loading and firing and cursing without the proper intermission, they had found time to regard him. And they now looked upon him as a war devil.

The friend came staggering to him. There was some fright and dismay in his voice. "Are yeh all right, Fleming? Do yeh feel all right? There ain't nothin' th' matter with yeh, Henry, is there?"

"No," said the youth with difficulty. His throat seemed full of knobs and burs.

These incidents made the youth ponder. It was revealed to him that he had been a barbarian, a beast. He had fought like a pagan who defends his religion. Regarding it, he saw that it was fine, wild, and, in some ways, easy. He had been a tremendous figure, no doubt. By this struggle he had overcome obstacles which he had admitted to be mountains. They had fallen like paper peaks, and he was now what he called a hero. And he had not been aware of the process. He had slept and, awakening, found himself a knight.

He lay and basked in the occasional stares of his comrades. Their faces were varied in degrees of blackness from the burned powder. Some were utterly smudged. They were reeking with perspiration, and their breaths came hard and wheezing. And from these soiled expanses they peered at him.

"Hot work! Hot work!" cried the lieutenant deliriously. He walked up and down, restless and eager. Sometimes his voice could be heard in a wild, incomprehensible laugh.

When he had a particularly profound thought upon the science of war he always unconsciously addressed himself to the youth.

There was some grim rejoicing by the men. "By thunder, I bet this army'll never see another new reg'ment like us!"

"You bet!"

> *"A dog, a woman, an' a walnut tree,*
> *Th' more yeh beat 'em, th' better they be!*

That's like us."

"Lost a piler men, they did. If an' ol' woman swep' up th' woods she'd git a dustpanful."

"Yes, an' if she'll come around ag'in in 'bout an' hour she'll git a pile more."

The forest still bore its burden of clamor. From off under the trees came the rolling clatter of the musketry. Each distant thicket seemed a strange porcupine with quills of flame. A cloud of dark smoke, as from smoldering ruins, went up toward the sun now bright and gay in the blue, enameled sky.

CHAPTER XVIII

The ragged line had respite for some minutes, but during its pause the struggle in the forest became magnified until the trees seemed to quiver from the firing and the ground to shake from the rushing of the men. The voices of the cannon were mingled in a long and interminable row. It seemed difficult to live in such an atmosphere. The chests of the men strained for a bit of freshness, and their throats craved water.

There was one shot through the body, who raised a cry of bitter lamentation when came this lull. Perhaps he had been calling out during the fighting also, but at that time no one had heard him. But now the men turned at the woeful complaints of him upon the ground.

"Who is it? Who is it?"

"It's Jimmie Rogers. Jimmie Rogers."

When their eyes first encountered him there was a sudden halt, as if they feared to go near. He was thrashing about in the grass, twisting his shuddering body into many strange postures. He was screaming loudly. This instant's hesitation seemed to fill him with a tremendous, fantastic contempt, and he damned them in shrieked sentences.

The youth's friend had a geographical illusion concerning a stream, and he obtained permission to go for some water. Immediately canteens were showered upon him. "Fill mine, will yeh?" "Bring me some, too." "And me, too." He departed, laden. The youth went with his friend, feeling a desire to throw his heated body onto the stream and, soaking there, drink quarts.

They made a hurried search for the supposed stream, but did not find it. "No water here," said the youth. They turned without delay and began to retrace their steps.

From their position as they again faced toward the place of the fighting, they could of course comprehend a greater amount of the battle than when their visions had been blurred by the hurling smoke of the line. They could see dark stretches winding along the land, and on one cleared space there was a row of guns making gray clouds, which were filled with large flashes of orange-colored flame. Over some foliage they could see the roof of a house. One window, glowing a deep murder red, shone squarely through the leaves. From the edifice a tall leaning tower of smoke went far into the sky.

Looking over their own troops, they saw mixed masses slowly getting into regular form. The sunlight made twinkling points

of the bright steel. To the rear there was a glimpse of a distant
roadway as it curved over a slope. It was crowded with retreating infantry. From all the interwoven forest arose the smoke
and bluster of the battle. The air was always occupied by a
blaring.

Near where they stood shells were flip-flapping and hooting.
Occasional bullets buzzed in the air and spanged into tree
trunks. Wounded men and other stragglers were slinking
through the woods.

Looking down an aisle of the grove, the youth and his companion saw a jangling general and his staff almost ride upon a
wounded man, who was crawling on his hands and knees. The
general reined strongly at his charger's opened and foamy
mouth and guided it with dexterous horsemanship past the
man. The latter scrambled in wild and torturing haste. His
strength evidently failed him as he reached a place of safety.
One of his arms suddenly weakened, and he fell, sliding over
upon his back. He lay stretched out, breathing gently.

A moment later the small, creaking cavalcade was directly
in front of the two soldiers. Another officer, riding with the
skillful abandon of a cowboy, galloped his horse to a position
directly before the general. The two unnoticed foot soldiers
made a little show of going on, but they lingered near in the
desire to overhear the conversation. Perhaps, they thought,
some great inner historical things would be said.

The general, whom the boys knew as the commander of their
division, looked at the other officer and spoke coolly, as if he
were criticising his clothes. "Th' enemy's formin' over there for
another charge," he said. "It'll be directed against Whiterside,
an' I fear they'll break through there unless we work like thunder t' stop them."

The other swore at his restive horse, and then cleared his
throat. He made a gesture toward his cap. "It'll be hell t' pay
stoppin' them," he said shortly.

"I presume so," remarked the general. Then he began to talk
rapidly and in a lower tone. He frequently illustrated his words

with a pointing finger. The two infantrymen could hear nothing until finally he asked: "What troops can you spare?"

The officer who rode like a cowboy reflected for an instant. "Well," he said, "I had to order in th' 12th to help th' 76th, an' I haven't really got any. But there's th' 304th. They fight like a lot 'a mule drivers. I can spare them best of any."

The youth and his friend exchanged glances of astonishment.

The general spoke sharply. "Get 'em ready, then. I'll watch developments from here, an' send you word when t' start them. It'll happen in five minutes."

As the other officer tossed his fingers toward his cap and wheeling his horse, started away, the general called out to him in a sober voice: "I don't believe many of your mule drivers will get back."

The other shouted something in reply. He smiled.

With scared faces, the youth and his companion hurried back to the line.

These happenings had occupied an incredibly short time, yet the youth felt that in them he had been made aged.[1] New eyes were given to him. And the most startling thing was to learn suddenly that he was very insignificant. The officer spoke of the regiment as if he referred to a broom. Some part of the woods needed sweeping, perhaps, and he merely indicated a broom in a tone properly indifferent to its fate. It was war, no doubt, but it appeared strange.

As the two boys approached the line, the lieutenant perceived them and swelled with wrath. "Fleming—Wilson—how long does it take yeh to git water, anyhow—where yeh been to."

But his oration ceased as he saw their eyes, which were large with great tales. "We're goin' t' charge—we're goin' t' charge!" cried the youth's friend, hastening with his news.

---

[1] *Manuscript SV contains a page that is blank except for one sentence representing the author's first attempt at this passage:* These happenings had occupied but an incredibly short time *unfinished. The page in SV is numbered in the author's handwriting as 149.*

"Charge?" said the lieutenant. "Charge? Well, b'Gawd! Now; this is real fightin'." Over his soiled countenance there went a boastful smile. "Charge? Well, b'Gawd!"

A little group of soldiers surrounded the two youths. "Are we, sure 'nough? Well, I'll be derned! Charge? What fer? What at? Wilson, you're lyin'." [2]

"I hope to die," said the youth, pitching his tones to the key of angry remonstrance. "Sure as shooting, I tell you."

And his friend spoke in re-enforcement. "Not by a blame sight, he ain't lyin'. We heard 'em talkin'."

They caught sight of two mounted figures a short distance from them. One was the colonel of the regiment and the other was the officer who had received orders from the commander of the division. They were gesticulating at each other. The soldier, pointing at them, interpreted the scene.

One man had a final objection: "How could yeh hear 'em talkin'?" But the men, for a large part, nodded, admitting that previously the two friends had spoken truth.

They settled back into reposeful attitudes with airs of having accepted the matter. And they mused upon it, with a hundred varieties of expression. It was an engrossing thing to think about. Many tightened their belts carefully and hitched at their trousers.

A moment later the officers began to bustle among the men, pushing them into a more compact mass and into a better alignment. They chased those that straggled and fumed at a few men who seemed to show by their attitudes that they had decided to remain at that spot. They were like critical shepherds struggling with sheep.

Presently, the regiment seemed to draw itself up and heave a deep breath. None of the men's faces were mirrors of large thoughts. The soldiers were bended and stooped like sprinters

---

[2] *The word of Wilson is here doubted just as in Chapter i, paragraph 5, the word of the tall soldier is doubted. Ironically, the word of the tall soldier was then disbelieved by Wilson himself:* "It's a lie! that's all it is—a thunderin' lie!" *said another private loudly.*

before a signal. Many pairs of glinting eyes peered from the grimy faces toward the curtains of the deeper woods. They seemed to be engaged in deep calculations of time and distance.

They were surrounded by the noises of the monstrous altercation between the two armies. The world was fully interested in other matters. Apparently, the regiment had its small affair to itself.

The youth, turning, shot a quick, inquiring glance at his friend. The latter returned to him the same manner of look. They were the only ones who possessed an inner knowledge. "Mule drivers—hell t' pay—don't believe many will get back." It was an ironical secret. Still, they saw no hesitation in each other's faces, and they nodded a mute and unprotesting assent when a shaggy man near them said in a meek voice: "We'll git swallowed."

CHAPTER XIX

The youth stared at the land in front of him. Its foliages now seemed to veil powers and horrors. He was unaware of the machinery of orders that started the charge, although from the corners of his eyes he saw an officer, who looked like a boy a-horseback, come galloping, waving his hat. Suddenly he felt a straining and heaving among the men. The line fell slowly forward like a toppling wall, and, with a convulsive gasp that was intended for a cheer, the regiment began its journey. The youth was pushed and jostled for a moment before he understood the movement at all, but directly he lunged ahead and began to run.

He fixed his eye upon a distant and prominent clump of trees where he had concluded the enemy were to be met, and he ran toward it as toward a goal. He had believed throughout that it was a mere question of getting over an unpleasant matter as quickly as possible, and he ran desperately, as if pursued for a murder. His face was drawn hard and tight with the stress of his endeavor. His eyes were fixed in a lurid glare. And with his

soiled and disordered dress, his red and inflamed features sur-
mounted by the dingy rag with its spot of blood, his wildly
swinging rifle and banging accouterments,[1] he looked to be an
insane soldier.

As the regiment swung from its position out into a cleared
space the woods and thickets before it awakened. Yellow flames
leaped toward it from many directions. The forest made a
tremendous objection.

The line lurched straight for a moment. Then the right wing
sprung forward; it in turn was surpassed by the left. Afterward
the center careered to the front until the regiment was a wedge-
shaped mass, but an instant later the opposition of the bushes,
trees, and uneven places on the ground split the command and
scattered it into detached clusters.

The youth, light-footed, was unconsciously in advance. His
eyes still kept note of the clump of trees. From all places near
it the clannish yell of the enemy could be heard. The little
flames of rifles leaped from it. The song of the bullets was in
the air and shells snarled among the tree-tops. One tumbled
directly into the middle of a hurrying group and exploded in
crimson fury. There was an instant's spectacle of a man, almost
over it, throwing up his hands to shield his eyes.

Other men, punched by bullets, fell in grotesque agonies.
The regiment left a coherent trail of bodies.

They had passed into a clearer atmosphere. There was an
effect like a revelation in the new appearance of the landscape.
Some men working madly at a battery were plain to them, and
the opposing infantry's lines were defined by the gray walls
and fringes of smoke.

It seemed to the youth that he saw everything. Each blade
of the green grass was bold and clear. He thought that he was
aware of every change in the thin, transparent vapor that
floated idly in sheets. The brown or gray trunks of the trees
showed each roughness of their surfaces. And the men of the
regiment, with their starting eyes and sweating faces, running

---

[1] *LV:* accoutrements.

madly, or falling, as if thrown headlong, to queer, heaped-up corpses—all were comprehended. His mind took a mechanical but firm impression, so that afterward everything was pictured and explained to him, save why he himself was there.

But there was a frenzy made from this furious rush. The men, pitching forward insanely, had burst into cheerings, moblike and barbaric, but tuned in strange keys that can arouse the dullard and the stoic. It made a mad enthusiasm that, it seemed, would be incapable of checking itself before granite and brass. There was the delirium that encounters despair and death, and is heedless and blind to the odds. It is a temporary but sublime absence of selfishness. And because it was of this order was the reason, perhaps, why the youth wondered, afterward, what reasons he could have had for being there.

Presently the straining pace ate up the energies of the men. As if by agreement, the leaders began to slacken their speed. The volleys directed against them had had a seeming windlike effect. The regiment snorted and blew. Among some stolid trees it began to falter and hesitate. The men, staring intently, began to wait for some of the distant walls of smoke to move and disclose to them the scene. Since much of their strength and their breath had vanished, they returned to caution. They were become men again.

The youth had a vague belief that he had run miles, and he thought, in a way, that he was now in some new and unknown land.

The moment the regiment ceased its advance the protesting splutter of musketry became a steadied roar. Long and accurate fringes of smoke spread out. From the top of a small hill came level belchings of yellow flame that caused an inhuman whistling in the air.

The men, halted, had opportunity to see some of their comrades dropping with moans and shrieks. A few lay under foot, still or wailing. And now for an instant the men stood, their rifles slack in their hands, and watched the regiment dwindle. They appeared dazed and stupid. This spectacle seemed to paralyze them, overcome them with a fatal fascination. They stared woodenly at the sights, and, lowering their eyes, looked from face to face. It was a strange pause, and a strange silence.

Then, above the sounds of the outside commotion, arose the roar of the lieutenant. He strode suddenly forth, his infantile features black with rage.

"Come on, yeh fools!" he bellowed. "Come on! Yeh can't stay here. Yeh must come on." He said more, but much of it could not be understood.

He started rapidly forward, with his head turned toward the men. "Come on," he was shouting. The men stared with blank and yokel-like eyes at him. He was obliged to halt and retrace his steps. He stood then with his back to the enemy and delivered gigantic curses into the faces of the men. His body vibrated from the weight and force of his imprecations. And he could string oaths with the facility of a maiden who strings beads.

The friend of the youth aroused. Lurching suddenly forward and dropping to his knees, he fired an angry shot at the persistent woods. This action awakened the men. They huddled no more like sheep. They seemed suddenly to bethink them of their weapons, and at once commenced firing. Belabored by their officers, they began to move forward. The regiment, involved like a cart involved in mud and muddle, started unevenly with many jolts and jerks. The men stopped now every few paces to fire and load, and in this manner moved slowly on from trees to trees.

The flaming opposition in their front grew with their advance until it seemed that all forward ways were barred by the thin leaping tongues, and off to the right an ominous demonstration could sometimes be dimly discerned. The smoke lately generated was in confusing clouds that made it difficult for the regiment to proceed with intelligence. As he passed through each curling mass the youth wondered what would confront him on the farther side.

The command went painfully forward until an open space interposed between them and the lurid lines. Here, crouching and cowering behind some trees, the men clung with desperation, as if threatened by a wave. They looked wild-eyed, and as if amazed at this furious disturbance they had stirred. In the storm there was an ironical expression of their importance. The faces of the men, too, showed a lack of a certain feeling of responsibility for being there. It was as if they had been driven. It was the dominant animal failing to remember in the supreme moments the forceful causes of various superficial qualities. The whole affair seemed incomprehensible to many of them.

As they halted thus the lieutenant again began to bellow profanely. Regardless of the vindictive threats of the bullets, he went about coaxing, berating, and bedamning. His lips, that were habitually in a soft and childlike curve, were now writhed into unholy contortions. He swore by all possible deities.

Once he grabbed the youth by the arm. "Come on, yeh lunkhead!" he roared. "Come on! We'll all git killed if we stay here. We've on'y got t' go across that lot. An' then"—the remainder of his idea disappeared in a blue haze of curses.

The youth stretched forth his arm. "Cross there?" His mouth was puckered in doubt and awe.

"Certainly. Jest 'cross th' lot! We can't stay here," screamed the lieutenant. He poked his face close to the youth and waved his bandaged hand. "Come on!" Presently he grappled with him as if for a wrestling bout. It was as if he planned to drag the youth by the ear on to the assault.

The private felt a sudden unspeakable indignation against his officer. He wrenched fiercely and shook him off.

"Come on yerself, then," he yelled. There was a bitter challenge in his voice.

They galloped together down the regimental front. The friend scrambled after them. In front of the colors the three men began to bawl: "Come on! come on!" They danced and gyrated like tortured savages.

The flag, obedient to these appeals, bended its glittering form and swept toward them. The men wavered in indecision for a moment, and then with a long, wailful cry the dilapidated regiment surged forward and began its new journey.

Over the field went the scurrying mass. It was a handful of men splattered into the faces of the enemy. Toward it instantly sprang the yellow tongues. A vast quantity of blue smoke hung before them. A mighty banging made ears valueless.

The youth ran like a madman to reach the woods before a bullet could discover him. He ducked his head low, like a football player. In his haste his eyes almost closed, and the scene was a wild blur. Pulsating saliva stood at the corners of his mouth.

Within him, as he hurled himself forward, was born a love, a despairing fondness for this flag which was near him. It was a creation of beauty and invulnerability. It was a goddess, radiant, that bended its form with an imperious gesture to him. It was a woman, red and white, hating and loving, that called him with the voice of his hopes. Because no harm could come to it he endowed it with power. He kept near, as if it could be a saver of lives, and an imploring cry went from his mind.

In the mad scramble he was aware that the color sergeant flinched suddenly, as if struck by a bludgeon. He faltered, and then became motionless, save for his quivering knees.

He made a spring and a clutch at the pole. At the same instant his friend grabbed it from the other side. They jerked at it, stout and furious, but the color sergeant was dead, and the corpse would not relinquish its trust. For a moment there was a grim encounter. The dead man, swinging with bended back, seemed to be obstinately tugging, in ludicrous and awful ways, for the possession of the flag.

It was past in an instant of time. They wrenched the flag furiously from the dead man, and, as they turned again, the corpse swayed forward with bowed head. One arm swung high, and the curved hand fell with heavy protest on the friend's unheeding shoulder.

CHAPTER XX

When the two youths turned with the flag they saw that much of the regiment had crumbled away, and the dejected remnant was coming back. The men, having hurled themselves in projectile fashion, had presently expended their forces. They slowly retreated, with their faces still toward the spluttering woods, and their hot rifles still replying to the din. Several officers were giving orders, their voices keyed to screams.

"Where in hell yeh goin'?" the lieutenant was asking in a sarcastic howl. And a red-bearded officer, whose voice of triple brass could plainly be heard, was commanding: "Shoot into 'em! Shoot into 'em, Gawd damn their souls!" There was a *mêlée* [1] of screeches, in which the men were ordered to do conflicting and impossible things.

The youth and his friend had a small scuffle over the flag. "Give it t' me!" "No, let me keep it!" Each felt satisfied with the other's possession of it, but each felt bound to declare, by an offer to carry the emblem, his willingness to further risk himself. The youth roughly pushed his friend away.

The regiment fell back to the stolid trees. There it halted for a moment to blaze at some dark forms that had begun to steal upon its track. Presently it resumed its march again, curving among the tree trunks. By the time the depleted regiment had again reached the first open space they were receiving a fast and merciless fire. There seemed to be mobs all about them.

The greater part of the men, discouraged, their spirits worn by the turmoil, acted as if stunned. They accepted the pelting of the bullets with bowed and weary heads. It was of no purpose to strive against walls. It was of no use to batter themselves against granite. And from this consciousness that they had attempted to conquer an unconquerable thing there seemed to arise a feeling that they had been betrayed. They glowered with bent brows, but dangerously, upon some of the

---

[1] *FAE: melée; LV:* melee.

officers, more particulary upon the red-bearded one with the voice of triple brass.

However, the rear of the regiment was fringed with men, who continued to shoot irritably at the advancing foes. They seemed resolved to make every trouble. The youthful lieutenant was perhaps the last man in the disordered mass. His forgotten back was toward the enemy. He had been shot in the arm. It hung straight and rigid. Occasionally he would cease to remember it, and be about to emphasize an oath with a sweeping gesture. The multiplied pain caused him to swear with incredible power.

The youth went along with slipping, uncertain feet. He kept watchful eyes rearward. A scowl of mortification and rage was upon his face. He had thought of a fine revenge upon the officer who had referred to him and his fellows as mule drivers. But he saw that it could not come to pass. His dreams had collapsed when the mule drivers, dwindling rapidly, had wavered and hesitated on the little clearing, and then had recoiled. And now the retreat of the mule drivers was a march of shame to him.

A dagger-pointed gaze from without his blackened face was held toward the enemy, but his greater hatred was riveted upon the man, who, not knowing him, had called him a mule driver.

When he knew that he and his comrades had failed to do anything in successful ways that might bring the little pangs of a kind of remorse upon the officer, the youth allowed the rage of the baffled to possess him. This cold officer upon a monument, who dropped epithets unconcernedly down, would be finer as a dead man, he thought. So grievous did he think it that he could never possess the secret right to taunt truly in answer.

He had pictured red letters of curious revenge. "We *are* mule drivers, are we?" And now he was compelled to throw them away.

He presently wrapped his heart in the cloak of his pride and kept the flag erect. He harangued his fellows, pushing against their chests with his free hand. To those he knew well he made frantic appeals, beseeching them by name. Between him and the lieutenant, scolding and near to losing his mind with rage, there was felt a subtle fellowship and equality. They supported each other in all manner of hoarse, howling protests.

But the regiment was a machine run down. The two men babbled at a forceless thing. The soldiers who had heart to go slowly were continually shaken in their resolves by a knowledge that comrades were slipping with speed back to the lines. It was difficult to think of reputation when others were thinking of skins. Wounded men were left crying on this black journey.

The smoke fringes and flames blustered always. The youth, peering once through a sudden rift in a cloud, saw a brown mass of troops, interwoven and magnified until they appeared to be thousands. A fierce-hued flag flashed before his vision.

Immediately, as if the uplifting of the smoke had been prearranged, the discovered troops burst into a rasping yell, and a hundred flames jetted toward the retreating band. A rolling gray cloud again interposed as the regiment doggedly replied. The youth had to depend again upon his misused ears, which were trembling and buzzing from the *mêlée* of musketry and yells.

The way seemed eternal. In the clouded haze men became panicstricken with the thought that the regiment had lost its path, and was proceeding in a perilous direction. Once the men who headed the wild procession turned and came pushing back against their comrades, screaming that they were being fired upon from points which they had considered to be toward their own lines. At this cry a hysterical fear and dismay beset the troops. A soldier, who heretofore had been ambitious to make the regiment into a wise little band that would proceed calmly amid the huge-appearing difficulties, suddenly sank down and buried his face in his arms with an air of bowing to a doom. From another a shrill lamentation rang out filled with profane illusions [2] to a general. Men ran hither and thither,

---

[2] *Same as in LV. Intended no doubt for the word:* allusions.

seeking with their eyes roads of escape. With serene regularity, as if controlled by a schedule, bullets buffed into men.

The youth walked stolidly into the midst of the mob, and with his flag in his hands took a stand as if he expected an attempt to push him to the ground. He unconsciously assumed the attitude of the color bearer in the fight of the preceding day. He passed over his brow a hand that trembled. His breath did not come freely. He was choking during this small wait for the crisis.

His friend came to him. "Well, Henry, I guess this is good-by—John."

"Oh, shut up, you damned fool!" replied the youth, and he would not look at the other.

The officers labored like politicians to beat the mass into a proper circle to face the menaces. The ground was uneven and torn. The men curled into depressions and fitted themselves snugly behind whatever would frustrate a bullet.

The youth noted with vague surprise that the lieutenant was standing mutely with his legs far apart and his sword [3] held in the manner of a cane.[4] The youth wondered what had happened to his vocal organs that he no more cursed.

There was something curious in this little intent pause of the lieutenant. He was like a babe which, having wept its fill, raises its eyes and fixes upon a distant toy. He was engrossed in this contemplation, and the soft under lip quivered from self-whispered words.

Some lazy and ignorant smoke curled slowly. The men, hiding from the bullets, waited anxiously for it to lift and disclose the plight of the regiment.

The silent ranks were suddenly thrilled by the eager voice of the youthful lieutenant bawling out: "Here they come!

---

[3] *LV:* cane *canceled.*

[4] *LV:* walking-stick *canceled. This canceled image, as well as the revised form of it, prepares for the phrase* oaths and walking sticks *appearing in the next to the last paragraph of Chapter xxiv. Crane's first intention was to end the novel with that phrase.*

Right on to us, b'Gawd!" His further words were lost in a roar of wicked thunder from the men's rifles.

The youth's eyes had instantly turned in the direction indicated by the awakened and agitated lieutenant, and he had seen the haze of treachery disclosing a body of soldiers of the enemy. They were so near that he could see their features. There was a recognition as he looked at the types of faces. Also he perceived with dim amazement that their uniforms were rather gay in effect, being light gray, accented with a brilliant-hued facing. Too, the clothes seemed new.

These troops had apparently been going forward with caution, their rifles held in readiness, when the youthful lieutenant had discovered them and their movement had been interrupted by the volley from the blue regiment. From the moment's glimpse, it was derived that they had been unaware of the proximity of their dark-suited foes or had mistaken the direction. Almost instantly they were shut utterly from the youth's sight by the smoke from the energetic rifles of his companions. He strained his vision to learn the accomplishment of the volley, but the smoke hung before him.

The two bodies of troops exchanged blows in the manner of a pair of boxers. The fast angry firings went back and forth. The men in blue were intent with the despair of their circumstances and they seized upon the revenge to be had at close range. Their thunder swelled loud and valiant. Their curving front bristled with flashes and the place resounded with the clangor of their ramrods. The youth ducked and dodged for a time and achieved a few unsatisfactory views of the enemy. There appeared to be many of them and they were replying swiftly. They seemed moving toward the blue regiment, step by step. He seated himself gloomily on the ground with his flag between his knees.

As he noted the vicious, wolflike temper of his comrades he had a sweet thought that if the enemy was about to swallow the regimental broom as a large prisoner, it could at least have the consolation of going down with bristles forward.

But the blows of the antagonist began to grow more weak. Fewer bullets ripped the air, and finally, when the men slackened to learn of the fight, they could see only dark, floating smoke. The regiment lay still and gazed. Presently some chance whim came to the pestering blur, and it began to coil heavily away. The men saw a ground vacant of fighters. It would have been an empty stage if it were not for a few corpses that lay thrown and twisted into fantastic shapes upon the sward.

At sight of this tableau, many of the men in blue sprang from behind their covers and made an ungainly dance of joy. Their eyes burned and a hoarse cheer of elation broke from their dry lips.

It had begun to seem to them that events were trying to prove that they were impotent. These little battles had evidently endeavored to demonstrate that the men could not fight well. When on the verge of submission to these opinions, the small duel had showed them that the proportions were not impossible, and by it they had revenged themselves upon their misgivings and upon the foe.

The impetus of enthusiasm was theirs again. They gazed about them with looks of uplifted pride, feeling new trust in the grim, always confident weapons in their hands. And they were men.

CHAPTER XXI

Presently they knew that no fighting threatened them. All ways seemed once more opened to them. The dusty blue lines of their friends were disclosed a short distance away. In the distance there were many colossal noises, but in all this part of the field there was a sudden stillness.

They perceived that they were free. The depleted band drew a long breath of relief and gathered itself into a bunch to complete its trip.

In this last length of journey the men began to show strange emotions. They hurried with nervous fear. Some who had been dark and unfaltering in the grimmest moments now could not

conceal an anxiety that made them frantic.[1] It was perhaps
that they dreaded to be killed in insignificant ways after the
times for proper military deaths had passed. Or, perhaps, they
thought it would be too ironical to get killed at the portals of
safety. With backward looks of perturbation, they hastened.

As they approached their own lines there was some sarcasm
exhibited on the part of a gaunt and bronzed regiment that lay
resting in the shade of trees. Questions were wafted to them.

"Where th' hell yeh been?"

"What yeh comin' back fer?"

"Why didn't yeh stay there?"

"Was it warm out there, sonny?"

"Goin' home now, boys?"

One shouted in taunting mimicry: "Oh, mother, come quick
an' look at th' sojers!"

There was no reply from the bruised and battered regiment,
save that one man made broadcast challenges to fist fights and
the red-bearded officer walked rather near and glared in great
swashbuckler style at a tall captain in the other regiment. But
the lieutenant suppressed the man who wished to fist fight,
and the tall captain, flushing at the little fanfare of the red-
bearded one, was obliged to look intently at some trees.

The youth's tender flesh was deeply stung by these remarks.
From under his creased brows he glowered with hate at the
mockers. He meditated upon a few revenges. Still, many in the
regiment hung their heads in criminal fashion, so that it came
to pass that the men trudged with sudden heaviness, as if they
bore upon their bended shoulders the coffin of their honor. And
the youthful lieutenant, recollecting himself, began to mutter
softly in black curses.

They turned when they arrived at their old position to regard
the ground over which they had charged.

The youth in this contemplation was smitten with a large
astonishment. He discovered that the distances, as compared

---

[1] In LV *a canceled passage:* They hastened with backward looks of
perturbation.

with the brilliant measurings of his mind, were trivial and ridiculous. The stolid trees, where much had taken place, seemed incredibly near. The time, too, now that he reflected, he saw to have been short. He wondered at the number of emotions and events that had been crowded into such little spaces. Elfin thoughts must have exaggerated and enlarged everything, he said.

It seemed, then, that there was bitter justice in the speeches of the gaunt and bronzed veterans. He veiled a glance of disdain at his fellows who strewed the ground, choking with dust, red from perspiration, misty-eyed, disheveled.

They were gulping at their canteens, fierce to wring every mite of water from them, and they polished at their swollen and watery features with coat sleeves and bunches of grass.

However, to the youth there was a considerable joy in musing upon his performances during the charge. He had had very little time previously in which to appreciate himself, so that there was now much satisfaction in quietly thinking of his actions. He recalled bits of color that in the flurry had stamped themselves unawares upon his engaged senses.

As the regiment lay heaving from its hot exertions the officer who had named them as mule drivers came galloping along the line. He had lost his cap. His tousled hair streamed wildly, and his face was dark with vexation and wrath. His temper was displayed with more clearness by the way in which he managed his horse. He jerked and wrenched savagely at his bridle, stopping the hard-breathing animal with a furious pull near the colonel of the regiment. He immediately exploded in reproaches which came unbidden to the ears of the men. They were suddenly alert, being always curious about black words between officers.

"Oh, thunder, MacChesnay, what an awful bull you made of this thing!" began the officer. He attempted low tones, but his indignation caused certain of the men to learn the sense of his words. "What an awful mess you made! Good Lord, man, you stopped about a hundred feet this side of a very pretty success!

If your men had gone a hundred feet farther you would have made a great charge, but as it is — what a lot of mud diggers you've got anyway!"

The men, listening with bated breath, now turned their curious eyes upon the colonel. They had a ragamuffin interest in this affair.

The colonel was seen to straighten his form and put one hand forth in oratorical fashion. He wore an injured air; it was as if a deacon had been accused of stealing. The men were wiggling in an ecstasy of excitement.

But of a sudden the colonel's manner changed from that of a deacon to that of a Frenchman. He shrugged his shoulders. "Oh, well, general, we went as far as we could," he said calmly.

"As far as you could? Did you, b'Gawd?" snorted the other. "Well, that wasn't very far, was it?" he added, with a glance of cold contempt into the other's eyes. "Not very far, I think. You were intended to make a diversion in favor of Whiterside. How well you succeeded your own ears can now tell you." He wheeled his horse and rode stiffly away.

The colonel, bidden to hear the jarring noises of an engagement in the woods to the left, broke out in vague damnations.

The lieutenant, who had listened with an air of impotent rage to the interview, spoke suddenly in firm and undaunted tones. "I don't care what a man is—whether he is a general or what—if he says th' boys didn't put up a good fight out there he's a damned fool."

"Lieutenant," began the colonel, severely, "this is my own affair, and I'll trouble you—"

The lieutenant made an obedient gesture. "All right, colonel, all right," he said. He sat down with an air of being content with himself.

The news that the regiment had been reproached went along the line. For a time the men were bewildered by it. "Good thunder!" they ejaculated, staring at the vanishing form of the general. They conceived it to be a huge mistake.

Presently, however, they began to believe that in truth their

efforts had been called light. The youth could see this conviction weigh upon the entire regiment until the men were
like cuffed and cursed animals, but withal rebellious.

The friend, with a grievance in his eye, went to the youth.
"I wonder what he does want," he said. "He must think we
went out there an' played marbles! I never see sech a man!"

The youth developed a tranquil philosophy for these moments of irritation. "Oh, well," he rejoined, "he probably didn't
see nothing of it at all and got mad as blazes, and concluded
we were a lot of sheep, just because we didn't do what he
wanted done. It's a pity old Grandpa Henderson got killed
yestirday—he'd have known that we did our best and fought
good. It's just our awful luck, that's what."

"I should say so," replied the friend. He seemed to be deeply
wounded at an injustice. "I should say we did have awful luck!
There's no fun in fightin' fer people when everything yeh do—
no matter what—ain't done right. I have a notion t' stay behind
next time an' let 'em take their ol' charge an' go t' th' devil
with it."

The youth spoke soothingly to his comrade. "Well, we both
did good. I'd like to see the fool what'd say we both didn't do
as good as we could!"

"Of course we did," declared the friend stoutly. "An' I'd
break th' feller's neck if he was as big as a church. But we're
all right, anyhow, for I heard one feller say that we two fit th'
best in th' reg'ment, an' they had a great argument 'bout it.
Another feller, 'a course, he had t' up an' say it was a lie—he
seen all what was goin' on an' he never seen us from th' beginnin' t' th' end. An' a lot more struck in an' ses it wasn't a
lie—we did fight like thunder, an' they give us quite a send-off.
But this is what I can't stand—these everlastin' ol' soldiers,
titterin' an' laughin', an' then that general, he's crazy."

The youth exclaimed with sudden exasperation: "He's a
lunkhead! He makes me mad. I wish he'd come along next
time. We'd show 'im what—"

He ceased because several men had come hurrying up. Their faces expressed a bringing of great news.

"O Flem, yeh jest oughta heard!" cried one, eagerly.

"Heard what?" said the youth.

"Yeh jest oughta heard!" repeated the other, and he arranged himself to tell his tidings. The others made an excited circle. "Well, sir, th' colonel met your lieutenant right by us—it was damnedest thing I ever heard—an' he ses: 'Ahem! ahem!' he ses. 'Mr. Hasbrouck!' he ses, 'by th' way, who was that lad what carried th' flag?' he ses. There, Flemin', what d' yeh think 'a that? 'Who was th' lad what carried th' flag?' he ses, an' th' lieutenant, he speaks up right away: 'That's Flemin', an' he's a jimhickey,' he ses, right away. What? I say he did. 'A jimhickey,' he ses—those 'r his words. He did, too. I say he did. If you kin tell this story better than I kin, go ahead an' tell it. Well, then, keep yer mouth shet. Th' lieutenant, he ses: 'He's a jimhickey,' an' th' colonel, he ses: 'Ahem! ahem! he is, indeed, a very good man t' have, ahem! He kep' th' flag 'way t' th' front. I saw 'im. He's a good un,' ses th' colonel. 'You bet,' ses th' lieutenant, 'he an' a feller named Wilson was at th' head 'a th' charge, an' howlin' like Indians all th' time,' he ses. 'Head a' th' charge all th' time,' he ses. 'A feller named Wilson,' he ses. There, Wilson, m'boy, put that in a letter an' send it hum t' yer mother, hay? 'A feller named Wilson,' he ses. An' th' colonel, he ses: 'Were they, indeed? Ahem! ahem! My sakes!' he ses. 'At th' head a' th' reg'ment?' he ses. 'They were,' ses th' lieutenant. 'My sakes!' ses th' colonel. He ses: 'Well, well, well,' he ses, 'those two babies?' 'They were,' ses th' lieutenant. 'Well, well,' ses th' colonel, 'they deserve t' be major-generals,' he ses. 'They deserve t' be major-generals.' "

The youth and his friend had said: "Huh!" "Yer lyin', Thompson." [2] "Oh, go t' blazes!" "He never sed it." "Oh, what a lie!"

---

[2] *This incident of disbelief of Thompson has its parallel in Chapter xviii, where Wilson and Fleming are disbelieved, and again in Chapter i, where Jim Conklin is doubted by Wilson and the whole regiment.*

"Huh!" But despite these youthful scoffings and embarrassments, they knew that their faces were deeply flushing from thrills of pleasure. They exchanged a secret glance of joy and congratulation.

They speedily forgot many things. The past held no pictures of error and disappointment. They were very happy, and their hearts swelled with grateful affection for the colonel and the youthful lieutenant.

CHAPTER XXII

When the woods again began to pour forth the dark-hued masses of the enemy the youth felt serene self-confidence. He smiled briefly when he saw men dodge and duck at the long screechings of shells that were thrown in giant handfuls over them. He stood, erect and tranquil, watching the attack begin against a part of the line that made a blue curve along the side of an adjacent hill. His vision being unmolested by smoke from the rifles of his companions, he had opportunities to see parts of the hard fight. It was a relief [1] to perceive at last from whence came some of these noises which had been roared into his ears.

Off a short way he saw two regiments fighting a little separate battle with two other regiments. It was in a cleared space, wearing a set-apart look. They were blazing as if upon a wager, giving and taking tremendous blows. The firings were incredibly fierce and rapid. These intent regiments apparently were oblivious of all larger purposes of war, and were slugging each other as if at a matched game.

In another direction he saw a magnificent brigade going with the evident intention of driving the enemy from a wood. They passed in out of sight and presently there was a most awe-inspiring racket in the wood. The noise was unspeakable. Having stirred this prodigious uproar, and, apparently, finding it too prodigious, the brigade, after a little time, came marching

---

[1] *LV:* revelation *canceled.*

airily out again with its fine formation in nowise disturbed. There were no traces of speed in its movements. The brigade was jaunty and seemed to point a proud thumb at the yelling wood.

On a slope to the left there was a long row of guns, gruff and maddened, denouncing the enemy, who, down through the woods, were forming for another attack in the pitiless monotony of conflicts. The round red discharges from the guns made a crimson flare and a high, thick smoke. Occasional glimpses could be caught of groups of the toiling artillerymen. In the rear of this row of guns stood a house, calm and white, amid bursting shells. A congregation of horses, tied to a long railing, were tugging frenziedly at their bridles. Men were running hither and thither.

The detached battle between the four regiments lasted for some time. There chanced to be no interference, and they settled their dispute by themselves. They struck savagely and powerfully at each other for a period of minutes, and then the lighter-hued regiments faltered and drew back, leaving the dark-blue lines shouting. The youth could see the two flags shaking with laughter amid the smoke remnants.

Presently there was a stillness, pregnant with meaning. The blue lines shifted and changed a trifle and stared expectantly at the silent woods and fields before them. The hush was solemn and churchlike, save for a distant battery that, evidently unable to remain quiet, sent a faint rolling thunder over the ground. It irritated, like the noises of unimpressed boys. The men imagined that it would prevent their perched ears from hearing the first words of the new battle.

Of a sudden the guns on the slope roared out a message of warning. A spluttering sound had begun in the woods. It swelled with amazing speed to a profound clamor that involved the earth in noises. The splitting crashes swept along the lines until an interminable roar was developed. To those in the midst of it it became a din fitted to the universe. It was the whirring and thumping of gigantic machinery, complications among the smaller stars. The youth's ears were filled up. They were incapable of hearing more.

On an incline over which a road wound he saw wild and desperate rushes of men perpetually backward and forward in riotous surges. These parts of the opposing armies were two long waves that pitched upon each other madly at dictated points. To and fro they swelled. Sometimes, one side by its yells and cheers would proclaim decisive blows, but a moment later the other side would be all yells and cheers. Once the youth saw a spray of light forms go in houndlike leaps toward the waving blue lines. There was much howling, and presently it went away with a vast mouthful of prisoners. Again, he saw a blue wave dash with such thunderous force against a gray obstruction that it seemed to clear the earth of it and leave nothing but trampled sod. And always in their swift and deadly rushes to and fro the men screamed and yelled like maniacs.

Particular pieces of fence or secure positions behind collections of trees were wrangled over, as gold thrones or pearl bedsteads. There were desperate lunges at these chosen spots seemingly every instant, and most of them were bandied like light toys between the contending forces. The youth could not tell from the battle flags flying like crimson foam in many directions which color of cloth was winning.

His emaciated regiment bustled forth with undiminished fierceness when its time came. When assaulted again by bullets, the men burst out in a barbaric cry of rage and pain. They bent their heads in aims of intent hatred behind the projected hammers of their guns. Their ramrods clanged loud with fury as their eager arms pounded the cartridges into the rifle barrels. The front of the regiment was a smoke-wall penetrated by the flashing points of yellow and red.

Wallowing in the fight, they were in an astonishingly short time resmudged. They surpassed in stain and dirt all their previous appearances. Moving to and fro with strained exertion, jabbering the while, they were, with their swaying bodies, black faces, and glowing eyes, like strange and ugly fiends [2] jigging heavily in the smoke.

The lieutenant, returning from a tour after a bandage, produced from a hidden receptacle of his mind new and portentous oaths suited to the emergency. Strings of expletives he swung lashlike over the backs of his men, and it was evident that his previous efforts had in nowise impaired his resources.

The youth, still the bearer of the colors, did not feel his idleness. He was deeply absorbed as a spectator. The crash and swing of the great drama made him lean forward, intent-eyed, his face working in small contortions. Sometimes he prattled, words coming unconsciously from him in grotesque exclamations. He did not know that he breathed; that the flag hung silently over him, so absorbed was he.

A formidable line of the enemy came within dangerous range. They could be seen plainly—tall, gaunt men with excited faces running with long strides toward a wandering fence.

At sight of this danger the men suddenly ceased their cursing monotone. There was an instant of strained silence before they threw up their rifles and fired a plumping volley at the foes. There had been no order given; the men, upon recognizing the menace, had immediately let drive their flock of bullets without waiting for word of command.

But the enemy were quick to gain the protection of the wandering line of fence. They slid down behind it with remarkable celerity, and from this position they began briskly to slice up the blue men.

These latter braced their energies for a great struggle. Often, white clinched teeth shone from the dusky faces. Many heads surged to and fro, floating upon a pale sea of smoke. Those behind the fence frequently shouted and yelped in taunts and gibelike cries, but the regiment maintained a stressed silence. Perhaps, at this new assault the men recalled the fact that they

---

[2] *FAE has:* friends.

had been named mud diggers, and it made their situation thrice bitter. They were breathlessly intent upon keeping the ground and thrusting away the rejoicing body of the enemy. They fought swiftly and with a despairing savageness denoted in their expressions.

The youth had resolved not to budge whatever should happen. Some arrows of scorn that had buried themselves in his heart had generated strange and unspeakable hatred. It was clear to him that his final and absolute revenge was to be achieved by his dead body lying, torn and gluttering,[3] upon the field. This was to be a poignant retaliation upon the officer who had said "mule drivers," and later "mud diggers," for in all the wild graspings of his mind for a unit responsible for his sufferings and commotions he always seized upon the man who had dubbed him wrongly. And it was his idea, vaguely formulated, that his corpse would be for those eyes a great and salt reproach.

The regiment bled extravagantly. Grunting bundles of blue began to drop. The orderly sergeant of the youth's company was shot through the cheeks. Its supports being injured, his jaw hung afar down, disclosing in the wide cavern of his mouth a pulsing mass of blood and teeth. And with all he made attempts to cry out. In his endeavor there was a dreadful earnestness, as if he conceived that one great shriek would make him well.

The youth saw him presently go rearward. His strength seemed in nowise impaired. He ran swiftly, casting wild glances for succor.

Others fell down about the feet of their companions. Some of the wounded crawled out and away, but many lay still, their bodies twisted into impossible shapes.

The youth looked once for his friend. He saw a vehement young man, powder-smeared and frowzled,[4] whom he knew to be him. The lieutenant, also, was unscathed in his position

---

[3] *LV:* gluttering *intended probably for* glittering.
[4] *LV: frowsled.*

at the rear. He had continued to curse, but it was now with the air of a man who was using his last box of oaths.

For the fire of the regiment had begun to wane and drip. The robust voice, that had come strangely from the thin ranks, was growing rapidly weak.

CHAPTER XXIII

The colonel came running along back of the line. There were other officers following him. "We must charge'm!" they shouted. "We must charge'm!" they cried with resentful voices, as if anticipating a rebellion against this plan by the men.

The youth, upon hearing the shouts, began to study the distance between him and the enemy. He made vague calculations. He saw that to be firm soldiers they must go forward. It would be death to stay in the present place, and with all the circumstances to go backward would exalt too many others. Their hope was to push the galling foes away from the fence.

He expected that his companions, weary and stiffened, would have to be driven to this assault, but as he turned toward them he perceived with a certain surprise that they were giving quick and unqualified expressions of assent. There was an ominous, clanging overture to the charge when the shafts of the bayonets rattled upon the rifle barrels. At the yelled words of command the soldiers sprang forward in eager leaps. There was new and unexpected force in the movement of the regiment. A knowledge of its faded and jaded condition made the charge appear like a paroxysm, a display of the strength that comes before a final feebleness. The men scampered in insane fever of haste, racing as if to achieve a sudden success before an exhilarating fluid should leave them. It was a blind and despairing rush by the collection of men in dusty and tattered blue, over a green sward and under a sapphire sky, toward a fence, dimly outlined in smoke, from behind which spluttered the fierce rifles of enemies.

The youth kept the bright colors to the front. He was waving his free arm in furious circles, the while shrieking mad calls and appeals, urging on those that did not need to be urged, for it seemed that the mob of blue men hurling themselves on the dangerous group of rifles were again grown suddenly wild with an enthusiasm of unselfishness. From the many firings starting toward them, it looked as if they would merely succeed in making a great sprinkling of corpses on the grass between their former position and the fence. But they were in a state of frenzy, perhaps because of forgotten vanities, and it made an exhibition of sublime recklessness. There was no obvious questioning, nor figurings, nor diagrams. There was, apparently, no considered loopholes. It appeared that the swift wings of their desires would have shattered against the iron gates of the impossible.

He himself felt the daring spirit of a savage religion mad.[1] He was capable of profound sacrifices, a tremendous death. He had no time for dissections, but he knew that he thought of the bullets only as things that could prevent him from reaching the place of his endeavor. There were subtle flashings of joy within him that thus should be his mind.

He strained all his strength. His eyesight was shaken and dazzled by the tension of thought and muscle. He did not see anything excepting the mist of smoke gashed by the little knives of fire, but he knew that in it lay the aged fence of a vanished farmer protecting the snuggled bodies of the gray men.

As he ran a thought of the shock of contact gleamed in his mind. He expected a great concussion when the two bodies of troops crashed together. This became a part of his wild battle madness. He could feel the onward swing of the regiment about him and he conceived of a thunderous, crushing blow that would prostrate the resistance and spread consternation and amazement for miles. The flying regiment was going to have a catapultian effect. This dream made him run faster among his comrades, who were giving vent to hoarse and frantic cheers.

But presently he could see that many of the men in gray did not intend to abide the blow. The smoke, rolling, disclosed men

---

[1] *LV*: a savage, religion-mad.

who ran, their faces still turned. These grew to a crowd, who retired stubbornly. Individuals wheeled frequently to send a bullet at the blue wave.

But at one part of the line there was a grim and obdurate group that made no movement. They were settled firmly down behind posts and rails. A flag, ruffled and fierce, waved over them and their rifles dinned fiercely.

The blue whirl of men got very near, until it seemed that in truth there would be a close and frightful scuffle. There was an expressed disdain in the opposition of the little group, that changed the meaning of the cheers of the men in blue. They became yells of wrath, directed, personal. The cries of the two parties were now in sound an interchange of scathing insults.

They in blue showed their teeth; their eyes shone all white. They launched themselves as at the throats of those who stood resisting. The space between dwindled to an insignificant distance.

The youth had centered the gaze of his soul upon that other flag. Its possession would be high pride. It would express bloody minglings, near blows. He had a gigantic hatred for those who made great difficulties and complications. They caused it to be as a craved treasure of mythology, hung amid tasks and contrivances of danger.

He plunged like a mad horse at it. He was resolved it should not escape if wild blows and darings of blows could seize it. His own emblem, quivering and aflare, was winging toward the other. It seemed there would shortly be an encounter of strange beaks and claws, as of eagles.

The swirling body of blue men came to a sudden halt at close and disastrous range and roared a swift volley. The group in gray was split and broken by this fire, but its riddled body still fought. The men in blue yelled again and rushed in upon it.

The youth, in his leapings, saw, as through a mist, a picture of four or five men stretched upon the ground or writhing upon their knees with bowed heads as if they had been stricken by bolts from the sky. Tottering among them was the rival color bearer, whom [2] the youth saw had been bitten vitally by the bullets of the last formidable volley. He perceived this man fighting a last struggle, the struggle of one whose legs are grasped by demons. It was a ghastly battle. Over his face was the bleach of death, but set upon it was the dark and hard lines of desperate purpose. With this terrible grin of resolution he hugged his precious flag to him and was stumbling and staggering in his design to go the way that led to safety for it.

But his wounds always made it seem that his feet were retarded, held, and he fought a grim fight, as with invisible ghouls fastened greedily upon his limbs. Those in advance of the scampering blue men, howling cheers, leaped at the fence. The despair of the lost was in his eyes as he glanced back at them.

The youth's friend went over the obstruction in a tumbling heap and sprang at the flag as a panther at prey. He pulled at it and, wrenching it free, swung up its red brilliancy with a mad cry of exultation even as the color bearer, gasping, lurched over in a final throe and, stiffening convulsively, turned his dead face to the ground. There was much blood upon the grass blades.

At the place of success there began more wild clamorings of cheers. The men gesticulated and bellowed in an ecstasy. When they spoke it was as if they considered their listener to be a mile away. What hats and caps were left to them they often slung high in the air.

At one part of the line four men had been swooped upon, and they now sat as prisoners. Some blue men were about them in an eager and curious circle. The soldiers had trapped strange birds, and there was an examination. A flurry of fast questions was in the air.

One of the prisoners was nursing a superficial wound in the foot. He cuddled it, baby-wise, but he looked up from it often to curse with an astonishing utter abandon straight at the noses

---

[2] *Same in LV.*

of his captors. He consigned them to red regions; he called upon the pestilential wrath of strange gods. And with it all he was singularly free from recognition of the finer points of the conduct of prisoners of war. It was as if a clumsy clod had trod upon his toe and he conceived it to be his privilege, his duty, to use deep, resentful oaths.

Another, who was a boy in years, took his plight with great calmness and apparent good nature. He conversed with the men in blue, studying their faces with his bright and keen eyes. They spoke of battle and conditions. There was an acute interest in all their faces during this exchange of view points. It seemed a great satisfaction to hear voices from where all had been darkness and speculation.

The third captive sat with a morose countenance. He preserved a stoical and cold attitude. To all advances he made one reply without variation, "Ah, go t' hell!"

The last of the four was always silent, and, for the most part, kept his face turned in unmolested directions. From the views the youth received he seemed to be in a state of absolute dejection. Shame was upon him, and with it profound regret that he was, perhaps, no more to be counted in the ranks of his fellows. The youth could detect no expression that would allow him to believe that the other was giving a thought to his narrowed future, the pictured dungeons, perhaps, and starvations and brutalities, liable to the imagination. All to be seen was shame for captivity and regret for the right to antagonize.

After the men had celebrated sufficiently they settled down behind the old rail fence, on the opposite side to the one from which their foes had been driven. A few shot perfunctorily at distant marks.

There was some long grass. The youth nestled in it and rested, making a convenient rail support the flag. His friend, jubilant and glorified, holding his treasure with vanity, came to him there. They sat side by side and congratulated each other.

CHAPTER XXIV

The roarings that had stretched in a long line of sound across the face of the forest began to grow intermittent and weaker. The stentorian speeches of the artillery continued in some distant encounter, but the crashes of the musketry had almost ceased. The youth and his friend of a sudden looked up, feeling a deadened form of distress at the waning of these noises, which had become a part of life. They could see changes going on among the troops. There were marchings this way and that way. A battery wheeled leisurely. On the crest of a small hill was the thick gleam of many departing muskets.

The youth arose. "Well, what now, I wonder?" he said. By his tone he seemed to be preparing to resent some new monstrosity in the way of dins and smashes. He shaded his eyes with his grimy hand and gazed over the field.

His friend also arose and stared. "I bet we're goin' t' git along out of this an' back over th' river," said he.

"Well, I swan!" said the youth.

They waited, watching. Within a little while the regiment received orders to retrace its way. The men got up grunting from the grass, regretting the soft repose.[1] They jerked their stiffened legs, and stretched their arms over their heads. One man swore as he rubbed his eyes. They all groaned "O Lord!" They had as many objections to this change as they would have had to a proposal for a new battle.

They trampled slowly back over the field across which they had run in a mad scamper. [The fence, deserted, resumed with its careening posts and disjointed bars, an air of quiet and rural depravity. Beyond it, there lay spread a few corpses. Conspicuous was the contorted body of the color-bearer in grey whose flag the youth's friend was now bearing away.]

The regiment marched until it had joined its fellows. The reformed brigade, in column, aimed through a wood at the

---

[1] *LV:* reposes.

road. Directly they were in a mass of dust-covered troops, and were trudging along in a way parallel to the enemy's lines as these had been defined by the previous turmoil.

They passed within view of a stolid white house, and saw in front of it groups of their comrades lying in wait behind a neat breastwork. A row of guns were booming at a distant enemy. Shells thrown in reply were raising clouds of dust and splinters. Horsemen dashed along the line of intrenchments.

[As they passed near other commands, men of the delapidated regiment procured the captured flag from Wilson and, tossing it high into the air cheered tumultuously as it turned, with apparent reluctance, slowly over and over.]

At this point of its march the division curved away from the field and went winding off in the direction of the river. When the significance of this movement had impressed itself upon the youth he turned his head and looked over his shoulder toward the trampled and *débris*-strewed [2] ground. He breathed a breath of new satisfaction. He finally nudged his friend. "Well, it's all over," he said to him.

His friend gazed backward. "B'Gawd, it is," he assented. They mused. [3]

For a time the youth was obliged to reflect in a puzzled and uncertain way. His mind was undergoing a subtle change. It took moments for it to cast off its battleful ways and resume its accustomed course of thought. Gradually his brain emerged from the clogged clouds, and at last was enabled to more closely comprehend himself and circumstance.

He understood then that the existence of shot and countershot was in the past. He had dwelt in a land of strange, squalling upheavals and had come forth. He had been where there was red of blood and black of passion, and he was escaped. His first thoughts were given to rejoicings at this fact.

Later he began to study his deeds, his failures, and his achievements. Thus, fresh from scenes where many of his usual

---

[2] *LV:* debris-strewed.

[3] *In LV* They mused *is written as a new paragraph.*

machines of reflection had been idle, from where he had proceeded sheeplike, he struggled to marshal all his acts.

At last they marched before him clearly. From this present view point he was enabled to look them in spectator fashion and to criticize them with some correctness, for his new condition had already defeated certain sympathies.

[His friend, too, seemed engaged with some retrospection, for he suddenly gestured and said: "Good Lord!"

"What?" asked the youth.

"Good Lord!" repeated his friend. "Yeh know Jimmie Rogers? Well, he—gosh, when he was hurt I started t' git some water fer 'im an', thunder, I aint seen 'im from that time 'til this. I clean forgot what I—say, has anybody seen Jimmie Rogers?"

"Seen 'im? No! He's dead," they told him.

His friend swore.

But the youth, regarding his procession of memory, felt] gleeful and unregretting, for in it his public deeds were paraded in great and shining prominence. Those performances which had been witnessed by his fellows marched now in wide purple and gold, having various deflections. They went gayly with music. It was pleasure to watch these things. He spent delightful minutes viewing the gilded images of memory.

He saw that he was good. He recalled with a thrill of joy the respectful comments of his fellows upon his conduct. [He said to himself again the sentence of the insane lieutenant: [4] "If I had ten thousand wild-cats like you, I could tear th' stomach outa this war in less'n a week." It was a little coronation.[5]]

Nevertheless, the ghost of his flight from the first engagement appeared to him and danced. [Echoes of his terrible combat with the arrayed forces of the universe came to his ears.] There were small shoutings in his brain about these matters.

---

[4] *That the lieutenant is here called insane whereas he is elsewhere described as youthful is ironically weighted to upset the scales of Henry's egotism.*

[5] *This echoes another passage new to the text and here restored (p. 320, line 27), the passage where Henry vaingloriously regards himself as one fit to be led to a crown.*

For a moment he blushed, and the light of his soul flickered with shame.

[However, he presently procured an explanation and an apology. He said that those tempestuous moments were of the wild mistakes and ravings of a novice who did not comprehend. He had been a mere man railing at a condition, but now he was out of it and could see that it had been very proper and just. It had been necessary for him to swallow swords that he might have a better throat for grapes. Fate had in truth been kind to him; she had stabbed him with benign purpose and diligently cudgeled him for his own sake. In his rebellion, he had been very portentious, no doubt, and sincere, and anxious for humanity, but now that he stood safe, with no lack of blood, it was suddenly clear to him that he had been wrong not to kiss the knife and bow to the cudgel. He had foolishly squirmed.

But the sky would forget. It was true, he admitted, that in the world it was the habit to cry devil at persons who refused to trust what they could not trust, but he thought that perhaps the stars dealt differently. The imperturbable sun shines on insult and worship.[6]

As he was thus fraternizing again with nature, a spectre] of reproach came to him. There loomed the dogging memory of the tattered soldier—he who, gored by bullets and faint for blood, had fretted concerning an imagined wound in another; he who had loaned his last of strength and intellect for the tall soldier; he who, blind with weariness and pain, had been deserted in the field.

For an instant a wretched chill of sweat was upon him at the thought that he might be detected in the thing. As he stood persistently before his vision, he gave vent to a cry of sharp irritation and agony.

---

[6] *And just so it shone on Henry Fleming when he insulted the sun, metaphorically imaged as an object of worship in Chapter ix. See text and note, p. 287, and, for interpretation, the Introduction to Part II (A), secs. 5 and 6.*

His friend turned. "What's the matter, Henry?" he demanded. The youth's reply was an outburst of crimson oaths.

As he marched along the little branch-hung roadway among his prattling companions this vision of cruelty brooded over him. It clung near him always and darkened his view of these deeds in purple and gold. Whichever way his thoughts turned they were followed by the somber phantom of the desertion in the fields. He looked stealthily at his companions, feeling sure that they must discern in his face evidences of this pursuit. But they were plodding in ragged array, discussing with quick tongues the accomplishments of the late battle.

"Oh, if a man should come up an' ask me, I'd say we got a dum good lickin'."

"Lickin'—in yer eye! We ain't licked, sonny. We're going down here aways, swing aroun', an' come in behint 'em."

"Oh, hush, with your comin' in behint 'em. I've seen all 'a that I wanta. Don't tell me about comin' in behint—"

"Bill Smithers, he ses he'd rather been in ten hundred battles than been in that heluva hospital. He ses they got shootin' in th' night-time, an' shells dropped plum among 'em in th' hospital. He ses sech hollerin' he never see."

"Hasbrouck? He's th' best off'cer in this here reg'ment. He's a whale."

"Didn't I tell yeh we'd come aroun' in behint 'em? Didn't I tell yeh so? We—"

"Oh, shet yer mouth!"

["You make me sick."

"G' home, yeh fool."]

For a time this pursuing recollection of the tattered man took all elation from the youth's [7] veins. He saw his vivid error, and he was afraid that it would stand before him all his life. He took no share in the chatter of his comrades, nor did he look at them or know them, save when he felt sudden suspicion that they were seeing his thoughts and scrutinizing each detail of the scene with the tattered soldier.

---

[7] *LV:* Fleming's *canceled. This is the last of name alterations.*

Yet gradually he mustered force to put the sin at a distance. [And then he regarded it with what he thought to be great calmness. At last, he concluded that he saw in it quaint uses. He exclaimed that its importance in the aftertime would be great to him if it even succeeded in hindering the workings of his egotism. It would make a sobering balance. It would become a good part of him. He would have upon him often the consciousness of a great mistake. And he would be taught to deal gently and with care. He would be a man.

This plan for the utilization of a sin did not give him complete joy but it was the best sentiment he could formulate under the circumstances, and when it was combined with his success, or public deeds, he knew that he was quite contented.] And at last his eyes seemed to open to some new ways. He found that he could look back upon the brass and bombast of his earlier gospels and see them truly. He was gleeful when he discovered that he now despised them.

[He was emerged from his struggles, with a large sympathy for the machinery of the universe. With his new eyes, he could see that the secret and open blows which were being dealt about the world with such heavenly lavishness were in truth blessings. It was a diety laying about him with the bludgeon of correction.

His loud mouth against these things had been lost as the storm ceased. He would no more stand upon places high and false, and denounce the distant planets. He beheld that he was tiny but not inconsequent to the sun. In the space-wide whirl of events no grain like him would be lost.]

With this [8] conviction came a store of assurance. He felt a quiet manhood, nonassertive but of sturdy and strong blood. He knew that he would no more quail before his guides wherever they should point. He had been to touch the great death, and found that, after all, it was but the great death [and was for others]. He was a man.

So it came to pass that as he trudged from the place of blood

---

[8] FAE *and* LV: this; *several other editions incorrectly:* the.

and wrath his soul changed.[9] He came from hot plowshares to prospects of clover tranquilly, and it was as if hot plowshares were not. Scars faded as flowers.

It rained. The procession of weary soldiers became a bedraggled train, despondent and muttering, marching with churning effort in a trough of liquid brown mud under a low, wretched sky. Yet the youth smiled, for he saw that the world was a world for him, though many discovered it to be made of oaths and walking sticks.[1] He had rid himself of the red sickness of battle. The sultry nightmare was in the past. He had been an animal blistered and sweating in the heat and pain of war. He turned now with a lover's thirst to images of tranquil skies, fresh meadows, cool brooks—an existence of soft and eternal peace.[2]

Over the river a golden ray of sun came through the hosts of leaden rain clouds.[3]

---

[9] *The Biblical phrasing, used on three previous occasions, here has deliberate ironic intent. That Henry's soul has not changed is indicated in the evoked meaning of the final image of the book.*

[1] *Here the novel ended, and that Crane first intended to end the novel here is shown by the words* The End *written immediately after this image on p. 192 of Manuscript LV. See Introduction to Part II (A), sec. 6.*

[2] *Here is Crane's second ending for the novel, intended so in Manuscript LV as this passage of fifty-five words was appended to the first* oaths and walking sticks *ending. This second ending prepares for the third and final one, the single concluding image of the book; the first ending prepares for the second and third endings.*

[3] *This third and final ending does not appear in the LV Manuscript and was unquestionably added in typescript by Crane himself. See Introduction to Part II (A), sec. 6. That Crane plotted the entire novel by images and situations evoking contradictory moods of despair and hope is evidenced not only in this terminal image of the book but in the opening image of Chapter i, or again in Chapter vii with its flat statement of conscious intention (notably in the word* again*):* Again the youth was in despair.

Page 189 of Manuscript LV suggests the possibility that Crane's first intention was to terminate the novel here—with the paragraph: His friend turned. "What's the matter, Henry?" he demanded. The youth's reply was an outburst of crimson oaths. *My reason for this supposition is that one half of page 189 is blank except for a wavy line slanting downward across the page.*

PART II [B]

War Tales

INTRODUCTION

Here are the three best war tales Crane wrote: *A Mystery of Heroism*, *The Upturned Face*, and *An Episode of War*. All three are inventions, like *The Red Badge*. For their conception and for their photographic resemblance to reality, as one contemporary review put it, "the author might have stayed for the one as for the other in his own armchair, and never have gone at all to the wars" (the *Academy*, October 6, 1900). Two of these imaginary pieces are staged in the Civil War; the third—*The Upturned Face*—belongs to no actual war or time or place. The scene is Rostina, the army is the "Spitzbergen army," and Timothy Lean belongs to the legendary "Twelfth Regiment of the Line."

This "Kicking Twelfth" Regiment is dealt with in four related pieces, two of them no more than fragments. In the first of this group, *Kim Up, the Kickers*, we meet the same Timothy Lean. The second one is good only in its title: *The Shrapnel of their Friends*. The third, *The End of the Battle*, is sentimental, the theme or meaning evoked being in excess of the motivating situation. Two soldiers pilfer an orchard and get reprimanded by the sergeant: "You're the kind of soldiers a man wants to choose for a dangerous outpost duty, ain't you?" Apparently, his men are not fit to belong to the Twelfth Regiment, but they die heroes—these culprits. One of the enemy, surprised to find the dead men so few in number, says: "God, I should have estimated them at least a hundred strong." It is a limp ending for a drama of such force, and it comes all too neat and pat. The beginning situation predicts too much, especially for a story whose theme is the unpredictableness of human nature.

Crane is always dealing with the paradox of man. That defines what his stories are really all about. Paradox patterns all his best stories; it defines their kinship one to another. The reading of fear as the "theme" of everything he wrote ignores about as many of his stories as, superficially, it accounts for. The soldiers in *The End of the Battle* are as fearless as the sheriff in *The Bride Comes to Yellow Sky*. *Maggie* and *George's Mother* have nothing to do with fear, and there is no trace of panic in *An Episode of War*.

On February 15, 1896 Crane, writing to the editor of the *Critic* from his brother's home at Hartwood, said: "I am now finishing a little novelette for S. S. McClure called *The Little Regiment* which represents my work at its best I think and is positively my last thing dealing with battle." But Crane did not keep to this intention. He published a second collection of war sketches in 1900, *Wounds in the Rain*; a downright bad war novel in 1899, *Active Service*; and among the last things he wrote was *Great Battles of the World*, potboiler Grub Street stuff published just before he died in 1900. War figures, too, in the title of his last book of poems, *War is Kind* (1899). By no stretch of terms can *The Little Regiment* (1896) be said to be a "little novelette": the six stories bear no relationship to each other except in subject; nor can that book be said to represent "my work at its best." *A Mystery of Heroism* is the only story in that volume having designed significance.

A Mystery of Heroism was written before Crane had occasion to witness actual warfare; *An Episode of War* likewise portrays a war he never saw; and *The Upturned Face* deals with a war that never existed. But no matter; what counts is the created illusion of reality, and in any work of art fact cannot be divided from fiction. *A Mystery of Heroism* was probably written in Mexico during the summer of 1895 when Crane was out west looking for material to supply the Bacheller syndicate. It appeared first on August 1–2 in the *Philadelphia Press*, the newspaper that had serialized *The Red Badge* the year before (December 3–8, 1894), and so in point of publication made its appearance before the novel—*The Red Badge* being published in September 1895. The other two stories, written much later, were not published in America until 1921

(in *Men, Women and Boats*), though they had English publication in 1902 in the posthumous *Last Words*. *The Upturned
Face* came out in *Ainslee's Magazine* in March 1900, just two
months before Crane died. *A Mystery of Heroism, The Upturned Face*, and *An Episode of War* have never before been
brought together.

The Upturned Face, though wholly imaginary, was inspired
by the Spanish-American War. Timothy Lean and the adjutant must bury their comrade amidst riflefire, and they are
puzzled about how to perform this delicate task. The story
opens and ends with a question. " 'What do we do now?' said
the adjutant, troubled and excited. 'Bury him,' said Timothy
Lean." That opening question evokes the mood of hesitation
and doubt, and Lean's answer—"bury him"—intensifies the
question and does not answer it. It is the question of how to
come to terms with the real thing. Even after burying him
they are still in doubt. It is as though their coming to terms
with the actuality has exploded their theory about it. " 'Perhaps
we have been wrong,' said the adjutant. His glance wavered
stupidly. 'It might have been better if we hadn't buried him
just at this time.' 'Damn you,' said Lean, 'shut your mouth!' He
was not the senior officer." In cursing the adjutant, Lean was
breaking code, and this has its parallel in the abstract code or
ritual of burial, which is shattered by its impingement upon a
point in time. The final question in the story is, as it were,
the unspoken query of the corpse, "which from its chalkblue
face looked keenly out from the grave."

The one moment *before* the first shovel-load of earth is
emptied upon the corpse pinpoints the whole story. It is the
moment *while* the shovel is "held poised above the corpse,"
fixed "for *a moment of inexplicable hesitation*. . . ." Keenly,
"in curious *abstraction* they looked at the body." They cannot
bring themselves to face up to the real thing—"Both were
particular that their fingers should not feel the corpse." But
the abstract code becomes far more terrifyingly real to them
than the bullets spitting overhead, and, in a sense, more real

than the corpse. Louder than any riflefire is the sound of the earth landing upon the upturned face—"plop!" How poignant the reality of life, all its values realized in that impact! It is this burden that fills the grave. (In Bierce's *An Occurrence at Owl Creek Bridge* the same theme is evoked, and the same structural conception underlies the story: illusion shattered by realities.) "And from Thy superb heights," says Lean, reading the burial service. But he can remember only two lines of it. All that is now remaining of this ritual is but a fragment. "'Oh, well,' he cried suddenly, 'let us—let us say something—while he can hear us.'" It is as though he were denying the fact; it is as though the dead man were *alive*. Then the first shovel is emptied "on—on the feet. Timothy Lean felt as if tons had been swiftly lifted from off his forehead." It is as though the living man had been thus *exhumed*. But the key paradox is that in honoring their beloved comrade they dishonor him and honor themselves. Their consecration is a desecration: the ritual consecrates him, but the act of the ritual desecrates him. "Always the earth made that sound—plop!" So all relationships, like this one, involve that shock of reality by which intentions are contradicted by the act.

The story is a parable and, like *An Episode of War*, it is built on a paradox. The wounded lieutenant in *An Episode of War* sees life with new insight because, being wounded, he is removed from the flux of things and can observe life instead of merely experiencing it.

In *War Memories* Crane wrote: "'But to get at the real thing!' cried Vernall, the war-correspondent. 'It seems impossible! It is because war is neither magnificent nor squalid; it is simply life, and an expression of life can always evade us. We can never tell life, one to another, although sometimes we think we can.'" Life evades us when we try to recapture it, as Crane attempted in *War Memories* to recapture his experiences. More real is the unreal, the imagined experience.

An Episode of War is about the withdrawal of the wounded lieutenant from the real world into an imaginary world.

Wounded, he was puzzled what to do with his unsheathed sword: "this weapon had of a sudden become a strange thing to him. He looked at it in a kind of stupefaction, as if he had been endowed with a trident, a sceptre, or a spade." He has become another person, a king or mythical figure, and his wounded arm seems fabulous—"made of very brittle glass." The wound is the symbol of his change of vision, enabling him now "to see many things which as a participant in the fight were unknown to him." The wounded, "no longer having part in the battle, knew more of it than others." "A wound gives strange dignity to him who bears it. Well men shy from this new and terrible majesty." The real world seen from the point of view of the wounded spectator now seems unreal, more like something in "a historical painting," and the men who belong to it seem immobilized as they gaze "statue-like and silent." *An Episode* thus bears comparison with *The Upturned Face* and, in its theme of a change of vision, it links with *A Mystery of Heroism* and *The Red Badge of Courage*. In structure *An Episode* is exactly like *The Red Badge*. It is formed of alternations of moods: perspectives of motion and change shifting into picture-postcard impressions where everything is felt as fixed and static. Henry Fleming is duped by realities; Collins is likewise disillusioned; and the lieutenant is deceived. "I won't amputate it," says the surgeon when asked about the wounded arm. "Come along. Don't be a baby." Like *The Red Badge*, *A Mystery of Heroism* is an analysis of disillusionment. The mood of disillusionment is evoked in the final symbol of the story: "The bucket lay on the ground, empty."

Crane's best stories are all of a piece, similar in theme and design. What Carl Van Doren said about *A Mystery of Heroism*—"pure, concentrated Crane"—applies equally to *An Episode* and *The Upturned Face*. The germinal situations of these two stories reappear in *The Price of the Harness*, a story of the Spanish-American War published in 1898 and probably written before them. *The Upturned Face* is a reworking, apparently, of this episode:

—Cover his face—said Grierson, in a low and husky voice afterwards.

—What'll I cover it with?—said Watkins.

They looked at themselves. They stood in their shirts, trousers, leggings, shoes; they had nothing.

Oh—said Grierson—here's his hat—He brought it and laid it on the face of the dead man. They stood for a time. It was apparent that they thought it essential and decent to say or do something.

And *An Episode of War* has its parallel in this episode in *The Price of the Harness*:

. . . —I'm hit, sir—he said.

The lieutenant was very busy. —All right, all right—he said, just heeding the man enough to learn where he was wounded. —Go over that way. You ought to see a dressing-station under those trees.—

Martin found himself dizzy and sick. The sensation in his arm was distinctly galvanic. The feeling was so strange that he could wonder at times if a wound was really what ailed him.

As *The Price of the Harness* repeats several episodes and images from *The Red Badge*, so *An Episode of War* harks back to the novel too, to the incident of the wounded lieutenant there (chapter iv). More important are the external kinships between Crane's stories—*A Mystery* and *An Episode*—and Hemingway's novels of the wounded hero or outcast. In *The Sun Also Rises* Hemingway employs the same symbolism of wound as Crane in *An Episode* and in *The Red Badge*. Hemingway's social outcasts stand in line of descent as much from Crane's mental outcasts—Henry Fleming and, in *A Mystery,* Collins—as from Twain's Huck Finn.

A MYSTERY OF HEROISM

THE DARK uniforms of the men were so coated with dust from the incessant wrestling of the two armies that the regiment almost seemed a part of the clay bank which shielded them from the shells. On the top of the hill a battery was arguing in tremendous roars with some other guns, and to the eye of the infantry the artillerymen, the guns, the caissons, the horses, were distinctly outlined upon the blue sky. When a piece was fired, a red streak as round as a log flashed low in the heavens, like a monstrous bolt of lightning. The men of the battery wore white duck trousers, which somehow emphasized their legs; and when they ran and crowded in little groups at the bidding of the shouting officers, it was more impressive than usual to the infantry.

Fred Collins, of A Company, was saying: "Thunder! I wisht I had a drink. Ain't there any water round here?" Then somebody yelled: "There goes th' bugler!"

As the eyes of half the regiment swept in one machine-like movement, there was an instant's picture of a horse in a great convulsive leap of a death-wound and a rider leaning back with a crooked arm and spread fingers before his face. On the ground was the crimson terror of an exploding shell, with fibres of flame that seemed like lances. A glittering bugle swung clear of the rider's back as fell headlong the horse and the man. In the air was an odour as from a conflagration.

Sometimes they of the infantry looked down at a fair little meadow which spread at their feet. Its long green grass was rippling gently in a breeze. Beyond it was the grey form of a house half torn to pieces by shells and by the busy axes of soldiers who had pursued firewood. The line of an old fence was now dimly marked by long weeds and by an occasional post. A shell had blown the well-house to fragments. Little lines of grey smoke ribboning upward from some embers indicated the place where had stood the barn.

From beyond a curtain of green woods there came the sound of some stupendous scuffle, as if two animals of the size of islands were fighting. At a distance there were occasional appearances of swift-moving men, horses, batteries, flags, and with the crashing of infantry volleys were heard, often, wild and frenzied cheers. In the midst of it all Smith and Ferguson, two privates of A Company, were engaged in a heated discussion which involved the greatest questions of the national existence.

The battery on the hill presently engaged in a frightful duel. The white legs of the gunners scampered this way and that way, and the officers redoubled their shouts. The guns, with their demeanours of stolidity and courage, were typical of something infinitely self-possessed in this clamour of death that swirled around the hill.

One of a "swing" team was suddenly smitten quivering to the ground, and his maddened brethren dragged his torn body in their struggle to escape from this turmoil and danger. A young soldier astride one of the leaders swore and fumed in his saddle and furiously jerked at the bridle. An officer screamed out an order so violently that his voice broke and ended the sentence in a falsetto shriek.

The leading company of the infantry regiment was somewhat exposed, and the colonel ordered it moved more fully under the shelter of the hill. There was the clank of steel against steel.

A lieutenant of the battery rode down and passed them, holding his right arm carefully in his left hand. And it was as if this arm was not at all a part of him, but belonged to another man. His sober and reflective charger went slowly. The officer's face was grimy and perspiring, and his uniform was tousled as if he had been in direct grapple with an enemy. He smiled grimly when the men stared at him. He turned his horse toward the meadow.

Collins, of A Company, said: "I wisht I had a drink. I bet there's water in that there ol' well yonder!"

"Yes; but how you goin' to git it?"

For the little meadow which intervened was now suffering a terrible onslaught of shells. Its green and beautiful calm had vanished utterly. Brown earth was being flung in monstrous handfuls. And there was a massacre of the young blades of grass. They were being torn, burned, obliterated. Some curious fortune of the battle had made this gentle little meadow the object of the red hate of the shells, and each one as it exploded seemed like an imprecation in the face of a maiden.

The wounded officer who was riding across this expanse said to himself: "Why, they couldn't shoot any harder if the whole army was massed here!"

A shell struck the grey ruins of the house, and as, after the roar, the shattered wall fell in fragments, there was a noise which resembled the flapping of shutters during a wild gale of winter. Indeed, the infantry paused in the shelter of the bank appeared as men standing upon a shore contemplating a madness of the sea. The angel of calamity had under its glance the battery upon the hill. Fewer white-legged men laboured about the guns. A shell had smitten one of the pieces, and after the flare, the smoke, the dust, the wrath of this blow were gone, it was possible to see white legs stretched horizontally upon the ground. And at that interval to the rear where it is the business of battery horses to stand with their noses to the fight, awaiting the command to drag their guns out of the destruction, or into it, or wheresoever these incomprehensible humans demanded with whip and spur—in this line of passive and dumb spectators, whose fluttering hearts yet would not let them forget the iron laws of man's control of them—in this rank of brute-soldiers there had been relentless and hideous carnage. From the ruck of bleeding and prostrate horses, the men of the infantry could see one animal raising its stricken body with its forelegs and turning its nose with mystic and profound eloquence toward the sky.

Some comrades joked Collins about his thirst. "Well, if yeh want a drink so bad, why don't yeh go git it?"

"Well, I will in a minnet, if yeh don't shut up!"

A lieutenant of artillery floundered his horse straight down the hill with as little concern as if it were level ground. As he galloped past the colonel of the infantry, he threw up his hand in swift salute. "We've got to get out of that," he roared angrily. He was a black-bearded officer, and his eyes, which resembled beads, sparkled like those of an insane man. His jumping horse sped along the column of infantry.

The fat major, standing carelessly with his sword held horizontally behind him and with his legs far apart, looked after the receding horseman and laughed. "He wants to get back with orders pretty quick, or there'll be no batt'ry left," he observed.

The wise young captain of the second company hazarded to the lieutenant-colonel that the enemy's infantry would probably soon attack the hill, and the lieutenant-colonel snubbed him.

A private in one of the rear companies looked out over the meadow, and then turned to a companion and said, "Look there, Jim!" It was the wounded officer from the battery, who some time before had started to ride across the meadow, supporting his right arm carefully with his left hand. This man had encountered a shell, apparently, at a time when no one perceived him, and he could now be seen lying face downward with a stirruped foot stretched across the body of his dead horse. A leg of the charger extended slantingly upward, precisely as stiff as a stake. Around this motionless pair the shells still howled.

There was a quarrel in A Company. Collins was shaking his fist in the faces of some laughing comrades. "Dern yeh! I ain't afraid t' go. If yeh say much, I will go!"

"Of course, yeh will! You'll run through that there medder, won't yeh?"

Collins said, in a terrible voice: "You see now!"

At this ominous threat his comrades broke into renewed jeers.

Collins gave them a dark scowl, and went to find his captain. The latter was conversing with the colonel of the regiment.

"Captain," said Collins, saluting and standing at attention—in those days all trousers bagged at the knees—"Captain, I want t' get permission to go git some water from that there well over yonder!"

The colonel and the captain swung about simultaneously and stared across the meadow. The captain laughed. "You must be pretty thirsty, Collins?"

"Yes, sir, I am."

"Well—ah," said the captain. After a moment, he asked, "Can't you wait?"

"No, sir."

The colonel was watching Collins's face. "Look here, my lad," he said, in a pious sort of voice—"Look here, my lad"—Collins was not a lad—"don't you think that's taking pretty big risks for a little drink of water?"

"I dunno," said Collins uncomfortably. Some of the resentment toward his companions, which perhaps had forced him into this affair, was beginning to fade. "I dunno w'ether 'tis."

The colonel and the captain contemplated him for a time.

"Well," said the captain finally.

"Well," said the colonel, "if you want to go, why, go."

Collins saluted. "Much obliged t' yeh."

As he moved away the colonel called after him. "Take some of the other boys' canteens with you, an' hurry back, now."

"Yes, sir, I will."

The colonel and the captain looked at each other then, for it had suddenly occurred that they could not for the life of them tell whether Collins wanted to go or whether he did not.

They turned to regard Collins, and as they perceived him surrounded by gesticulating comrades, the colonel said: "Well, by thunder! I guess he's going."

Collins appeared as a man dreaming. In the midst of the questions, the advice, the warnings, all the excited talk of his company mates, he maintained a curious silence.

They were very busy in preparing him for his ordeal. When they inspected him carefully, it was somewhat like the examination that grooms give a horse before a race; and they were amazed, staggered, by the whole affair. Their astonishment found vent in strange repetitions.

"Are yeh sure a-goin'?" they demanded again and again.

"Certainly I am," cried Collins at last, furiously.

He strode sullenly away from them. He was swinging five or six canteens by their cords. It seemed that his cap would not remain firmly on his head, and often he reached and pulled it down over his brow.

There was a general movement in the compact column. The long animal-like thing moved slightly. Its four hundred eyes were turned upon the figure of Collins.

"Well, sir, if that ain't th' derndest thing! I never thought Fred Collins had the blood in him for that kind of business."

"What's he goin' to do, anyhow?"

"He's goin' to that well there after water."

"We ain't dyin' of thirst, are we? That's foolishness."

"Well, somebody put him up to it, an' he's doin' it."

"Say, he must be a desperate cuss."

When Collins faced the meadow and walked away from the regiment, he was vaguely conscious that a chasm, the deep valley of all prides, was suddenly between him and his comrades. It was provisional, but the provision was that he return as a victor. He had blindly been led by quaint emotions, and laid himself under an obligation to walk squarely up to the face of death.

But he was not sure that he wished to make a retraction, even if he could do so without shame. As a matter of truth, he was sure of very little. He was mainly surprised.

It seemed to him supernaturally strange that he had allowed

his mind to manœuvre his body into such a situation. He understood that it might be called dramatically great.

However, he had no full appreciation of anything, excepting that he was actually conscious of being dazed. He could feel his dulled mind groping after the form and colour of this incident. He wondered why he did not feel some keen agony of fear cutting his sense like a knife. He wondered at this, because human expression had said loudly for centuries that men should feel afraid of certain things, and that all men who did not feel this fear were phenomena—heroes.

He was, then, a hero. He suffered that disappointment which we would all have if we discovered that we were ourselves capable of those deeds which we most admire in history and legend. This, then, was a hero. After all, heroes were not much.

No, it could not be true. He was not a hero. Heroes had no shames in their lives, and, as for him, he remembered borrowing fifteen dollars from a friend and promising to pay it back the next day, and then avoiding that friend for ten months. When, at home, his mother had aroused him for the early labour of his life on the farm, it had often been his fashion to be irritable, childish, diabolical; and his mother had died since he had come to the war.

He saw that, in this matter of the well, the canteens, the shells, he was an intruder in the land of fine deeds.

He was now about thirty paces from his comrades. The regiment had just turned its many faces toward him.

From the forest of terrific noises there suddenly emerged a little uneven line of men. They fired fiercely and rapidly at distant foliage on which appeared little puffs of white smoke. The spatter of skirmish firing was added to the thunder of the guns on the hill. The little line of men ran forward. A colour-sergeant fell flat with his flag as if he had slipped on ice. There was hoarse cheering from this distant field.

Collins suddenly felt that two demon fingers were pressed

into his ears. He could see nothing but flying arrows, flaming red. He lurched from the shock of this explosion, but he made a mad rush for the house, which he viewed as a man submerged to the neck in a boiling surf might view the shore. In the air little pieces of shell howled, and the earthquake explosions drove him insane with the menace of their roar. As he ran the canteens knocked together with a rhythmical tinkling.

As he neared the house, each detail of the scene became vivid to him. He was aware of some bricks of the vanished chimney lying on the sod. There was a door which hung by one hinge.

Rifle bullets called forth by the insistent skirmishers came from the far-off bank of foliage. They mingled with the shells and the pieces of shells until the air was torn in all directions by hootings, yells, howls. The sky was full of fiends who directed all their wild rage at his head.

When he came to the well, he flung himself face downward and peered into its darkness. There were furtive silver glintings some feet from the surface. He grabbed one of the canteens and, unfastening its cap, swung it down by the cord. The water flowed slowly in with an indolent gurgle.

And now, as he lay with his face turned away, he was suddenly smitten with the terror. It came upon his heart like the grasp of claws. All the power faded from his muscles. For an instant he was no more than a dead man.

The canteen filled with a maddening slowness, in the manner of all bottles. Presently he recovered his strength and addressed a screaming oath to it. He leaned over until it seemed as if he intended to try to push water into it with his hands. His eyes as he gazed down into the well shone like two pieces of metal, and in their expression was a great appeal and a great curse. The stupid water derided him.

There was the blaring thunder of a shell. Crimson light shone through the swift-boiling smoke and made a pink reflection on part of the wall of the well. Collins jerked out his arm and canteen with the same motion that a man would use in withdrawing his head from a furnace.

He scrambled erect and glared and hesitated. On the ground near him lay the old well bucket, with a length of rusty chain. He lowered it swiftly into the well. The bucket struck the water and then, turning lazily over, sank. When, with hand reaching tremblingly over hand, he hauled it out, it knocked often against the walls of the well and spilled some of its contents.

In running with a filled bucket, a man can adopt but one kind of gait. So, through this terrible field over which screamed practical angels of death, Collins ran in the manner of a farmer chased out of a dairy by a bull.

His face went staring white with anticipation—anticipation of a blow that would whirl him around and down. He would fall as he had seen other men fall, the life knocked out of them so suddenly that their knees were no more quick to touch the ground than their heads. He saw the long blue line of the regiment, but his comrades were standing looking at him from the edge of an impossible star. He was aware of some deep wheel-ruts and hoofprints in the sod beneath his feet.

The artillery officer who had fallen in this meadow had been making groans in the teeth of the tempest of sound. These futile cries, wrenched from him by his agony, were heard only by shells, bullets. When wild-eyed Collins came running, this officer raised himself. His face contorted and blanched from pain, he was about to utter some great beseeching cry. But suddenly his face straightened, and he called: "Say, young man, give me a drink of water, will you?"

Collins had no room amid his emotions for surprise. He was mad from the threats of destruction.

"I can't!" he screamed, and in his reply was a full description of his quaking apprehension. His cap was gone and his hair was riotous. His clothes made it appear that he had been dragged over the ground by the heels. He ran on.

The officer's head sank down, and one elbow crooked. His

foot in its brass-bound stirrup still stretched over the body of his horse, and the other leg was under the steed.

But Collins turned. He came dashing back. His face had now turned grey, and in his eyes was all terror. "Here it is! here it is!"

The officer was as a man gone in drink. His arm bent like a twig. His head drooped as if his neck were of willow. He was sinking to the ground, to lie face downward.

Collins grabbed him by the shoulder. "Here it is. Here's your drink. Turn over. Turn over, man, for God's sake!"

With Collins hauling at his shoulder, the officer twisted his body and fell with his face turned toward that region where lived the unspeakable noises of the swirling missiles. There was the faintest shadow of a smile on his lips as he looked at Collins. He gave a sigh, a little primitive breath like that from a child.

Collins tried to hold the bucket steadily, but his shaking hands caused the water to splash all over the face of the dying man. Then he jerked it away and ran on.

The regiment gave him a welcoming roar. The grimed faces were wrinkled in laughter.

His captain waved the bucket away. "Give it to the men!"

The two genial, skylarking young lieutenants were the first to gain possession of it. They played over it in their fashion.

When one tried to drink, the other teasingly knocked his elbow. "Don't Billie! You'll make me spill it," said the one. The other laughed.

Suddenly there was an oath, the thud of wood on the ground, and a swift murmur of astonishment among the ranks. The two lieutenants glared at each other. The bucket lay on the ground, empty.

THE UPTURNED FACE

Wʜᴀᴛ will we do now?" said the adjutant, troubled and excited.

"Bury him," said Timothy Lean.

The two officers looked down close to their toes where lay the body of their comrade. The face was chalk-blue; gleaming eyes stared at the sky. Over the two upright figures was a windy sound of bullets, and on the top of the hill Lean's prostrate company of Spitzbergen infantry was firing measured volleys.

"Don't you think it would be better—" began the adjutant. "We might leave him until to-morrow."

"No," said Lean. "I can't hold that post an hour longer. I've got to fall back, and we've got to bury old Bill."

"Of course," said the adjutant, at once. "Your men got entrenching tools?"

Lean shouted back to his little line, and two men came slowly, one with a pick, one with a shovel. They started in the direction of the Rostina sharpshooters. Bullets cracked near their ears. "Dig here," said Lean gruffly. The men, thus caused to lower their glances to the turf, became hurried and frightened, merely because they could not look to see whence the bullets came. The dull beat of the pick striking the earth sounded amid the swift snap of close bullets. Presently the other private began to shovel.

"I suppose," said the adjutant, slowly, "we'd better search his clothes for—things."

Lean nodded. Together in curious abstraction they looked at the body. Then Lean stirred his shoulders suddenly, arousing himself.

"Yes," he said, "we'd better see what he's got." He dropped to his knees, and his hands approached the body of the dead officer. But his hands wavered over the buttons of the tunic. The first button was brick-red with drying blood, and he did not seem to dare touch it.

"Go on," said the adjutant, hoarsely.

Lean stretched his wooden hand, and his fingers fumbled the bloodstained buttons. At last he rose with ghastly face. He had gathered a watch, a whistle, a pipe, a tobacco-pouch, a handkerchief, a little case of cards and papers. He looked at the adjutant. There was a silence. The adjutant was feeling that he had been a coward to make Lean do all the grisly business.

"Well," said Lean, "that's all, I think. You have his sword and revolver?"

"Yes," said the adjutant, his face working, and then he burst out in a sudden strange fury at the two privates. "Why don't you hurry up with that grave? What are you doing, anyhow? Hurry, do you hear? I never saw such stupid—"

Even as he cried out in his passion the two men were labouring for their lives. Ever overhead the bullets were spitting.

The grave was finished. It was not a masterpiece—a poor little shallow thing. Lean and the adjutant again looked at each other in a curious silent communication.

Suddenly the adjutant croaked out a weird laugh. It was a terrible laugh, which had its origin in that part of the mind which is first moved by the singing of the nerves. "Well," he said humorously to Lean, "I suppose we had best tumble him in."

"Yes," said Lean. The two privates stood waiting, bent over their implements. "I suppose," said Lean, "it would be better if we laid him in ourselves."

"Yes," said the adjutant. Then, apparently remembering that he had made Lean search the body, he stooped with great fortitude and took hold of the dead officer's clothing. Lean joined him. Both were particular that their fingers should not feel the corpse. They tugged away; the corpse lifted, heaved, toppled, flopped into the grave, and the two officers, straightening, looked again at each other—they were always looking at each other. They sighed with relief.

The adjutant said, "I suppose we should—we should say something. Do you know the service, Tim?"

"They don't read the service until the grave is filled in," said Lean, pressing his lips to an academic expression.

"Don't they?" said the adjutant, shocked that he had made the mistake. "Oh, well," he cried, suddenly, "let us—let us say something—while he can hear us."

"All right," said Lean. "Do you know the service?"

"I can't remember a line of it,' said the adjutant.

Lean was extremely dubious. "I can repeat two lines, but—"

"Well, do it," said the adjutant. "Go as far as you can. That's better than nothing. And the beasts have got our range exactly."

Lean looked at his two men. "Attention," he barked. The privates came to attention with a click, looking much aggrieved. The adjutant lowered his helmet to his knee. Lean, bareheaded, stood over the grave. The Rostina sharpshooters fired briskly.

"O Father, our friend has sunk in the deep waters of death, but his spirit has leaped toward Thee as the bubble arises from the lips of the drowning. Perceive, we beseech, O Father, the little flying bubble, and—"

Lean, although husky and ashamed, had suffered no hesitation up to this point, but he stopped with a hopeless feeling and looked at the corpse.

The adjutant moved uneasily. "And from Thy superb heights—" he began, and then he too came to an end.

"And from Thy superb heights," said Lean.

The adjutant suddenly remembered a phrase in the back of the Spitzbergen burial service, and he exploited it with the triumphant manner of a man who has recalled everything, and can go on.

"O God, have mercy—"

"O God, have mercy—" said Lean.

"Mercy," repeated the adjutant, in quick failure.

"Mercy," said Lean. And then he was moved by some violence of feeling, for he turned upon his two men and tigerishly said, "Throw the dirt in."

The fire of the Rostina sharpshooters was accurate and continuous.

One of the aggrieved privates came forward with his shovel. He lifted his first shovel-load of earth, and for a moment of inexplicable hesitation it was held poised above this corpse, which from its chalk-blue face looked keenly out from the grave. Then the soldier emptied his shovel on—on the feet.

Timothy Lean felt as if tons had been swiftly lifted from off his forehead. He had felt that perhaps the private might empty the shovel on—on the face. It had been emptied on the feet. There was a great point gained there—ha, ha!—the first shovelful had been emptied on the feet. How satisfactory!

The adjutant began to babble. "Well, of course—a man we've messed with all these years—impossible—you can't, you know, leave your intimate friends rotting on the field. Go on, for God's sake, and shovel, you."

The man with the shovel suddenly ducked, grabbed his left arm with his right hand, and looked at his officer for orders. Lean picked the shovel from the ground. "Go to the rear," he said to the wounded man. He also addressed the other private. "You get under cover, too; I'll finish this business."

The wounded man scrambled hard still for the top of the ridge without devoting any glances to the direction from whence the bullets came, and the other man followed at an equal pace; but he was different, in that he looked back anxiously three times.

This is merely the way—often—of the hit and unhit.

Timothy Lean filled the shovel, hesitated, and then, in a movement which was like a gesture of abhorrence, he flung

the dirt into the grave, and as it landed it made a sound—plop.
Lean suddenly stopped and mopped his brow—a tired labourer.
"Perhaps we have been wrong," said the adjutant. His
glance wavered stupidly. "It might have been better if we
hadn't buried him just at this time. Of course, if we advance
to-morrow the body would have been—"

"Damn you," said Lean, "shut your mouth." He was not the
senior officer.

He again filled the shovel and flung the earth. Always the
earth made that sound—plop. For a space Lean worked frantically, like a man digging himself out of danger.

Soon there was nothing to be seen but the chalk-blue face.
Lean filled the shovel. "Good God," he cried to the adjutant.
"Why didn't you turn him somehow when you put him in?
This—" Then Lean began to stutter.

The adjutant understood. He was pale to the lips. "Go on,
man," he cried, beseechingly, almost in a shout.

Lean swung back the shovel. It went forward in a pendulum
curve. When the earth landed it made a sound—plop.

AN EPISODE OF WAR

THE LIEUTENANT's rubber blanket lay on the ground, and upon it he had poured the company's supply of coffee. Corporals and other representatives of the grimy and hot-throated men who lined the breast-work had come for each squad's portion.

The lieutenant was frowning and serious at this task of division. His lips pursed as he drew with his sword various crevices in the heap, until brown squares of coffee, astoundingly equal in size, appeared on the blanket. He was on the verge of a great triumph in mathematics, and the corporals were thronging forward, each to reap a little square, when suddenly the lieutenant cried out and looked quickly at a man near him as if he suspected it was a case of personal assault. The others cried out also when they saw blood upon the lieutenant's sleeve.

He had winced like a man stung, swayed dangerously, and then straightened. The sound of his hoarse breathing was plainly audible. He looked sadly, mystically, over the breast-work at the green face of a wood, where now were many little puffs of white smoke. During this moment the men about him gazed statue-like and silent, astonished and awed by this catastrophe which happened when catastrophes were not expected—when they had leisure to observe it.

As the lieutenant stared at the wood, they too swung their heads, so that for another instant all hands, still silent, contemplated the distant forest as if their minds were fixed upon the mystery of a bullet's journey.

The officer had, of course, been compelled to take his sword into his left hand. He did not hold it by the hilt. He gripped it at the middle of the blade, awkwardly. Turning his eyes from the hostile wood, he looked at the sword as he held it there, and seemed puzzled as to what to do with it, where to put it. In short, this weapon had of a sudden become a strange thing to him. He looked at it in a kind of stupefaction, as if he had been endowed with a trident, a sceptre, or a spade.

Finally he tried to sheathe it. To sheathe a sword held by the left hand, at the middle of the blade, in a scabbard hung at the left hip, is a feat worthy of a sawdust ring. This wounded officer engaged in a desperate struggle with the sword and the wobbling scabbard, and during the time of it he breathed like a wrestler.

But at this instant the men, the spectators, awoke from their stone-like poses and crowded forward sympathetically. The orderly-sergeant took the sword and tenderly placed it in the scabbard. At the time, he leaned nervously backward, and did not allow even his finger to brush the body of the lieutenant. A wound gives strange dignity to him who bears it. Well men shy from this new and terrible majesty. It is as if the wounded man's hand is upon the curtain which hangs before the revelations of all existence—the meaning of ants, potentates, wars, cities, sunshine, snow, a feather dropped from a bird's wing; and the power of it sheds radiance upon a bloody form, and makes the other men understand sometimes that they are little. His comrades look at him with large eyes thoughtfully. Moreover, they fear vaguely that the weight of a finger upon him might send him headlong, precipitate the tragedy, hurl him at once into the dim, grey unknown. And so the orderly-sergeant, while sheathing the sword, leaned nervously backward.

There were others who proffered assistance. One timidly presented his shoulder and asked the lieutenant if he cared to lean upon it, but the latter waved him away mournfully. He wore the look of one who knows he is the victim of a terrible disease and understands his helplessness. He again stared over the breast-work at the forest, and then, turning, went slowly rearward. He held his right wrist tenderly in his left hand as if the wounded arm was made of very brittle glass.

And the men in silence stared at the wood, then at the departing lieutenant; then at the wood, then at the lieutenant.

As the wounded officer passed from the line of battle, he was enabled to see many things which as a participant in the fight were unknown to him. He saw a general on a black horse gazing over the lines of blue infantry at the green woods which veiled his problems. An aide galloped furiously, dragged his horse suddenly to a halt, saluted, and presented a paper. It was, for a wonder, precisely like a historical painting.

To the rear of the general and his staff a group, composed of a bugler, two or three orderlies, and the bearer of the corps standard, all upon maniacal horses, were working like slaves to hold their ground, preserve their respectful interval, while the shells boomed in the air about them, and caused their chargers to make furious quivering leaps.

A battery, a tumultuous and shining mass, was swirling toward the right. The wild thud of hoofs, the cries of the riders shouting blame and praise, menace and encouragement, and, last, the roar of the wheels, the slant of the glistening guns, brought the lieutenant to an intent pause. The battery swept in curves that stirred the heart; it made halts as dramatic as the crash of a wave on the rocks, and when it fled onward this aggregation of wheels, levers, motors had a beautiful unity, as if it were a missile. The sound of it was a war-chorus that reached into the depths of man's emotion.

The lieutenant, still holding his arm as if it were of glass, stood watching this battery until all detail of it was lost, save the figures of the riders, which rose and fell and waved lashes over the black mass.

Later, he turned his eyes toward the battle, where the shooting sometimes crackled like bush-fires, sometimes sputtered with exasperating irregularity, and sometimes reverberated like the thunder. He saw the smoke rolling upward and saw crowds of men who ran and cheered, or stood and blazed away at the inscrutable distance.

He came upon some stragglers, and they told him how to

find the field hospital. They described its exact location. In fact, these men, no longer having part in the battle, knew more of it than others. They told the performance of every corps, every division, the opinion of every general. The lieutenant, carrying his wounded arm rearward, looked upon them with wonder.

At the roadside a brigade was making coffee and buzzing with talk like a girls' boarding-school. Several officers came out to him and inquired concerning things of which he knew nothing. One, seeing his arm, began to scold. "Why, man, that's no way to do. You want to fix that thing." He appropriated the lieutenant and the lieutenant's wound. He cut the sleeve and laid bare the arm, every nerve of which softly fluttered under his touch. He bound his handerchief over the wound, scolding away in the meantime. His tone allowed one to think that he was in the habit of being wounded every day. The lieutenant hung his head, feeling, in this presence, that he did not know how to be correctly wounded.

The low white tents of the hospital were grouped around an old schoolhouse. There was here a singular commotion. In the foreground two ambulances interlocked wheels in the deep mud. The drivers were tossing the blame of it back and forth, gesticulating and berating, while from the ambulances, both crammed with wounded, there came an occasional groan. An interminable crowd of bandaged men were coming and going. Great numbers sat under the trees nursing heads or arms or legs. There was a dispute of some kind raging on the steps of the schoolhouse. Sitting with his back against a tree a man with a face as grey as a new army blanket was serenely smoking a corncob pipe. The lieutenant wished to rush forward and inform him that he was dying.

A busy surgeon was passing near the lieutenant. "Good-morning," he said, with a friendly smile. Then he caught sight of the lieutenant's arm, and his face at once changed. "Well, let's have a look at it." He seemed possessed suddenly of a great contempt for the lieutenant. This wound evidently placed the latter on a very low social plane. The doctor cried out impatiently: "What mutton-head had tied it up that way anyhow?" The lieutenant answered, "Oh, a man."

When the wound was disclosed the doctor fingered it disdainfully. "Humph," he said. "You come along with me and I'll 'tend to you." His voice contained the same scorn as if he were saying: "You will have to go to jail."

The lieutenant had been very meek, but now his face flushed, and he looked into the doctor's eyes. "I guess I won't have it amputated," he said.

"Nonsense, man! Nonsense! Nonsense!" cried the doctor. "Come along, now. I won't amputate it. Come along. Don't be a baby."

"Let go of me," said the lieutenant, holding back wrathfully, his glance fixed upon the door of the old schoolhouse, as sinister to him as the portals of death.

And this is the story of how the lieutenant lost his arm. When he reached home, his sisters, his mother, his wife, sobbed for a long time at the sight of the flat sleeve. "Oh, well," he said, standing shamefaced amid these tears, "I don't suppose it matters so much as all that."

STEPHEN CRANE'S VIVID STORY
OF THE BATTLE OF SAN JUAN [1]

☼ ☼ ☼

Victory Gained Not by the Officers, but by the Audacious Bravery of the Men

---

"GRAND POPULAR MOVEMENT"

With or Without Orders, They Marched Doggedly Forward in the Face of Death

---

DESPERATE VALOR AT EL CANEY

Cuban Soldiers Demoralized, Lazy, Worthless and Heartily Despised by the American Troops

IN FRONT OF SANTIAGO, July 4, via Old Point Comfort, Va., July 13.—The action at San Juan on July 1 was, particularly speaking, a soldiers' battle. It was like Inkerman, where the English fought half leaderless all day in a fog. Only the Cuban forest was worse than any fog.

No doubt when history begins to grind out her story we will find that many a thundering, fine, grand order was given for that day's work: but after all there will be no harm in contending that the fighting line, the men and their regimental officers, took the hill chiefly because they knew they could take it, some having no orders and others disobeying whatever orders they had.

In civil life the newspapers would have called it a grand,

---

[1] Reprinted verbatim from the *World*, New York, Thursday, July 14, 1898, p. 3.

popular movement. It will never be forgotten as long as America has a military history.

A line of intrenched hills held by men armed with a weapon like the Mauser is not to be taken by a front attack of infantry unless the trenches have first been heavily shaken by artillery fire. Any theorist will say that it is impossible, and prove it to be impossible. But it was done, and we owe the success to the splendid gallantry of the American private soldier.

As near as one can learn, headquarters expected little or no fighting on the 1st. Lawton's division was to go by the Caney road, chase the Spaniards out of that interesting village, and then, wheeling half to the left, march down to join the other divisions in some kind of attack on San Juan at daybreak on the 2d.

MISINFORMED AS TO SPANISH STRENGTH

But somebody had been entirely misinformed as to the strength and disposition of the Spanish forces at Caney, and instead of taking Lawton six minutes to capture the town it took him nearly all day, as well it might.

The other divisions lying under fire, waiting for Lawton, grew annoyed at a delay which was, of course, not explained to them, and suddenly arose and took the formidable hills of San Juan. It was impatience suddenly exalted to one of the sublime passions.

Lawton was well out toward Caney soon after daybreak, and by 7 o'clock we could hear the boom of Capron's guns in support of the infantry. The remaining divisions—Kent's and Wheeler's—were trudging slowly along the muddy trail through the forest.

When the first gun was fired a grim murmur passed along the lean column. "They're off!" somebody said.

The marching was of necessity very slow, and even then the narrow road was often blocked. The men, weighted with their packs, cartridge belts and rifles, forded many streams, climbed hills, slid down banks and forced their way through thickets.

Suddenly there was a roar of guns just ahead and a little to the left. This was Grimes's battery going into action on the hill which is called El Paso. Then, all in a moment, the quiet column moving forward was opposed by men carrying terrible burdens. Wounded Cubans were being carried to the rear. Most of them were horribly mangled.

The second brigade of dismounted American cavalry had been in support of the battery, its position being directly to the rear. Some Cubans had joined there. The Spanish shrapnel fired at the battery was often cut too long, and, passing over, burst amid the supports and the Cubans.

SHORT LULL IN THE BATTLE

The loss of the battery, the cavalry and the Cubans from this fire was forty men in killed and wounded, the First regular cavalry probably suffering most grievously. Presently there was a lull in the artillery fire, and down through spaces in the trees we could see the infantry still plodding with its packs steadily toward the front.

The artillerymen were greatly excited. Some showed with glee fragments of Spanish shells which had come dangerously near their heads. They had gone through their ordeal and were talking over it lightly.

In the mean time Lawton's division, some three miles away, was making plenty of noise. Caney is just at the base of a high willow-green, crinkled mountain, and Lawton was making his way over little knolls which might be termed foothills. We could see the great white clouds of smoke from Capron's guns and hear their roar punctuating the incessant drumming of the infantry. It was plain even then that Lawton was having considerably more of a fete than anybody had supposed previously.

At about 2,500 yards in front of Grimes's position on El Paso arose the gentle green hills of San Juan, dotted not too plentifully with trees—hills that resembled the sloping orchards of Orange County in summer. Here and there were houses built, evidently as summer villas, but now loopholed and barricaded. They had heavy roofs of red tiles and were shaped much like Japanese, or, better, Javanese, houses. Here and there, too, along the crests of these curving hillocks were ashen streaks, the rifle-pits of the Spaniards.

At the principal position of the enemy were a flag, a redoubt, a block-house and some sort of pagoda, in the shade of which Spanish officers were wont to promenade during lulls and negligently gossip about the battle. There was one man in a summer-resort straw hat. He did a deal of sauntering in the coolest manner possible, walking out in the clear sunshine and gazing languidly in our direction. He seemed to be carrying a little cane.

GRIMES SMASHED THEM

At 11.25 our artillery reopened on the central block-house and intrenchments. The Spanish fire had been remarkably fine, but it was our turn now. Grimes had his ranges to a nicety. After the great "shout of the gun" came the broad, windy, diminishing noise of the flung shell: then a fainter boom and a cloud of red debris out of the block-house or up from the ground near the trenches.

The Spanish infantry in the trenches fired a little volley immediately after every one of the American shells. It puzzled many to decide at what they could be firing, but it was finally resolved that they were firing just to show us that they were still there and were not afraid.

It must have been about 2 o'clock when the enemy's battery again retorted.

The cruel thing about this artillery duel was that our battery had nothing but old-fashioned powder, and its position was always as clearly defined as if it had been the Chicago fire. There is no secrecy about a battery that uses that kind of powder. The great billowy white smoke can be seen for miles.

On the other hand, the Spaniards were using the best smokeless. There is no use groaning over what was to be, but!—

However, fate elected that the Spanish shooting should be very bad. Only two-thirds of their shells exploded in this second affair. They all whistled high, and those that exploded raked the ground long since evacuated by the supports and the timbers. No one was hurt.

A MISPLACED BALLOON

From El Paso to San Juan there is a broad expanse of dense forest, spotted infrequently with vividly green fields. It is traversed by a single narrow road which leads straight between the two positions, fording two little streams. Along this road had gone our infantry and also the military balloon. Why it was ever taken to such a position nobody knows, but there it was—huge, fat, yellow, quivering—being dragged straight into a zone of fire that would surely ruin it.

There were two officers in the car for the greater part of the way, and there surely were never two men who valued their lives less. But they both escaped unhurt, while the balloon sank down, torn to death by the bullets that were volleyed at it by the nervous Spaniards, who suspected dynamite. It was never brought out of the woods where it recklessly met its fate.

In these woods, unknown to some, including the Spaniards, was fulminated the gorgeous plan of taking an impregnable position.

One saw a thin line of black figures moving across a field. They disappeared in the forest. The enemy was keeping up a terrific fire. Then suddenly somebody yelled, "By God, there go our boys up the hill!"

There is many a good American who would give an arm to get the thrill of patriotic insanity that coursed through us when we heard that yell.

Yes, they were going up the hill, up the hill. It was the best moment of anybody's life. An officer said to me afterward: "If we had been in that position and the Spaniards had come at us, we would have piled them up so high the last man couldn't have climbed over." But up went the regiments with no music save that ceaseless, fierce crashing of rifles.

FOREIGN ATTACHES SAID "IMPOSSIBLE"

The foreign attaches were shocked. "It is very gallant, but very foolish," said one sternly.

"Why, they can't take it, you know. Never in the world," cried another, much agitated. "It is slaughter, absolute slaughter."

The little Japanese shrugged his shoulders. He was one who said nothing.

The road from El Paso to San Juan was now a terrible road. It should have a tragic fame like the sunken road at Waterloo. Why we did not later hang some of the gentry who contributed from the trees to the terror of this road is not known.

The wounded were stringing back from the front, hundreds of them. Some walked unaided, an arm or a shoulder having been dressed at a field station. They stopped often enough to answer the universal hail "How is it going?" Others hobbled or clung to a friend's shoulders. Their slit trousers exposed red bandages. A few were shot horribly in the face and were led, bleeding and blind, by their mates.

And then there were the slow pacing stretcher-bearers with the dying or the insensible, the badly wounded, still figures with blood often drying brick color on their hot bandages.

Prostrate at the roadside were many, others who had made their way thus far and were waiting for strength. Everywhere moved the sure-handed, invaluable Red Cross men.

Over this scene was a sort of haze of bullets. They were of two kinds. First, the Spanish lines were firing just a trifle high. Their bullets swept over our firing lines and poured into this devoted roadway, the single exit, even as it had been the single approach. The second fire was from guerillas concealed in the trees and in the thickets along the trail. They had come in under the very wings of our strong advance, taken good positions on either side of the road and were peppering our line of communication whenever they got a good target, no matter, apparently, what the target might be.

Red Cross men, wounded men, sick men, correspondents and attaches were all one to the guerilla. The move of sending an irregular force around the flanks of the enemy as he is making his front attack is so legitimate that some of us could not believe at first that the men hidden in the forest were really blazing away at the non-combatants or the wounded. Viewed simply as a bit of tactics, the scheme was admirable. But there is no doubt now that they intentionally fired at anybody they thought they could kill.

You can't mistake an ambulance driver when he is driving his ambulance. You can't mistake a wounded man when he is lying down and being bandaged. And when you see a field hospital you don't mistake it for a squadron of cavalry or a brigade of infantry.

PROFOUND PATIENCE OF THE WOUNDED

As we went along the road we suddenly heard a cry behind us. "Oh, come quick! Come quick!" We turned and saw a young soldier spinning around frantically and grabbing at his leg. Evidently he had been going to the stream to fill his canteen, but a guerilla had barred him from that drink. Two Red Cross men rushed for him.

At the last ford, and in the shelter of the muddy bank, lay a dismal band, forty men on their backs with doctors working at them and bullets singing in flocks over their heads. They rolled their eyes quietly at us. There was no groaning. They exhibited that profound patience which has been the marvel of every one.

After the ford was passed the woods cleared. The road passed through lines of barbed wire. There were, in fact, barbed wire fences running in almost every direction.

The mule train, galloping like a troop of cavalry, dashed up with a reinforcement of ammunition, every mule on the jump, the cowboys swinging their whips. They were under a fairly strong fire, but up they went.

One does not expect gallantry in a pack train, but incidentally it may be said that this charge, led by the bell mare, was one of the sights of the day.

BURROWE'S DYNAMITE GUN

At a place where the road cut through the crest of the ridge Burrowe and some of his men were working over his dynamite gun. After the fifth discharge something had got jammed. There was never such devotion to an inanimate thing as these men give to their dynamite gun. They will quarrel for her, starve for her, lose sleep for her and fight for her to the last ditch.

In the army there have always been two opinions of the dynamite gun. Some have said it was a most terrific engine of destruction, while others have called it a toy. With the bullets winging their long flights not very high overhead, Burrowe and his crowd, at sight of us, began their little hymn of praise, the chief note of which was one of almost pathetic insistence. If they ever get that gun into action again, they will make her hum.

The discomfited Spaniards, recovering from their panic, opened from their second line a most furious fire. It was first directed against one part of our line and then against another, as if they were feeling for our weakest point, fumbling around after the throat of the army.

Somebody on the left caught it for a time, and then suddenly the enemy apparently devoted their entire attention to the position occupied by the Rough Riders. Some shrapnel, with fuses cut too long, passed over and burst from 100 to 200 yards to the rear. They acted precisely like things with strings to them. When the string was jerked, bang! went the hurtling explosive. But the infantry fire was very heavy, albeit high.

The American reply was in measured volleys. Part of a regiment would remain on the firing line while the other companies rested near by under the brow of the hill. Parties were sent after the packs. The commands knew with what other organizations they were in touch on the two flanks. Otherwise they knew nothing, save that they were going to hold their ground. They said so.

From our line could be seen a long, gray, Spanish intrenchment, from 400 to 1,000 yards away, according to what part of our line one measured from. From it floated no smoke and no men appeared there, but it was making a noise like a million champagne corks.

Back of their entrenchments, perhaps another thousand yards, was a long building of masonry tinted pink. It flew many Red Cross flags and near it were other smaller structures also flying Red Cross flags. In fact, the enemy's third line of defense seemed to be composed of hospitals.

The city itself slanted down toward the bay, just a glimpse of silver. In the clear, white sunshine the houses of the suburbs, the hospitals and the long gray trenches were so vivid that they seemed far closer than they were.

To the rear, over the ground that the army had taken, a breeze was gently stirring the long grass and ruffling the surface of a pool that lay in a sort of meadow. The army took its glory calmly. Having nothing else to do, the army sat down and looked tranquilly at the scenery. There was not that exuberance of enthusiasm which surrounds the vicinity of a candidate for the Assembly.

The army was dusty, dishevelled, its hair matted to its forehead with sweat, its shirts glued to its back with the same, and indescribably dirty, thirsty, hungry, and a-weary from its bundles and its marches and its fights. It sat down on the conquered crest and felt satisfied.

"Well, hell! here we are."

LAWTON'S HEAVY LOSSES

News began to pass along the line. Lawton had taken Caney after a long fight and had lost heavily. The siege pieces were being unloaded at Siboney. Pando had succeeded in reinforcing Santiago that very morning with 8,400 men, 6,000 men, 4,500 men. Pando had not succeeded. And so on.

At dusk a comparative stillness settled upon the ridge. The shooting subsided to little nervous outbursts. In the trenches taken by our troops lay dead Spaniards.

The road to the rear increased its terrors in the darkness. The wounded men, stumbling along in the mud, a miasmic mist from the swampish ground filling their nostrils, heard often in the air the whiplash sound of a bullet that was meant for them by the lurking guerillas. A mile, two miles, two miles and a half to the rear, great populous hospitals had been formed.

CAMPING ON THE GROUND THEY WON

The long lines of the hill began to intrench under cover of night, each regiment for itself, still, however, keeping in touch on the flanks. Each regiment dug in the ground that it had taken by its own valor. Some commands had two or three shovels, an axe or two, maybe a pick. Other regiments dug with their bayonets and shovelled out the dirt with their meat ration cans.

Darkness swallowed Santiago and the new intrenchments. The large tropic stars illumined the sky. On the safe side of the ridge our men had built some little red fires, no larger than hats, at which they cooked what food they possessed. There was no sound save to the rear, where throughout the night our pickets could be faintly heard exchanging shots with the guerillas.

On the very moment, it seemed, of the break of day, bang! the fight was on again. The firing broke out from one end of the prodigious V-shaped formation to the other. Our artillery took new advanced positions, but they were driven away by the swirling Mauser fire.

When the day was in full bloom Lawton's division, having

marched all night, appeared in the road. The long, long column wound around the base of the ridge and disappeared among the woods and knolls on the right of Wheeler's line. The army was now concentrated in a splendid position.

CUBANS HELD IN CONTEMPT

It becomes necessary to speak of the men's opinion of the Cubans. To put it shortly, both officers and privates have the most lively contempt for the Cubans. They despise them. They came down here expecting to fight side by side with an ally, but this ally has done little but stay in the rear and eat army rations, manifesting an indifference to the cause of Cuban liberty which could not be exceeded by some one who had never heard of it.

In the great charge up the hills of San Juan the American soldiers who, for their part, sprinkled a thousand bodies in the grass, were not able to see a single Cuban assisting in what might easily turn out to be the decisive battle for Cuban freedom.

At Caney a company of Cubans came into action on the left flank of one of the American regiments just before the place was taken. Later they engaged a block-house at 2,000 yards and fired away all their ammunition. They sent back to the American commander for more, but they got only a snort of indignation.

As a matter of fact, the Cuban soldier, ignorant as only such isolation as has been his can make him, does not appreciate the ethics of the situation.

This great American army he views is furious, too, because the Cubans apparently consider themselves under no obligation to take part in an engagement; because the Cubans will stay at the rear and collect haversacks, blankets, coats and shelter tents dropped by our troops.

The average Cuban here will not speak to an American unless to beg. He forgets his morning, afternoon or evening salutation unless he is reminded. If he takes a dislike to you he talks about you before your face, using a derisive undertone.

DEMORALIZED BY AID

The truth probably is that the food, raiment and security furnished by the Americans have completely demoralized the insurgents. When the force under Gomez came to Guantanamo to assist the marines they were a most efficient body of men. They guided the marines to the enemy and fought with them shoulder to shoulder, not very skilfully in the matter of shooting, but still with courage and determination.

After this action there ensued at Guantanamo a long peace. The Cubans built themselves a permanent camp and they began to eat, eat much, and to sleep long, day and night, until now, behold, there is no more useless body of men anywhere! A trifle less than half of them are on Dr. Edgar's sick list, and the others are practically insubordinate. So much food seems to act upon them like a drug.

Here with the army the demoralization has occurred on a big scale. It is dangerous, too, for the Cuban. If he stupidly, drowsily remains out of these fights, what weight is his voice to have later in the final adjustments? The officers and men of the army, if their feeling remains the same, will not be happy to see him have any at all. The situation needs a Gomez. It is more serious than these bestarred machete bearers know how to appreciate, and it is the worst thing for the cause of an independent Cuba that could possibly exist.

THE BATTLE OF JULY 2

At San Juan the 2d of July was a smaller edition of the 1st. The men deepened their intrenchments, shot, slept and ate. On the 1st every man had been put into the fighting line. There was not a reserve as big as your hat. If the enemy broke through any part of the line there was nothing to stop them short of Siboney. On the 2d, however, some time after the arrival of Lawton, the Ninth Massachusetts and the Thirty-fourth Michigan came up.

Along the road from El Paso they had to pass some pretty grim sights. And there were some pretty grim odors, but the men were steady enough. "How far are they off?" they asked of a passing regular. "Oh, not far; but it's all right. We think they may run out of ammunition in the course of a week or ten days."

The volunteers laughed. But the pitiful thing about this advance was to see in the hands of the boys those terrible old rifles that smoke like brush fires and give the regimental line away to the enemy as plainly as an illuminated sign.

I remember that on the first day men of the Seventy-first who had lost their command would try to join one of the regular regiments, but the regulars would have none of them. "Get out of here with that —— gun!" the regulars would say. During the battle just one shot from a Springfield would call a volley, for the Spaniards then knew just where to shoot. It was very hard on the Seventy-first New York and the Second Massachusetts.

At Caney about two hundred prisoners were taken. Two big squads of them were soldiers of the regular Spanish infantry in the usual blue-and-white pajamas. The others were the rummiest-looking set of men one could possibly imagine. They were native-born Cubans, reconcentrados, traitors, guerillas of the kind that bushwacked us so unmercifully. Some were doddering old men, shaking with the palsy of their many years. Some were slim, dirty, bad-eyed boys. They were all of a lower class than one could find in any United States jail.

At first they had all expected to be butchered. In fact, to encourage them to fight, their officers had told them that if they gave in they need expect no mercy from the dreadful Americans.

Our great, good, motherly old country has nothing in her heart but mercy, and nothing in her pockets but beef, hardtack and coffee for all of them—lemon-colored refugee from Santiago, wild-eyed prisoner from the trenches, Spanish guerilla from out the thickets, half-naked insurgent from the mountains—all of them.

STEPHEN CRANE

PART III

A Tale of the Sea

A TALE OF THE SEA

INTRODUCTION

IN the winter of 1892-3 Crane roomed with some young painters and newspaper illustrators at the Art Students' League on Twenty-third Street, and he used to visit the near-by studio of one of these artist friends, Corwin Linson.

Sitting on my couch, rings of gray smoke circling about him, a pad on his knee, he would turn out a complete story in a half-hour. Sometimes it was a fragment that would be laid by for future use. Several sparkling sketches were invented and written in that atmosphere of melancholy, while I sat at my easel dabbling at a drawing and wondering how a new illustrator could get in his "wedge." [1]

One morning when Linson called at Crane's room he discovered him "feverishly writing. He waved me to a seat, and soon handed me the first pages of a story. 'Been at it most of the night, and it's nearly finished.'" Short stories, Crane told another friend, "are the easiest things to write."

Three years later, when Crane was living at Hartwood "very quietly and alone mostly," he looked back on the array of writings he had published and remarked in a letter to his former schoolmate C. L. Peaslee: "it appears that I have worked, but as a matter of truth I am very lazy, hating work and only taking up a pen when circumstances drive me." [2] Two of his major books were finished and his third was under way in that wonderful year 1893, and he did a lot of other pieces. One of these, written that spring, was *The Reluctant Voyagers* —his first attempt at a sea-story. It is a kind of *New Yorker*

---

[1] "Little Stories of 'Steve' Crane," *Saturday Evening Post*, April 11, 1903, p. 19.

[2] This letter appears in "The College Days of Stephen Crane," *Monthly Illustrator*, 13 (1896), 27.

sketch about two men who are carried out to sea on a derelict raft, rescued by a coast schooner, and deposited at New York harbor in their bathing suits. Corwin Linson drew illustrations for it, using Crane to pose for "the tall man." But the sketch did not pay off. No magazine would take *The Reluctant Voyagers*, and it never reached print until 1902, in the posthumous *Last Words*. It is fifth-rate Crane. The plot drifts like the raft itself, breaking loose from what looked like a good beginning.

Crane did not have to invent any plot for *The Open Boat*: he transcribed the whole from his own experience. Yet it is as much an invention as *The Reluctant Voyagers*. Crane always was concerned to get facts down with scrupulous fidelity to the truth of experience, and he went to extraordinary pains to be certain that the facts in *The Open Boat* squared with what actually happened. To find out whether he had them right, he checked them with the captain of the *Commodore*. Their conversation was overheard by Ralph Paine and recorded in his *Roads of Adventure* (1922):

—Listen, Ed, I want to have this *right*, from your point of view. How does it sound so far?—
—You've got it, Steve—said the other man.—That is just how it happened, and how we felt. Read me some more of it.—

Accounts of the wreck in dispatches to the *New York Press* and the *Florida Times-Union* (here abridged and collected for the first time, pages 448–64), together with Crane's own report, furnished a history of the tragedy. Crane did not alter the facts or their sequence, yet the difference between what happened and what Crane reconstructed from his experience is immense. It is the difference that distinguishes life from art. In *The Open Boat* the whole event is charged with significance. Every fact has been charged with meaning and patterned into a scheme of relationships. Realistic details have been converted into symbols, and their sequence forms a designed whole possessing a life of its own.

By what methods has Crane brought about this symbolic conversion? Let us examine some of his symbols and see how symbols are created.

Symbols are created by establishing correlations between the plight of the characters and their environment (for example, battlefield, forest, or sea). The mental state, feeling, or mood is transposed and objectified in things, in natural objects or in other persons whose plight parallels the central situation or stands in contrast to it. Thus in *The Red Badge* Henry's mental state is objectified in a single recurrent object, the flag, and the meaning of the whole book gradually accretes around this dominant or focal symbol. In *The Open Boat* the confused mental state of the men is identified with the confused and "broken sea," and it is obversely objectified in the contradictory gulls that hover "comfortably" over them, gruesome and ominous birds utterly indifferent to the plight of the men. The bird's "black eyes were *wistfully* fixed upon the captain's head." The unconcern of the universe is symbolized by the wind-tower as it appears to them when they head for the beach:

This tower was a giant, standing with its back to the plight of the ants. It represented in a degree, to the correspondent, the serenity of nature amid the struggles of the individual—nature in the wind, and nature in the vision of the men. She did not seem cruel to him then, nor beneficent, nor treacherous, nor wise. But she was indifferent, flatly indifferent.

Symbols are generated by parallelisms and repetitions. A symbolic detail at the very beginning of *The Open Boat* prepares for the final incident, the death of the oiler. He is represented by the oar he steers: "It was a thin little oar and it seemed often ready to snap." In *The Red Badge* the chattering fear of a frightened squirrel, fleeing when Henry Fleming throws a pine cone at him (Chapter vii), parallels the plight of the hero under shellfire.

Symbols are at their most effective when they radiate

multiple correspondences or different contents—at different times or at the same time. Colors, used *only* as decorative pattern in *Maggie* and *An Experiment in Misery*, are symbolically employed in *The Red Badge*. Here the symbolic value of any given color varies according to its location in a specific context. Symbolic patterns of life and death are established, for example, by the *same* color. The one is signified by the *yellow* of the sun and the other by the *yellow* of uniforms on dead soldiers.

The Open Boat and *The Red Badge* are identical in form, in theme, and even in their patterns of leitmotivs and imagery. In *The Open Boat* the despair-hope mood of the men is established (and the point of view prepared for) in the opening sentence: "None of them knew the colour of the sky"; and the final scene repeats the same contrast mood. At the end, when the men are tossed upon "the lonely and indifferent shore," the once barbarously abrupt waves now pace "to and fro in the moonlight." As the sea changes, so the men change. They experience a change of heart. Their serenity, we are made to feel, is signified by the seemingly quieted waves. But the serenity of the waves is deceptive, for the violent sea actually remains unabated. Their victory over nature has cost them one of their brotherhood—the oiler lies face-downward in the shallows.

The death of Higgins symbolizes nature's injustice, her treachery and indifference, but it is *through* his death that this truth is revealed to the others. It is his death that changes their vision. (Similarly, in *The Red Badge*, it is the death of Jim Conklin that changes Henry Fleming's vision.) At the end, when the men hear "the great sea's voice," they understand what it says, what life means, because they have suffered the worst that the sea can exact from them—"they felt that they could *then* be interpreters." Life—represented by the ritual of comfort bestowed on the saved men by the people on the beach—life now becomes "sacred to their minds."

This theme of insight through suffering is prepared for by

the very first image of the story: "None of them knew the colour of the sky." It is foreshadowed and epitomized in the song that the correspondent recites to himself: "A soldier of the Legion lay dying in Algiers." The correspondent had known this verse when a child, but *then* he had not regarded the death of that soldier as important or meaningful. He had never felt any sympathy for the soldier's plight because he himself had not yet experienced it. "It was less to him than the breaking of a pencil's point." The soldier's plight parallels and foremirrors the oiler's plight. The image of the delicate pencil point correlates with the image of the thin oar of the oiler that "seemed often ready to snap." The whole meaning of *The Open Boat* is focused in the death of the oiler.

The Open Boat was sold by Irvin Bacheller to *Scribner's Magazine* for three hundred and fifty dollars. It appeared there in June 1897 and in *The Open Boat and Other Stories* the next year, with Crane's dedication to "the late William Higgins and to Captain Edward Murphy and Steward C. B. Montgomery. . . ." *The Open Boat*, said H. G. Wells, is "beyond all question, the crown of all his work." Conrad deeply admired it: "the deep and simple humanity of its presentation seems somehow to illustrate the essentials of life itself, like a symbolic tale."

Both Conrad and Crane showed themselves very early in their career to be symbolic artists—Conrad in his very first story, *The Lagoon*, and Crane in one of his earliest, *The Men in the Storm*. The greater number of Crane's stories, however, are non-symbolic. When he does attempt symbolism, the potential symbols all too often collapse. The beginning of *The Reluctant Voyagers* is wasted by what follows, and the pathetic episode of *An Auction*, while intending a symbolism, remains merely pathetic. Crane's technique is best studied in *The Red Badge* and *The Open Boat*. The device of a double vision, for instance, was first introduced in *The Open Boat*. Things viewed by the men at sea are viewed *as though* they were men on land. In *An Episode of War*, similarly, we get the point of view of the wounded simultaneously with the point of view of the unwounded. It is this technical trick that Joyce employed so expertly in *The Dead*. In *The Open Boat* this double vision manifests the two-part contrast of Crane's theme: sea and land symbolizing two opposite ways of life.

Of all Crane's works *The Open Boat* is the most direct manifestation of his belief that no man can interpret life without first experiencing it. The key to the whole work of Crane is that he passionately believed in this theme and that as artist he put his belief into practice. And that is the paradox of his whole career: *The Red Badge* is the product of his *imaginative* belief in the same theme. What is important to the artist is not that he experience his theme but that he believe in it.

I have said that *The Open Boat* and *The Red Badge* embody the same theme. In change lies salvation. This theme of immersion and regeneration is exploited in *King Lear*; it is uttered by Heyst in Conrad's *Victory*; and it is expressed as the credo of Stein in *Lord Jim*. The way is to immerse oneself in the destructive element. In *The Red Badge* the destructive element is the battle; in *The Open Boat* it is the sea. The rescue of the men from the sea has cost them "a terrible grace"—the oiler lies face-downward in the shallows. To the correspondent the man on the shore seemed like a savior. He had a halo "about his head, and he shone like a saint."

THE OPEN BOAT

A Tale Intended to be after the Fact:
Being the Experience of Four Men
from the Sunk Steamer Commodore

I

NONE of them knew the colour of the sky. Their eyes glanced level, and were fastened upon the waves that swept toward them. These waves were of the hue of slate, save for the tops, which were of foaming white, and all of the men knew the colours of the sea. The horizon narrowed and widened, and dipped and rose, and at all times its edge was jagged with waves that seemed thrust up in points like rocks.

Many a man ought to have a bathtub larger than the boat which here rode upon the sea. These waves were most wrongfully and barbarously abrupt and tall, and each froth-top was a problem in small-boat navigation.

The cook squatted in the bottom, and looked with both eyes at the six inches of gunwale which separated him from the ocean. His sleeves were rolled over his fat forearms, and the two flaps of his unbuttoned vest dangled as he bent to bail out the boat. Often he said, "Gawd! that was a narrow clip." As he remarked it he invariably gazed eastward over the broken sea.

The oiler, steering with one of the two oars in the boat, sometimes raised himself suddenly to keep clear of water that swirled in over the stern. It was a thin little oar, and it seemed often ready to snap.

The correspondent, pulling at the other oar, watched the waves and wondered why he was there.

The injured captain, lying in the bow, was at this time buried in that profound dejection and indifference which comes, temporarily at least, to even the bravest and most enduring when, willy-nilly, the firm fails, the army loses, the ship goes down. The mind of the master of a vessel is rooted deep in the timbers of her, though he command for a day or a decade; and this captain had on him the stern impression of a scene in the greys of dawn of seven turned faces, and later a stump of a topmast with a white ball on it, that slashed to and fro at the waves, went low and lower, and down. Thereafter there was something strange in his voice. Although steady, it was deep with mourning, and of a quality beyond oration or tears.

"Keep 'er a little more south, Billie," said he.

"A little more south, sir," said the oiler in the stern.

A seat in his boat was not unlike a seat upon a bucking broncho, and by the same token a broncho is not much smaller. The craft pranced and reared and plunged like an animal. As each wave came, and she rose for it, she seemed like a horse making at a fence outrageously high. The manner of her scramble over these walls of water is a mystic thing, and, moreover, at the top of them were ordinarily these problems in white water, the foam racing down from the summit of each wave requiring a new leap, and a leap from the air. Then, after scornfully bumping a crest, she would slide and race and splash down a long incline, and arrive bobbing and nodding in front of the next menace.

A singular disadvantage of the sea lies in the fact that after successfully surmounting one wave you discover that there is another behind it just as important and just as nervously anxious to do something effective in the way of swamping boats. In a ten-foot dinghy one can get an idea of the resources of the sea in the line of waves that is not probable to the average experience which is never at sea in a dinghy. As each slaty wall of water approached, it shut all else from the view of the men in the boat, and it was not difficult to imagine that this particular wave was the final outburst of the ocean, the last effort of the grim water. There was a terrible grace in the move of the waves, and they came in silence, save for the snarling of the crests.

In the wan light the faces of the men must have been grey. Their eyes must have glinted in strange ways as they gazed steadily astern. Viewed from a balcony, the whole thing would doubtless have been weirdly picturesque. But the men in the boat had no time to see it, and if they had had leisure, there were other things to occupy their minds. The sun swung steadily up the sky, and they knew it was broad day because the colour of the sea changed from slate to emerald green streaked with amber lights, and the foam was like tumbling snow. The process of the breaking day was unknown to them. They were aware only of this effect upon the colour of the waves that rolled toward them.

In disjointed sentences the cook and the correspondent argued as to the difference between a life-saving station and a house of refuge. The cook had said: "There's a house of refuge just north of the Mosquito Inlet Light, and as soon as they see us they'll come off in their boat and pick us up."

"As soon as who see us?" said the correspondent.

"The crew," said the cook.

"Houses of refuge don't have crews," said the correspondent. "As I understand them, they are only places where clothes and grub are stored for the benefit of shipwrecked people. They don't carry crews."

"Oh, yes, they do," said the cook.

"No, they don't," said the correspondent.

"Well, we're not there yet, anyhow," said the oiler, in the stern.

"Well," said the cook, "perhaps it's not a house of refuge that I'm thinking of as being near Mosquito Inlet Light; perhaps it's a life-saving station."

"We're not there yet," said the oiler in the stern.

II

As the boat bounced from the top of each wave the wind tore through the hair of the hatless men, and as the craft plopped her stern down again the spray slashed past them. The crest of each of these waves was a hill, from the top of which the men surveyed for a moment a broad tumultuous expanse, shining and wind-riven. It was probably splendid, it was probably glorious, this play of the free sea, wild with lights of emerald and white and amber.

"Bully good thing it's an on-shore wind," said the cook. "If not, where would we be? Wouldn't have a show."

"That's right," said the correspondent.

The busy oiler nodded his assent.

Then the captain, in the bow, chuckled in a way that expressed humour, contempt, tragedy, all in one. "Do you think we've got much of a show now, boys?" said he.

Whereupon the three were silent, save for a trifle of hemming and hawing. To express any particular optimism at this time they felt to be childish and stupid, but they all doubtless possessed this sense of the situation in their minds. A young man thinks doggedly at such times. On the other hand, the ethics of their condition was decidedly against any open suggestion of hopelessness. So they were silent.

"Oh, well," said the captain, soothing his children, "we'll get ashore all right."

But there was that in his tone which made them think; so the oiler quoth, "Yes! if this wind holds."

The cook was bailing. "Yes! if we don't catch hell in the surf."

Canton-flannel gulls flew near and far. Sometimes they sat down on the sea, near patches of brown seaweed that rolled over the waves with a movement like carpets on a line in a gale. The birds sat comfortably in groups, and they were envied by some in the dinghy, for the wrath of the sea was no more to them than it was to a covey of prairie chickens a thousand miles inland. Often they came very close and stared at the men with black bead-like eyes. At these times they were uncanny and sinister in their unblinking scrutiny, and the men hooted angrily at them, telling them to be gone. One came, and evidently decided to alight on the top of the captain's head. The bird flew parallel to the boat and did not circle, but made short sidelong jumps in the air in chicken-fashion. His black eyes were wistfully fixed upon the captain's head. "Ugly brute," said the oiler to the bird. "You look as if you were made with a jackknife." The cook and the correspondent swore darkly at the creature. The captain naturally wished to knock it away with the end of the heavy painter, but he did not dare do it, because anything resembling an emphatic gesture would have capsized this freighted boat; and so, with his open hand, the captain gently and carefully waved the gull away. After it had been discouraged from the pursuit the captain breathed easier on account of his hair, and others breathed easier because the bird struck their minds at this time as being somehow gruesome and ominous.

In the meantime the oiler and the correspondent rowed. And also they rowed. They sat together in the same seat, and each rowed an oar. Then the oiler took both oars; then the correspondent took both oars; then the oiler; then the correspondent. They rowed and they rowed. The very ticklish part of the business was when the time came for the reclining one in the stern to take his turn at the oars. By the very last star of truth, it is easier to steal eggs from under a hen than it was to change seats in the dinghy. First the man in the stern slid his hand along the thwart and moved with care, as if he were of Sèvres. Then the man in the rowing-seat slid his hand along the other thwart. It was all done with the most extraordinary care. As the two sidled past each other, the whole party kept watchful eyes on the coming wave, and the captain cried: "Look out, now! Steady, there!"

The brown mats of seaweed that appeared from time to time were like islands, bits of earth. They were travelling, apparently, neither one way nor the other. They were, to all intents, stationary. They informed the men in the boat that it was making progress slowly toward the land.

The captain, rearing cautiously in the bow after the dinghy soared on a great swell, said that he had seen the lighthouse at Mosquito Inlet. Presently the cook remarked that he had seen it. The correspondent was at the oars then, and for some reason he too wished to look at the lighthouse; but his back was toward the far shore, and the waves were important, and for some time he could not seize an opportunity to turn his head. But at last there came a wave more gentle than the others, and when at the crest of it he swiftly scoured the western horizon.

"See it?" said the captain.

"No," said the correspondent, slowly; "I didn't see anything."

"Look again," said the captain. He pointed. "It's exactly in that direction."

At the top of another wave the correspondent did as he was bid, and this time his eyes chanced on a small, still thing on the edge of the swaying horizon. It was precisely like the point of a pin. It took an anxious eye to find a lighthouse so tiny.

"Think we'll make it, Captain?"

"If this wind holds and the boat don't swamp, we can't do much else," said the captain.

The little boat, lifted by each towering sea and splashed viciously by the crests, made progress that in the absence of seaweed was not apparent to those in her. She semed just a wee thing wallowing, miraculously top up, at the mercy of five oceans. Occasionally a great spread of water, like white flames, swarmed into her.

"Bail her, cook," said the captain, serenely.

"All right, Captain," said the cheerful cook.

III

It would be difficult to describe the subtle brotherhood of men that was here established on the seas. No one said that it was so. No one mentioned it. But it dwelt in the boat, and each man felt it warm him. They were a captain, an oiler, a cook, and a correspondent, and they were friends—friends in a more curiously iron-bound degree than may be common. The hurt captain, lying against the water-jar in the bow, spoke always in a low voice and calmly; but he could never command a more ready and swiftly obedient crew than the motley three of the dinghy. It was more than a mere recognition of what was best for the common safety. There was surely in it a quality that was personal and heart-felt. And after this devotion to the commander of the boat, there was this comradeship, that the correspondent, for instance, who had been taught to be cynical of men, knew even at the time was the best experience of his life. But no one said that it was so. No one mentioned it.

"I wish we had a sail," remarked the captain. "We might try my overcoat on the end of an oar, and give you two boys a chance to rest." So the cook and the correspondent held the mast and spread wide the overcoat; the oiler steered; and the little boat made good way with her new rig. Sometimes the oiler had to scull sharply to keep a sea from breaking into the boat, but otherwise sailing was a success.

Meanwhile the lighthouse had been growing slowly larger. It had now almost assumed colour, and appeared like a little grey shadow on the sky. The man at the oars could not be prevented from turning his head rather often to try for a glimpse of this little grey shadow.

At last, from the top of each wave, the men in the tossing boat could see land. Even as the lighthouse was an upright shadow on the sky, this land seemed but a long black shadow on the sea. It certainly was thinner than paper. "We must be about opposite New Smyrna," said the cook, who had coasted this shore often in schooners. "Captain, by the way, I believe they abandoned that life-saving station there about a year ago."

"Did they?" said the captain.

The wind slowly died away. The cook and the correspondent

were not now obliged to slave in order to hold high the oar. But the waves continued their old impetuous swooping at the dinghy, and the little craft, no longer under way, struggled woundily over them. The oiler or the correspondent took the oars again.

Shipwrecks are apropos of nothing. If men could only train for them and have them occur when the men had reached pink condition, there would be less drowning at sea. Of the four in the dinghy none had slept any time worth mentioning for two days and two nights previous to embarking in the dinghy, and in the excitement of clambering about the deck of a foundering ship they had also forgotten to eat heartily.

For these reasons, and for others, neither the oiler nor the correspondent was fond of rowing at this time. The correspondent wondered ingenuously how in the name of all that was sane could there be people who thought it amusing to row a boat. It was not an amusement; it was a diabolical punishment, and even a genius of mental aberrations could never conclude that it was anything but a horror to the muscles and a crime against the back. He mentioned to the boat in general how the amusement of rowing struck him, and the weary-faced oiler smiled in full sympathy. Previously to the foundering, by the way, the oiler had worked a double watch in the engine-room of the ship.

"Take her easy now, boys," said the captain. "Don't spend yourselves. If we have to run a surf you'll need all your strength, because we'll sure have to swim for it. Take your time."

Slowly the land arose from the sea. From a black line it became a line of black and a line of white—trees and sand. Finally the captain said that he could make out a house on the shore. "That's the house of refuge, sure," said the cook. "They'll see us before long, and come out after us."

The distant lighthouse reared high. "The keeper ought to be able to make us out now, if he's looking through a glass," said the captain. "He'll notify the life-saving people."

"None of those other boats could have got ashore to give word of this wreck," said the oiler, in a low voice, "else the life-boat would be out hunting us."

Slowly and beautifully the land loomed out of the sea. The wind came again. It had veered from the north-east to the south-east. Finally a new sound struck the ears of the men in the boat. It was the low thunder of the surf on the shore. "We'll never be able to make the lighthouse now," said the captain. "Swing her head a little more north, Billie."

"A little more north, sir," said the oiler.

Whereupon the little boat turned her nose once more down the wind, and all but the oarsman watched the shore grow. Under the influence of this expansion doubt and direful apprehension were leaving the minds of the men. The management of the boat was still most absorbing, but it could not prevent a quiet cheerfulness. In an hour, perhaps, they would be ashore.

Their backbones had become thoroughly used to balancing in the boat, and they now rode this wild colt of a dinghy like circus men. The correspondent thought that he had been drenched to the skin, but happening to feel in the top pocket of his coat, he found therein eight cigars. Four of them were soaked with sea-water; four were perfectly scatheless. After a search, somebody produced three dry matches; and thereupon the four waifs rode impudently in their little boat and, with an assurance of an impending rescue shining in their eyes, puffed at the big cigars, and judged well and ill of all men. Everybody took a drink of water.

IV

"Cook," remarked the captain, "there don't seem to be any signs of life about your house of refuge."

"No," replied the cook. "Funny they don't see us!"

A broad stretch of lowly coast lay before the eyes of the men. It was of low dunes topped with dark vegetation. The roar of the surf was plain, and sometimes they could see the white lip of a wave as it spun up the beach. A tiny house was blocked out black upon the sky. Southward, the slim lighthouse lifted its little grey length.

Tide, wind, and waves were swinging the dinghy northward. "Funny they don't see us," said the men.

The surf's roar was here dulled, but its tone was nevertheless thunderous and mighty. As the boat swam over the great rollers the men sat listening to this roar. "We'll swamp sure," said everybody.

It is fair to say here that there was not a life-saving station within twenty miles in either direction; but the men did not know this fact, and in consequence they made dark and opprobrious remarks concerning the eyesight of the nation's life-savers. Four scowling men sat in the dinghy and surpassed records in the invention of epithets.

"Funny they don't see us."

The light-heartedness of a former time had completely faded. To their sharpened minds it was easy to conjure pictures of all kinds of incompetency and blindness and, indeed, cowardice. There was the shore of the populous land, and it was bitter and bitter to them that from it came no sign.

"Well," said the captain, ultimately, "I suppose we'll have to make a try for ourselves. If we stay out here too long, we'll none of us have strength left to swim after the boat swamps."

And so the oiler, who was at the oars, turned the boat straight for the shore. There was a sudden tightening of muscles. There was some thinking.

"If we don't all get ashore," said the captain—"if we don't all get ashore, I suppose you fellows know where to send news of my finish?"

They then briefly exchanged some addresses and admonitions. As for the reflections of the men, there was a great deal of rage in them. Perchance they might be formulated thus: "If I am going to be drowned—if I am going to be drowned—if I am going to be drowned, why, in the name of the seven mad gods who rule the sea, was I allowed to come thus far and contemplate sand and trees? Was I brought here merely to have my nose dragged away as I was about to nibble the sacred cheese of life? It is preposterous. If this old ninny-woman, Fate, cannot do better than this, she should be deprived of the management of men's fortunes. She is an old hen who knows not her intention. If she has decided to drown me, why did she not do it in the beginning and save me all this trouble? The whole affair is absurd.—But no; she cannot mean to drown me. She dare not drown me. She cannot drown me. Not after all this work." Afterward the man might have had an impulse to shake his fist at the clouds. "Just you drown me, now, and then hear what I call you!"

The billows that came at this time were more formidable. They seemed always just about to break and roll over the little boat in a turmoil of foam. There was a preparatory and long growl in the speech of them. No mind unused to the sea would have concluded that the dinghy could ascend these sheer heights in time. The shore was still afar. The oiler was a wily surfman. "Boys," he said swiftly, "she won't live three minutes more, and we're too far out to swim. Shall I take her to sea again, Captain?"

"Yes; go ahead!" said the captain.

This oiler, by a series of quick miracles and fast and steady oarsmanship, turned the boat in the middle of the surf and took her safely to sea again.

There was a considerable silence as the boat bumped over the furrowed sea to deeper water. Then somebody in gloom spoke: "Well, anyhow, they must have seen us from the shore by now."

The gulls went in slanting flight up the wind toward the grey, desolate east. A squall, marked by dingy clouds and clouds brick-red like smoke from a burning building, appeared from the south-east.

"What do you think of those life-saving people? Ain't they peaches?"

"Funny they haven't seen us."

"Maybe they think we're out here for sport! Maybe they think we're fishin'. Maybe they think we're damned fools."

It was a long afternoon. A changed tide tried to force them southward, but wind and wave said northward. Far ahead, where coast-line, sea, and sky formed their mighty angle, there were little dots which seemed to indicate a city on the shore.

"St. Augustine?"

The captain shook his head. "Too near Mosquito Inlet."

And the oiler rowed, and then the correspondent rowed; then the oiler rowed. It was a weary business. The human back can become the seat of more aches and pains than are registered in books for the composite anatomy of a regiment. It is a limited area, but it can become the theatre of innumerable muscular conflicts, tangles, wrenches, knots, and other comforts.

"Did you ever like to row, Billie?" asked the correspondent.

"No," said the oiler; "hang it!"

When one exchanged the rowing-seat for a place in the bottom of the boat, he suffered a bodily depression that caused him to be careless of everything save an obligation to wiggle one finger. There was cold sea-water swashing to and fro in the boat, and he lay in it. His head, pillowed on a thwart, was within an inch of the swirl of a wave-crest, and sometimes a particularly obstreperous sea came inboard and drenched him once more. But these matters did not annoy him. It is almost certain that if the boat had capsized he would have tumbled comfortably out upon the ocean as if he felt sure that it was a great soft mattress.

"Look! There's a man on the shore!"

"Where?"

"There! See 'im? See 'im?"

"Yes, sure! He's walking along."

"Now he's stopped. Look! He's facing us!"

"He's waving at us!"

"So he is! By thunder!"

"Ah, now we're all right! Now we're all right! There'll be a boat out here for us in half an hour."

"He's going on. He's running. He's going up to that house there."

The remote beach seemed lower than the sea, and it required a searching glance to discern the little black figure. The captain saw a floating stick, and they rowed to it. A bath towel was by some weird chance in the boat, and, tying this on the stick, the captain waved it. The oarsman did not dare turn his head, so he was obliged to ask questions.

"What's he doing now?"

"He's standing still again. He's looking, I think.—There he goes again—toward the house.—Now he's stopped again."

"Is he waving at us?"

"No, not now; he was, though."

"Look! There comes another man!"

"He's running."

"Look at him go, would you!"

"Why, he's on a bicycle. Now he's met the other man. They're both waving at us. Look!"

"There comes something up the beach."

"What the devil is that thing?"

"Why, it looks like a boat."

"Why, certainly, it's a boat."

"No; it's on wheels."

"Yes, so it is. Well, that must be the life-boat. They drag them along shore on a wagon."

"That's the life-boat, sure."

"No, by God, it's—it's an omnibus."

"I tell you it's a life-boat."

"It is not! It's an omnibus. I can see it plain. See? One of these big hotel omnibuses."

"By thunder, you're right. It's an omnibus, sure as fate. What do you suppose they are doing with an omnibus? Maybe they are going around collecting the life-crew, hey?"

"That's it, likely. Look! There's a fellow waving a little black flag. He's standing on the steps of the omnibus. There come those other two fellows. Now they're all talking together. Look at the fellow with the flag. Maybe he ain't waving it!"

"That ain't a flag, is it? That's his coat. Why, certainly, that's his coat."

"So it is; it's his coat. He's taken it off and is waving it around his head. But would you look at him swing it!"

"Oh, say, there isn't any life-saving station there. That's just a winter-resort hotel omnibus that has brought over some of the boarders to see us drown."

"What's that idiot with the coat mean? What's he signalling, anyhow?"

"It looks as if he were trying to tell us to go north. There must be a life-saving station up there."

"No; he thinks we're fishing. Just giving us a merry hand. See? Ah, there, Willie!"

"Well, I wish I could make something out of those signals. What do you suppose he means?"

"He don't mean anything; he's just playing."

"Well, if he'd just signal us to try the surf again, or to go to sea and wait, or go north, or go south, or go to hell, there would be some reason in it. But look at him! He just stands there and keeps his coat revolving like a wheel. The ass!"

"There come more people."

"Now there's quite a mob. Look! Isn't that a boat?"

"Where? Oh, I see where you mean. No, that's no boat."

"That fellow is still waving his coat."

"He must think we like to see him do that. Why don't he quit it? It don't mean anything."

"I don't know. I think he is trying to make us go north. It must be that there's a life-saving station there somewhere."

"Say, he ain't tired yet. Look at 'im wave!"

"Wonder how long he can keep that up. He's been revolving his coat ever since he caught sight of us. He's an idiot. Why aren't they getting men to bring a boat out? A fishing-boat—

one of those big yawls—could come out here all right. Why don't he do something?"

"Oh, it's all right now."

"They'll have a boat out here for us in less than no time, now that they've seen us."

A faint yellow tone came into the sky over the low land. The shadows on the sea slowly deepened. The wind bore coldness with it, and the men began to shiver.

"Holy smoke!" said one, allowing his voice to express his impious mood, "if we keep on monkeying out here! If we've got to flounder out here all night!"

"Oh, we'll never have to stay here all night! Don't you worry. They've seen us now, and it won't be long before they'll come chasing out after us."

The shore grew dusky. The man waving a coat blended gradually into this gloom, and it swallowed in the same manner the omnibus and the group of people. The spray, when it dashed uproariously over the side, made the voyagers shrink and swear like men who were being branded.

"I'd like to catch the chump who waved the coat. I feel like socking him one, just for luck."

"Why? What did he do?"

"Oh, nothing, but then he seemed so damned cheerful."

In the meantime the oiler rowed, and then the correspondent rowed, and then the oiler rowed. Grey-faced and bowed forward, they mechanically, turn by turn, plied the leaden oars. The form of the lighthouse had vanished from the southern horizon, but finally a pale star appeared, just lifting from the sea. The streaked saffron in the west passed before the all-merging darkness, and the sea to the east was black. The land had vanished, and was expressed only by the low and drear thunder of the surf.

"If I am going to be drowned—if I am going to be drowned— if I am going to be drowned, why, in the name of the seven mad gods who rule the sea, was I allowed to come thus far and contemplate sand and trees? Was I brought here merely to have my nose dragged away as I was about to nibble the sacred cheese of life?"

The patient captain, drooped over the water-jar, was sometimes obliged to speak to the oarsman.

"Keep her head up! Keep her head up!"

"Keep her head up, sir." The voices were weary and low.

This was surely a quiet evening. All save the oarsman lay heavily and listlessly in the boat's bottom. As for him, his eyes were just capable of noting the tall black waves that swept forward in a most sinister silence, save for an occasional subdued growl of a crest.

The cook's head was on a thwart, and he looked without interest at the water under his nose. He was deep in other scenes. Finally he spoke. "Billie," he murmured, dreamfully, "what kind of pie do you like best?"

V

"Pie!" said the oiler and the correspondent, agitatedly. "Don't talk about those things, blast you!"

"Well," said the cook, "I was just thinking about ham sandwiches and—"

A night on the sea in an open boat is a long night. As darkness settled finally, the shine of the light, lifting from the sea in the south, changed to full gold. On the northern horizon a new light appeared, a small bluish gleam on the edge of the waters. These two lights were the furniture of the world. Otherwise there was nothing but waves.

Two men huddled in the stern, and distances were so magnificent in the dinghy that the rower was enabled to keep his feet partly warm by thrusting them under his companions. Their legs indeed extended far under the rowing-seat until they touched the feet of the captain forward. Sometimes, despite the efforts of the tired oarsman, a wave came piling into the boat, an icy wave of the night, and the chilling water soaked them anew. They would twist their bodies for a moment and groan, and sleep the dead sleep once more, while the water in the boat gurgled about them as the craft rocked.

The plan of the oiler and the correspondent was for one to row until he lost the ability, and then arouse the other from his sea-water couch in the bottom of the boat.

The oiler plied the oars until his head drooped forward and the overpowering sleep blinded him; and he rowed yet afterward. Then he touched a man in the bottom of the boat, and called his name. "Will you spell me for a little while?" he said, meekly.

"Sure, Billie," said the correspondent, awaking and dragging himself to a sitting position. They exchanged places carefully, and the oiler, cuddling down in the sea-water at the cook's side, seemed to go to sleep instantly.

The particular violence of the sea had ceased. The waves came without snarling. The obligation of the man at the oars was to keep the boat headed so that the tilt of the rollers would not capsize her, and to preserve her from filling when the crests rushed past. The black waves were silent and hard to be seen in the darkness. Often one was almost upon the boat before the oarsman was aware.

In a low voice the correspondent addressed the captain. He was not sure that the captain was awake, although this iron man seemed to be always awake. "Captain, shall I keep her making for that light north, sir?"

The same steady voice answered him. "Yes. Keep it about two points off the port bow."

The cook had tied a life-belt around himself in order to get even the warmth which this clumsy cork contrivance could donate, and he seemed almost stove-like when a rower, whose teeth invariably chattered wildly as soon as he ceased his labour, dropped down to sleep.

The correspondent, as he rowed, looked down at the two men sleeping underfoot. The cook's arm was around the oiler's shoulders, and, with their fragmentary clothing and haggard faces, they were the babes of the sea—a grotesque rendering of the old babes in the wood.

Later he must have grown stupid at his work, for suddenly there was a growling of water, and a crest came with a roar and a swash into the boat, and it was a wonder that it did not set the cook afloat in his life-belt. The cook continued to sleep, but the oiler sat up, blinking his eyes and shaking with the new cold.

"Oh, I'm awful sorry, Billie," said the correspondent, contritely.

"That's all right, old boy," said the oiler, and lay down again and was asleep.

Presently it seemed that even the captain dozed, and the correspondent thought that he was the one man afloat on all the oceans. The wind had a voice as it came over the waves, and it was sadder than the end.

There was a long, loud swishing astern of the boat, and a gleaming trail of phosphorescence, like blue flame, was furrowed on the black waters. It might have been made by a monstrous knife.

Then there came a stillness, while the correspondent breathed with open mouth and looked at the sea.

Suddenly there was another swish and another long flash of bluish light, and this time it was alongside the boat, and might almost been reached with an oar. The correspondent saw an enormous fin speed like a shadow through the water, hurling the crystalline spray and leaving the long glowing trail.

The correspondent looked over his shoulder at the captain. His face was hidden, and he seemed to be asleep. He looked at the babes of the sea. They certainly were asleep. So, being bereft of sympathy, he leaned a little way to one side and swore softly into the sea.

But the thing did not then leave the vicinity of the boat. Ahead or astern, on one side or the other, at intervals long or short, fled the long sparkling streak, and there was to be heard the *whirroo* of the dark fin. The speed and power of the thing was greatly to be admired. It cut the water like a gigantic and keen projectile.

The presence of this biding thing did not affect the man with the same horror that it would if he had been a picnicker. He simply looked at the sea dully and swore in an undertone.

Nevertheless, it is true that he did not wish to be alone with the thing. He wished one of his companions to awake by chance and keep him company with it. But the captain hung motionless over the water-jar, and the oiler and the cook in the bottom of the boat were plunged in slumber.

VI

"If I am going to be drowned—if I am going to be drowned—if I am going to be drowned, why, in the name of the seven mad gods who rule the sea, was I allowed to come thus far and contemplate sand and trees?"

During this dismal night, it may be remarked that a man would conclude that it was really the intention of the seven mad gods to drown him, despite the abominable injustice of it. For it was certainly an abominable injustice to drown a man who had worked so hard, so hard. The man felt it would be a crime most unnatural. Other people had drowned at sea since galleys swarmed with painted sails, but still—

When it occurs to a man that nature does not regard him as important, and that she feels she would not maim the universe by disposing of him, he at first wishes to throw bricks at the temple, and he hates deeply the fact that there are no bricks and no temples. Any visible expression of nature would surely be pelleted with his jeers.

Then, if there be no tangible thing to hoot, he feels, perhaps, the desire to confront a personification and indulge in pleas, bowed to one knee, and with hands supplicant, saying, "Yes, but I love myself."

A high cold star on a winter's night is the word he feels that she says to him. Thereafter he knows the pathos of his situation.

The men in the dinghy had not discussed these matters, but

each had, no doubt, reflected upon them in silence and according to his mind. There was seldom any expression upon their faces save the general one of complete weariness. Speech was devoted to the business of the boat.

To chime the notes of his emotion, a verse mysteriously entered the correspondent's head. He had even forgotten that he had forgotten this verse, but it suddenly was in his mind.

A soldier of the Legion lay dying in Algiers;
There was lack of woman's nursing, there was dearth of woman's tears;
But a comrade stood beside him, and he took that comrade's hand,
And he said, "I never more shall see my own, my native land."

In his childhood the correspondent had been made acquainted with the fact that a soldier of the Legion lay dying in Algiers, but he had never regarded the fact as important. Myriads of his school-fellows had informed him of the soldier's plight, but the dinning had naturally ended by making him perfectly indifferent. He had never considered it his affair that a soldier of the Legion lay dying in Algiers, nor had it appeared to him as a matter for sorrow. It was less to him than the breaking of a pencil's point.

Now, however, it quaintly came to him as a human, living thing. It was no longer merely a picture of a few throes in the breast of a poet, meanwhile drinking tea and warming his feet at the grate; it was an actuality—stern, mournful, and fine.

The correspondent plainly saw the soldier. He lay on the sand with his feet out straight and still. While his pale left hand was upon his chest in an attempt to thwart the going of his life, the blood came between his fingers. In the far Algerian distance, a city of low square forms was set against a sky that was faint with the last sunset hues. The correspondent, plying the oars and dreaming of the slow and slower movements of the lips of the soldier, was moved by a profound and perfectly impersonal comprehension. He was sorry for the soldier of the Legion who lay dying in Algiers.

The thing which had followed the boat and waited had evidently grown bored at the delay. There was no longer to be heard the slash of the cutwater, and there was no longer the flame of the long trail. The light in the north still glimmered, but it was apparently no nearer to the boat. Sometimes the boom of the surf rang in the correspondent's ears, and he turned the craft seaward then and rowed harder. Southward, some one had evidently built a watch-fire on the beach. It was too low and too far to be seen, but it made a shimmering, roseate reflection upon the bluff in back of it, and this could be discerned from the boat. The wind came stronger, and sometimes a wave suddenly raged out like a mountain cat, and there was to be seen the sheen and sparkle of a broken crest.

The captain, in the bow, moved on his water-jar and sat erect. "Pretty long night," he observed to the correspondent. He looked at the shore. "Those life-saving people take their time."

"Did you see that shark playing around?"

"Yes, I saw him. He was a big fellow, all right."

"Wish I had known you were awake."

Later the correspondent spoke into the bottom of the boat. "Billie!" There was a slow and gradual disentanglement. "Billie, will you spell me?"

"Sure," said the oiler.

As soon as the correspondent touched the cold, comfortable sea-water in the bottom of the boat and had huddled close to the cook's life-belt he was deep in sleep, despite the fact that his teeth played all the popular airs. This sleep was so good to him that it was but a moment before he heard a voice call his name in a tone that demonstrated the last stages of exhaustion. "Will you spell me?"

"Sure, Billie."

The light in the north had mysteriously vanished, but the correspondent took his course from the wide-awake captain.

Later in the night they took the boat farther out to sea, and the captain directed the cook to take one oar at the stern and keep the boat facing the seas. He was to call out if he should hear the thunder of the surf. This plan enabled the oiler and the correspondent to get respite together. "We'll give those boys a chance to get into shape again," said the captain. They curled down and, after a few preliminary chatterings and trembles, slept once more the dead sleep. Neither knew they had bequeathed to the cook the company of another shark, or perhaps the same shark.

As the boat caroused on the waves, spray occasionally bumped over the side and gave them a fresh soaking, but this had no power to break their repose. The ominous slash of the wind and the water affected them as it would have affected mummies.

"Boys," said the cook, with the notes of every reluctance in his voice, "she's drifted in pretty close. I guess one of you had better take her to sea again." The correspondent, aroused, heard the crash of the toppled crests.

As he was rowing, the captain gave him some whisky-and-water, and this steadied the chills out of him. "If I ever get ashore and anybody shows me even a photograph of an oar—"

At last there was a short conversation.

"Billie!—Billie, will you spell me?"

"Sure," said the oiler.

VII

When the correspondent again opened his eyes, the sea and the sky were each of the grey hue of the dawning. Later, carmine and gold was painted upon the waters. The morning appeared finally, in its splendour, with a sky of pure blue, and the sunlight flamed on the tips of the waves.

On the distant dunes were set many little black cottages, and a tall white windmill reared above them. No man, nor dog, nor bicycle appeared on the beach. The cottages might have formed a deserted village.

The voyagers scanned the shore. A conference was held in the boat. "Well," said the captain, "if no help is coming, we might better try a run through the surf right away. If we stay out here much longer we will be too weak to do anything for ourselves at all." The others silently acquiesced in this reasoning. The boat was headed for the beach. The correspondent wondered if none ever ascended the tall wind-tower, and if then they never looked seaward. This tower was a giant, standing with its back to the plight of the ants. It represented in a degree, to the correspondent, the serenity of nature amid the struggles of the individual—nature in the wind, and nature in the vision of men. She did not seem cruel to him then, nor beneficent, nor treacherous, nor wise. But she was indifferent, flatly indifferent. It is, perhaps, plausible that a man in this situation, impressed with the unconcern of the universe, should see the innumerable flaws of his life, and have them taste wickedly in his mind, and wish for another chance. A distinction between right and wrong seems absurdly clear to him, then, in this new ignorance of the grave-edge, and he understands that if he were given another opportunity he would mend his conduct and his words, and be better and brighter during an introduction or at a tea.

"Now, boys," said the captain, "she is going to swamp sure. All we can do is to work her in as far as possible, and then when she swamps, pile out and scramble for the beach. Keep cool now, and don't jump until she swamps sure."

The oiler took the oars. Over his shoulders he scanned the surf. "Captain," he said, "I think I'd better bring her about and keep her head-on to the seas and back her in."

"All right, Billie," said the captain. "Back her in." The oiler swung the boat then, and, seated in the stern, the cook and the correspondent were obliged to look over their shoulders to contemplate the lonely and indifferent shore.

The monstrous inshore rollers heaved the boat high until the men were again enabled to see the white sheets of water scudding up the slanted beach. "We won't get in very close," said the captain. Each time a man could wrest his attention from the rollers, he turned his glance toward the shore, and in the expression of the eyes during this contemplation there was a singular quality. The correspondent, observing the others, knew that they were not afraid, but the full meaning of their glances was shrouded.

As for himself, he was too tired to grapple fundamentally with the fact. He tried to coerce his mind into thinking of it, but the mind was dominated at this time by the muscles, and the muscles said they did not care. It merely occurred to him that if he should drown it would be a shame.

There were no hurried words, no pallor, no plain agitation. The men simply looked at the shore. "Now, remember to get well clear of the boat when you jump," said the captain.

Seaward the crest of a roller suddenly fell with a thunderous crash, and the long white comber came roaring down upon the boat.

"Steady now," said the captain. The men were silent. They turned their eyes from the shore to the comber and waited. The boat slid up the incline, leaped at the furious top, bounced over it, and swung down the long back of the wave. Some water had been shipped, and the cook bailed it out.

But the next crest crashed also. The tumbling, boiling flood of white water caught the boat and whirled it almost perpendicular. Water swarmed in from all sides. The correspondent had his hands on the gunwale at this time, and when the water entered at that place he swiftly withdrew his fingers, as if he objected to wetting them.

The little boat, drunken with this weight of water, reeled and snuggled deeper into the sea.

"Bail her out, cook! Bail her out!" said the captain.

"All right, Captain," said the cook.

"Now, boys, the next one will do for us sure," said the oiler. "Mind to jump clear of the boat."

The third wave moved forward, huge, furious, implacable. It fairly swallowed the dinghy, and almost simultaneously the men tumbled into the sea. A piece of life-belt had lain in the bottom of the boat, and as the correspondent went overboard he held this to his chest with his left hand.

The January water was icy, and he reflected immediately
that it was colder than he had expected to find it off the
coast of Florida. This appeared to his dazed mind as a fact important enough to be noted at the time. The coldness of the
water was sad; it was tragic. This fact was somehow mixed
and confused with his opinion of his own situation, so that
it seemed almost a proper reason for tears. The water was
cold.

When he came to the surface he was conscious of little but
the noisy water. Afterward he saw his companions in the sea.
The oiler was ahead in the race. He was swimming strongly
and rapidly. Off to the correspondent's left, the cook's great
white and corked back bulged out of the water; and in the rear
the captain was hanging with his one good hand to the keel of
the overturned dinghy.

There is a certain immovable quality to a shore, and the
correspondent wondered at it amid the confusion of the sea.

It seemed also very attractive; but the correspondent knew
that it was a long journey, and he paddled leisurely. The piece
of life-preserver lay under him, and sometimes he whirled
down the incline of a wave as if he were on a hand-sled.

But finally he arrived at a place in the sea where travel was
beset with difficulty. He did not pause swimming to inquire
what manner of current had caught him, but there his progress
ceased. The shore was set before him like a bit of scenery on a
stage, and he looked at it and understood with his eyes each
detail of it.

As the cook passed, much farther to the left, the captain was
calling to him, "Turn over on your back, cook! Turn over on
your back and use the oar."

"All right, sir." The cook turned on his back, and, paddling
with an oar, went ahead as if he were a canoe.

Presently the boat also passed to the left of the correspondent, with the captain clinging with one hand to the keel. He
would have appeared like a man raising himself to look over
a board fence if it were not for the extraordinary gymnastics of

the boat. The correspondent marvelled that the captain could still hold to it.

They passed on nearer to shore—the oiler, the cook, the captain—and following them went the water-jar, bouncing gaily over the seas.

The correspondent remained in the grip of this strange new enemy—a current. The shore, with its white slope of sand and its green bluff topped with little silent cottages, was spread like a picture before him. It was very near to him then, but he was impressed as one who, in a gallery, looks at a scene from Brittany or Algiers.

He thought: "I am going to drown? Can it be possible? Can it be possible? Can it be possible?" Perhaps an individual must consider his own death to be the final phenomenon of nature.

But later a wave perhaps whirled him out of this small deadly current, for he found suddenly that he could again make progress toward the shore. Later still he was aware that the captain, clinging with one hand to the keel of the dinghy, had his face turned away from the shore and toward him, and was calling his name. "Come to the boat! Come to the boat!"

In his struggle to reach the captain and the boat, he reflected that when one gets properly wearied drowning must really be a comfortable arrangement—a cessation of hostilities accompanied by a large degree of relief; and he was glad of it, for the main thing in his mind for some moments had been horror of the temporary agony. He did not wish to be hurt.

Presently he saw a man running along the shore. He was undressing with most remarkable speed. Coat, trousers, shirt, everything flew magically off him.

"Come to the boat!" called the captain.

"All right, Captain." As the correspondent paddled, he saw the captain let himself down to bottom and leave the boat. Then the correspondent performed his one little marvel of the voyage. A large wave caught him and flung him with ease and supreme speed completely over the boat and far beyond it. It struck him even then as an event in gymnastics and a true miracle of the sea. An overturned boat in the surf is not a play-thing to a swimming man.

The correspondent arrived in water that reached only to his waist, but his condition did not enable him to stand for more than a moment. Each wave knocked him into a heap, and the undertow pulled at him.

Then he saw the man who had been running and undressing, and undressing and running, come bounding into the water. He dragged ashore the cook, and then waded toward the captain; but the captain waved him away and sent him to the correspond-ent. He was naked—naked as a tree in winter; but a halo was about his head, and he shone like a saint. He gave a strong pull, and a long drag, and a bully heave at the correspondent's hand. The correspondent, schooled in the minor formulæ, said, "Thanks, old man." But suddenly the man cried, "What's that?" He pointed a swift finger. The correspondent said, "Go."

In the shallows, face downward, lay the oiler. His forehead touched sand that was periodically, between each wave, clear of the sea.

The correspondent did not know all that transpired after-ward. When he achieved safe ground he fell, striking the sand with each particular part of his body. It was as if he had dropped from a roof, but the thud was grateful to him.

It seemed that instantly the beach was populated with men with blankets, clothes, and flasks, and women with coffee-pots and all the remedies sacred to their minds. The welcome of the land to the men from the sea was warm and generous; but a still and dripping shape was carried slowly up the beach, and the land's welcome for it could only be the different and sinister hospitality of the grave.

When it came night, the white waves paced to and fro in the moonlight, and the wind brought the sound of the great sea's voice to the men on the shore, and they felt that they could then be interpreters.

THE WRECK OF THE *COMMODORE*

✵   ✵   ✵

I

THE COMMODORE SINKS AT SEA [1]

The Little Vessel Lost with Her Cargo of Arms and
Ammunition

Her Numerous Company Reach Land in Safety

They are Compelled to Take to the Boats and Abandon
the Sinking Vessel

AN OVERLOAD OF COAL THE PROBABLE CAUSE

It is Thought That When the Vessel Went Ashore in
the St. Johns River, Her Heavy Shock Caused Her
Seams to Open—Cubans in Jacksonville Much Distressed Over the Serious Loss—An Unfounded Rumor
of Treachery

THE STEAMER COMMODORE, which left here Thursday
night with an expedition for the Cuban insurgents, is now resting on the bottom of the sea, twenty fathoms below the surface, about eighteen miles northeast of Mosquito Inlet.

All of the men on the vessel, twenty-eight in number, reached

---

[1] *Florida Times-Union*, Sunday, January 3, 1897, p. 1. These accounts
from the *Florida Times-Union* and the *New York Press* are reproduced
here for the first time.

the shore in safety, and twelve of them arrived in Jacksonville last night over the Florida East Coast railway. The other sixteen are still down the coast, but are expected to arrive here on a special train this morning. . . .

DETAILS OF THE ACCIDENT

From the accounts given by the different ones in the party, the following details of the accident were learned: The Commodore crossed the St. Johns bar at 2 o'clock Friday afternoon while the sea was running very high. As she was crossing the bar she got in the trough of the sea and came very near being swamped.

About 12 o'clock Friday night it was discovered that the boat was leaking badly. The swash of the water in the hold as the vessel rolled from side to side soon alarmed everyone on board. A panic ensued, but Captain Murphy, Stephen Crane, R. A. Delgado and one or two others soon quieted the excitement and put everybody to work on the pumps and with buckets. The steam pump was started and for two hours the water was poured over the sides in streams. The men worked with a will and in the meantime the steamer's bow had been turned to the westward, and she was making good time toward the shore, which was estimated to be at least forty miles away, for the steamer had headed due east after leaving the bar, as she wished to keep out of the way of the cruiser Newark.

At 2:30 a.m., it was seen that the water was steadily gaining, and it was then decided to abandon the vessel.

IN THE BOATS

Paul Rojo, R. A. Delgado, Franco Blanco, the old Cuban pilot, and nine other men took one of the boats and left the steamer. Captain Murphy, the first and second mate, the engineer and assistant, Stephen Crane and ten men took the large yawl boat, and at 3 o'clock they left the Commodore to her fate.

The night was dark and they could not see what became of her, but as she was rapidly filling with water, they are all confident that she is now resting on the bottom, and old Neptune has been supplied with enough arms and ammunition to blow up the island of Cuba. . . .

II

MORE OF THE FILIBUSTERS SAFE [2]

Commodore's Wrecked Seamen Struggle for Life
in a Heavy Surf

STEPHEN CRANE, NOVELIST, SWIMS ASHORE

Young New York Writer Astonishes the Sea Dogs by His
Courage in the Face of Death

CUBANS ASSERT A TRAITOR SUNK THE VESSEL

Federal Authorities Order Out the Three Friends to Aid
in the Work of Rescue

JACKSONVILLE, FLA., Jan. 3.—Seventeen men accounted for
out of the twenty-eight on the Cuban filibuster Commodore is
the record here to-night, with a slight chance of seven more yet
alive. Five men came ashore at Daytona this noon—Captain
Murphy, Stephen Crane, the novelist, the cook and two sailors.
One of the latter, William Higgins of Rhode Island, died soon
after reaching land from the effects of severe wounds received
while landing through the high surf. His family live in Boston.
One of the survivors gives the following graphic details:

STORY OF A SURVIVOR

"The tug sank at 7 o'clock Saturday morning, twenty miles
off New Smyrna, and the Americans on board remained till the

---

[2] *New York Press*, Monday, January 4, 1897, pp. 1–2.

last moment. A traitor in Spanish pay was the cause of the leak. Should he be found he will be dealt with severely. The leak was discovered at about 3 a.m. The pumps would not work long, though they did good service for awhile.

"Finding that the water gained on us, the captain called all hands and at 3 the vessel was turned shoreward. As she still continued to sink, two boat loads of Cubans, twelve men in all, were first sent off. One boat containing six men was capsized, and I am afraid that the men were lost. The Americans all remained on the tug till she sank. One of the lifeboats containing nine men was swamped and a hastily constructed raft was made up from materials thrown to them, and they then disappeared from our sight. Captain Murphy, Stephen Crane, the novelist and correspondent; Higgins, myself and one other sailor took to the ten-foot dingy at the last moment. We tried to save the men in the water around us, but the heavy seas and blinding wind swept them from us. The spray was so thick that we could see only a few rods. Their cries were heartrending, but we could do nothing, it requiring all our efforts to keep our small boat right side up.

THROWN INTO THE BREAKERS

'For twenty-four hours we battled with the heavy seas, constantly bailing, and at last land was sighted. As we attempted to land the wind drove us into the breakers and in an instant the boat was overturned and we were struggling for life. For an hour almost we battled for life, and then managed to crawl out on the sands, almost dead. Captain Murphy saved Mr. Crane by helping him when a cramp caught him. Higgins was struck on the head by floating timbers and he died soon after landing. He was a good sailor and a brave man. He worked to save his comrades.'" . . .

PRAISE FOR CRANE

DAYTONA, Fla., Jan. 3.—"That newspaper feller was a nervy man," said the cook of the ill-fated Commodore to-night in reference to Stephen Crane, the novelist, who is after material for stories. "He didn't seem to know what fear was. He was down on the ship's papers as an able seaman at $20 a month. When we started out he insisted upon doing a seaman's work, and he did it well, too. When aroused Saturday morning he never quailed when he came on deck and saw the foaming and raging billows and knew that the vessel was sinking and that it was only a question of time when we would be at the mercy of the terrible sea in a small ten-foot dingy.

"He stood on the bridge with glasses in hand, sweeping the horizon in an effort to get a glimpse of land. He had one of the sailor lads above him on the short mast, and once he mounted the rigging to get a better view. I thought sure that he would be swept off as the vessel rolled from side to side, her yards almost touching the water as she rolled down. One of the Cubans got rattled and tried to run out one of the boats before time, and Crane let him have it right from the shoulder, and the man rolled down the leeway, stunned for the moment.

"When the boats were launched he was the last one, except Captain Murphy, to get in, and his nerve greatly encouraged all hands. In the small dingy he rowed as well as the others, notwithstanding he was so worn out that he could hardly hold his oar straight in the terrific seas. At the last moment he rose on his seat, and, seeing the big wave coming that overthrew us, cried out, 'Look out, boys, there's trouble for us. Jump, captain!'

SAVES A DROWNING MAN

"Both he and Captain Murphy were thrown out on the same side. Crane was partially thrown under the overturned boat and but for Captain Murphy's readiness in catching him by the collar he would have gone under. We all battled there in the water for hours, it seemed to us. Crane was a good swimmer, and he really saved one of the sailors, as the man could not swim a stroke, and Crane had to keep him up by the aid of an oar. These newspaper fellers have got spunk, if they do tell such awful woppers at times," concluded the cook, as he took another big swig of the "life preservative" provided by the good people here. . . .

III

STEPHEN CRANE AND HIS WORK [3]

How He Came to Be on the Unlucky Commodore

TO WRITE FOR THE PRESS

Brilliant Author Not of the Sort to Give Up His Cuban
Letters Because of Shipwreck

STEPHEN CRANE, the writer, is safe and readers of The
Press may expect in a short time a treat from his versatile
pen. . . .

Mr. Crane was on the way to Cuba to write about the war
there. He will get to Cuba as soon as he can. He is not of the
sort who are frightened by an experience in a lifeboat. His
letters will appear in The Press as soon as they arrive.

Mr. Crane has not intimated just what he is going to write;
probably he does not know himself. But that his letters will
be intensely interesting and true to life readers of his stories,
"The Red Badge of Courage," "The Third Violet," "George's
Mother" and "Maggie, a Girl of the Streets," feel assured.

EXPERIENCE AS A REPORTER

Stephen Crane has been talked about more in New York
than any writer of recent years. He was a New York reporter
at the age of 16. In his newspaper work he early showed remarkable command of the English language, but his nature
revolted at the slavish devotion to facts which makes a successful reporter. So he took to writing stories.

The Tenderloin was gayer then than now. Its lights and

---

[3] *New York Press,* Monday, January 4, 1897, p. 2.

shadows attracted his artistic genius. There he found the whole gamut of human emotions. He listened and studied. His stories had as their background the slums oftener than the palaces. They were intensely realistic. His training as a reporter accounts in part for that, and his English flowed simple and pure.

HIS GENIUS RECOGNIZED

Though but a boy in years, his work became the subject of gossip in literary circles. The critics recognized the merit of his stories. The old novelists read with wonder. They found his war scenes so vivid that they could scarcely believe they were painted by one who never had smelled gunpowder except at a shooting match. . . .

A TALE OF THE SEA

IV

TWELVE MEN LOST THROUGH TREACHERY [4]

Sinking of the Commodore Caused by a Traitor, Says
Montgomery

STEAM PUMPS TAMPERED WITH, IS THE SUSPICION

Eight Men Are Now at Sea on a Raft, and Four Others
are Still Missing

STOKER KILLED WHILE LANDING IN THE SURF

Captain Murphy, Stephen Crane and C. M. Mont-
gomery Now at Daytona—Three Friends Delayed
Thirty Hours from Going to the Rescue Through Red
Tape of Treasury Department Officials—The Newark's
Searchlight to be Used

. . . . .

THE RAFT LOST

"THE mate's boat, containing nine Americans, was smashed and
the mate, two engineers, six firemen and sailors were lashed
to a raft which Captain Murphy attempted to tow ashore
twenty miles away, but the terrible sea and northeast gale
swept them away.

"The dingy, occupied by the captain and companions, was
twenty-seven hours at sea, Montgomery and Crane holding
Captain Murphy's overcoat as a sail until the beach was

---

[4] *Florida Times-Union*, Tuesday, January 5, 1897, p. 1.

sighted. High seas were breaking a half mile from shore. Montgomery, Crane and Murphy were washed onto the beach where
citizens provided them with medical attendance. Higgins was
killed at the overturning of the boat which made ten American and six Cubans lost. . . ."

A TALE OF THE SEA

V

CAPTAIN MURPHY'S SHIPWRECKED CREW [5]

Twenty Men Are Now Safe in Jacksonville With Friends

BUT EIGHT OTHERS MAY BE AT THE BOTTOM

Story of the Wreck of the Commodore Told by the
Commander of the Ill-Fated Vessel

THERE IS STILL SOME TALK OF TREACHERY

Three Men Were Drowned as the Steamer Sunk—
One Died on the Beach and Five Are at Sea on a
Raft—The Newark and Three Friends Are Still Look-
ing for Them, but There Is Little or No Hope That
Any More Will be Saved

.　.　.　.　.　.

CAPTAIN MURPHY's story is as follows:

"The engineer reported to me, about midnight, that the
vessel was gaining water in her hold and that he was unable
to get the pumps to work. They had tried to get the water out,
but the pumps would not heave the water. The pipe was evidently choked or the suction gone. It is customary to keep the
water clear of the hold. All necessary was to run the steam
pumps now and then. If the water is allowed to get up into the
coal, the coal is washed down and chokes the pumps. All the
water that entered the ship was in the engine room."

"Was it treachery, do you think?" asked the Times-Union
reporter.

---

[5] *Florida Times-Union*, Tuesday, January 5, 1897, p. 6.

"No, I don't think so. It was neglect, more than anything else.

"I gave the order to use the buckets: also an order to pile into the furnace wood, oil and alcohol, hoping to get up sufficient steam to run into Mosquito Inlet, about eighteen miles almost due west of us. The men used the buckets with a will. None stood back, but to our chagrin the water gained upon us slowly and surely, and we had not proceeded three miles when the fires were quenched. There was no hope then of saving the ship. I let go the anchor to get her head to the sea and told the men to quietly proceed to man the boats. We got two of the boats off. They contained all the Cubans.

"One boat was in command of Julio Rodriguez Baz, and those with him were Manuel Gonzalez, Luis Sierra Mederos and Jesus Alvarez.

"The other, in command of Paul F. Rojo, contained Ricardo Delgado, Felix de los Rios, Emelio Marquez, Ventura Linares, Romeo Hernandez, J. Francisco Blanco, Jose Hernandez, T. Bencenor, Lino Soldera, Gabriel Martinez and Santiago Diaz. Senor Baz's boat stood by for a considerable time to render us assistance, but finally, as we had boats sufficient for the rescue of all those left aboard, we told them to go ahead. Later on we launched the ship's boat, with seven men, in charge of Mate Grane. I told all those to go who desired to do so. All went except Mr. Crane, a brave little gentleman, Steward Montgomery and William Higgins. I intended to stand by the ship and then put ashore in the dingy. Later on we also embarked. We had proceeded but a few yards when we heard a cry from the ship:

ONE BOAT STOVE IN

"'The big boat is stove!' They were also flying a distress flag.

"I don't know how this happened unless the mate returned and attempted to get some article that he had forgotten. We immediately put back in the dingy, and I told the men to construct a raft. They made three and got on these. Meanwhile, our little boat was remaining distant about 200 yards.

"Finally, they begged us to take them in tow. We put back against the waves and wind and made a towline fast. The first sea nearly filled our boat, and we were compelled to let go and bail our own craft dry. We went back again and once more made fast, but the first sea parted the rafts and broke over our towline. The rafts all parted and were scattered. I told them to return to the vessel and make another raft while I bailed out. When fifty yards away, the vessel went down broadside. Three men went down with her, like heroes with no cry of despair, not a murmur. I remained by the rafts twenty minutes longer, but as the boat was being filled by almost every sea, and as the wind was constantly increasing in force, we allowed our boat to go whither the elements carried her.

HOW THEY LANDED

"Saturday afternoon at 4 o'clock, we came in sight of the coast north of Mosquito inlet. We saw people on shore and I flew a flag of distress, and repeatedly fired my pistol to attract their attention. I do not see how they could have failed to see us and appreciate our perilous position, for we were only a half mile from shore. Feeling certain that we had been seen, and thinking that they would send to us a staunch surf boat, we waited at the spot, pulling like Trojans against the heavy sea and wind all that afternoon and all that night. I do not see now, looking back upon it, how human strength could have successfully contended against the fierce odds of nature. We had a little store of brandy and this stood us in good stead. The next morning we found ourselves off the beach opposite Daytona, and seeing no one, resolved to make one last desperate effort with our little remaining strength to reach shore through the breakers. I gave one life belt to the steward and one to Mr. Crane. (The captain does not say that he, with a badly injured arm and shoulder, took none himself.) The sea upset the boat and washed us all away. I grabbed it and got on the bottom, but she was rolled over again. Higgins tried to swim, but sank. I tried to encourage him, and he made another attempt. The boat went over again, and I saw no more of him until his corpse came up on the beach.

DEATH OF HIGGINS

"John Getchell, one of nature's noblemen, who lives upon the beach, saw our dreadful predicament. He stripped to the skin and plunged into the surf and helped the steward and Mr. Crane in. I was safe in shallow water. I then saw Higgins' body on the wet sand. We rolled him and made every effort to bring him to life, but unfortunately failed. Poor fellow, he was brave and did his duty faithfully.

"We had not been on the beach long before the good women of the town came to us with hot coffee and all kinds of restoratives. Their attentions warmed a man's heart to the appreciation of human charity. Not one of these women came to us without some present of food, clothing, and all with offers of shelter. The people of Daytona buried poor Higgins at their own expense." . . .

VI

COMMODORE SAID TO BE OVERLADEN [6]

Many Think That Fact, and Not Treachery, Sunk Her

FOUR MORE MEN RESCUED

Half-Famished Filibusters Land at Port Orange—
Captain Murphy Compliments Crane

.   .   .   .   .   .

CAPTAIN MURPHY TALKS

. . . Captain Murphy had his arm in a sling, but otherwise
seemed all right. All of them looked tired and worn out.

The captain paid a marked compliment to his men for their
orderly conduct. He said that Higgins was a game man, and
fought hard for his life and to aid his shipmates. Higgins was
buried at Daytona yesterday.

Captain Murphy, in response to a direct question, answered
evasively as to the report of the treachery, and stated that the
leaks were not there early Friday evening, but were there at
midnight.

Cubans here feel much dispirited over the sad affair, and the
terrible ending of the expedition from which so much was expected.

CRANE'S SPLENDID GRIT

"That man Crane is the spunkiest fellow out," said Captain
Murphy to-night to The Press correspondent, in speaking of
the wreck and incidents pertaining to it. "The sea was so

---

[6] *New York Press,* Tuesday, January 5, 1897, p. 1.

rough that even old sailors got seasick when we struck the open sea after leaving the bar, but Crane behaved like a born sailor. He and I were about the only ones not affected by the big seas which tossed us about. As we went south he sat in the pilot house with me, smoking and telling yarns. When the leak was discovered he was the first man to volunteer aid.

JOKES AMID DANGER

"His shoes, new ones, were slippery on the deck, and he took them off and tossed them overboard, saying, with a laugh: 'Well, captain, I guess I won't need them if we have to swim.' He stood on the deck by me all the while, smoking his cigarette, and aided me greatly while the boats were getting off. When in the dingey he suggested putting up the overcoat for a sail, and he took his turn at the oars or holding up the oar mast.

TRIES TO SAVE HIGGINS

"When we went over I called to him to see that his life preserver was on all right and he replied in his usual tones, saying that he would obey orders. He was under the boat once, but got out in some way. He held up Higgins when the latter got so terribly tired and endeavored to bring him in, but the sailor was so far gone that he could hardly help himself. When we were thrown up by the waves, Crane was the first man to stagger up the beach looking for houses. He's a thoroughbred," concluded the captain, "and a brave man, too, with plenty of grit."

A TALE OF THE SEA

VII

STEPHEN CRANE'S OWN STORY

———

He Tells How the Commodore Was Wrecked and How He Escaped

———

FEAR-CRAZED NEGRO NEARLY SWAMPS BOAT

———

Young Writer Compelled to Work in Stifling Atmosphere of the Fire Room

———

BRAVERY OF CAPTAIN MURPHY AND HIGGINS

———

Tried to Tow Their Companions Who Were on the Raft— Last Dash for the Shore Through the Surf

———

JACKSONVILLE, FLA., Jan. 6.—It was the afternoon of New Year's. The Commodore lay at her dock in Jacksonville and negro stevedores processioned steadily toward her with box after box of ammunition and bundle after bundle of rifles. Her hatch, like the mouth of a monster, engulfed them. It might have been the feeding time of some legendary creature of the sea. It was in broad daylight and the crowd of gleeful Cubans on the pier did not forbear to sing the strange patriotic ballads of their island.

Everything was perfectly open. The Commodore was cleared with a cargo of arms and munition for Cuba. There was none of that extreme modesty about the proceeding which had marked previous departures of the famous tug. She loaded up as placidly as if she were going to carry oranges to New York, instead of Remingtons to Cuba. Down the river, furthermore, the revenue cutter Boutwell, the old isosceles triangle that protects United States interests in the St. John's, lay at anchor, with no sign of excitement aboard her.

EXCHANGING FAREWELLS

On the decks of the Commodore there were exchanges of farewells in two languages. Many of the men who were to sail upon her had many intimates in the old Southern town, and we who had left our friends in the remote North received our first touch of melancholy on witnessing these strenuous and earnest goodbys.

It seems, however, that there was more difficulty at the custom house. The officers of the ship and the Cuban leaders were detained there until a mournful twilight settled upon the St. John's, and through a heavy fog the lights of Jacksonville blinked dimly. Then at last the Commodore swung clear of the dock, amid a tumult of goodbys. As she turned her bow toward the distant sea the Cubans ashore cheered and cheered. In response the Commodore gave three long blasts of her whistle, which even to this time impressed me with their sadness. Somehow, they sounded as wails.

Then at last we began to feel like filibusters. I don't suppose that the most stolid brain could contrive to believe that there is not a mere trifle of danger in filibustering, and so as we watched the lights of Jacksonville swing past us and heard the regular thump, thump, thump of the engines we did considerable reflecting.

But I am sure that there were no hifalutin emotions visible upon any of the faces which fronted the speeding shore. In fact, from cook's boy to captain, we were all enveloped in a gentle satisfaction and cheerfulness. But less than two miles from Jacksonville, this atrocious fog caused the pilot to ram the bow of the Commodore hard upon the mud and in this ignominious position we were compelled to stay until daybreak.

HELP FROM THE BOUTWELL

It was to all of us more than a physical calamity. We were now no longer filibusters. We were men on a ship stuck in the mud. A certain mental somersault was made once more necessary.

But word had been sent to Jacksonville to the captain of the revenue cutter Boutwell, and Captain Kilgore turned out promptly and generously fired up his old triangle, and came at full speed to our assistance. She dragged us out of the mud, and again we headed for the mouth of the river. The revenue cutter pounded along a half mile astern of us, to make sure that we did not take on board at some place along the river men for the Cuban army.

This was the early morning of New Year's Day, and the fine golden southern sunlight fell full upon the river. It flashed over the ancient Boutwell, until her white sides gleamed like pearl, and her rigging was spun into little threads of gold.

Cheers greeted the old Commodore from passing ship and from the shore. It was a cheerful, almost merry, beginning to our voyage. At Mayport, however, we changed our river pilot for a man who could take her to open sea, and again the Commodore was beached. The Boutwell was fussing around us in her venerable way, and, upon seeing our predicament, she came again to assist us, but this time, with engines reversed, the Commodore dragged herself away from the grip of the sand and again headed for the open sea.

The captain of the revenue cutter grew curious. He hailed the Commodore: "Are you fellows going to sea to-day?"

Captain Murphy of the Commodore called back: "Yes, sir."

And then as the whistle of the Commodore saluted him, Captain Kilgore doffed his cap and said: "Well, gentlemen, I hope you have a pleasant cruise," and this was our last word from shore.

When the Commodore came to enormous rollers that flee

over the bar a certain light-heartedness departed from the ship's company.

SLEEP IMPOSSIBLE

As darkness came upon the waters, the Commodore was a broad, flaming path of blue and silver phosphorescence, and as her stout bow lunged at the great black waves she threw flashing, roaring cascades to either side. And all that was to be heard was the rhythmical and mighty pounding of the engines. Being an inexperienced filibuster, the writer had undergone considerable mental excitement since the starting of the ship, and in consequence he had not yet been to sleep and so I went to the first mate's bunk to indulge myself in all the physical delights of holding one's-self in bed. Every time the ship lurched I expected to be fired through a bulkhead, and it was neither amusing nor instructive to see in the dim light a certain accursed valise aiming itself at the top of my stomach with every lurch of the vessel.

THE COOK IS HOPEFUL

The cook was asleep on a bench in the galley. He is of a portly and noble exterior, and by means of a checker board he had himself wedged on this bench in such a manner the motion of the ship would be unable to dislodge him. He woke as I entered the galley and delivered himself of some dolorous sentiments: "God," he said in the course of his observations, "I don't feel right about this ship, somehow. It strikes me that something is going to happen to us. I don't know what it is, but the old ship is going to get it in the neck, I think."

"Well, how about the men on board of her?" said I. "Are any of us going to get out, prophet?"

"Yes," said the cook. "Sometimes I have these damned feelings come over me, and they are always right, and it seems to me, somehow, that you and I will both get and meet again somewhere, down at Coney Island, perhaps, or some place like that."

ONE MAN HAS ENOUGH

Finding it impossible to sleep, I went back to the pilot house. An old seaman, Tom Smith, from Charleston, was then at the wheel. In the darkness I could not see Tom's face, except at those times when he leaned forward to scan the compass and the dim light from the box came upon his weatherbeaten features.

"Well, Tom," said I, "how do you like filibustering?"

He said "I think I am about through with it. I've been in a number of these expeditions and the pay is good, but I think if I ever get back safe this time I will cut it."

I sat down in the corner of the pilot house and almost went to sleep. In the meantime the captain came on duty and he was standing near me when the chief engineer rushed up the stairs and cried hurriedly to the captain that there was something wrong in the engine room. He and the captain departed swiftly.

I was drowsing there in my corner when the captain returned, and, going to the door of the little room directly back of the pilothouse, he cried to the Cuban leader:

"Say, can't you get those fellows to work. I can't talk their language and I can't get them started. Come on and get them going."

HELPS IN THE FIREROOM

The Cuban leader turned to me and said: "Go help in the fireroom. They are going to bail with buckets."

The engine room, by the way, represented a scene at this time taken from the middle kitchen of hades. In the first place, it was insufferably warm, and the lights burned faintly in a way to cause mystic and grewsome shadows. There was a quantity of soapish sea water swirling and sweeping and swishing among machinery that roared and banged and clattered and steamed, and, in the second place, it was a devil of a ways down below.

Here I first came to know a certain young oiler named Billy Higgins. He was sloshing around this inferno filling buckets with water and passing them to a chain of men that extended up the ship's side. Afterward we got orders to change our point of attack on water and to operate through a little door on the windward side of the ship that led into the engine room.

NO PANIC ON BOARD

During this time there was much talk of pumps out of order and many other statements of a mechanical kind, which I did not altogether comprehend but understood to mean that there was a general and sudden ruin in the engine room.

There was no particular agitation at this time, and even later there was never a panic on board the Commodore. The party of men who worked with Higgins and me at this time were all Cubans, and we were under the direction of the Cuban leaders. Presently we were ordered again to the after-hold, and there was some hesitation about going into the abominable fireroom again, but Higgins dashed down the companionway with a bucket.

LOWERING BOATS

The heat and hard work in the fireroom affected me and I was obliged to come on deck again. Going forward, I heard as I went talk of lowering the boats. Near the corner of the galley the mate was talking with a man.

"Why don't you send up a rocket?" said this unknown man. And the mate replied: "What the hell do we want to send up a rocket for? The ship is all right."

Returning with a little rubber and cloth overcoat, I saw the first boat about to be lowered. A certain man was the first person in this first boat, and they were handing him in a valise about as large as a hotel. I had not entirely recovered from astonishment and pleasure in witnessing this noble deed when I saw another valise go to him.

HUMAN HOG APPEARS

This valise was not perhaps so large as a hotel, but it was a big valise anyhow. Afterward there went to him something which looked to me like an overcoat.

Seeing the chief engineer leaning out of his little window, I remarked to him:

"What do you think of that blank, blank, blank?"

"Oh, he's a bird," said the old chief.

It was now that was heard the order to get away the lifeboat, which was stowed on top of the deckhouse. The deckhouse was a mighty slippery place, and with each roll of the ship, the men there thought themselves likely to take headers into the deadly black sea.

Higgins was on top of the deckhouse, and, with the first mate and two colored stokers, we wrestled with that boat, which, I am willing to swear, weighed as much as a Broadway cable car. She might have been spiked to the deck. We could have pushed a little brick schoolhouse along a corduroy road as easily as we could have moved this boat. But the first mate got a tackle to her from a leeward davit, and on the deck below the captain corralled enough men to make an impression upon the boat.

We were ordered to cease hauling then, and in this lull the cook of the ship came to me and said: "What are you going to do?"

I told him of my plans, and he said:

"Well, my God, that's what I am going to do."

A WHISTLE OF DESPAIR

Now the whistle of the Commodore had been turned loose, and if there ever was a voice of despair and death, it was in the voice of this whistle. It had gained a new tone. It was as if its throat was already choked by the water, and this cry on the sea at night, with a wind blowing the spray over the ship, and the waves roaring over the bow, and swirling white along the decks, was to each of us probably a song of man's end.

It was now that the first mate showed a sign of losing his grip. To us who were trying in all stages of competence and experience to launch the lifeboat he raged in all terms of fiery satire and hammerlike abuse. But the boat moved at last and swung down toward the water.

Afterward, when I went aft, I saw the captain standing, with his arm in a sling, holding on to a stay with his one good hand and directing the launching of the boat. He gave me a five-gallon jug of water to hold, and asked me what I was going to do. I told him what I thought was about the proper thing, and he told me then that the cook had the same idea, and ordered me to go forward and be ready to launch the ten-foot dingy.

IN THE TEN-FOOT DINGY

I remember well that he turned then to swear at a colored stoker who was prowling around, done up in life preservers until he looked like a feather bed. I went forward with my five-gallon jug of water, and when the captain came we launched the dingy, and they put me over the side to fend her off from the ship with an oar.

They handed me down the water jug, and then the cook came into the boat, and we sat there in the darkness, wondering why, by all our hopes of future happiness, the captain was so long in coming over to the side and ordering us away from the doomed ship.

The captain was waiting for the other boat to go. Finally he hailed in the darkness: "Are you all right, Mr. Graines?"

The first mate answered: "All right, sir."

"Shove off, then," cried the captain.

The captain was just about to swing over the rail when a dark form came forward and a voice said: "Captain, I go with you."

The captain answered: "Yes, Billy; get in."

HIGGINS LAST TO LEAVE SHIP

It was Billy Higgins, the oiler. Billy dropped into the boat and a moment later the captain followed, bringing with him an end of about forty yards of lead line. The other end was attached to the rail of the ship.

As we swung back to leeward the captain said: "Boys, we will stay right near the ship till she goes down."

This cheerful information, of course, filled us all with glee. The line kept us headed properly into the wind, and as we rode over the monstrous waves we saw upon each rise the swaying lights of the dying Commodore.

When came the gray shade of dawn, the form of the Commodore grew slowly clear to us as our little ten-foot boat rose over each swell. She was floating with such an air of buoyancy that we laughed when we had time, and said "What a gag it would be on those other fellows if she didn't sink at all."

But later we saw men aboard of her, and later still they began to hail us.

HELPING THEIR MATES

I had forgot to mention that previously we had loosened the end of the lead line and dropped much further to leeward. The men on board were a mystery to us, of course, as we had seen all the boats leave the ship. We rowed back to the ship, but did not approach too near, because we were four men in a ten-foot boat, and we knew that the touch of a hand on our gunwale would assuredly swamp us.

The first mate cried out from the ship that the third boat had foundered alongside. He cried that they had made rafts, and wished us to tow them.

The captain said, "All right."

Their rafts were floating astern. "Jump in!" cried the captain, but there was a singular and most harrowing hesitation. There were five white men and two negroes. This scene in the gray light of morning impressed one as would a view into some place where ghosts move slowly. These seven men on the stern of the sinking Commodore were silent. Save the words of the mate to the captain there was no talk. Here was death, but here also was a most singular and indefinable kind of fortitude.

Four men, I remember, clambered over the railing and stood there watching the cold, steely sheen of the sweeping waves. "Jump," cried the captain again.

The old chief engineer first obeyed the order. He landed on the outside raft and the captain told him how to grip the raft and he obeyed as promptly and as docilely as a scholar in riding school.

THE MATE'S MAD PLUNGE

A stoker followed him, and then the first mate threw his hands over his head and plunged into the sea. He had no life belt and for my part, even when he did this horrible thing, I somehow felt that I could see in the expression of his hands, and in the very toss of his head, as he leaped thus to death, that it was rage, rage, rage unspeakable that was in his heart at the time.

And then I saw Tom Smith, the man who was going to quit filibustering after this expedition, jump to a raft and turn his face toward us. On board the Commodore three men strode, still in silence and with their faces turned toward us. One man had his arms folded and was leaning against the deckhouse. His feet were crossed, so that the toe of his left foot pointed downward. There they stood gazing at us, and neither from the deck nor from the rafts was a voice raised. Still was there this silence.

TRIED TO TOW THE RAFTS

The colored stoker on the first raft threw us a line and we began to tow. Of course, we perfectly understood the absolute impossibility of any such thing; our dingy was within six inches of the water's edge, there was an enormous sea running, and I knew that under the circumstances a tugboat would have no light task in moving these rafts.

But we tried it, and would have continued to try it indefinitely, but that something critical came to pass. I was at an oar and so faced the rafts. The cook controlled the line. Suddenly the boat began to go backward and then we saw this negro on the first raft pulling on the line hand over hand and drawing us to him.

He had turned into a demon. He was wild—wild as a tiger. He was crouched on this raft and ready to spring. Every muscle of him seemed to be turned into an elastic spring. His eyes were almost white. His face was the face of a lost man reaching upward, and we knew that the weight of his hand on our gunwale doomed us.

THE COMMODORE SINKS

The cook let go of the line. We rowed around to see if we could not get a line from the chief engineer, and all this time, mind you, there were no shrieks, no groans, but silence, silence and silence, and then the Commodore sank.

She lurched to windward, then swung afar back, righted and dove into the sea, and the rafts were suddenly swallowed by this frightful maw of the ocean. And then by the men on the ten-foot dingy were words said that were still not words—something far beyond words.

The lighthouse of Mosquito Inlet stuck up above the horizon like the point of a pin. We turned our dingy toward the shore.

The history of life in an open boat for thirty hours would no doubt be instructive for the young, but none is to be told here and now. For my part I would prefer to tell the story at once, because from it would shine the splendid manhood of Captain Edward Murphy and of William Higgins, the oiler, but let it suffice at this time to say that when we were swamped in the surf and making the best of our way toward the shore the captain gave orders amid the wildness of the breakers as clearly as if he had been on the quarter deck of a battleship.

John Kitchell [7] of Daytona came running down the beach, and as he ran the air was filled with clothes. If he had pulled a single lever and undressed, even as the fire horses harness, he could not seem to me to have stripped with more speed. He dashed into the water and dragged the cook. Then he went after the captain, but the captain sent him to me, and then it was that he saw Billy Higgins lying with his forehead on sand that was clear of the water, and he was dead.

STEPHEN CRANE [8]

---

[7] Getchell, according to the Captain's account.

[8] Reprinted from the *New York Press*, January 7, 1897, p. 1.

PART IV

Western Tales

INTRODUCTION

The *Bride Comes to Yellow Sky* is the best short story Crane
wrote beyond his major achievements: *Maggie, The Red
Badge,* and *The Open Boat.* It is the single perfect bead on his
string of Western tales. Crane spent most of his twenty-third
year out in the Far West and in Mexico. Frederic Remington's
pictures and Mark Twain's *Huckleberry Finn* and *Life on the
Mississippi* inspired him to want to see cowboys and the big
river, but his main purpose in going west was to collect short-
story and sketch material. Writing, he said, is a business like
any other. One trained one's mind to observe and a man should
be able to say something "worth while" about any event
(quoted from Beer, page 252). "When I was 23, I devoted
most of my time to travelling for the Bacheller and Johnson
syndicate and in writing short stories for English magazines."
When he was out west he wrote a war tale—*A Mystery of
Heroism*—and only one Western piece. The only Western story
he wrote this year (1895) was *Horses—One Dash!* He wrote
the first draft of this story in Philadelphia (see letter to
Hawkins for September 18, 1895). And of his six Western
sketches or stories,[1] only one was published in an English
magazine, and this one—*Twelve O'clock*—did not appear until
December 1899. So he did not write his Westerns in the West;
they were written the next year and some of them much later:

---

[1] In order of publication the Western tales are *Horses—One Dash!*
(*Philadelphia Press,* January 1896), *A Man and Some Others* (*Century,*
February 1897), *The Bride Comes to Yellow Sky* (*McClure's Magazine,*
February 1898), *Five White Mice* (New York *World,* April 1898), *The
Blue Hotel* (*Collier's Weekly,* November 26, 1898), and *Twelve O'Clock*
(*Pall Mall Gazette,* December 1899). Four of these appeared in *The Open
Boat and Other Stories* (1898). *The Blue Hotel* received first book pub-
lication in *The Monster* (1899 and 1901), and *Twelve O'Clock* in *The
Monster* (1901).

That is, after *The Open Boat* (1897). The style of *The Bride Comes to Yellow Sky* is different from the style of *The Open Boat*. *The Open Boat* was written first. He wrote *The Bride* in England and sent it to his American agent, Paul Reynolds, with a note that *The Bride* "is a daisy and don't let them talk funny about it."

Out West Crane wrote such journalistic pieces as *Mexican Sights and Street Scenes*, published in the *Philadelphia Press*, May 19. *Horses—One Dash!* is a direct transcript of personal experience, but none of the other Western stories draws upon his own adventures. *The Blue Hotel* and *A Man and Some Others* make use of the persons he met, an incident he witnessed, the scenery, and his knowledge of the frontier code, but the dramatic situation in both stories was invented. *A Man and Some Others* had its beginning in a story told him by a Bowery fellow whom Crane met in a Mexican lodging-house. Some Mexicans tried to run this sheep-herder off his land, and he shot them down. Crane recast even this germinal part. In the story it is Bill, the former Bowery saloon-keeper, who is shot down by the Mexicans. Conrad wrote: "But my great excitement was reading your stories. Garnett's right. *A Man and Some Others* is immense. . . . I admire it without reserve. It is an amazing bit of biography." But there's nothing "immense" about it except its length—the whole thing is very badly put together, with a false middle and a melodramatic end. I can't conceive what Conrad saw in this piece to say: "I am envious of you—horribly." His reason for envy should have been *The Bride* and the opening part of *The Blue Hotel*.

As in *The Red Badge*, so in all the Mexican and Texan sketches, as Beer says, there appears "a vision of man's identity faced by its end, by incomprehensible death." In *Horses—One Dash!* the Mexican José and Richardson, whose experience mirrors Crane's own, are forced to ride for their lives to escape a Mexican band of cutthroats out to murder them for the possession of a pair of boots. This experience, supposedly, terrified

Crane; no other occasion in all his life instilled in him such
fear. And so, according to this critic, "from Richardson's emotions we learn something of the author's" (*Stephen Crane*,
1950, p. 104). Perhaps so, but I think that in so far as Crane's
stories attain to perfection this question of the personal equation never arises. What do you learn about Shakespeare's
emotions from *Macbeth*? Criticism constantly confuses these
two kinds of literary discussion, the one having to do with the
creative process by which the work came into being and the
other with the work as a thing in itself. The critical point to
make about *Horses—One Dash!* is that it has not a dash of
significance. No significance emerges from the story of Richardson; it is his plight not mine. And like many other Crane
pieces, this story is not in Crane's own idiom and could have
been written by some other author. Although it is an autobiographical sketch, it might very well have come from the
pen of Cunninghame Graham. It has been doubted whether
anyone has ever rendered better than Crane the exotic spirit
and color of Latin America. But it is Cunninghame Graham,
that romantic adventurer and most picturesque personality of
the nineties, who captures it with photographic fidelity.
Crane, as comparison with Graham's sensory kodaking shows,
was no realist. But he was the superior artist, using in his best
works only so much realistic detail as his design required.

The Blue Hotel was written in early 1898 and finished in
February at Brede Place in England three years after Crane
visited a desolate junction town in Nebraska (in February
1895) and saw there a hotel that was painted a light blue.
Crane begged Paul Reynolds: "Try to sell it as soon as possible. I must have some money by the first of April." Reynolds
sold it to *Collier's* for three hundred dollars, but before it was
accepted there it had been turned down by *Scribner's* in March
and by the *Atlantic Monthly* in April (1898). Crane said: "to
my mind, it is a daisy." But he said the same about *The Bride*,
and in a letter to William (October 29, 1897) he wrote: "My

next short thing after the novelette (The Monster) was The
Bride Comes to Yellow Sky. All my friends come here [*sic*]
say it is my very best thing." Crane was not sure which one
was his best, and his critics have not yet decided for him. *The
Blue Hotel* happens to be Hemingway's favorite, and one or
another Crane critic has rated it "one of the most vivid short
stories ever written by an American." This story, said Mencken
in 1927, "is superlative among short stories." Howells, however,
thought *The Monster* "the greatest short story ever written by
an American." John Berryman claims that *The Blue Hotel*
forms with *The Open Boat* Crane's "masterwork." And *The
Monster* is *The Blue Hotel* "in more terrible form." So one
critic applauds the story because its values are to him social
and political, and another because he too finds in it what he is
looking for—psychological source-material. It is Crane's mind,
not Crane's story, that concerns him. *The Blue Hotel* localizes
Crane's own "thrust toward suicide." The Swede in the blizzard
is Crane in the blizzard "hearing the *bugles* of the tempest;
and he *likes* this weather, 'I like it. It suits me.' Crane was
going to war again." By my reading of the story, however, the
Swede is Crane's diametric opposite. The man who wrote
Maggie believed that our environment shapes our life; yet he
himself did nothing to shape his own. He shared with Conrad
a fatalistic resignation to what happens. The Swede in *The
Blue Hotel* distrusts life and runs to meet and shape his
destiny.

But consider the story *critically*, and you see at once that
Crane has here violated his own artistic canon. He intrudes to
preach a deliberate moral. The story ends with the grotesque
image of the murdered Swede whose eyes stare "upon a dreadful legend that dwelt atop of the cash-machine: 'This registers
the amount of your purchase.'" This point marks the legitimate
end of the story. Crane spoiled the whole thing by tacking on
a moralizing appendix. The off-key tone is at odds with the
tone of the preceding part, and the theme that his beginning
prepared for stands at odds with the trumped-up theme an-

nounced in the totally irrelevant and non-ironic conclusion. In *The Upturned Face*, a slight thing but a perfection, Crane's grotesquerie is integral to his theme. In *The Blue Hotel* it is there on the page and it is misspent.

Ford Madox Ford said that *The Bride Comes to Yellow Sky* was the story that had "influenced" him "more than anything else I ever read." But then, elsewhere, he also said that it was Crane's *Five White Mice*. Ford was given to distortion of facts, misquotation, and faulty memory. Of some dozen portraits he has sketched of Crane, this one, exaggerated but in substance likely enough, puts us in mind of *The Bride*, which Crane wrote about this time. Ford says that Crane "in those days, and for my benefit, was in the habit of posing as an almost fabulous Billy the Kid." This Stephen Crane looks more like Scratchy Wilson himself:

I can see him sitting in the singularly ugly drawing room of the singularly hideous villa he lived in for a time at Oxted. Then he wore—I dare say to shock me—cowboy breeches and no coat, and all the time he was talking he wagged in his hand an immense thing that he called a gun and that we should call a revolver. From time to time he would attempt to slay with the bead-sight of this Colt such flies as settled on the table, and a good deal of his conversation would be taken up with fantastic boasts about what can be done with these lethal instruments. I don't know that he celebrated his own prowess, but he boasted about what heroes in the Far West were capable of. I did not much believe him then and I believe him still less now. *I don't believe any one is capable of anything with a revolver.*[2]

But neither did Crane believe that; Ford has lifted his belief from Crane's story of Jack Potter. Scratchy Wilson "is a wonder with a gun—a perfect wonder," but the point of the story is that no man "is capable of anything with a revolver."

The whole story turns on a single ironic moment. The sheriff, whose business is gunfire, carries no gun; and Wilson, who

---

[2] "Stevie & Co.," *New York Times Book Review*, January 2, 1927, p. 1.

always shoots, is disarmed by no gun at all. Potter's weapon is a spiritual one.

—I ain't got a gun because I've just come from San Anton' with my wife. I'm married—said Potter. . . .
—Married?—said Scratchy. Seemingly for the first time, he saw the drooping, drowning woman at the other man's side.—No!—he said. He was like a creature allowed a glimpse of another world.

Potter has married, as it were, a vision, and it is this dream— "all the glory of the marriage, the environment of the new estate"—that buoys him up through the crisis. He is a new man now, and his new world saves him. It is Wilson's getting a glimpse of it that saves him, too. When the shock of recognition comes he feels ashamed. His abasement is symbolized thus: "His feet made *funnel-shaped* tracks in the *heavy* sand." The only code he has ever known to live by, the frontier code that Potter no longer lives by, seems for once to have failed him. Potter and Wilson represent two opposite worlds or points of view: the idealistic world of spiritual values whose force lies in its innocence, and the non-imaginative world of crass realities. *This same conflict, the conflict between ideals and realities, ruled Crane's struggle as artist and gave his life and his art all their bitter ironies.*

The Bride is built on a paradoxical reversal of situation. Structurally it has close affinities, therefore, with Crane's *Mystery of Heroism*, *The Upturned Face*, and *An Episode of War*. In all four stories, that which is predictable—a code, a theory, or an ideal—is discovered to be unpredictable when faced by the realities. Wilson's "theory" about the sheriff collapses; the trapped man is Wilson himself. It is the same with Henry Fleming. The trapped or "baited" man is the characteristic ingredient of a Crane tale. The corollary is an ironic turnabout, a reversal of situation. Crane's fiction at its best combines these two ironic ingredients. No reversal occurs in *The Blue Hotel*, and there the baited character has set his own trap. Potter, unlike the Swede, accepts his moment of destiny. It has been shaped for him by a man who (allegorically speaking) is not "married." In that crucial moment of impending death Potter attains spiritual triumph. *The Bride Comes to Yellow Sky* thus anticipates in both its theme and its structure Hemingway's *Short Happy Life of Francis Macomber.*

THE BRIDE COMES TO YELLOW SKY

I

THE GREAT Pullman was whirling onward with such dignity of motion that a glance from the window seemed simply to prove that the plains of Texas were pouring eastward. Vast flats of green grass, dull-hued spaces of mesquit and cactus, little groups of frame houses, woods of light and tender trees, all were sweeping into the east, sweeping over the horizon, a precipice.

A newly married pair had boarded this coach at San Antonio. The man's face was reddened from many days in the wind and sun, and a direct result of his new black clothes was that his brick-coloured hands were constantly performing in a most conscious fashion. From time to time he looked down respectfully at his attire. He sat with a hand on each knee, like a man waiting in a barber's shop. The glances he devoted to other passengers were furtive and shy.

The bride was not pretty, nor was she very young. She wore a dress of blue cashmere, with small reservations of velvet here and there, and with steel buttons abounding. She continually twisted her head to regard her puff sleeves, very stiff, straight, and high. They embarrassed her. It was quite apparent that she had cooked, and that she expected to cook, dutifully. The blushes caused by the careless scrutiny of some passengers as she had entered the car were strange to see upon this plain, under-class countenance, which was drawn in placid, almost emotionless lines.

They were evidently very happy. "Ever been in a parlour-car before?" he asked, smiling with delight.

"No," she answered; "I never was. It's fine, ain't it?"

"Great! And then after a while we'll go forward to the diner, and get a big lay-out. Finest meal in the world. Charge a dollar."

"Oh, do they?" cried the bride. "Charge a dollar? Why, that's too much—for us—ain't it, Jack?"

"Not this trip, anyhow," he answered bravely. "We're going to go the whole thing."

Later he explained to her about the trains. "You see, it's a thousand miles from one end of Texas to the other; and this train runs right across it, and never stops but four times." He had the pride of an owner. He pointed out to her the dazzling fittings of the coach; and in truth her eyes opened wider as she contemplated the sea-green figured velvet, the shining brass, silver, and glass, the wood that gleamed as darkly brilliant as the surface of a pool of oil. At one end a bronze figure sturdily held a support for a separated chamber, and at convenient places on the ceiling were frescos in olive and silver.

To the minds of the pair, their surroundings reflected the glory of their marriage that morning in San Antonio; this was the environment of their new estate; and the man's face in particular beamed with an elation that made him appear ridiculous to the negro porter. This individual at times surveyed them from afar with an amused and superior grin. On other occasions he bullied them with skill in ways that did not make it exactly plain to them that they were being bullied. He subtly used all the manners of the most unconquerable kind of snobbery. He oppressed them; but of this oppression they had small knowledge, and they speedily forgot that infrequently a number of travellers covered them with stares of derisive enjoyment. Historically there was supposed to be something infinitely humorous in their situation.

"We are due in Yellow Sky at 3:42," he said, looking tenderly into her eyes.

"Oh, are we?" she said, as if she had not been aware of it. To evince surprise at her husband's statement was part of her wifely amiability. She took from a pocket a little silver watch;

and as she held it before her, and stared at it with a frown of attention, the new husband's face shone.

"I bought it in San Anton' from a friend of mine," he told her gleefully.

"It's seventeen minutes past twelve," she said, looking up at him with a kind of shy and clumsy coquetry. A passenger, noting this play, grew excessively sardonic, and winked at himself in one of the numerous mirrors.

At last they went to the dining-car. Two rows of negro waiters, in glowing white suits, surveyed their entrance with the interest, and also the equanimity, of men who had been forewarned. The pair fell to the lot of a waiter who happened to feel pleasure in steering them through their meal. He viewed them with the manner of a fatherly pilot, his countenance radiant with benevolence. The patronage, entwined with the ordinary deference, was not plain to them. And yet, as they returned to their coach, they showed in their faces a sense of escape.

To the left, miles down a long purple slope, was a little ribbon of mist where moved the keening Rio Grande. The train was approaching it at an angle, and the apex was Yellow Sky. Presently it was apparent that, as the distance from Yellow Sky grew shorter, the husband became commensurately restless. His brick-red hands were more insistent in their prominence. Occasionally he was even rather absent-minded and far-away when the bride leaned forward and addressed him.

As a matter of truth, Jack Potter was beginning to find the shadow of a deed weigh upon him like a leaden slab. He, the town marshal of Yellow Sky, a man known, liked, and feared in his corner, a prominent person, had gone to San Antonio to meet a girl he believed he loved, and there, after the usual prayers, had actually induced her to marry him, without consulting Yellow Sky for any part of the transaction. He was now bringing his bride before an innocent and unsuspecting community.

Of course people in Yellow Sky married as it pleased them,

in accordance with a general custom; but such was Potter's thought of his duty to his friends, or of their idea of his duty, or of an unspoken form which does not control men in these matters, that he felt he was heinous. He had committed an extraordinary crime. Face to face with this girl in San Antonio, and spurred by his sharp impulse, he had gone headlong over all the social hedges. At San Antonio he was like a man hidden in the dark. A knife to sever any friendly duty, any form, was easy to his hand in that remote city. But the hour of Yellow Sky—the hour of daylight—was approaching.

He knew full well that his marriage was an important thing to his town. It could only be exceeded by the burning of the new hotel. His friends could not forgive him. Frequently he had reflected on the advisability of telling them by telegraph, but a new cowardice had been upon him. He feared to do it. And now the train was hurrying him toward a scene of amazement, glee, and reproach. He glanced out of the window at the line of haze swinging slowly in toward the train.

Yellow Sky had a kind of brass band, which played painfully, to the delight of the populace. He laughed without heart as he thought of it. If the citizens could dream of his prospective arrival with his bride, they would parade the band at the station and escort them, amid cheers and laughing congratulations, to his adobe home.

He resolved that he would use all the devices of speed and plainscraft in making the journey from the station to his house. Once within that safe citadel, he could issue some sort of vocal bulletin, and then not go among the citizens until they had time to wear off a little of their enthusiasm.

The bride looked anxiously at him. "What's worrying you, Jack?"

He laughed again. "I'm not worrying, girl; I'm only thinking of Yellow Sky."

She flushed in comprehension.

A sense of mutual guilt invaded their minds and developed a finer tenderness. They looked at each other with eyes softly aglow. But Potter often laughed the same nervous laugh; the flush upon the bride's face seemed quite permanent.

The traitor to the feelings of Yellow Sky narrowly watched the speeding landscape. "We're nearly there," he said.

Presently the porter came and announced the proximity of Potter's home. He held a brush in his hand, and, with all his airy superiority gone, he brushed Potter's new clothes as the latter slowly turned this way and that way. Potter fumbled out a coin and gave it to the porter, as he had seen others do. It was a heavy and muscle-bound business, as that of a man shoeing his first horse.

The porter took their bag, and as the train began to slow they moved forward to the hooded platform of the car. Presently the two engines and their long string of coaches rushed into the station of Yellow Sky.

"They have to take water here," said Potter, from a constricted throat and in mournful cadence, as one announcing death. Before the train stopped his eye had swept the length of the platform, and he was glad and astonished to see there was none upon it but the station-agent, who, with a slightly hurried and anxious air, was walking toward the water-tanks. When the train had halted, the porter alighted first, and placed in position a little temporary step.

"Come on, girl," said Potter, hoarsely. As he helped her down they each laughed on a false note. He took the bag from the negro, and bade his wife cling to his arm. As they slunk rapidly away, his hang-dog glance perceived that they were unloading the two trunks, and also that the station-agent, far ahead near the baggage-car, had turned and was running toward him, making gestures. He laughed, and groaned as he laughed, when he noted the first effect of his marital bliss upon Yellow Sky. He gripped his wife's arm firmly to his side, and they fled. Behind them the porter stood, chuckling fatuously.

II

The California express on the Southern Railway was due at
Yellow Sky in twenty-one minutes. There were six men at the
bar of the Weary Gentleman saloon. One was a drummer who
talked a great deal and rapidly; three were Texans who did
not care to talk at that time; and two were Mexican sheep-
herders, who did not talk as a general practice in the Weary
Gentleman saloon. The barkeeper's dog lay on the board walk
that crossed in front of the door. His head was on his paws,
and he glanced drowsily here and there with the constant
vigilance of a dog that is kicked on occasion. Across the sandy
street were some vivid green grass-plots, so wonderful in
appearance, amid the sands that burned near them in a blazing
sun, that they caused a doubt in the mind. They exactly resembled the grass mats used to represent lawns on the stage.
At the cooler end of the railway station, a man without a coat
sat in a tilted chair and smoked his pipe. The fresh-cut bank
of the Rio Grande circled near the town, and there could be
seen beyond it a great plum-coloured plain of mesquit.

Save for the busy drummer and his companions in the saloon,
Yellow Sky was dozing. The new-comer leaned gracefully
upon the bar, and recited many tales with the confidence of
a bard who has come upon a new field.

"—and at the moment that the old man fell downstairs with
the bureau in his arms, the old woman was coming up with
two scuttles of coal, and of course—"

The drummer's tale was interrupted by a young man who
suddenly appeared in the open door. He cried: "Scratchy
Wilson's drunk, and has turned loose with both hands." The
two Mexicans at once set down their glasses and faded out of
the rear entrance of the saloon.

The drummer, innocent and jocular, answered: "All right,
old man. S'pose he has? Come in and have a drink, anyhow."

But the information had made such an obvious cleft in
every skull in the room that the drummer was obliged to see

its importance. All had become instantly solemn. "Say," said he, mystified, "what is this?" His three companions made the introductory gesture of eloquent speech; but the young man at the door forestalled them.

"It means, my friend," he answered, as he came into the saloon, "that for the next two hours this town won't be a health resort."

The barkeeper went to the door, and locked and barred it; reaching out of the window, he pulled in heavy wooden shutters, and barred them. Immediately a solemn, chapel-like gloom was upon the place. The drummer was looking from one to another.

"But say," he cried, "what is this, anyhow? You don't mean there is going to be a gun-fight?"

"Don't know whether there'll be a fight or not," answered one man, grimly; "but there'll be some shootin'—some good shootin'."

The young man who had warned them waved his hand. "Oh, there'll be a fight fast enough, if any one wants it. Anybody can get a fight out there in the street. There's a fight just waiting."

The drummer seemed to be swayed between the interest of a foreigner and a perception of personal danger.

"What did you say his name was?" he asked.

"Scratchy Wilson," they answered in chorus.

"And will he kill anybody? What are you going to do? Does this happen often? Does he rampage around like this once a week or so? Can he break in that door?"

"No; he can't break down that door," replied the barkeeper. "He's tried it three times. But when he comes you'd better lay down on the floor, stranger. He's dead sure to shoot at it, and a bullet may come through."

Thereafter the drummer kept a strict eye upon the door. The time had not yet been called for him to hug the floor, but, as a minor precaution, he sidled near to the wall. "Will he kill anybody?" he said again.

The men laughed low and scornfully at the question.

"He's out to shoot, and he's out for trouble. Don't see any good in experimentin' with him."

"But what do you do in a case like this? What do you do?"

A man responded: "Why, he and Jack Potter—"

"But," in chorus the other men interrupted, "Jack Potter's in San Anton'."

"Well, who is he? What's he got to do with it?"

"Oh, he's the town marshal. He goes out and fights Scratchy when he gets on one of these tears."

"Wow!" said the drummer, mopping his brow. "Nice job he's got."

The voices had toned away to mere whisperings. The drummer wished to ask further questions, which were born of an increasing anxiety and bewilderment; but when he attempted them, the men merely looked at him in irritation and motioned him to remain silent. A tense waiting hush was upon them. In the deep shadows of the room their eyes shone as they listened for sounds from the street. One man made three gestures at the barkeeper; and the latter, moving like a ghost, handed him a glass and a bottle. The man poured a full glass of whisky, and set down the bottle noiselessly. He gulped the whisky in a swallow, and turned again toward the door in immovable silence. The drummer saw that the barkeeper, without a sound, had taken a Winchester from beneath the bar. Later he saw this individual beckoning to him, so he tiptoed across the room.

"You better come with me back of the bar."

"No, thanks," said the drummer, perspiring; "I'd rather be where I can make a break for the back door."

Whereupon the man of bottles made a kindly but peremptory gesture. The drummer obeyed it, and, finding himself seated on a box with his head below the level of the bar, balm was laid upon his soul at sight of various zinc and copper fittings that bore a resemblance to armour-plate. The barkeeper took a seat comfortably upon an adjacent box.

"You see," he whispered, "this here Scratchy Wilson is a wonder with a gun—a perfect wonder; and when he goes on the war-trail, we hunt our holes—naturally. He's about the last one of the old gang that used to hang out along the river here. He's a terror when he's drunk. When he's sober he's all right—kind of simple—wouldn't hurt a fly—nicest fellow in town. But when he's drunk—whoo!"

There were periods of stillness. "I wish Jack Potter was back from San Anton'," said the barkeeper. "He shot Wilson up once—in the leg—and he would sail in and pull out the kinks in this thing."

Presently they heard from a distance the sound of a shot, followed by three wild yowls. It instantly removed a bond from the men in the darkened saloon. There was a shuffling of feet. They looked at each other. "Here he comes," they said.

III

A man in a maroon-coloured flannel shirt, which had been purchased for purposes of decoration, and made principally by some Jewish women on the East Side of New York, rounded a corner and walked into the middle of the main street of Yellow Sky. In either hand the man held a long, heavy, blue-black revolver. Often he yelled, and these cries rang through a semblance of a deserted village, shrilly flying over the roofs in a volume that seemed to have no relation to the ordinary vocal strength of a man. It was as if the surrounding stillness formed the arch of a tomb over him. These cries of ferocious challenge rang against walls of silence. And his boots had red tops with gilded imprints, of the kind beloved in winter by little sledding boys on the hillsides of New England.

The man's face flamed in a rage begot of whisky. His eyes, rolling, and yet keen for ambush, hunted the still doorways and windows. He walked with the creeping movement of the midnight cat. As it occurred to him, he roared menacing information. The long revolvers in his hands were as easy as straws; they were moved with an electric swiftness. The little fingers of each hand played sometimes in a musician's way. Plain from the low collar of the shirt, the cords of his neck straightened and sank, straightened and sank, as passion moved him. The only sounds were his terrible invitations. The calm adobes preserved their demeanour at the passing of this small thing in the middle of the street.

There was no offer of fight—no offer of fight. The man called to the sky. There were no attractions. He bellowed and fumed and swayed his revolvers here and everywhere.

The dog of the barkeeper of the Weary Gentleman saloon had not appreciated the advance of events. He yet lay dozing in front of his master's door. At sight of the dog, the man paused and raised his revolver humorously. At sight of the man, the dog sprang up and walked diagonally away, with a sullen head, and growling. The man yelled, and the dog broke into a gallop. As it was about to enter an alley, there was a loud noise, a whistling, and something spat the ground directly before it. The dog screamed, and, wheeling in terror, galloped headlong in a new direction. Again there was a noise, a whistling, and sand was kicked viciously before it. Fear-stricken, the dog turned and flurried like an animal in a pen. The man stood laughing, his weapons at his hips.

Ultimately the man was attracted by the closed door of the Weary Gentleman saloon. He went to it and, hammering with a revolver, demanded drink.

The door remaining imperturbable, he picked a bit of paper from the walk, and nailed it to the framework with a knife. He then turned his back contemptuously upon this popular resort and, walking to the opposite side of the street and spinning there on his heel quickly and lithely, fired at the bit of paper. He missed it by a half-inch. He swore at himself, and went away. Later he comfortably fusilladed the windows of his most intimate friend. The man was playing with this town; it was a toy for him.

But still there was no offer of fight. The name of Jack Potter, his ancient antagonist, entered his mind, and he concluded that it would be a glad thing if he should go to Potter's house, and by bombardment induce him to come out and fight. He moved in the direction of his desire, chanting Apache scalp-music.

When he arrived at it, Potter's house presented the same still front as had the other adobes. Taking up a strategic position, the man howled a challenge. But this house regarded him as might a great stone god. It gave no sign. After a decent wait, the man howled further challenges, mingling with them wonderful epithets.

Presently there came the spectacle of a man churning himself into deepest rage over the immobility of a house. He fumed at it as the winter wind attacks a prairie cabin in the North. To the distance there should have gone the sound of a tumult like the fighting of two hundred Mexicans. As necessity bade him, he paused for breath or to reload his revolvers.

IV

Potter and his bride walked sheepishly and with speed. Some-times they laughed together shamefacedly and low.

"Next corner, dear," he said finally.

They put forth the efforts of a pair walking bowed against a strong wind. Potter was about to raise a finger to point the first appearance of the new home when, as they circled the corner, they came face to face with a man in a maroon-coloured shirt, who was feverishly pushing cartridges into a large revolver. Upon the instant the man dropped his revolver to the ground and, like lightning, whipped another from its holster. The second weapon was aimed at the bridegroom's chest.

There was a silence. Potter's mouth seemed to be merely a grave for his tongue. He exhibited an instinct to at once loosen his arm from the woman's grip, and he dropped the bag to the sand. As for the bride, her face had gone as yellow as old cloth. She was a slave to hideous rites, gazing at the apparitional snake.

The two men faced each other at a distance of three paces. He of the revolver smiled with a new and quiet ferocity.

"Tried to sneak up on me," he said. "Tried to sneak up on me!" His eyes grew more baleful. As Potter made a slight movement, the man thrust his revolver venomously forward. "No; don't you do it, Jack Potter. Don't you move a finger toward a gun just yet. Don't you move an eyelash. The time has come for me to settle with you, and I'm goin' to do it my own way, and loaf along with no interferin'. So if you don't want a gun bent on you, just mind what I tell you."

Potter looked at his enemy. "I ain't got a gun on me Scratchy," he said. "Honest, I ain't." He was stiffening and steadying, but yet somewhere at the back of his mind a vision of the Pullman floated: the sea-green figured velvet, the shining brass, silver, and glass, the wood that gleamed as darkly brilliant as the surface of a pool of oil—all the glory of the marriage, the environment of the new estate. "You know I fight when it comes to fighting, Scratchy Wilson; but I ain't got a gun on me. You'll have to do all the shootin' yourself."

His enemy's face went livid. He stepped forward, and lashed his weapon to and fro before Potter's chest. "Don't you tell me you ain't got no gun on you, you whelp. Don't tell me no lie like that. There ain't a man in Texas ever seen you without no gun. Don't take me for no kid." His eyes blazed with light, and his throat worked like a pump.

"I ain't takin' you for no kid," answered Potter. His heels had not moved an inch backward. "I'm takin' you for a damn fool. I tell you I ain't got a gun, and I ain't. If you're goin' to shoot me up, you better begin now; you'll never get a chance like this again."

So much enforced reasoning had told on Wilson's rage; he was calmer. "If you ain't got a gun, why ain't you got a gun?" he sneered. "Been to Sunday-school?"

"I ain't got a gun because I've just come from San Anton' with my wife. I'm married," said Potter. "And if I'd thought there was going to be any galoots like you prowling around when I brought my wife home, I'd had a gun, and don't you forget it."

"Married!" said Scratchy, not at all comprehending.

"Yes, married. I'm married," said Potter, distinctly.

"Married?" said Scratchy. Seemingly for the first time, he saw the drooping, drowning woman at the other man's side. "No!" he said. He was like a creature allowed a glimpse of another world. He moved a pace backward, and his arm, with the revolver, dropped to his side. "Is this the lady?" he asked.

"Yes; this is the lady," answered Potter.

There was another period of silence.

"Well," said Wilson at last, slowly, "I s'pose it's all off now."

"It's all off if you say so, Scratchy. You know I didn't make the trouble." Potter lifted his valise.

"Well, I 'low it's off, Jack," said Wilson. He was looking at the ground. "Married!" He was not a student of chivalry; it was merely that in the presence of this foreign condition he was a simple child of the earlier plains. He picked up his starboard revolver, and, placing both weapons in their holsters, he went away. His feet made funnel-shaped tracks in the heavy sand.

THE BLUE HOTEL

I

The Palace Hotel at Fort Romper was painted a light blue, a shade that is on the legs of a kind of heron, causing the bird to declare its position against any background. The Palace Hotel, then, was always screaming and howling in a way that made the dazzling winter landscape of Nebraska seem only a grey swampish hush. It stood alone on the prairie, and when the snow was falling the town two hundred yards away was not visible. But when the traveller alighted at the railway station he was obliged to pass the Palace Hotel before he could come upon the company of low clapboard houses which composed Fort Romper, and it was not to be thought that any traveller could pass the Palace Hotel without looking at it. Pat Scully, the proprietor, had proved himself a master of strategy when he chose his paints. It is true that on clear days, when the great transcontinental expresses, long lines of swaying Pullmans, swept through Fort Romper, passengers were overcome at the sight, and the cult that knows the brown-reds and the subdivisions of the dark greens of the East expressed shame, pity, horror, in a laugh. But to the citizens of this prairie town and to the people who would naturally stop there, Pat Scully had performed a feat. With this opulence and splendour, these creeds, classes, egotisms, that streamed through Romper on the rails day after day, they had no colour in common.

As if the displayed delights of such a blue hotel were not sufficiently enticing, it was Scully's habit to go every morning and evening to meet the leisurely trains that stopped at Romper and work his seductions upon any man that he might see wavering, gripsack in hand.

One morning, when a snow-crusted engine dragged its long

string of freight cars and its one passenger coach to the station, Scully performed the marvel of catching three men. One was a shaky and quick-eyed Swede, with a great shining cheap valise; one was a tall bronzed cowboy, who was on his way to a ranch near the Dakota line; one was a little silent man from the East, who didn't look it, and didn't announce it. Scully practically made them prisoners. He was so nimble and merry and kindly that each probably felt it would be the height of brutality to try to escape. They trudged off over the creaking board sidewalks in the wake of the eager little Irishman. He wore a heavy fur cap squeezed tightly down on his head. It caused his two red ears to stick out stiffly, as if they were made of tin.

At last, Scully, elaborately, with boisterous hospitality, conducted them through the portals of the blue hotel. The room which they entered was small. It seemed to be merely a proper temple for an enormous stove, which, in the centre, was humming with godlike violence. At various points on its surface the iron had become luminous and glowed yellow from the heat. Beside the stove Scully's son Johnnie was playing High-Five with an old farmer who had whiskers both grey and sandy. They were quarrelling. Frequently the old farmer turned his face toward a box of sawdust—coloured brown from tobacco juice—that was behind the stove, and spat with an air of great impatience and irritation. With a loud flourish of words Scully destroyed the game of cards, and bustled his son upstairs with part of the baggage of the new guests. He himself conducted them to three basins of the coldest water in the world. The cowboy and the Easterner burnished themselves fiery red with this water, until it seemed to be some kind of metal-polish. The Swede, however, merely dipped his fingers gingerly and with trepidation. It was notable that throughout this series of small ceremonies the three travellers were made to feel that Scully was very benevolent. He was conferring great favours upon them. He handed the towel from one to another with an air of philanthropic impulse.

Afterward they went to the first room, and, sitting about the stove, listened to Scully's officious clamour at his daughters, who were preparing the midday meal. They reflected in the silence of experienced men who tread carefully amid new people. Nevertheless, the old farmer, stationary, invincible in his chair near the warmest part of the stove, turned his face from the sawdust-box frequently and addressed a glowing commonplace to the strangers. Usually he was answered in short but adequate sentences by either the cowboy or the Easterner. The Swede said nothing. He seemed to be occupied in making furtive estimates of each man in the room. One might have thought that he had the sense of silly suspicion which comes to guilt. He resembled a badly frightened man.

Later, at dinner, he spoke a little, addressing his conversation entirely to Scully. He volunteered that he had come from New York, where for ten years he had worked as a tailor. These facts seemed to strike Scully as fascinating, and afterward he volunteered that he had lived at Romper for fourteen years. The Swede asked about the crops and the price of labour. He seemed barely to listen to Scully's extended replies. His eyes continued to rove from man to man.

Finally, with a laugh and a wink, he said that some of these Western communities were very dangerous; and after his statement he straightened his legs under the table, tilted his head, and laughed again, loudly. It was plain that the demonstration had no meaning to the others. They looked at him wondering and in silence.

II

As the men trooped heavily back into the front room, the two little windows presented views of a turmoiling sea of snow. The huge arms of the wind were making attempts—mighty, circular, futile—to embrace the flakes as they sped. A gate-post like a still man with a blanched face stood aghast amid this profligate fury. In a hearty voice Scully announced the presence of a blizzard. The guests of the blue hotel, lighting their pipes, assented with grunts of lazy masculine contentment. No island of the sea could be exempt in the degree of this little room with its humming stove. Johnnie, son of Scully, in a tone which defined his opinion of his ability as a card-player, challenged the old farmer of both grey and sandy whiskers to a game of High-Five. The farmer agreed with a contemptuous and bitter scoff. They sat close to the stove, and squared their knees under a wide board. The cowboy and the Easterner watched the game with interest. The Swede remained near the window, aloof, but with a countenance that showed signs of an inexplicable excitement.

The play of Johnnie and the grey-beard was suddenly ended by another quarrel. The old man arose while casting a look of heated scorn at his adversary. He slowly buttoned his coat, and then stalked with fabulous dignity from the room. In the discreet silence of all the other men the Swede laughed. His laughter rang somehow childish. Men by this time had begun to look at him askance, as if they wished to inquire what ailed him.

A new game was formed jocosely. The cowboy volunteered to become the partner of Johnnie, and they all then turned to ask the Swede to throw in his lot with the little Easterner. He asked some questions about the game, and, learning that it wore many names, and that he had played it when it was under an alias, he accepted the invitation. He strode toward the men nervously, as if he expected to be assaulted. Finally, seated, he gazed from face to face and laughed shrilly. This laugh was so strange that the Easterner looked up quickly, the cowboy sat intent and with his mouth open, and Johnnie paused, holding the cards with still fingers.

Afterward there was a short silence. Then Johnnie said, "Well, let's get at it. Come on now!" They pulled their chairs forward until their knees were bunched under the board. They began to play, and their interest in the game caused the others to forget the manner of the Swede.

The cowboy was a board-whacker. Each time that he held

superior cards he whanged them, one by one, with exceeding force, down upon the improvised table, and took the tricks with a glowing air of prowess and pride that sent thrills of indignation into the hearts of his opponents. A game with a board-whacker in it is sure to become intense. The countenances of the Easterner and the Swede were miserable whenever the cowboy thundered down his aces and kings, while Johnnie, his eyes gleaming with joy, chuckled and chuckled.

Because of the absorbing play none considered the strange ways of the Swede. They paid strict heed to the game. Finally, during a lull caused by a new deal, the Swede suddenly addressed Johnnie: "I suppose there have been a good many men killed in this room." The jaws of the others dropped and they looked at him.

"What in hell are you talking about?" said Johnnie.

The Swede laughed again his blatant laugh, full of a kind of false courage and defiance. "Oh, you know what I mean all right," he answered.

"I'm a liar if I do!" Johnnie protested. The card was halted, and the men stared at the Swede. Johnnie evidently felt that as the son of the proprietor he should make a direct inquiry. "Now, what might you be drivin' at, mister?" he asked. The Swede winked at him. It was a wink full of cunning. His fingers shook on the edge of the board. "Oh, maybe you think I have been to nowheres. Maybe you think I'm a tenderfoot?"

"I don't know nothin' about you," answered Johnnie, "and I don't give a damn where you've been. All I got to say is that I don't know what you're driving at. There hain't never been nobody killed in this room."

The cowboy, who had been steadily gazing at the Swede, then spoke: "What's wrong with you, mister?"

Apparently it seemed to the Swede that he was formidably menaced. He shivered and turned white near the corners of his mouth. He sent an appealing glance in the direction of the little Easterner. During these moments he did not forget to wear his air of advanced pot-valour. "They say they don't know what I mean," he remarked mockingly to the Easterner.

The latter answered after prolonged and cautious reflection. "I don't understand you," he said, impassively.

The Swede made a movement then which announced that he thought he had encountered treachery from the only quarter where he had expected sympathy, if not help. "Oh, I see you are all against me. I see—"

The cowboy was in a state of deep stupefaction. "Say," he cried, as he tumbled the deck violently down upon the board, "say, what are you gittin' at, hey?"

The Swede sprang up with the celerity of a man escaping from a snake on the floor. "I don't want to fight!" he shouted. "I don't want to fight!"

The cowboy stretched his long legs indolently and deliberately. His hands were in his pockets. He spat into the sawdust-box. "Well, who the hell thought you did?" he inquired.

The Swede backed rapidly toward a corner of the room. His hands were out protectingly in front of his chest, but he was making an obvious struggle to control his fright. "Gentlemen," he quavered, "I suppose I am going to be killed before I can leave this house! I suppose I am going to be killed before I can leave this house!" In his eyes was the dying-swan look. Through the windows could be seen the snow turning blue in the shadow of dusk. The wind tore at the house, and some loose thing beat regularly against the clapboards like a spirit tapping.

A door opened, and Scully himself entered. He paused in surprise as he noted the tragic attitude of the Swede. Then he said, "What's the matter here?"

The Swede answered him swiftly and eagerly: "These men are going to kill me."

"Kill you!" ejaculated Scully. "Kill you! What are you talkin'?"

The Swede made the gesture of a martyr.

Scully wheeled sternly upon his son. "What is this, Johnnie?"

The lad had grown sullen. "Damned if I know," he answered.

"I can't make no sense to it." He began to shuffle the cards, fluttering them together with an angry snap. "He says a good many men have been killed in this room, or something like that. And he says he's goin' to be killed here too. I don't know what ails him. He's crazy, I shouldn't wonder."

Scully then looked for explanation to the cowboy, but the cowboy simply shrugged his shoulders.

"Kill you?" said Scully again to the Swede. "Kill you? Man, you're off your nut."

"Oh, I know," burst out the Swede. "I know what will happen. Yes, I'm crazy—yes. Yes, of course, I'm crazy—yes. But I know one thing—" There was a sort of sweat of misery and terror upon his face. "I know I won't get out of here alive."

The cowboy drew a deep breath, as if his mind was passing into the last stages of dissolution. "Well, I'm doggoned," he whispered to himself.

Scully wheeled suddenly and faced his son. "You've been troublin' this man!"

Johnnie's voice was loud with its burden of grievance. "Why, good Gawd, I ain't done nothin' to 'im."

The Swede broke in. "Gentlemen, do not disturb yourselves. I will leave this house. I will go away, because"—he accused them dramatically with his glance—"because I do not want to be killed."

Scully was furious with his son. "Will you tell me what is the matter, you young divil? What's the matter, anyhow? Speak out!"

"Blame it!" cried Johnnie in despair, "don't I tell you I don't know? He—he says we want to kill him, and that's all I know. I can't tell what ails him."

The Swede continued to repeat: "Never mind, Mr. Scully; never mind. I will leave this house. I will go away, because I do not wish to be killed. Yes, of course, I am crazy—yes. But I know one thing! I will go away. I will leave this house. Never mind, Mr. Scully; never mind. I will go away."

"You will not go 'way," said Scully. "You will not go 'way

until I hear the reason of this business. If anybody has troubled you I will take care of him. This is my house. You are under my roof, and I will not allow any peaceable man to be troubled here." He cast a terrible eye upon Johnnie, the cowboy, and the Easterner.

"Never mind, Mr. Scully; never mind. I will go away. I do not wish to be killed." The Swede moved toward the door which opened upon the stairs. It was evidently his intention to go at once for his baggage.

"No, no," shouted Scully peremptorily; but the white-faced man slid by him and disappeared. "Now," said Scully severely, "what does this mane?"

Johnnie and the cowboy cried together: "Why, we didn't do nothin' to 'im!"

Scully's eyes were cold. "No," he said, "you didn't?"

Johnnie swore a deep oath. "Why, this is the wildest loon I ever see. We didn't do nothin' at all. We were jest sittin' here playin' cards, and he—"

The father suddenly spoke to the Easterner. "Mr. Blanc," he asked, "what has these boys been doin'?"

The Easterner reflected again. "I didn't see anything wrong at all," he said at last, slowly.

Scully began to howl. "But what does it mane?" He stared ferociously at his son. "I have a mind to lather you for this, me boy."

Johnnie was frantic. "Well, what have I done?" he bawled at his father.

III

"I think you are tongue-tied," said Scully finally to his son, the cowboy, and the Easterner; and at the end of this scornful sentence he left the room.

Upstairs the Swede was swiftly fastening the straps of his great valise. Once his back happened to be half turned toward the door, and, hearing a noise there, he wheeled and sprang up, uttering a loud cry. Scully's wrinkled visage showed grimly in the light of the small lamp he carried. This yellow effulgence, streaming upward, coloured only his prominent features, and left his eyes, for instance, in mysterious shadow. He resembled a murderer.

"Man! man!" he exclaimed, "have you gone daffy?"

"Oh, no! Oh, no!" rejoined the other. "There are people in this world who know pretty nearly as much as you do—understand?"

For a moment they stood gazing at each other. Upon the Swede's deathly pale cheeks were two spots brightly crimson and sharply edged, as if they had been carefully painted. Scully placed the light on the table and sat himself on the edge of the bed. He spoke ruminatively. "By cracky, I never heard of such a thing in my life. It's a complete muddle. I can't, for the soul of me, think how you ever got this idea into your head." Presently he lifted his eyes and asked: "And did you sure think they were going to kill you?"

The Swede scanned the old man as if he wished to see into his mind. "I did," he said at last. He obviously suspected that this answer might precipitate an outbreak. As he pulled on a strap his whole arm shook, the elbow wavering like a bit of paper.

Scully banged his hand impressively on the footboard of the bed. "Why, man, we're goin' to have a line of ilictric street-cars in this town next spring."

"'A line of electric street-cars,'" repeated the Swede, stupidly.

"And," said Scully, "there's a new railroad goin' to be built down from Broken Arm to here. Not to mintion the four churches and the smashin' big brick school-house. Then there's the big factory, too. Why, in two years Romper'll be a met-tro-pol-is."

Having finished the preparation of his baggage, the Swede straightened himself. "Mr. Scully," he said, with sudden hardihood, "how much do I owe you?"

"You don't owe me anythin'," said the old man, angrily.

"Yes, I do," retorted the Swede. He took seventy-five cents from his pocket and tendered it to Scully; but the latter snapped his fingers in disdainful refusal. However, it happened that they both stood gazing in a strange fashion at three silver pieces on the Swede's open palm.

"I'll not take your money," said Scully at last. "Not after what's been goin' on here." Then a plan seemed to strike him. "Here," he cried, picking up his lamp and moving toward the door. "Here! Come with me a minute."

"No," said the Swede, in overwhelming alarm.

"Yes," urged the old man. "Come on! I want you to come and see a picter—just across the hall—in my room."

The Swede must have concluded that his hour was come. His jaw dropped and his teeth showed like a dead man's. He ultimately followed Scully across the corridor, but he had the step of one hung in chains.

Scully flashed the light high on the wall of his own chamber. There was revealed a ridiculous photograph of a little girl. She was leaning against a balustrade of gorgeous decoration, and the formidable bang to her hair was prominent. The figure was as graceful as an upright sled-stake, and, withal, it was of the hue of lead. "There," said Scully, tenderly, "that's the picter of my little girl that died. Her name was Carrie. She had the purtiest hair you ever saw! I was that fond of her, she—"

Turning then, he saw that the Swede was not contemplating the picture at all, but, instead, was keeping keen watch on the gloom in the rear.

"Look, man!" cried Scully, heartily. "That's the picter of my little gal that died. Her name was Carrie. And then here's the picter of my oldest boy, Michael. He's a lawyer in Lincoln, an' doin' well. I gave that boy a grand eddication, and I'm glad for it now. He's a fine boy. Look at 'im now. Ain't he bold as blazes, him there in Lincoln, an honoured an' respicted gintleman! An honoured and respicted gintleman," concluded Scully with a flourish. And, so saying, he smote the Swede jovially on the back.

The Swede faintly smiled.

"Now," said the old man, "there's only one more thing." He dropped suddenly to the floor and thrust his head beneath the bed. The Swede could hear his muffled voice. "I'd keep it under me piller if it wasn't for that boy Johnnie. Then there's the old woman— Where is it now? I never put it twice in the same place. Ah, now come out with you!"

Presently he backed clumsily from under the bed, dragging with him an old coat rolled into a bundle. "I've fetched him," he muttered. Kneeling on the floor, he unrolled the coat and extracted from its heart a large yellow-brown whisky-bottle.

His first manœuvre was to hold the bottle up to the light. Reassured, apparently, that nobody had been tampering with it, he thrust it with a generous movement toward the Swede.

The weak-kneed Swede was about to eagerly clutch this element of strength, but he suddenly jerked his hand away and cast a look of horror upon Scully.

"Drink," said the old man affectionately. He had risen to his feet, and now stood facing the Swede.

There was a silence. Then again Scully said: "Drink!"

The Swede laughed wildly. He grabbed the bottle, put it to his mouth; and as his lips curled absurdly around the opening and his throat worked, he kept his glance, burning with hatred, upon the old man's face.

IV

After the departure of Scully the three men, with the cardboard still upon their knees, preserved for a long time an astounded silence. Then Johnnie said: "That's the doddangedest Swede I ever see."

"He ain't no Swede," said the cowboy, scornfully.

"Well, what is he then?" cried Johnnie. "What is he then?"

"It's my opinion," replied the cowboy deliberately, "he's some kind of a Dutchman." It was a venerable custom of the country to entitle as Swedes all light-haired men who spoke with a heavy tongue. In consequence the idea of the cowboy was not without its daring. "Yes, sir," he repeated. "It's my opinion this feller is some kind of a Dutchman."

"Well, he says he's a Swede, anyhow," muttered Johnnie, sulkily. He turned to the Easterner: "What do you think, Mr. Blanc?"

"Oh, I don't know," replied the Easterner.

"Well, what do you think makes him act that way?" asked the cowboy.

"Why, he's frightened." The Easterner knocked his pipe against a rim of the stove. "He's clear frightened out of his boots."

"What at?" cried Johnnie and the cowboy together.

The Easterner reflected over his answer.

"What at?" cried the others again.

"Oh, I don't know, but it seems to me this man has been reading dime novels, and he thinks he's right out in the middle of it—the shootin' and stabbin' and all."

"But," said the cowboy, deeply scandalized, "this ain't Wyoming, ner none of them places. This is Nebrasker."

"Yes," added Johnnie, "an' why don't he wait till he gits *out* West?"

The travelled Easterner laughed. "It isn't different there even—not in these days. But he thinks he's right in the middle of hell."

Johnnie and the cowboy mused long.

"It's awful funny," remarked Johnnie at last.

"Yes," said the cowboy. "This is a queer game. I hope we don't git snowed in, because then we'd have to stand this here man bein' around with us all the time. That wouldn't be no good."

"I wish pop would throw him out," said Johnnie.

Presently they heard a loud stamping on the stairs, accompanied by ringing jokes in the voice of old Scully, and laughter, evidently from the Swede. The men around the stove stared vacantly at each other. "Gosh!" said the cowboy. The door flew open, and old Scully, flushed and anecdotal, came into the room. He was jabbering at the Swede, who followed him, laughing bravely. It was the entry of two roisterers from a banquet hall.

"Come now," said Scully sharply to the three seated men, "move up and give us a chance at the stove." The cowboy and the Easterner obediently sidled their chairs to make room for the new-comers. Johnnie, however, simply arranged himself in a more indolent attitude, and then remained motionless.

"Come! Git over, there," said Scully.

"Plenty of room on the other side of the stove," said Johnnie.

"Do you think we want to sit in the draught?" roared the father.

But the Swede here interposed with a grandeur of confidence. "No, no. Let the boy sit where he likes," he cried in a bullying voice to the father.

"All right! All right!" said Scully, deferentially. The cowboy and the Easterner exchanged glances of wonder.

The five chairs were formed in a crescent about one side of the stove. The Swede began to talk; he talked arrogantly, profanely, angrily. Johnnie, the cowboy, and the Easterner maintained a morose silence, while old Scully appeared to be receptive and eager, breaking in constantly with sympathetic ejaculations.

Finally the Swede announced that he was thirsty. He moved in his chair, and said that he would go for a drink of water.

"I'll git it for you," cried Scully at once.

"No," said the Swede, contemptuously. "I'll get it for myself." He arose and stalked with the air of an owner off into the executive parts of the hotel.

As soon as the Swede was out of hearing Scully sprang to his feet and whispered intensely to the others: "Upstairs he thought I was tryin' to poison 'im."

"Say," said Johnnie, "this makes me sick. Why don't you throw 'im out in the snow?"

"Why, he's all right now," declared Scully. "It was only that he was from the East, and he thought this was a tough place. That's all. He's all right now."

The cowboy looked with admiration upon the Easterner. "You were straight," he said. "You were on to that there Dutchman."

"Well," said Johnnie to his father, "he may be all right now, but I don't see it. Other time he was scared, but now he's too fresh."

Scully's speech was always a combination of Irish brogue and idiom, Western twang and idiom, and scraps of curiously formal diction taken from the story-books and newspapers. He now hurled a strange mass of language at the head of his son. "What do I keep? What do I keep? What do I keep?" he demanded, in a voice of thunder. He slapped his knee impressively, to indicate that he himself was going to make reply, and that all should heed. "I keep a hotel," he shouted. "A hotel, do you mind? A guest under my roof has sacred privileges. He is to be intimidated by none. Not one word shall he hear that would prijudice him in favour of goin' away. I'll not have it. There's no place in this here town where they can say they iver took in a guest of mine because he was afraid to stay here." He wheeled suddenly upon the cowboy and the Easterner. "Am I right?"

"Yes, Mr. Scully," said the cowboy, "I think you're right."

"Yes, Mr. Scully," said the Easterner, "I think you're right."

V

At six-o'clock supper, the Swede fizzed like a fire-wheel. He sometimes seemed on the point of bursting into riotous song, and in all his madness he was encouraged by old Scully. The Easterner was encased in reserve; the cowboy sat in wide-mouthed amazement, forgetting to eat, while Johnnie wrathily demolished great plates of food. The daughters of the house, when they were obliged to replenish the biscuits, approached as warily as Indians, and, having succeeded in their purpose, fled with ill-concealed trepidation. The Swede domineered the whole feast, and he gave it the appearance of a cruel bacchanal. He seemed to have grown suddenly taller; he gazed, brutally disdainful, into every face. His voice rang through the room. Once when he jabbed out harpoon-fashion with his fork to pinion a biscuit, the weapon nearly impaled the hand of the Easterner, which had been stretched quietly out for the same biscuit.

After supper, as the men filed toward the other room, the Swede smote Scully ruthlessly on the shoulder. "Well, old boy, that was a good, square meal." Johnnie looked hopefully at his father; he knew that shoulder was tender from an old fall; and, indeed, it appeared for a moment as if Scully was going to flame out over the matter, but in the end he smiled a sickly smile and remained silent. The others understood from his manner that he was admitting his responsibility for the Swede's new view-point.

Johnnie, however, addressed his parent in an aside. "Why don't you license somebody to kick you downstairs?" Scully scowled darkly by way of reply.

When they were gathered about the stove, the Swede insisted on another game of High-Five. Scully gently deprecated the plan at first, but the Swede turned a wolfish glare upon him. The old man subsided, and the Swede canvassed the others. In his tone there was always a great threat. The cowboy and the Easterner both remarked indifferently that they would play. Scully said that he would presently have to go to meet the 6.58 train, and so the Swede turned menacingly upon Johnnie. For a moment their glances crossed like blades, and then Johnnie smiled and said, "Yes, I'll play."

They formed a square, with the little board on their knees. The Easterner and the Swede were again partners. As the play went on, it was noticeable that the cowboy was not board-whacking as usual. Meanwhile, Scully, near the lamp, had put on his spectacles and, with an appearance curiously like an old priest, was reading a newspaper. In time he went out to meet the 6.58 train, and, despite his precautions, a gust of polar

wind whirled into the room as he opened the door. Besides
scattering the cards, it chilled the players to the marrow. The
Swede cursed frightfully. When Scully returned, his entrance
disturbed a cosy and friendly scene. The Swede again cursed.
But presently they were once more intent, their heads bent
forward and their hands moving swiftly. The Swede had
adopted the fashion of board-whacking.

Scully took up his paper and for a long time remained
immersed in matters which were extraordinarily remote from
him. The lamp burned badly, and once he stopped to adjust
the wick. The newspaper, as he turned from page to page,
rustled with a slow and comfortable sound. Then suddenly he
heard three terrible words: "You are cheatin'!"

Such scenes often prove that there can be little of dramatic
import in environment. Any room can present a tragic front;
any room can be comic. This little den was now hideous as a
torture-chamber. The new faces of the men themselves had
changed it upon the instant. The Swede held a huge fist in
front of Johnnie's face, while the latter looked steadily over it
into the blazing orbs of his accuser. The Easterner had grown
pallid; the cowboy's jaw had dropped in that expression of
bovine amazement which was one of his important mannerisms. After the three words, the first sound in the room was
made by Scully's paper as it floated forgotten to his feet. His
spectacles had also fallen from his nose, but by a clutch he had
saved them in air. His hand, grasping the spectacles, now remained poised awkwardly and near his shoulder. He stared
at the card-players.

Probably the silence was while a second elapsed. Then, if
the floor had been suddenly twitched out from under the men
they could not have moved quicker. The five had projected
themselves headlong toward a common point. It happened that
Johnnie, in rising to hurl himself upon the Swede, had stumbled
slightly because of his curiously instinctive care for the cards
and the board. The loss of the moment allowed time for the

arrival of Scully, and also allowed the cowboy time to give the Swede a great push which sent him staggering back. The men found tongue together, and hoarse shouts of rage, appeal, or fear burst from every throat. The cowboy pushed and jostled feverishly at the Swede, and the Easterner and Scully clung wildly to Johnnie; but through the smoky air, above the swaying bodies of the peace-compellers, the eyes of the two warriors ever sought each other in glances of challenge that were at once hot and steely.

Of course the board had been overturned, and now the whole company of cards was scattered over the floor, where the boots of the men trampled the fat and painted kings and queens as they gazed with their silly eyes at the war that was waging above them.

Scully's voice was dominating the yells. "Stop now! Stop, I say! Stop, now—"

Johnnie, as he struggled to burst through the rank formed by Scully and the Easterner, was crying, "Well, he says I cheated! He says I cheated! I won't allow no man to say I cheated! If he says I cheated, he's a —— —— !"

The cowboy was telling the Swede, "Quit, now! Quit, d'ye hear—"

The screams of the Swede never ceased: "He did cheat! I saw him! I saw him—"

As for the Easterner, he was importuning in a voice that was not heeded: "Wait a moment, can't you? Oh, wait a moment. What's the good of a fight over a game of cards? Wait a moment—"

In this tumult no complete sentences were clear. "Cheat"— "Quit"—"He says"—these fragments pierced the uproar and rang out sharply. It was remarkable that, whereas Scully undoubtedly made the most noise, he was the least heard of any of the riotous band.

Then suddenly there was a great cessation. It was as if each man had paused for breath; and although the room was still lighted with the anger of men, it could be seen that there was no danger of immediate conflict, and at once Johnnie, shouldering his way forward, almost succeeded in confronting the Swede. "What did you say I cheated for? What did you say I cheated for? I don't cheat, and I won't let no man say I do!"

The Swede said, "I saw you! I saw you!"

"Well," cried Johnnie, "I'll fight any man what says I cheat!"

"No, you won't," said the cowboy. "Not here."

"Ah, be still, can't you?" said Scully, coming between them.

The quiet was sufficient to allow the Easterner's voice to be heard. He was repeating, "Oh, wait a moment, can't you? What's the good of a fight over a game of cards? Wait a moment!"

Johnnie, his red face appearing above his father's shoulder, hailed the Swede again. "Did you say I cheated?"

The Swede showed his teeth. "Yes."

"Then," said Johnnie, "we must fight."

"Yes, fight," roared the Swede. He was like a demoniac. "Yes, fight! I'll show you what kind of a man I am! I'll show you who you want to fight! Maybe you think I can't fight! Maybe you think I can't! I'll show you, you skin, you card-sharp! Yes, you cheated! You cheated! You cheated!"

"Well, let's go at it, then, mister," said Johnnie, coolly.

The cowboy's brow was beaded with sweat from his efforts in intercepting all sorts of raids. He turned in despair to Scully. "What are you goin' to do now?"

A change had come over the Celtic visage of the old man. He now seemed all eagerness; his eyes glowed.

"We'll let them fight," he answered, stalwartly. "I can't put up with it any longer. I've stood this damned Swede till I'm sick. We'll let them fight."

VI

The men prepared to go out of doors. The Easterner was so nervous that he had great difficulty in getting his arms into the sleeves of his new leather coat. As the cowboy drew his fur cap down over his ears his hands trembled. In fact, Johnnie and old Scully were the only ones who displayed no agitation. These preliminaries were conducted without words.

Scully threw open the door. "Well, come on," he said. Instantly a terrific wind caused the flame of the lamp to struggle at its wick, while a puff of black smoke sprang from the chimney-top. The stove was in mid-current of the blast, and its voice swelled to equal the roar of the storm. Some of the scarred and bedabbled cards were caught up from the floor and dashed helplessly against the farther wall. The men lowered their heads and plunged into the tempest as into a sea.

No snow was falling, but great whirls and clouds of flakes, swept up from the ground by the frantic winds, were streaming southward with the speed of bullets. The covered land was blue with the sheen of an unearthly satin, and there was no other hue save where, at the low, black railway station—which seemed incredibly distant—one light gleamed like a tiny jewel. As the men floundered into a thigh-deep drift, it was known that the Swede was bawling out something. Scully went to him, put a hand on his shoulder, and projected an ear. "What's that you say?" he shouted.

"I say," bawled the Swede again, "I won't stand much show against this gang. I know you'll all pitch on me."

Scully smote him reproachfully on the arm. "Tut, man!" he yelled. The wind tore the words from Scully's lips and scattered them far alee.

"You are all a gang of—" boomed the Swede, but the storm also seized the remainder of this sentence.

Immediately turning their backs upon the wind, the men had swung around a corner to the sheltered side of the hotel. It was the function of the little house to preserve here, amid this great devastation of snow, an irregular V-shape of heavily encrusted grass, which crackled beneath the feet. One could imagine the great drifts piled against the windward side. When the party reached the comparative peace of this spot it was found that the Swede was still bellowing.

"Oh, I know what kind of a thing this is! I know you'll all pitch on me. I can't lick you all!"

Scully turned upon him panther-fashion. "You'll not have to whip all of us. You'll have to whip my son Johnnie. An' the man what troubles you durin' that time will have me to dale with."

The arrangements were swiftly made. The two men faced each other, obedient to the harsh commands of Scully, whose face, in the subtly luminous gloom, could be seen set in the austere impersonal lines that are pictured on the countenances of the Roman veterans. The Easterner's teeth were chattering, and he was hopping up and down like a mechanical toy. The cowboy stood rock-like.

The contestants had not stripped off any clothing. Each was in his ordinary attire. Their fists were up, and they eyed each other in a calm that had the elemnets of leonine cruelty in it.

During this pause, the Easterner's mind, like a film, took lasting impressions of three men—the iron-nerved master of the ceremony; the Swede, pale, motionless, terrible; and Johnnie, serene yet ferocious, brutish yet heroic. The entire prelude had in it a tragedy greater than the tragedy of action, and this aspect was accentuated by the long, mellow cry of the blizzard, as it sped the tumbling and wailing flakes into the black abyss of the south.

"Now!" said Scully.

The two combatants leaped forward and crashed together like bullocks. There was heard the cushioned sound of blows, and of a curse squeezing out from between the tight teeth of one.

As for the spectators, the Easterner's pent-up breath exploded from him with a pop of relief, absolute relief from the tension of the preliminaries. The cowboy bounded into the air with a yowl. Scully was immovable as from supreme amazement and fear at the fury of the fight which he himself had permitted and arranged.

For a time the encounter in the darkness was such a perplexity of flying arms that it presented no more detail than
would a swiftly revolving wheel. Occasionally a face, as if
illumined by a flash of light, would shine out, ghastly and
marked with pink spots. A moment later, the men might have
been known as shadows, if it were not for the involuntary
utterance of oaths that came from them in whispers.

Suddenly a holocaust of warlike desire caught the cowboy,
and he bolted forward with the speed of a broncho. "Go it,
Johnnie! go it! Kill him! Kill him!"

Scully confronted him. "Kape back," he said; and by his
glance the cowboy could tell that this man was Johnnie's
father.

To the Easterner there was a monotony of unchangeable
fighting that was an abomination. This confused mingling was
eternal to his sense, which was concentrated in a longing for
the end, the priceless end. Once the fighters lurched near him,
and as he scrambled hastily backward he heard them breathe
like men on the rack.

"Kill him, Johnnie! Kill him! Kill him! Kill him!" The cowboy's face was contorted like one of those agony masks in
museums.

"Keep still," said Scully, icily.

Then there was a sudden loud grunt, incomplete, cut short,
and Johnnie's body swung away from the Swede and fell with
sickening heaviness to the grass. The cowboy was barely in
time to prevent the mad Swede from flinging himself upon
his prone adversary. "No, you don't," said the cowboy, inter-
posing an arm. "Wait a second."

Scully was at his son's side. "Johnnie! Johnnie, me boy!" His
voice had a quality of melancholy tenderness. "Johnnie! Can
you go on with it?" He looked anxiously down into the bloody,
pulpy face of his son.

There was a moment of silence, and then Johnnie answered
in his ordinary voice, "Yes, I—it—yes."

Assisted by his father he struggled to his feet. "Wait a bit now till you git your wind," said the old man.

A few paces away the cowboy was lecturing the Swede. "No, you don't! Wait a second!"

The Easterner was plucking at Scully's sleeve. "Oh, this is enough," he pleaded. "This is enough! Let it go as it stands. This is enough!"

"Bill," said Scully, "git out of the road." The cowboy stepped aside. "Now." The combatants were actuated by a new caution as they advanced toward collision. They glared at each other, and then the Swede aimed a lightning blow that carried with it his entire weight. Johnnie was evidently half stupid from weakness, but he miraculously dodged, and his fist sent the overbalanced Swede sprawling.

The cowboy, Scully, and the Easterner burst into a cheer that was like a chorus of triumphant soldiery, but before its conclusion the Swede had scuffled agilely to his feet and come in berserk abandon at his foe. There was another perplexity of flying arms, and Johnnie's body again swung away and fell, even as a bundle might fall from a roof. The Swede instantly staggered to a little wind-waved tree and leaned upon it, breathing like an engine, while his savage and flame-lit eyes roamed from face to face as the men bent over Johnnie. There was a splendour of isolation in his situation at this time which the Easterner felt once when, lifting his eyes from the man on the ground, he beheld that mysterious and lonely figure, waiting.

"Are you any good yet, Johnnie?" asked Scully in a broken voice.

The son gasped and opened his eyes languidly. After a moment he answered, "No—I ain't—any good—any—more." Then, from shame and bodily ill, he began to weep, the tears furrowing down through the blood-stains on his face. "He was too—too—too heavy for me."

Scully straightened and addressed the waiting figure.

"Stranger," he said, evenly, "it's all up with our side." Then his voice changed into that vibrant huskiness which is commonly the tone of the most simple and deadly announcements. "Johnnie is whipped."

Without replying, the victor moved off on the route to the front door of the hotel.

The cowboy was formulating new and unspellable blasphemies. The Easterner was startled to find that they were out in a wind that seemed to come direct from the shadowed arctic floes. He heard again the wail of the snow as it was flung to its grave in the south. He knew now that all this time the cold had been sinking into him deeper and deeper, and he wondered that he had not perished. He felt indifferent to the condition of the vanquished man.

"Johnnie, can you walk?" asked Scully.

"Did I hurt—hurt him any?" asked the son.

"Can you walk, boy? Can you walk?"

Johnnie's voice was suddenly strong. There was a robust impatience in it. "I asked you whether I hurt him any!"

"Yes, yes, Johnnie," answered the cowboy, consolingly; "he's hurt a good deal."

They raised him from the ground, and as soon as he was on his feet he went tottering off, rebuffing all attempts at assistance. When the party rounded the corner they were fairly blinded by the pelting of the snow. It burned their faces like fire. The cowboy carried Johnnie through the drift to the door. As they entered, some cards again rose from the floor and beat against the wall.

The Easterner rushed to the stove. He was so profoundly chilled that he almost dared to embrace the glowing iron. The Swede was not in the room. Johnnie sank into a chair and, folding his arms on his knees, buried his face in them. Scully, warming one foot and then the other at a rim of the stove, muttered to himself with Celtic mournfulness. The cowboy had removed his fur cap, and with a dazed and rueful air he was running one hand through his tousled locks. From overhead they could hear the creaking of boards, as the Swede tramped here and there in his room.

The sad quiet was broken by the sudden flinging open of a door that led toward the kitchen. It was instantly followed by an inrush of women. They precipitated themselves upon Johnnie amid a chorus of lamentation. Before they carried their prey off to the kitchen, there to be bathed and harangued with that mixture of sympathy and abuse which is a feat of their sex, the mother straightened herself and fixed old Scully with an eye of stern reproach. "Shame be upon you, Patrick Scully!" she cried. "Your own son, too. Shame be upon you!"

"There, now! Be quiet, now!" said the old man, weakly.

"Shame be upon you, Patrick Scully!" The girls, rallying to this slogan, sniffed disdainfully in the direction of those trembling accomplices, the cowboy and the Easterner. Presently they bore Johnnie away, and left the three men to dismal reflection.

VII

"I'd like to fight this here Dutchman myself," said the cowboy, breaking a long silence.

Scully wagged his head sadly. "No, that wouldn't do. It wouldn't be right. It wouldn't be right."

"Well, why wouldn't it?" argued the cowboy. "I don't see no harm in it."

"No," answered Scully, with mournful heroism. "It wouldn't be right. It was Johnnie's fight, and now we mustn't whip the man just because he whipped Johnnie."

"Yes, that's true enough," said the cowboy; "but—he better not get fresh with me, because I couldn't stand no more of it."

"You'll not say a word to him," commanded Scully, and even then they heard the tread of the Swede on the stairs. His entrance was made theatric. He swept the door back with a bang and swaggered to the middle of the room. No one looked at him. "Well," he cried, insolently, at Scully, "I s'pose you'll tell me now how much I owe you?"

The old man remained stolid. "You don't owe me nothin'."

"Huh!" said the Swede, "huh! Don't owe 'im nothin'."

The cowboy addressed the Swede. "Stranger, I don't see how you come to be so gay around here."

Old Scully was instantly alert. "Stop!" he shouted, holding his hand forth, fingers upward. "Bill, you shut up!"

The cowboy spat carelessly into the sawdust-box. "I didn't say a word, did I?" he asked.

"Mr. Scully," called the Swede, "how much do I owe you?" It was seen that he was attired for departure, and that he had his valise in his hand.

"You don't owe me nothin'," repeated Scully in the same imperturbable way.

"Huh!" said the Swede. "I guess you're right. I guess if it was any way at all, you'd owe me somethin'. That's what I guess." He turned to the cowboy. " 'Kill him! Kill him! Kill him!' " he mimicked, and then guffawed victoriously. " 'Kill him!' " He was convulsed with ironical humour.

But he might have been jeering the dead. The three men were immovable and silent, staring with glassy eyes at the stove.

The Swede opened the door and passed into the storm, giving one derisive glance backward at the still group.

As soon as the door was closed, Scully and the cowboy leaped to their feet and began to curse. They trampled to and fro, waving their arms and smashing into the air with their fists. "Oh, but that was a hard minute!" wailed Scully. "That was a hard minute! Him there leerin' and scoffin'! One bang at his nose was worth forty dollars to me that minute! How did you stand it, Bill?"

"How did I stand it?" cried the cowboy in a quivering voice. "How did I stand it? Oh!"

The old man burst into sudden brogue. "I'd loike to take that Swade," he wailed, "and hould 'im down on a shtone flure and bate 'im to a jelly wid a shtick!"

The cowboy groaned in sympathy. "I'd like to git him by the

neck and ha-ammer him"—he brought his hand down on a chair with a noise like a pistol-shot—"hammer that there Dutchman until he couldn't tell himself from a dead coyote!"

"I'd bate 'im until he—"

"I'd show *him* some things—"

And then together they raised a yearning, fanatic cry—"Oho-oh! if we only could—"

"Yes!"

"Yes!"

"And then I'd—"

"O-o-oh!"

VIII

The Swede, tightly gripping his valise, tacked across the face of the storm as if he carried sails. He was following a line of little naked, grasping trees which, he knew, must mark the way of the road. His face, fresh from the pounding of Johnnie's fists, felt more pleasure than pain in the wind and the driving snow. A number of square shapes loomed upon him finally, and he knew them as the houses of the main body of the town. He found a street and made travel along it, leaning heavily upon the wind whenever, at a corner, a terrific blast caught him.

He might have been in a deserted village. We picture the world as thick with conquering and elate humanity, but here, with the bugles of the tempest pealing, it was hard to imagine a peopled earth. One viewed the existence of man then as a marvel, and conceded a glamour of wonder to these lice which were caused to cling to a whirling, fire-smitten, ice-locked, disease-stricken, space-lost bulb. The conceit of man was explained by this storm to be the very engine of life. One was a coxcomb not to die in it. However, the Swede found a saloon.

In front of it an indomitable red light was burning, and the snowflakes were made blood-colour as they flew through the circumscribed territory of the lamp's shining. The Swede pushed open the door of the saloon and entered. A sanded expanse was before him, and at the end of it four men sat about a table drinking. Down one side of the room extended a radiant bar, and its guardian was leaning upon his elbows listening to the talk of the men at the table. The Swede dropped his valise upon the floor and, smiling fraternally upon the bar-keeper, said, "Gimme some whisky, will you?" The man placed a bottle, a whisky-glass, and a glass of ice-thick water upon the bar. The Swede poured himself an abnormal portion of whisky and drank it in three gulps. "Pretty bad night," remarked the bartender, indifferently. He was making the pretension of blindness which is usually a distinction of his class; but it could have been seen that he was furtively studying the half-erased blood-stains on the face of the Swede. "Bad night," he said again.

"Oh, it's good enough for me," replied the Swede, hardily, as he poured himself some more whisky. The barkeeper took his coin and manœuvred it through its reception by the highly nickelled cash-machine. A bell rang; a card labelled "20 cts." had appeared.

"No," continued the Swede, "this isn't too bad weather. It's good enough for me."

"So?" murmured the barkeeper, languidly.

The copious drams made the Swede's eyes swim, and he breathed a trifle heavier. "Yes, I like this weather. I like it. It suits me." It was apparently his design to impart a deep significance to these words.

"So?" murmured the bartender again. He turned to gaze dreamily at the scroll-like birds and bird-like scrolls which had been drawn with soap upon the mirrors in back of the bar.

"Well, I guess I'll take another drink," said the Swede, presently. "Have something?"

"No, thanks; I'm not drinkin'," answered the bartender. Afterward he asked, "How did you hurt your face?"

The Swede immediately began to boast loudly. "Why, in a fight. I thumped the soul out of a man down here at Scully's hotel."

The interest of the four men at the table was at last aroused. "Who was it?" said one.

"Johnnie Scully," blustered the Swede. "Son of the man what runs it. He will be pretty near dead for some weeks, I can tell you. I made a nice thing of him, I did. He couldn't get up. They carried him in the house. Have a drink?"

Instantly the men in some subtle way encased themselves in reserve. "No, thanks," said one. The group was of curious formation. Two were prominent local business men; one was the district attorney; and one was a professional gambler of the kind known as "square." But a scrutiny of the group would not have enabled an observer to pick the gambler from the men of more reputable pursuits. He was, in fact, a man so delicate in manner, when among people of fair class, and so judicious in his choice of victims, that in the strictly masculine part of the town's life he had come to be explicitly trusted and admired. People called him a thoroughbred. The fear and contempt with which his craft was regarded were undoubtedly the reason why his quiet dignity shone conspicuous above the quiet dignity of men who might be merely hatters, billiard-markers, or grocery clerks. Beyond an occasional unwary traveller who came by rail, this gambler was supposed to prey solely upon reckless and senile farmers, who, when flush with good crops, drove into town in all the pride and confidence of an absolutely invulnerable stupidity. Hearing at times in circuitous fashion of the despoilment of such a farmer, the important men of Romper invariably laughed in contempt of the victim, and if they thought of the wolf at all, it was with a kind of pride at the knowledge that he would never dare think of attacking their wisdom and courage. Besides, it was popular that this gambler had a real wife and two real children in a neat cottage in a suburb, where he led an exemplary home life; and when any one even suggested a discrepancy in his character, the crowd immediately vociferated descriptions of this virtuous family circle. Then men who led exemplary home lives, and men who did not lead exemplary home lives, all subsided in a bunch, remarking that there was nothing more to be said.

However, when a restriction was placed upon him—as, for instance, when a strong clique of members of the new Pollywog Club refused to permit him, even as a spectator, to appear in the rooms of the organization—the candour and gentleness with which he accepted the judgment disarmed many of his foes and made his friends more desperately partisan. He invariably distinguished between himself and a respectable Romper man so quickly and frankly that his manner actually appeared to be a continual broadcast compliment.

And one must not forget to declare the fundamental fact of his entire position in Romper. It is irrefutable that in all affairs outside his business, in all matters that occur eternally and commonly between man and man, this thieving card-player was so generous, so just, so moral, that, in a contest, he could have put to flight the consciences of nine tenths of the citizens of Romper.

And so it happened that he was seated in this saloon with the two prominent local merchants and the district attorney.

The Swede continued to drink raw whisky, meanwhile babbling at the barkeeper and trying to induce him to indulge in potations. "Come on. Have a drink. Come on. What—no? Well, have a little one, then. By gawd, I've whipped a man to-night, and I want to celebrate. I whipped him good, too. Gentlemen," the Swede cried to the men at the table, "have a drink?"

"Ssh!" said the barkeeper.

The group at the table, although furtively attentive, had been pretending to be deep in talk, but now a man lifted his eyes toward the Swede and said, shortly, "Thanks. We don't want any more."

At this reply the Swede ruffled out his chest like a rooster. "Well," he exploded, "it seems I can't get anybody to drink with me in this town. Seems so, don't it? Well!"

"Ssh!" said the barkeeper.

"Say," snarled the Swede, "don't you try to shut me up. I won't have it. I'm a gentleman, and I want people to drink with me. And I want 'em to drink with me now. *Now*—do you understand?" He rapped the bar with his knuckles.

Years of experience had calloused the bartender. He merely grew sulky. "I hear you," he answered.

"Well," cried the Swede, "listen hard then. See those men over there? Well, they're going to drink with me, and don't you forget it. Now you watch."

"Hi!" yelled the barkeeper, "this won't do!"

"Why won't it?" demanded the Swede. He stalked over to the table, and by chance laid his hand upon the shoulder of the gambler. "How about this?" he asked wrathfully. "I asked you to drink with me."

The gambler simply twisted his head and spoke over his shoulder. "My friend, I don't know you."

"Oh, hell!" answered the Swede, "come and have a drink."

"Now, my boy," advised the gambler, kindly, "take your hand off my shoulder and go 'way and mind your own business." He was a little, slim man, and it seemed strange to hear him use this tone of heroic patronage to the burly Swede. The other men at the table said nothing.

"What! You won't drink with me, you little dude? I'll make you, then! I'll make you!" The Swede had grasped the gambler frenziedly at the throat, and was dragging him from his chair. The other men sprang up. The barkeeper dashed around the corner of his bar. There was a great tumult, and then was seen a long blade in the hand of the gambler. It shot forward, and a human body, this citadel of virtue, wisdom, power, was pierced as easily as if it had been a melon. The Swede fell with a cry of supreme astonishment.

The prominent merchants and the district attorney must have at once tumbled out of the place backward. The bartender found himself hanging limply to the arm of a chair and gazing into the eyes of a murderer.

"Henry," said the latter, as he wiped his knife on one of

the towels that hung beneath the bar rail, "you tell 'em where to find me. I'll be home, waiting for 'em." Then he vanished. A moment afterward the barkeeper was in the street dinning through the storm for help and, moreover, companionship.

The corpse of the Swede, alone in the saloon, had its eyes fixed upon a dreadful legend that dwelt atop of the cash-machine: "This registers the amount of your purchase."

IX

Months later, the cowboy was frying pork over the stove of a little ranch near the Dakota line, when there was a quick thud of hoofs outside, and presently the Easterner entered with the letters and the papers.

"Well," said the Easterner at once, "the chap that killed the Swede has got three years. Wasn't much, was it?"

"He has? Three years?" The cowboy poised his pan of pork, while he ruminated upon the news. "Three years. That ain't much."

"No. It was a light sentence," replied the Easterner as he unbuckled his spurs. "Seems there was a good deal of sympathy for him in Romper."

"If the bartender had been any good," observed the cowboy, thoughtfully, "he would have gone in and cracked that there Dutchman on the head with a bottle in the beginnin' of it and stopped all this here murderin'."

"Yes, a thousand things might have happened," said the Easterner, tartly.

The cowboy returned his pan of pork to the fire, but his philosophy continued. "It's funny, ain't it? If he hadn't said Johnnie was cheatin' he'd be alive this minute. He was an awful fool. Game played for fun, too. Not for money. I believe he was crazy."

"I feel sorry for that gambler," said the Easterner.

"Oh, so do I," said the cowboy. "He don't deserve none of it for killin' who he did."

"The Swede might not have been killed if everything had been square."

"Might not have been killed?" exclaimed the cowboy. "Everythin' square? Why, when he said that Johnnie was cheatin' and acted like such a jackass? And then in the saloon he fairly walked up to git hurt?" With these arguments the cowboy browbeat the Easterner and reduced him to rage.

"You're a fool!" cried the Easterner, viciously. "You're a bigger jackass than the Swede by a million majority. Now let me tell you one thing. Let me tell you something. Listen! Johnnie *was* cheating!"

"'Johnnie,'" said the cowboy, blankly. There was a minute of silence, and then he said, robustly, "Why, no. The game was only for fun."

"Fun or not," said the Easterner, "Johnnie was cheating. I saw him. I know it. I saw him. And I refused to stand up and be a man. I let the Swede fight it out alone. And you—you were simply puffing around the place and wanting to fight. And then old Scully himself! We are all in it! This poor gambler isn't even a noun. He is kind of an adverb. Every sin is the result of a collaboration. We, five of us, have collaborated in the murder of this Swede. Usually there are from a dozen to forty women really involved in every murder, but in this case it seems to be only five men—you, I, Johnnie, old Scully; and that fool of an unfortunate gambler came merely as a culmination, the apex of a human movement, and gets all the punishment."

The cowboy, injured and rebellious, cried out blindly into this fog of mysterious theory: "Well, I didn't do anythin', did I?"

PART V

Whilomville Stories

INTRODUCTION

Whilomville—where Crane lived *for a while*—is chiefly Port Jervis, New York, where he spent three years of his boyhood (1879–82). The stories have their composite setting not only in Port Jervis but in the various New Jersey towns where the Cranes lived—Bloomington, Patterson, Jersey City, and subsequently Asbury Park, where Stephen attended school (1882–8). It is any boy's town. And Jimmie Trescott is as much Tom Sawyer as he is Stephen Crane. He is Stephen in the haircutting incident of *An Angel Child* and in the comedy of *Lynx-Hunting*, where Jimmie shoots a cow. According to Crane's niece (*Literary Digest*, March 1926, "He himself tried to shoot a cow with a toy gun my father [William Crane] gave him." Dr. Trescott is modeled on William, who thought that the portrait flattered him, "and we and our friends and cousins helped to supply the material for them. We were an active, healthy band of savages, keen as briars, father says, out-of-doors all day, and receiving a boy's training." It was Edmund who gave the children of *Angel Child* the money for the haircuts and (to the wrath of their mother) sheared Stephen's curls away. Later (in 1894 in Albany) Crane himself encountered two small boys with long curls and black velvet suits and lace collars, tricked out by their mothers in imitation of Little Lord Fauntleroy, and he gave the pitiful victims money: "You take this money and go down to Jake's barber shop and tell him to cut your hair and do a good job of it." The mothers fainted, had hysterics, wept, and denounced him, but one of the fathers—if we can credit this legend—"averred that his son now looked like a convict, but he was secretly pleased . . . and sent Crane an anonymous box of cigars with a card inscribed: 'From a grateful public'" (*Bookman*, March 1927).

But if Crane is Jimmie Trescott, he is also the painter in

Angel Child and *The Stove*, a painter so famous that "almost everybody in the United States who knew about art and its travail knew about him." Jimmie falls in love with the Angel Child, whose name is Cora—after Crane's wife. At the tea-party in *The Stove*, "A few came to see if they could not find out the faults of the painter's wife." That echoes with personal undertones. Crane wrote the thirteen *Whilomville Stories* at Brede Place, England. Published in *Harper's* starting in August 1899, and posthumously in book form, with drawings by Peter Newell, in 1900, they were his last work. Another Whilomville story, much better than these with the one exception of *The Knife*, is *His New Mittens*. It was published in *McClure's Magazine* in November 1898, but was not collected in the Whilomville group until Volume V of the *Work* appeared in 1926. It was the first Whilomville story Crane wrote, and it was written on board the dispatch-boat *The Three Friends* during the Santiago blockade (1898). The name of the barber in *An Angel Child* was lifted from the name of one of the wounded whom Crane met in the Cuban campaign, Reuben McNab. The farmer in *Lynx-Hunting* and the hero in *The Veteran* are Henry Fleming now grown old, and Dr. Trescott is transposed from *The Monster*. *The Veteran* and *The Knife* are not stories about children; on the other hand, the baby sketches Crane did in 1893, though not Whilomville stories, belong with them—particularly *A Dark Brown Dog* and *An Ominous Baby*. They too deal with the cruelty of childhood. *An Indiana Campaign*, a Civil War incident, has the same mellow humor as some of the *Whilomville Stories* and might as well be laid in Whilomville as in a village called Wigglesville. The grotesquerie of *An Illusion in Red and White*, apparently a murder story but actually a satire on journalists, is all too violent for Whilomville, but the stonily perverse Jones children on whom the story centers behave not unlike Whilomville kids—"young Freddy's mind began to work like ketchup."

As Beer points out in *The Mauve Decade*, Mark Twain had discovered in *Huckleberry Finn* that "the personality of a child could be used to project realistic views and pictures of a society, and that trick begins to appear in the latter ' '90's, more and more." Twain established the mode, not Crane, and from him Crane probably learned also dialect and irony. It is irony that differentiates the *Whilomville Stories* from Booth Tarkington's *Penrod*. It was Mark Twain's *Roughing It* and *Life on the Mississippi* that Crane drew upon in writing the *Whilomville Stories. The Stove* is sheer Twain:

—Well, we ain't goin' to hurt your old stable, are we?—asked Jimmie, ironically.
—Dat you ain't, Jim! Not so long's I keep my two eyes right plumb squaah p'inted at ol' Jim. No, seh!—Peter began to chuckle in derision.

So too is *The Carriage Lamps*: Jimmie is a prisoner in his upstairs room, and Willie Dalzel attempts to rescue him—in emulation, as it were, of Tom Sawyer and Huck Finn. Peter Washington, the Negro, reappears again in *The Knife*—the best of the *Whilomville Stories.*

The Knife in its theme of deception harks back to *Huckleberry Finn*, where Huck learns all about social guile. Fabrication, equivocation, deceit, the mask of the lie—these equip man for society and protect him from it. To lie is to be saved. In *The Knife* Alek saves Peter, the betrayer, by lying to the white man, Bryant. This Judas is outwitted by the all-saving lie. White against black, the Negro's salvation lies in fidelity. The trap is set by the white man: "I found a knife and thought it might be yours." When Alek denies owning the knife, Bryant tries another trap: "Is he a very close friend of yourn?" At this Alek stutters, and his stuttering is emblematic of his plight. "Well, seems like he *was* er frien', an' then agin, it seems like he"— "It seems like he *wasn't?*" asked Bryant. Each equivocates, not trusting the other. Alek's only recourse is to lie: the knife belongs to Sam Jackson. Ironically, the lie is the truth, as Peter is no true friend.

Crane believed in his *Whilomville Stories* so thoroughly that he thought his best was in them, he told the editor of *Harper's Magazine*; but Crane was anything but consistent in critical opinion. Contradicting himself, he rated at one time or another some half dozen of his works as being his best and for some of these he straddled the fence. One of his inscriptions reads: "This work [*Maggie*] is a mudpuddle, I am told on the best authority. Wade in and have a swim." The answer is, it seems to me, that the Whilomville collection, sometimes charming but more often boring, is lightweight stuff. The romps and scrapes of children and the tortures their parents also suffer cannot themselves have literary interest, and their chief appeal is to readers who have experienced similar incidents in childhood and find pleasure in self-identification. To say that *Lynx-Hunting* touches "the level of *The Monster*" and that *Shame* is "a story genial, charming, and natural" sidesteps judgment with merely impressionistic opinion. To the critical point: the language is dead, the diction flat or (worse) "educated," and the point of view as well as the language badly miscalculated: the telling of these stories is directed to adults in language suitable for them but not for children. Crane was off key from the start. Furthermore, only four of the batch embody any artistic significance or attempt to embody a formed meaning: *The Knife, His New Mittens, Shame, The Fight*. The other ten stories are completely devoid of theme and design. They are a straight line with no ironic turnabout in direction, no angling downward from straight or literal progression. The others have a twist to them. But *Shame* is faulty in the suggested symbolism, and *The Fight* is not so important as a thing in itself as it is for themes of shame and flight, Johnnie Hedge being a miniature of the outcast who redeems himself—Henry Fleming in *The Red Badge of Courage*. Crane in the *Whilomville Stories* unmasks Innocence. They link thus with *The Bride Comes to Yellow Sky* and other variations on the theme: "what innocence can do if it has the opportunity." *His New Mittens* is a study of boy morals, but (as Edward Garnett remarked) "when Crane breathes an everyday, common atmosphere his æsthetic power always weakens." What saves, or almost saves, the whole thing from sheer sentimentalism is the final scene with its symbolic turnabout: "Aunt Martha turned defiantly upon the butcher, because her face betrayed her. She was crying. She made a gesture half military, half feminine. 'Won't you have a glass of our root-beer, Mr. Stickney. *We made it ourselves.*'" Our plight is what we ourselves brew. It is the same in *George's Mother*, whereas *Maggie* represents an inversion of this theme. Which theme did Crane believe in?

THE KNIFE

I

Si Bryant's place was on the shore of the lake, and his garden patch, shielded from the north by a bold little promontory
and a higher ridge inland, was accounted the most successful
and surprising in all Whilomville township. One afternoon Si
was working in the garden patch, when Doctor Trescott's man,
Peter Washington, came trudging slowly along the road, observing nature. He scanned the white man's fine agricultural
results. "Take your eye off them there mellons, you rascal," said
Si, placidly.

The negro's face widened in a grin of delight. "Well, Mist'
Bryant, I raikon I ain't on'y make m'se'f covertous er-lookin' at
dem yere mellums, sure 'nough. Dey suhtainly is grand."

"That's all right," responded Si, with affected bitterness of
spirit. "That's all right. Just don't you admire 'em too much,
that's all."

Peter chuckled and chuckled. "Ma Lode! Mist' Bryant, y-y-
you don' think I'm gwine come prowlin' in dish yer gawden?"

"No, I know you hain't," said Si, with solemnity. "B'cause,
if you did, I'd shoot you so full of holes you couldn't tell yourself from a sponge."

"Um—no, seh! No, seh! I don' raikon you'll get chance at
Pete, Mist' Bryant. No, seh. I'll take an' run 'long an' rob er
bank 'fore I'll come foolishin' 'round *your* gawden, Mist' Bryant."

Bryant, gnarled and strong as an old tree, leaned on his hoe
and laughed a Yankee laugh. His mouth remained tightly
closed, but the sinister lines which ran from the sides of his
nose to the meetings of his lips developed to form a comic oval,
and he emitted a series of grunts, while his eyes gleamed mer-

rily and his shoulders shook. Pete, on the contrary, threw back his head and guffawed thunderously. The effete joke in regard to an American negro's fondness for watermelons was still an admirable pleasantry to them, and this was not the first time they had engaged in badinage over it. In fact, this venerable survival had formed between them a friendship of casual roadside quality.

Afterward Peter went on up the road. He continued to chuckle until he was far away. He was going to pay a visit to old Alek Williams, a negro who lived with a large family in a hut clinging to the side of a mountain. The scattered colony of negroes which hovered near Whilomville was of interesting origin, being the result of some contrabands who had drifted as far north as Whilomville during the great civil war. The descendants of these adventurers were mainly conspicuous for their bewildering number and the facility which they possessed for adding even to this number. Speaking, for example, of the Jacksons—one couldn't hurl a stone into the hills about Whilomville without having it land on the roof of a hut full of Jacksons. The town reaped little in labour from these curious suburbs. There were a few men who came in regularly to work in gardens, to drive teams, to care for horses, and there were a few women who came in to cook or to wash. These latter had usually drunken husbands. In the main the colony loafed in high spirits, and the industrious minority gained no direct honour from their fellows, unless they spent their earnings on raiment, in which case they were naturally treated with distinction. On the whole, the hardships of these people were the wind, the rain, the snow, and any other physical difficulties which they could cultivate. About twice a year the lady philanthropists of Whilomville went up against them, and came away poorer in goods but rich in complacence. After one of these attacks the colony would preserve a comic air of rectitude for two days, and then relapse again to the genial irresponsibility of a crew of monkeys.

Peter Washington was one of the industrious class who occupied a position of distinction, for he surely spent his money on personal decoration. On occasion he would dress better than the Mayor of Whilomville himself, or at least in more colours, which was the main thing to the minds of his admirers. His ideal had been the late gallant Henry Johnson, whose conquests in Watermelon Alley, as well as in the hill shanties, had proved him the equal if not the superior of any Pullman car porter in the country. Perhaps Peter had too much Virginia laziness and humour in him to be a wholly adequate successor to the fastidious Henry Johnson, but, at any rate, he admired his memory so attentively as to be openly termed a dude by envious people.

On this afternoon he was going to call on old Alek Williams because Alek's eldest girl was just turned seventeen and, to Peter's mind, was a triumph of beauty. He was not wearing his best clothes, because on his last visit Alek's half-breed hound Susie had taken occasion to forcefully extract a quite large and valuable part of the visitor's trousers. When Peter arrived at the end of the rocky field which contained old Alek's shanty he stooped and provided himself with several large stones, weighing them carefully in his hand, and finally continuing his journey with three stones of about eight ounces each. When he was near the house, three gaunt hounds, Rover and Carlo and Susie, came sweeping down upon him. His impression was that they were going to climb him as if he were a tree, but at the critical moment they swerved and went growling and snapping around him, their heads low, their eyes malignant. The afternoon caller waited until Susie presented her side to him; then he heaved one of his eight-ounce rocks. When it landed, her hollow ribs gave forth a drum-like sound, and she was knocked sprawling, her legs in the air. The other hounds at once fled in horror, and she followed as soon as she was able, yelping at the top of her lungs. The afternoon caller resumed his march.

At the wild expressions of Susie's anguish old Alek had flung open the door and come hastily into the sunshine. "Yah, you

Suse, come erlong outa dat now. What fer you— Oh, how do, how do, Mist' Wash'ton—how do?"

"How do, Mist' Willums? I done foun' it necessa'y fer ter damnearkill dish yer dawg a' yourn, Mist' Willums."

"Come in, come in, Mist' Wash'ton. Dawg no'count, Mist' Wash'ton." Then he turned to address the unfortunate animal. "Hu't, did it? Hu't? 'Pears like you gwine lun some saince by time somebody brek yer back. 'Pears like I gwine club yer inter er frazzle 'fore you fin' out some saince. G'w'on 'way f'm yah!"

As the old man and his guest entered the shanty a body of black children spread out in crescent-shape formation and observed Peter with awe. Fat old Mrs. Williams greeted him turbulently, while the eldest girl, Mollie, lurked in a corner and giggled with finished imbecility, gazing at the visitor with eyes that were shy and bold by turns. She seemed at times absurdly over-confident, at times foolishly afraid; but her giggle consistently endured. It was a giggle on which an irascible but right-minded judge would have ordered her forthwith to be buried alive.

Amid a great deal of hospitable gabbling, Peter was conducted to the best chair out of the three that the house contained. Enthroned therein, he made himself charming in talk to the old people, who beamed upon him joyously. As for Mollie, he affected to be unaware of her existence. This may have been a method for entrapping the sentimental interest of that young gazelle, or it may be that the giggle had worked upon him.

He was absolutely fascinating to the old people. They could talk like rotary snow-ploughs, and he gave them every chance, while his face was illumined with appreciation. They pressed him to stay for supper, and he consented, after a glance at the pot on the stove which was too furtive to be noted.

During the meal old Alek recounted the high state of Judge Hagenthorpe's kitchen garden, which Alek said was due to his unremitting industry and fine intelligence. Alek was a gardener, whenever impending starvation forced him to cease temporarily from being a lily of the field.

"Mist' Bryant he suhtainly got er grand gawden," observed Peter.

"Dat so, dat so, Mist' Wash'ton," assented Alek. "He got fine gawden."

"Seems like I nev' *did* see sech mellums, big as er bar'l, layin' dere. I don't raikon an'body in dish yer county kin hol' it with Mist' Bryant when comes ter mellums."

"Dat so, Mist' Wash'ton."

They did not talk of watermelons until their heads held nothing else, as the phrase goes. But they talked of watermelons until, when Peter started for home that night over a lonely road, they held a certain dominant position in his mind. Alek had come with him as far as the fence, in order to protect him from possible attack by the mongrels. There they had cheerfully parted, two honest men.

The night was dark, and heavy with moisture. Peter found it uncomfortable to walk rapidly. He merely loitered on the road. When opposite Si Bryant's place he paused and looked over the fence into the garden. He imagined he could see the form of a huge melon lying in dim stateliness not ten yards away. He looked at the Bryant house. Two windows, downstairs, were lighted. The Bryants kept no dog, old Si's favourite child having once been bitten by a dog, and having since died, within that year, of pneumonia.

Peering over the fence, Peter fancied that if any low-minded night prowler should happen to note the melon, he would not find it difficult to possess himself of it. This person would merely wait until the lights were out in the house, and the people presumably asleep. Then he would climb the fence, reach the melon in a few strides, sever the stem with his ready knife, and in a trice be back in the road with his prize. There need be no noise, and, after all, the house was some distance.

Selecting a smooth bit of turf, Peter took a seat by the roadside. From time to time he glanced at the lighted window.

II

When Peter and Alek had said good-bye, the old man turned back in the rocky field and shaped a slow course toward that high dim light which marked the little window of his shanty. It would be incorrect to say that Alek could think of nothing but watermelons. But it was true that Si Bryant's watermelon patch occupied a certain conspicuous position in his thoughts.

He sighed; he almost wished that he was again a conscienceless pickaninny, instead of being one of the most ornate, solemn, and look-at-me-sinner deacons that ever graced the handle of a collection basket. At this time it made him quite sad to reflect upon his granite integrity. A weaker man might perhaps bow his moral head to the temptation, but for him such a fall was impossible. He was a prince of the church, and if he had been nine princes of the church he could not have been more proud. In fact, religion was to the old man a sort of personal dignity. And he was on Sundays so obtrusively good that you could see his sanctity through a door. He forced it on you until you would have felt its influence even in a forecastle.

It was clear in his mind that he must put watermelon thoughts from him, and after a moment he told himself, with much ostentation, that he had done so. But it was cooler under the sky than in the shanty, and as he was not sleepy, he decided to take a stroll down to Si Bryant's place and look at the melons from a pinnacle of spotless innocence. Reaching the road, he paused to listen. It would not do to let Peter hear him, because that graceless rapscallion would probably misunderstand him. But, assuring himself that Peter was well on his way, he set out, walking briskly until he was within four hundred yards of Bryant's place. Here he went to the side of the road, and walked thereafter on the damp, yielding turf. He made no sound.

He did not go on to that point in the main road which was directly opposite the watermelon patch. He did not wish to have his ascetic contemplation disturbed by some chance wayfarer. He turned off along a short lane which led to Si Bryant's barn. Here he reached a place where he could see, over the fence, the faint shapes of the melons.

Alek was affected. The house was some distance away, there was no dog, and doubtless the Bryants would soon extinguish their lights and go to bed. Then some poor lost lamb of sin might come and scale the fence, reach a melon in a moment, sever the stem with his ready knife, and in a trice be back in the road with his prize. And this poor lost lamb of sin might even be a bishop, but no one would ever know it. Alek singled out with his eye a very large melon, and thought that the lamb would prove his judgment if he took that one.

He found a soft place in the grass, and arranged himself comfortably. He watched the lights in the windows.

III

It seemed to Peter Washington that the Bryants absolutely consulted their own wishes in regard to the time for retiring; but at last he saw the lighted windows fade briskly from left to right, and after a moment a window on the second floor blazed out against the darkness. Si was going to bed. In five minutes this window abruptly vanished, and all the world was night.

Peter spent the ensuing quarter-hour in no mental debate. His mind was fixed. He was here, and the melon was there. He would have it. But an idea of being caught appalled him. He thought of his position. He was the beau of his community, honoured right and left. He pictured the consternation of his friends and the cheers of his enemies if the hands of the redoubtable Si Bryant should grip him in his shame.

He arose and, going to the fence, listened. No sound broke the stillness, save the rhythmical incessant clicking of myriad insects and the guttural chanting of the frogs in the reeds at the lake-side. Moved by sudden decision, he climbed the fence and crept silently and swiftly down upon the melon. His open knife was in his hand. There was the melon, cool, fair to see, as pompous in its fatness as the cook in a monastery.

Peter put out a hand to steady it while he cut the stem. But at the instant he was aware that a black form had dropped over the fence lining the lane in front of him and was coming stealthily toward him. In a palsy of terror he dropped flat upon the ground, not having strength enough to run away. The next moment he was looking into the amazed and agonized face of old Alek Williams.

There was a moment of loaded silence, and then Peter was overcome by a mad inspiration. He suddenly dropped his knife and leaped upon Alek. "I got che!" he hissed. "I got che! I got che!" The old man sank down as limp as rags. "I got che! I got che! Steal Mist' Bryant's mellums, hey?"

Alek, in a low voice, began to beg. "Oh, Mist' Peter Wash'-ton, don' go fer ter be too ha'd on er ole man! I nev' come yere fer ter steal 'em. 'Deed I didn't, Mist' Wash'ton! I come yere jes' fer ter *feel* 'em. Oh, please, Mist' Wash'ton—"

"Come erlong outa yere, you ol' rip," said Peter, "an' don' trumple on dese yer baids. I gwine put you w'ah you won' ketch col'."

Without difficulty he tumbled the whining Alek over the fence to the roadway and followed him with sheriff-like expedition. He took him by the scruff. "Come erlong, deacon. I raikon I gwine put you w'ah you kin pray, deacon. Come erlong, deacon."

The emphasis and reiteration of his layman's title in the church produced a deadly effect upon Alek. He felt to his marrow the heinous crime into which this treacherous night had betrayed him. As Peter marched his prisoner up the road toward the mouth of the lane, he continued his remarks: "Come erlong, deacon. Nev' see er man so anxious-like erbout er mellum-paitch, deacon. Seem like you jes' must see 'em er-growin' an' *feel* 'em, deacon. Mist' Bryant he'll be s'prised, deacon, findin' out you come fer ter *feel* his mellums. Come erlong, deacon. Mist' Bryant he expectin' some ole rip like you come soon."

They had almost reached the lane when Alek's cur Susie, who

had followed her master, approached in the silence which attends dangerous dogs; and seeing indications of what she took to be war, she appended herself swiftly but firmly to the calf of Peter's left leg. The mêlée was short, but spirited. Alek had no wish to have his dog complicate his already serious misfortunes, and went manfully to the defence of his captor. He procured a large stone, and by beating this with both hands down upon the resounding skull of the animal, he induced her to quit her grip. Breathing heavily, Peter dropped into the long grass at the roadside. He said nothing.

"Mist' Wash'ton," said Alek at last, in a quavering voice, "I raikon I gwine wait yere see what you gwine do ter me."

Whereupon Peter passed into a spasmodic state, in which he rolled to and fro and shook.

"Mist' Wash'ton, I hope dish yer dog ain't gone an' give you fitses?"

Peter sat up suddenly. "No, she ain't," he answered; "but she gin me er big skeer; an' fer yer 'sistance with er cobblestone, Mist' Willums, I tell you what I gwine do—I tell you what I gwine do." He waited an impressive moment. "I gwine 'lease you!"

Old Alek trembled like a little bush in a wind. "Mist' Wash'ton?"

Quoth Peter, deliberately, "I gwine 'lease you."

The old man was filled with a desire to negotiate this statement at once, but he felt the necessity of carrying off the event without an appearance of haste. "Yes, seh; thank 'e, seh; thank 'e, Mist' Wash'ton. I raikon I ramble home pressenly."

He waited an interval, and then dubiously said, "Good-evenin', Mist' Wash'ton."

"Good-evenin', deacon. Don' come foolin' roun' *feelin'* no mellums, and I say troof. Good-evenin', deacon."

Alek took off his hat and made three profound bows. "Thank 'e, seh. Thank 'e, seh. Thank 'e, seh."

Peter underwent another severe spasm, but the old man walked off toward his home with a humble and contrite heart.

IV

The next morning Alek proceeded from his shanty under the complete but customary illusion that he was going to work. He trudged manfully along until he reached the vicinity of Si Bryant's place. Then, by stages, he relapsed into a slink. He was passing the garden patch under full steam when, at some distance ahead of him, he saw Si Bryant leaning casually on the garden fence.

"Good-mornin', Alek."

"Good-mawnin', Mist' Bryant," answered Alek, with a new deference. He was marching on, when he was halted by a word—"Alek!"

He stopped. "Yes, seh."

"I found a knife this mornin' in th' road," drawled Si, "an' I thought maybe it was yourn."

Improved in mind by this divergence from the direct line of attack, Alek stepped up easily to look at the knife. "No, seh," he said, scanning it as it lay in Si's palm, while the cold steel-blue eyes of the white man looked down into his stomach, "'tain't no knife er mine." But he knew the knife. He knew it as if it had been his mother. And at the same moment a spark flashed through his head and made wise his understanding. He knew everything. "'Tain't much of er knife, Mist' Bryant," he said, deprecatingly.

"'Tain't much of a knife, I know that," cried Si, in sudden heat, "but I found it this mornin' in my watermelon patch—hear?"

"Watahmellum paitch?" yelled Alek, not astounded.

"Yes, in my watermelon patch," sneered Si, "an' I think you know something about it, too!"

"Me?" cried Alek. "Me?"

"Yes—you!" said Si, with icy ferocity. "Yes—you!" He had become convinced that Alek was not in any way guilty, but he was certain that the old man knew the owner of the knife, and so he pressed him at first on criminal lines. "Alek, you might as well own up now. You've been meddlin' with my water-melons!"

"Me?" cried Alek again. "Yah's *ma* knife. I done cah'e it foh yeahs."

Bryant changed his ways. "Look here, Alek," he said, con-fidentially: "I know you and you know me, and there ain't no use in any more skirmishin'. *I* know that *you* know whose knife that is. Now whose is it?"

This challenge was so formidable in character that Alek temporarily quailed and began to stammer. "Er—now—Mist' Bryant—you—you—frien' er mine—"

"I know I'm a friend of yours, but," said Bryant, inexorably, "who owns this knife?"

Alek gathered unto himself some remnants of dignity and spoke with reproach: "Mist' Bryant, dish yer knife ain' mine."

"No," said Bryant, "it ain't. But you know who it belongs to, an' I want you to tell me—quick."

"Well, Mist' Bryant," answered Alek, scratching his wool, "I won't say 's I *do* know who b'longs ter dish yer knife, an' I won't say 's I *don't*."

Bryant again laughed his Yankee laugh, but this time there was little humour in it. It was dangerous.

Alek, seeing that he had got himself into hot water by the fine diplomacy of his last sentence, immediately began to flounder and totally submerge himself. "No, Mist' Bryant," he repeated, "I won't say 's I *do* know who b'longs ter dish yer knife, an' I won't say 's I *don't*." And he began to parrot this fatal sentence again and again. It seemed wound about his tongue. He could not rid himself of it. Its very power to make trouble for him seemed to originate the mysterious Afric reason for its repetition.

"Is he a very close friend of yourn?" said Bryant, softly.

"F-frien'?" stuttered Alek. He appeared to weigh this ques-tion with much care. "Well, seems like he *was* er frien', an' then agin, it seems like he—"

"It seems like he *wasn't*?" asked Bryant.

"Yes, seh, jest so, jest so," cried Alek. "Sometimes it seems like he *wasn't*. Then again—" He stopped for profound meditation.

The patience of the white man seemed inexhaustible. At length his low and oily voice broke the stillness. "Oh, well, of course if he's a friend of yourn, Alek! You know I wouldn't want to make no trouble for a friend of yourn."

"Yes, seh," cried the negro at once. "He's er frien' er mine. He is dat."

"Well, then, it seems as if about the only thing to do is for you to tell me his name so's I can send him his knife, and that's all there is to it."

Alek took off his hat, and in perplexity ran his hand over his wool. He studied the ground. But several times he raised his eyes to take a sly peep at the imperturbable visage of the white man. "Y-y-yes, Mist' Bryant.—I raikon dat's erbout all what kin be done. I gwine tell you who b'longs ter dish yer knife."

"Of course," said the smooth Bryant, "it ain't a very nice thing to have to do, but—"

"No, seh," cried Alek, brightly; "I'm gwine tell you, Mist' Bryant. I gwine tell you erbout dat knife. Mist' Bryant," he asked, solemnly, "does you know who b'longs ter dat knife?"

"No, I—"

"Well, I gwine tell. I gwine tell who. Mist' Bryant—" The old man drew himself to a stately pose and held forth his arm. "I gwine tell who. Mist' Bryant, *dish yer knife b'longs ter Sam Jackson!*"

Bryant was startled into indignation. "Who in hell is Sam Jackson?" he growled.

"He's a nigger," said Alek, impressively, "and he wuks in er lumber-yawd up yere in Hoswego."

HIS NEW MITTENS

I

LITTLE HORACE was walking home from school, brilliantly decorated by a pair of new red mittens. A number of boys were snowballing gleefully in a field. They hailed him. "Come on, Horace! We're having a battle."

Horace was sad. "No," he said, "I can't. I've got to go home." At noon his mother had admonished him: "Now, Horace, you come straight home as soon as school is out. Do you hear? And don't you get them nice new mittens all wet, either. Do you hear?" Also his aunt had said: "I declare, Emily, it's a shame the way you allow that child to ruin his things." She had meant mittens. To his mother, Horace had dutifully replied, "Yes'm." But he now loitered in the vicinity of the group of uproarious boys, who were yelling like hawks as the white balls flew.

Some of them immediately analysed this extraordinary hesitancy. "Hah!" they paused to scoff, "afraid of your new mittens, ain't you?" Some smaller boys, who were not yet so wise in discerning motives, applauded this attack with unreasonable vehemence. "A-fray-ed of his mit-tens! A-fray-ed of his mittens." They sang these lines to cruel and monotonous music which is as old perhaps as American childhood, and which it is the privilege of the emancipated adult to completely forget. "A-fray-ed of his mit-tens!"

Horace cast a tortured glance toward his playmates and then dropped his eyes to the snow at his feet. Presently he turned to the trunk of one of the great maple trees that lined the curb. He made a pretence of closely examining the rough and virile bark. To his mind, this familiar street of Whilomville seemed to grow dark in the thick shadow of shame. The trees and the houses were now palled in purple.

"A-fray-ed of his mit-tens!" The terrible music had in it a meaning from the moonlit war-drums of chanting cannibals.

At last Horace, with supreme effort, raised his head. "'Tain't them I care about," he said, gruffly. "I've got to go home. That's all."

Whereupon each boy held his left forefinger as if it were a pencil and began to sharpen it derisively with his right forefinger. They came closer, and sang like a trained chorus, "A-fray-ed of his mittens!"

When he raised his voice to deny the charge it was simply lost in the screams of the mob. He was alone, fronting all the traditions of boyhood held before him by inexorable representatives. To such a low state had he fallen that one lad, a mere baby, outflanked him and then struck him in the cheek with a heavy snowball. The act was acclaimed with loud jeers. Horace turned to dart at his assailant, but there was an immediate demonstration on the other flank, and he found himself obliged to keep his face toward the hilarious crew of tormentors. The baby retreated in safety to the rear of the crowd, where he was received with fulsome compliments upon his daring. Horace retreated slowly up the walk. He continually tried to make them heed him, but the only sound was the chant, "A-fray-ed of his mit-tens!" In this desperate withdrawal the beset and haggard boy suffered more than is the common lot of man.

Being a boy himself, he did not understand boys at all. He had, of course, the dismal conviction that they were going to dog him to his grave. But near the corner of the field they suddenly seemed to forget all about it. Indeed, they possessed only the malevolence of so many flitter-headed sparrows. The interest had swung capriciously to some other matter. In a moment they were off in the field again, carousing amid the snow. Some authoritative boy had probably said, "Aw, come on!"

As the pursuit ceased, Horace ceased his retreat. He spent some time in what was evidently an attempt to adjust his self-respect, and then began to wander furtively down toward the

group. He, too, had undergone an important change. Perhaps
his sharp agony was only as durable as the malevolence of the
others. In this boyish life obedience to some unformulated
creed of manners was enforced with capricious but merciless
rigour. However, they were, after all, his comrades, his friends.
They did not heed his return. They were engaged in an altercation. It had evidently been planned that this battle was
between Indians and soldiers. The smaller and weaker boys
had been induced to appear as Indians in the initial skirmish,
but they were now very sick of it, and were reluctantly but
steadfastly affirming their desire for a change of caste. The
larger boys had all won great distinction, devastating Indians
materially, and they wished the war to go on as planned. They
explained vociferously that it was proper for the soldiers always
to thrash the Indians. The little boys did not pretend to deny
the truth of this argument; they confined themselves to the
simple statement that, in that case, they wished to be soldiers.
Each little boy willingly appealed to the others to remain Indians, but as for himself he reiterated his desire to enlist as a
soldier. The larger boys were in despair over this dearth of
enthusiasm in the small Indians. They alternately wheedled
and bullied, but they could not persuade the little boys, who
were really suffering dreadful humiliation rather than submit
to another onslaught of soldiers. They were called all the baby
names that had the power of stinging deep into their pride, but
they remained firm.

Then a formidable lad, a leader of reputation, one who
could whip many boys that wore long trousers, suddenly blew
out his cheeks and shouted, "Well, all right then. I'll be an Indian myself. Now." The little boys greeted with cheers this
addition to their wearied ranks, and seemed then content. But
matters were not mended in the least, because all the personal
following of the formidable lad, with the addition of every
outsider, spontaneously forsook the flag and declared themselves Indians. There were now no soldiers. The Indians had
carried everything unanimously. The formidable lad used his

influence, but his influence could not shake the loyalty of his friends, who refused to fight under any colours but his colours.

Plainly there was nothing for it but to coerce the little ones. The formidable lad again became a soldier, and then graciously permitted to join him all the real fighting strength of the crowd, leaving behind a most forlorn band of little Indians. Then the soldiers attacked the Indians, exhorting them to opposition at the same time.

The Indians at first adopted a policy of hurried surrender, but this had no success, as none of the surrenders were accepted. They then turned to flee, bawling out protests. The ferocious soldiers pursued them amid shouts. The battle widened, developing all manner of marvellous detail.

Horace had turned toward home several times, but, as a matter of fact, this scene held him in a spell. It was fascinating beyond anything which the grown man understands. He had always in the back of his head a sense of guilt, even a sense of impending punishment for disobedience, but they could not weigh with the delirium of this snow-battle.

II

One of the raiding soldiers, espying Horace, called out in passing, "A-fray-ed of his mit-tens!" Horace flinched at this renewal, and the other lad paused to taunt him again. Horace scooped some snow, moulded it into a ball, and flung it at the other. "Ho!" cried the boy, "you're an Indian, are you? Hey, fellers, here's an Indian that ain't been killed yet." He and Horace engaged in a duel in which both were in such haste to mould snowballs that they had little time for aiming.

Horace once struck his opponent squarely in the chest. "Hey," he shouted, "you're dead. You can't fight any more, Pete. I killed you. You're dead."

The other boy flushed red, but he continued frantically to make ammunition. "You never touched me!" he retorted, glowering. "You never touched me! Where, now?" he added, defiantly. "Where did you hit me?"

"On the coat! Right on your breast! You can't fight any more! You're dead!"

"You never!"

"I did, too! Hey, fellers, ain't he dead? I hit 'im square!"

"He never!"

Nobody had seen the affair, but some of the boys took sides in absolute accordance with their friendship for one of the concerned parties. Horace's opponent went about contending, "He never touched me! He never came near me! He never came near me!"

The formidable leader now came forward and accosted Horace. "What was you? An Indian? Well, then, you're dead— that's all. He hit you. I saw him."

"Me?" shrieked Horace. "He never came within a mile of me—"

At that moment he heard his name called in a certain familiar tune of two notes, with the last note shrill and prolonged. He looked toward the sidewalk, and saw his mother standing there in her widow's weeds, with two brown paper parcels under her arm. A silence had fallen upon all the boys. Horace moved slowly toward his mother. She did not seem to note his approach; she was gazing austerely off through the naked branches of the maples where two crimson sunset bars lay on the deep blue sky.

At a distance of ten paces Horace made a desperate venture. "Oh, ma," he whined, "can't I stay out for a while?"

"No," she answered solemnly, "you come with me." Horace knew that profile; it was the inexorable profile. But he continued to plead, because it was not beyond his mind that a great show of suffering now might diminish his suffering later.

He did not dare to look back at his playmates. It was already a public scandal that he could not stay out as late as other boys, and he could imagine his standing now that he had been again dragged off by his mother in sight of the whole world. He was a profoundly miserable human being.

Aunt Martha opened the door for them. Light streamed

about her straight skirt. "Oh," she said, "so you found him on the road, eh? Well, I declare! It was about time!"

Horace slunk into the kitchen. The stove, straddling out on its four iron legs, was gently humming. Aunt Martha had evidently just lighted the lamp, for she went to it and began to twist the wick experimentally.

"Now," said the mother, "let's see them mittens."

Horace's chin sank. The aspiration of the criminal, the passionate desire for an asylum from retribution, from justice, was aflame in his heart. "I—I—don't—don't know where they are," he gasped finally, as he passed his hand over his pockets.

"Horace," intoned his mother, "you are tellin' me a story!"

"'Tain't a story," he answered, just above his breath. He looked like a sheep-stealer.

His mother held him by the arm, and began to search his pockets. Almost at once she was able to bring forth a pair of very wet mittens. "Well, I declare!" cried Aunt Martha. The two women went close to the lamp, and minutely examined the mittens, turning them over and over. Afterward, when Horace looked up, his mother's sad-lined, homely face was turned toward him. He burst into tears.

His mother drew a chair near the stove. "Just you sit there now, until I tell you to git off." He sidled meekly into the chair. His mother and his aunt went briskly about the business of preparing supper. They did not display a knowledge of his existence; they carried an effect of oblivion so far that they even did not speak to each other. Presently they went into the dining- and living-room; Horace could hear the dishes rattling. His Aunt Martha brought a plate of food, placed it on a chair near him, and went away without a word.

Horace instantly decided that he would not touch a morsel of the food. He had often used this ruse in dealing with his mother. He did not know why it brought her to terms, but certainly it sometimes did.

The mother looked up when the aunt returned to the other room. "Is he eatin' his supper?" she asked.

The maiden aunt, fortified in ignorance, gazed with pity and contempt upon this interest. "Well, now, Emily, how do I know?" she queried. "Was I goin' to stand over 'im? Of all the worryin' you do about that child! It's a shame the way you're bringin' up that child."

"Well, he ought to eat somethin'. It won't do fer him to go without eatin'," the mother retorted weakly.

Aunt Martha, profoundly scorning the policy of concession which these words meant, uttered a long, contemptuous sigh.

III

Alone in the kitchen, Horace stared with sombre eyes at the plate of food. For a long time he betrayed no sign of yielding. His mood was adamantine. He was resolved not to sell his vengeance for bread, cold ham, and a pickle, and yet it must be known that the sight of them affected him powerfully. The pickle in particular was notable for its seductive charm. He surveyed it darkly.

But at last, unable to longer endure his state, his attitude in the presence of the pickle, he put out an inquisitive finger and touched it, and it was cool and green and plump. Then a full conception of the cruel woe of his situation swept upon him suddenly, and his eyes filled with tears, which began to move down his cheeks. He sniffled. His heart was black with hatred. He painted in his mind scenes of deadly retribution. His mother would be taught that he was not one to endure persecution meekly, without raising an arm in his defence. And so his dreams were of a slaughter of feelings, and near the end of them his mother was pictured as coming, bowed with pain, to his feet. Weeping, she implored his charity. Would he forgive her? No; his once tender heart had been turned to stone by her injustice. He could not forgive her. She must pay the inexorable penalty.

The first item in this horrible plan was the refusal of the food. This he knew by experience would work havoc in his mother's heart. And so he grimly waited.

But suddenly it occurred to him that the first part of his revenge was in danger of failing. The thought struck him that his mother might not capitulate in the usual way. According to his recollection, the time was more than due when she should come in, worried, sadly affectionate, and ask him if he was ill. It had then been his custom to hint in a resigned voice that he was the victim of secret disease, but that he preferred to suffer in silence and alone. If she was obdurate in her anxiety, he always asked her in a gloomy, low voice to go away and leave him to suffer in silence and alone in the darkness without food. He had known this manœuvring to result even in pie.

But what was the meaning of the long pause and the stillness? Had his old and valued ruse betrayed him? As the truth sank into his mind, he supremely loathed life, the world, his mother. Her heart was beating back the besiegers; he was a defeated child.

He wept for a time before deciding upon the final stroke. He would run away. In a remote corner of the world he would become some sort of bloody-handed person driven to a life of crime by the barbarity of his mother. She should never know his fate. He would torture her for years with doubts and doubts, and drive her implacably to a repentant grave. Nor would his Aunt Martha escape. Some day, a century hence, when his mother was dead, he would write to his Aunt Martha, and point out her part in the blighting of his life. For one blow against him now he would, in time, deal back a thousand—ay, ten thousand.

He arose and took his coat and cap. As he moved stealthily toward the door he cast a glance backward at the pickle. He was tempted to take it, but he knew that if he left the plate inviolate his mother would feel even worse.

A blue snow was falling. People, bowed forward, were moving briskly along the walks. The electric lamps hummed amid showers of flakes. As Horace emerged from the kitchen, a shrill squall drove the flakes around the corner of the house. He cowered away from it, and its violence illumined his mind vaguely in new directions. He deliberated upon a choice of remote corners of the globe. He found that he had no plans which were definite enough in a geographical way, but without much loss of time he decided upon California. He moved briskly as far as his mother's front gate on the road to California. He was off at last. His success was a trifle dreadful; his throat choked.

But at the gate he paused. He did not know if his journey to California would be shorter if he went down Niagara Avenue or off through Hogan Street. As the storm was very cold and the point was very important, he decided to withdraw for reflection to the wood-shed. He entered the dark shanty, and took seat upon the old chopping-block upon which he was supposed to perform for a few minutes every afternoon when he returned from school. The wind screamed and shouted at the loose boards, and there was a rift of snow on the floor to leeward of a crack.

Here the idea of starting for California on such a night departed from his mind, leaving him ruminating miserably upon his martyrdom. He saw nothing for it but to sleep all night in the wood-shed and start for California in the morning bright and early. Thinking of his bed, he kicked over the floor and found that the innumerable chips were all frozen tightly, bedded in ice.

Later he viewed with joy some signs of excitement in the house. The flare of a lamp moved rapidly from window to window. Then the kitchen door slammed loudly and a shawled figure sped toward the gate. At last he was making them feel his power. The shivering child's face was lit with saturnine glee as in the darkness of the wood-shed he gloated over the evidences of consternation in his home. The shawled figure had been his Aunt Martha dashing with the alarm to the neighbours.

The cold of the wood-shed was tormenting him. He endured only because of the terror he was causing. But then it occurred to him that, if they instituted a search for him, they would

probably examine the wood-shed. He knew that it would not
be manful to be caught so soon. He was not positive now that
he was going to remain away for ever, but at any rate he was
bound to inflict some more damage before allowing himself to
be captured. If he merely succeeded in making his mother
angry, she would thrash him on sight. He must prolong the
time in order to be safe. If he held out properly, he was
sure of a welcome of love, even though he should drip with
crimes.

Evidently the storm had increased, for when he went out it
swung him violently with its rough and merciless strength.
Panting, stung, half blinded with the driving flakes, he was now
a waif, exiled, friendless, and poor. With a bursting heart, he
thought of his home and his mother. To his forlorn vision they
were as far away as heaven.

IV

Horace was undergoing changes of feeling so rapidly that he
was merely moved hither and then thither like a kite. He was
now aghast at the merciless ferocity of his mother. It was she
who had thrust him into this wild storm, and she was perfectly
indifferent to his fate, perfectly indifferent. The forlorn wanderer could no longer weep. The strong sobs caught at his
throat, making his breath come in short, quick snuffles. All in
him was conquered save the enigmatical childish ideal of form,
manner. This principle still held out, and it was the only
thing between him and submission. When he surrendered, he
must surrender in a way that deferred to the undefined code.
He longed simply to go to the kitchen and stumble in, but his
unfathomable sense of fitness forbade him.

Presently he found himself at the head of Niagara Avenue,
staring through the snow into the blazing windows of Stickney's butcher-shop. Stickney was the family butcher, not so
much because of a superiority to other Whilomville butchers as
because he lived next door and had been an intimate friend of
the father of Horace. Rows of glowing pigs hung head down-

ward behind the tables, which bore huge pieces of red beef. Clumps of attenuated turkeys were suspended here and there. Stickney, hale and smiling, was bantering with a woman in a cloak, who, with a monster basket on her arm, was dickering for eight cents' worth of something. Horace watched them through a crusted pane. When the woman came out and passed him, he went toward the door. He touched the latch with his finger, but withdrew again suddenly to the sidewalk. Inside Stickney was whistling cheerily and assorting his knives.

Finally Horace went desperately forward, opened the door, and entered the shop. His head hung low. Stickney stopped whistling. "Hello, young man," he cried; "what brings you here?"

Horace halted, but said nothing. He swung one foot to and fro over the sawdust floor.

Stickney had placed his two fat hands palms downward and wide apart on the table, in the attitude of a butcher facing a customer, but now he straightened. "Here," he said, "what's wrong? What's wrong, kid?"

"Nothin'," answered Horace, huskily. He laboured for a moment with something in his throat, and afterwards added, "O'ny—I've—I've run away, and—"

"Run away!" shouted Stickney. "Run away from what? Who?"

"From—home," answered Horace. "I don't like it there any more. I—" He had arranged an oration to win the sympathy of the butcher; he had prepared a table setting forth the merits of his case in the most logical fashion, but it was as if the wind had been knocked out of his mind. "I've run away. I—"

Stickney reached an enormous hand over the array of beef, and firmly grappled the emigrant. Then he swung himself to Horace's side. His face was stretched with laughter, and he playfully shook his prisoner. "Come—come—come. What dashed nonsense is this? Run away, hey? Run away?" Whereupon the child's long-tried spirit found vent in howls.

"Come, come," said Stickney, busily. "Never mind now,

never mind. You just come along with me. It'll be all right. I'll
fix it. Never you mind."

Five minutes later the butcher, with a great ulster over his
apron, was leading the boy homeward.

At the very threshold, Horace raised his last flag of pride.
"No—no," he sobbed. "I don't want to. I don't want to go in
there." He braced his foot against the step and made a very
respectable resistance.

"Now, Horace," cried the butcher. He thrust open the door
with a bang. "Hello there!" Across the dark kitchen the door to
the living-room opened and Aunt Martha appeared. "You've
found him!" she screamed.

"We've come to make a call," roared the butcher. At the entrance to the living-room a silence fell upon them all. Upon a
couch Horace saw his mother lying limp, pale as death, her
eyes gleaming with pain. There was an electric pause before
she swung a waxen hand toward Horace. "My child," she murmured, tremulously. Whereupon the sinister person addressed,
with a prolonged wail of grief and joy, ran to her with speed.
"Mam-ma! Mam-ma! Oh, mam-ma!" She was not able to speak
in a known tongue as she folded him in her weak arms.

Aunt Martha turned defiantly upon the butcher, because her
face betrayed her. She was crying. She made a gesture half
military, half feminine. "Won't you have a glass of our root-
beer, Mr. Stickney? We make it ourselves."

PART VI

Poems

INTRODUCTION

ONE morning in April 1893, a few weeks after Garland was shown the first draft of *The Red Badge*, Crane appeared at Garland's Harlem apartment with another roll of manuscript in his pocket, a smaller roll containing a dozen short poems written on legal-cap paper. Garland asked him when he had written them, and Crane said: "This morning," and then, "putting the tip of his finger to his right temple, quaintly added, 'I have four or five more standing in a row up here—all they need is to be drawn off; but I can't write among those "Indians." ' " (The "Indians," as Crane called them, were the art students he was living with in the old Art Students' League building on East Twenty-third Street.) Garland was skeptical and asked for some proof:

—Do you mean to say that these lines are arranged in your head, complete in every detail?—
—Yes, I could do one right now.—
—Very well. Take a seat at my desk and do one for me.— Thereupon with my pen he wrote steadily, composedly, without a moment's hesitation, one of his most powerful poems. It flowed from his pen like oil, but when I examined it, I found it not only without blot or erasure, but perfectly correct in punctuation.[1]

The poem Crane drew off in Garland's presence was No. XXI in *The Black Riders and Other Lines*. This volume of Crane's first poems was published in the spring of 1895—before the book publication of *The Red Badge of Courage*.

In March, Howells had invited Crane for tea and had read him some of Emily Dickinson's poetry. Crane was busy writing *The Red Badge* when this inspiration for poetry cut across

---

[1] In *Roadside Meetings* (1930), p. 194.

his path.[2] He wrote the first poems in a single creative spurt of three days (so a college friend reports); they were the outcome of a mood of desperation. "No one would print a line of mine," he subsequently told Harvey Wickham, "and I just had to do something odd to attract attention."[3] In April he told Garland "I'd trade my entire future for twenty-three dollars in cash." Crane himself did not call his poems poetry, they were "lines." Yet he had a higher opinion of his poetic output than of all his fiction. It was because the poems said something important that he thought them more important than *Maggie* or *The Red Badge*. My poems "give my ideas of life as a whole, so far as I know it." But Crane is constantly contradicting himself: a novel must not be didactic, but a poem should *say* what it means. His "lines" seemed to him more "sincere" and "honest" because they were not contrived. *Maggie* and *The Red Badge* were preconceived and consciously designed, whereas the poems were spontaneously produced by Pure Inspiration.

Garland was much impressed by the poet's "air of detachment. *It was precisely as if some alien spirit were delivering these lines through his hand as a medium.*"[4] Garland joked about Crane's having a poetic ghost at his shoulder. "He wrote steadily in beautifully clear script with perfect alignment and spacing, precisely as if he were copying something already written and before his eyes":

---

[2] Crane's statement: "I wrote the things in February of 1893," cannot be true, says Beer, because he had not yet dined with Howells. Garland's meeting with Crane's poetic ghost occurred shortly after April 1. See Beer, p. 297.

[3] "Stephen Crane at College," *American Mercury*, 7 (March 1926), 291–7.

[4] "There is a ghost at your shoulder," I said in mock seriousness, "but not the ghost who gave you *The Red Badge of Courage*. This is the ghost of militant agnosticism—a satirical ghost." What this also tells us is that Garland saw *first* the manuscript of *The Red Badge* and *then* the manuscript of the poems. (In Berryman's account this sequence of visits to Garland is reversed.) The above quotation is taken from Garland's "Stephen Crane as I Knew Him," *Yale Review*, 3 (April 1914, 494–506. The italics are his.

> *There was, before me,*
> *Mile upon mile*
> *Of snow, ice, burning sand.*
> *And yet I could look beyond all this,*
> *To a place of infinite beauty;*
> *And I could see the loveliness of her*
> *Who walked in the garden of the trees.*
> *When I gazed,*
> *All was lost*
> *But this place of beauty and her.*
> *When I gazed,*
> *And in my gazing, desired,*
> *Then came again*
> *Mile upon mile*
> *Of snow, ice, burning sand.*

For several days after that first visit Crane came regularly to Garland "bringing these curious fragments, and then gradually the number of the poems dwindled until he had but one or two." His poetic ghost disappeared. Garland asked him, pointing at his head, whether he had any more poems up there, and Crane replied with a touch of melancholy: "they're all gone now—the place is empty." [5] But Garland is incorrect in saying that Crane wrote no more poems, for in a letter of May 1894 Crane wrote him when Garland was in Chicago: "Everything is coming along nicely now. I have got the poetic spout so that I can turn it on or off."

The Black Riders (dedicated to Hamlin Garland) was brutally treated by the reviewers. Even his best poem—"Do not weep, maiden, for war is kind"—was damned when it first appeared the next year, in a magazine for February 1896. That poem, said Jeannette Gilder in the New York *World* that same month, is not poetry—"not poetry as Tennyson understood it. . . ." It would take a professor to find any poetry in these

---

[5] "Stephen Crane as I Knew Him," *Yale Review*, 3 (April 1914), 494–506. A later version of this account, in *Roadside Meetings* (1930), is somewhat different and considerably extended. A third version appeared in the *Bookman* for January 1930, pp. 525–8.

poems; his *Black Riders* "had better be forgotten." Despite critical onslaught, however, *Black Riders* went into six printings during 1895–6.

Inspired by Emily Dickinson's poetry but not modeled upon it, Crane's poems derive their cadence and sometimes their framework from the Bible (as Amy Lowell was first to observe). Half the poems in *Black Riders* are epigrammatic parables; several of these have close affinity with the parable-poems of Ambrose Bierce and his epigrams in *The Devil's Dictionary*. In Olive Schreiner's *Dreams,* poetic parables of savage philosophy, Garland spotted another source. *Black Riders* and *War is Kind* have a family kinship with the free verse of W. E. Henley, Emily Dickinson, and Walt Whitman. Crane was talked about as a second Walt Whitman; the *Nation* for October 24, 1895, said that the poems were at once Whitman condensed and Dickinson expanded. As formless as Whitman, "these 'lines' are in other respects the antipodes of his; while Whitman dilutes mercilessly, Crane condenses almost as formidably." The influence of Dickinson has recently been denied, but there are several points of relationship. Both poets express unorthodox sentiments, use metaphor, and delight in paradox. An idea is glanced at from two points of view and then left there undeveloped. Occasionally you hear a Dickinson ghost rime, as in "success or calamity/Would attend all in equality." Crane's lines are pithy and short like Dickinson's, though more irregular. Straight Whitman or straight Carl Sandburg is "A newspaper is a collection of half-injustices" (*War is Kind,* No. XII), with its Whitmanesque cataloguing of flat statements, its bombast and formlessness.

Some of Crane's poems echo Whitman in phrase ("making cunning noiseless travel down the ways"), but in form they identify themselves with Bierce. "Forth went the candid man" (in *War is Kind,* 1899) is built exactly like Bierce's parable *Moral Principle and Material Interest.* Bierce's structure of ironic reversal is paralleled again in "A man said to the universe" and in earlier poems such as "I saw a man pursuing the horizon" and "A youth in apparel that glittered." Crane's epigrams, as Horace Gregory remarks, provide a bridge from Bierce to the first imagist anthologies and the early epigrammatic Ezra Pound. Amy Lowell said that Crane was no poet, but it was Crane who anticipated the very program she took over from T. E. Hulme and Pound, and it was Crane who fulfilled certain tenets of imagism more truly than the imagists themselves. (See Edith Wyatt in the *New Republic* for September 11, 1915.) They regarded his verse as experimental; Crane of course did not deliberately pioneer, or experiment, or write according to program as the imagists did. Pound spoke of Crane appreciatively, and so did Carl Sandburg. In "Letters to Dead Imagists," in *Chicago Poems* (1916), Sandburg acknowledged Crane's influence as a contemporary. By accidental resemblance to vers-librist and imagist verse, Crane thus heralded and somewhat influenced the poetic renaissance of 1912.

2

At their best the poems have the same structural design and (some of them) even the same plot or mood as the short stories. "A youth in apparel that glittered" (No. XXVII in *The Black Riders*) is a miniature copy of *The Red Badge of Courage*. The would-be assassin of the youth meets an impasse. It is the youth's romantic notion of wanting to die a happy heroic death in the best medieval fashion. The poem is like a short story, of which the distinguishing ingredient is a conflict. In *A Mystery of Heroism, The Upturned Face, An Episode of War,* and *The Bride*, the conflict is between theory or code and fact, the theory or ideal being exploded by the facts of reality. The conflict in the poem about the indomitable youth is between *illusion and reality*. But here it is reality, the assassin of dreams, that finds itself compromised.

> *A youth in apparel that glittered*
> *Went to walk in a grim forest.*
> *There he met an assassin*
> *Attired all in garb of old days;*
> *He, scowling through the thickets,*

> *And dagger poised quivering,*
> *Rushed upon the youth.*
> *"Sir," said this latter,*
> *"I am enchanted, believe me,*
> *To die, thus,*
> *In this mediæval fashion,*
> *According to the best legends;*
> *Ah, what joy!"*
> *Then took he the wound, smiling,*
> *And died, content.*
>
> (BR, XXVII)

In *The Bride*, similarly, the dreamer—the newly wedded sheriff—disarms his would-be assassin.

"A man adrift on a slim spar" reproduces the plight of the men in *The Open Boat*, and the germinal situation that Crane developed in *The Blue Hotel* is stated in this syllogistic three-line poem:

> *A man feared that he might find an assassin;*
> *Another that he might find a victim.*
> *One was more wise than the other.*
>
> (BR, LVI)

The parable-poem "I saw a man pursuing the horizon" recalls Henry Fleming and other Crane heroes who are men "pursuing the horizon." Dream or ideal is the quest, but he who seeks truth is derided. You can never find what you seek; always it is beyond the horizon. In "I stood musing in a black world" (BR, XLIX) the seeker is too blind to see the thing he desires.

Black Riders poem No. IX epitomizes Hawthorne's story *Young Goodman Brown*. Here illusion is shattered by realities.

> *I stood upon a high place,*
> *And saw, below, many devils*
> *Running, leaping,*
> *And carousing in sin.*
> *One looked up, grinning,*
> *And said, "Comrade! Brother!"*

The obverse of this theme is presented in

> *There was, before me,*
> *Mile upon mile*
> *Of snow, ice, burning sand . . .*
> (BR, XXI)

Here the real world seems to the lover but a mirage; what is real is his dream.

Crane's poems fall into two categories of form: the logical and the non-logical. Contrast shapes both types. The non-syllogistic poems are built upon a contrast of moods.

> *Should the wide world roll away,*
> *Leaving black terror,*
> *Limitless night,*
> *Nor God, nor man, nor place to stand*
> *Would be to me essential,*
> *If thou and thy white arms were there,*
> *And the fall to doom a long way.*
> (BR, X)

Despair attaching to limitless space is set in contrast with hope and faith attaching to a small and finite thing.

This sequence of moods is reversed in the hope-despair contrast of No. XX in *Black Riders*—"A learned man came to me once"—and in No. III of *War is Kind*:

> *To the maiden*
> *The sea was blue meadow,*
> *Alive with little froth-people*
> *Singing.*

The second part of the poem turns against the first. The sea evokes the contrary mood when seen from another point of view.

> *To the sailor, wrecked,*
> *The sea was dead grey walls*
> *Superlative in vacancy,*

> *Upon which nevertheless at fateful time*
> *Was written*
> *The grim hatred of nature.*

Illusion canceled out by disillusionment fashions the two-part form of "Upon the road of my life" (br, lx). The same form is seen in this imagistic piece, the first part contradicted by the second—illusion versus reality:

> *Fast rode the knight*
> *With spurs, hot and reeking,*
> *Ever waving an eager sword,*
> *"To save my lady!"*
> *Fast rode the knight,*
> *And leaped from saddle to war.*
> *Men of steel flickered and gleamed*
> *Like riot of silver lights,*
> *And the gold of the knight's good banner*
> *Still waved on a castle wall.*
>
> *A horse,*
> *Blowing, staggering, bloody thing,*
> *Forgotten at foot of castle wall.*
> *A horse*
> *Dead at foot of castle wall.*
>   (WK, VIII)

One variation of this form is the poem of a single mood: for example, "A man adrift on a slim spar." "Do not weep, maiden, for war is kind," the title poem of Crane's second volume, is likewise a poem of single mood, repetitive in form. It stands apart from, and is superior to, the other piece by its ironic point of view. A second variation of the form is the poem of three parts, the middle contrasted against the opening and closing mood. One example is No. XXI of *Black Riders*—"There was, before me" (quoted above). No. XXIV inverts the sequence. Here it is hope-despair-hope:

> *I saw a man pursuing the horizon;*
> *Round and round they sped.*

> I was disturbed at this;
> I accosted the man.
> "It is futile," I said,
> "You can never—"
>
> "You lie," he cried,
> And ran on.

There is a double mood of despair-hope in the opening part of No. XLII:

> I walked in a desert.
> And I cried,   (A)
> "Ah, God, take me from this place!"
>
> A voice said, "It is no desert."   (B)

The same double mood concludes the poem:

> I cried, "Well, but—   (A¹)
> The sand, the heat, the vacant horizon."
>
> A voice said, "It is no desert."   (B¹)

The poems belonging to the second category of form employ the same substance of paradox and parable, but here the ironic turnabout is shaped by contradiction of logic rather than by contradiction of mood. In the poems of double mood two situations are presented in contrast with each other, but without logical link between them. Poem No. V in *Black Riders* is quite different in structure from poem No. III in *War is Kind*, quoted above, for here instead of two parallel situations there is a reversal of situation. The one works by contrast, the other by contradiction of directions. The one turns in terms of contrast of mood, the other turns in terms of contradiction of proposition or statement.

> "Think as I think," said a man,
> "Or you are abominably wicked;
> You are a toad."

This premise, diagrammatically the poem's line of direction, is contradicted by the tangential:

> *And after I had thought of it,*
> *I said, "I will, then, be a toad."*
> (*BR*, XLVII)

These poems presume a logic that does not exist; it is a logic that contradicts "logic."

> *A man said to the universe:*
> *"Sir, I exist!"*
> *"However," replied the universe,*
> *"The fact has not created in me*
> *A sense of obligation."*
> (*WK*, XXI)

The poems built by double mood provide no situations of choice. The characteristic of syllogistic form is illustrated in the already quoted triad "A man feared that he might find an assassin" (BR, LVI). That one out-Bierces Bierce. The same triple partitioning occurs in:

> *In the desert*
> *I saw a creature, naked, bestial,*
> *Who, squatting upon the ground,*
> *Held his heart in his hands,*
> *And ate of it.*
> *I said, "Is it good, friend?"*

Next the contradiction:

> *"It is bitter—bitter," he answered.*

This turn, prepared for by the premise, constitutes the point of the angle and prepares for the final thrust:

> *"But I like it*
> *Because it is bitter,*
> *And because it is my heart."*
> (*BR*, III)

It is Crane's priority in this historical perspective that places him as important. As unified wholes his poems are negligible, being chiefly fragments of unformed meaning. Although they are mannered in style, style is not their main concern; their meaning is everything. They are certainly not notable for innovations of poetic technique and form. In technique they are bad models; in form nothing could be simpler; and in texture they are flat, their language being nonreflexive and rhetorical. *Crane used language poetically not in his verse, but in his prose.*

Other poems in Crane's day looked like poems (Omar Khayyám's, for instance), but Crane's poems did not. And other poets looked like poets and dressed the role of The Poet: flowing tie, flowing beard or mane, eyes "in a fine frenzy rolling." So Richard Hovey played it. Not Crane, who detested pose of any kind. Yet his own verse is not free from pose.

Here are some of Crane's best poems besides those quoted complete in this introduction:

BR V

Once there came a man
Who said,
"Range me all men of the world in rows."
And instantly
There was terrific clamour among the people
Against being ranged in rows.
There was a loud quarrel, world-wide.
It endured for ages;
And blood was shed
By those who would not stand in rows,
And by those who pined to stand in rows,
Eventually, the man went to death, weeping.
And those who stayed in bloody scuffle
Knew not the great simplicity.

WK XIII

The wayfarer,
Perceiving the pathway to truth,
Was struck with astonishment.
It was thickly grown with weeds.
"Ha," he said,
"I see that none has passed here
In a long time."
Later he saw that each weed
Was a singular knife.
"Well," he mumbled at last,
"Doubtless there are other roads."

WK I

Do not weep, maiden, for war is kind.
Because your lover threw wild hands toward the sky
And the affrighted steed ran on alone,
Do not weep.
War is kind.

Hoarse, booming drums of the regiment,
Little souls who thirst for fight,
These men were born to drill and die.
The unexplained glory flies above them,
Great is the battle-god, great, and his kingdom—
A field where a thousand corpses lie.

Do not weep, babe, for war is kind.
Because your father tumbled in the yellow trenches,
Raged at his breast, gulped and died,
Do not weep.
War is kind.

Swift blazing flag of the regiment,
Eagle with crest of red and gold,
These men were born to drill and die.
Point for them the virtue of slaughter,
Make plain to them the excellence of killing
And a field where a thousand corpses lie.

Mother whose heart hung humble as a button
On the bright splendid shroud of your son,
Do not weep.
War is kind.

NO. I FROM "THREE POEMS"

A man adrift on a slim spar
A horizon smaller than the rim of a bottle
Tented waves rearing lashy dark points
The near whine of froth in circles.
                    God is cold.

The incessant raise and swing of the sea
And growl after growl of crest
The sinkings, green, seething, endless
The upheaval half-completed.
                    God is cold.

The seas are in the hollow of The Hand;
Oceans may be turned to a spray
Raining down through the stars
Because of a gesture of pity toward a babe.
Oceans may become grey ashes,
Die with a long moan and a roar
Amid the tumult of the fishes
And the cries of the ships,

Because The Hand beckons the mice.
A horizon smaller than a doomed assassin's cap,
Inky, surging tumults
A reeling, drunken sky and no sky
A pale hand sliding from a polished spar.
                    God is cold.

The puff of a coat imprisoning air:
A face kissing the water-death
A weary slow sway of a lost hand
And the sea, the moving sea, the sea.
                    God is cold.

PART VII

Letters

INTRODUCTION

T<small>HIS</small> first collection of Crane's letters—120 in all, 57 of them published for the first time—constitutes an important addition to the Crane biography. This collection does not comprise the whole story. Crane wrote several hundred letters, not just the few that Thomas Beer knew about. Crane was not a great letter-writer, but then, he made no conscious effort to be one; he did not write with any megrim about posterity looking over his shoulder. On the other hand, it is not true, as has been said, that Crane's scarce letters are not often interesting. Almost all of them are autobiographically interesting, and several have critical significance. Only a few show what Beer describes as "a formal running tone, now and then lifted by a phrase." (The ones in this manner are chiefly the twenty-four letters to Ripley Hitchcock, now in the Berg Collection at the New York Public Library.)

Crane, it has been said, "carried into his correspondence little of the glamor of his creative work." But that is as it should be; the one cannot very well compete with the other. Yet his letters are characterized by several points of reference, and even of resemblance, to his creative work. For one thing, many of them are deliberately enigmatic. Also, they are full of wisdom and humor. Quite a different Stephen Crane from the one portrayed by Beer in his biography is said to be revealed in Crane's letters to Miss Nellie Crouse, which no biographer has yet been permitted to use. Crane poured out his soul to her in seven letters ranging from five to twenty pages, and what these letters reveal—according to a published report about them made by Jerry Mangione, the one person so far permitted to describe them [1]—is that Crane "could not refer to his own life

---

[1] "Stephen Crane's Unpublished Letters," *Chap Book*, May 1930, pp. 8–10.

without suggesting a tense struggle going on within himself." This struggle, we are told, "is the struggle between uncompromising realities and deeply rooted ideals, one which filled Crane's soul with irony and despair."

A correlation thus exists between the personal revelations made in Crane's letters to Miss Crouse and Crane's own creative work. The crux of his poetry and fiction manifests this same conflict: the conflict between illusory theories or ideals, empty forms or abstractions, and unpredictable realities. The basis for this interpretation lies in the works themselves, not in the external evidence of Crane's letters. Letters serve the critic only as corroborative evidence. What they reveal reinforces or stands at odds with his critical interpretation of the works, but in either case such external evidence as letters or notebooks provide is coincidental, supererogatory; however interesting, it is critically irrelevant for establishing the meaning of the works *as* works of art. There can be no substitute for our critical scrutiny of the realized thing, and it is there that the artist's intention or meaning resides.

The critic's greatest hazard lies in the assumption that what the work means must be the same as what the artist himself said his work means or intends. Artists are notoriously self-contradictory. They make public pronouncements in their prefaces, and then in private letters contradict what they there professed (Conrad for one). They contradict themselves in their own works by treating obversely the theme or convictions expressed in one work in the theme or convictions expressed in their very next. Conrad not only concealed from his public his secret intentions, but even disguised them by planting bogus trade secrets about his literary aims in his Author's Notes, false clues to what his books are really all about. Crane's *Red Badge of Courage* is not *only* what he said he intended it to be, "a psychological portrayal of fear"—it is that, but it is also a great deal more. The reader needs only D. H. Lawrence's pointer to tip him off: "Never trust the artist. Trust the tale."

The concern of literary criticism is with the work itself. Letters and notebooks frequently furnish some clues for understanding it, but the validity of critical interpretation must be based upon internal evidence alone. Critical inquiry is, as it were, a one-way traffic: it is directed *away* from personal documents *toward* the work of art. Reverse the traffic, and you are interpreting the work solely for a reconstruction of the biography, which is to reduce the work of art back into the history from which it came. Critical error lies in a mistaken identification of the work with the personality of the man who wrote it. Is the Stephen Crane revealed in his letters the Stephen Crane who wrote *The Open Boat* or *The Bride Comes to Yellow Sky*? His letters open up certain sides of his nature not reflected in his literary works (as well as some characteristics identifiable there); they are filled largely with such residual stuff as incidents and emotions not made use of in his art, moods not relevant to his creative one, and so on. There is the artist writing, and there is the man not writing—or rather the man writing only letters. They are two distinct personalities, each of which is probably many-sided. It is not the man who is in his work; it is the artist.

The letters reveal the man. Crane's letters throw a vivid light on his character. They have use not only for the biographer, but also for the critic, for they re-establish and correct both the chronology of Crane's personal events and the composition-dates of his writings, and they document his views on art and the creative process.

It is interesting to find the many sides of Crane's contradictory nature disclosed in his letters. His love for outdoor life is shown in the letters written while vacationing at a camp in northern Pennsylvania two months after his return from the West and just after reading the proofs of *The Red Badge of Courage*, and this is even more lyrically expressed in the letters written while he was reworking the manuscript of *George's Mother* at his brother's house in Hartwood, New York. And then, in conflict with his love for the outdoors, he expresses his fondness for sociability and city life in some letters preparing for poker games with his friends, for meetings with members of the Lantern Club, or for the dinner given in his honor by the Philistine Society. For Crane, experiencing life went hand in hand with writing about it, but his compulsion to withdraw from it stands nevertheless in conflict with his compulsion to experience it to the full. Ironically enough, even in the midst of retreating to the woods he is confronted and threatened by the forces of "engagement *versus* withdrawal" when six girls show up at the camp in Parker's Glen: "There are six girls in camp and it is with the greatest difficulty that I can think coherently on any other subject" (letter of August 9, 1895).

The letters in this first collection cover the main events of Crane's career, and the letters to Willis Hawkins add a new chapter to the biography. The friendship they record brings to light here for the first time the most intimate and rewarding of all the many friendships Crane's magnetic personality won for him. Not before published or known to exist, these letters provide the most important addition to Craneana that has appeared in over two decades. In 1930 the *Colophon* reproduced in facsimile a letter which was hailed at that time as "the most important Crane discovery of recent years." It is the letter Crane wrote to the editor of the *Critic,* reprinted here from the Crane Collection of Mr. Clifton Waller Barrett.

Letters and manuscripts by Crane are very scarce. Crane's latest biographer rests his conclusions about Crane "heavily upon unpublished materials, including three extensive, important sources which I am not permitted to cite" (Berryman, p. xiv). His sources include (I surmise) three long letters to Cora Taylor. One wonders whether the letters to Cora Taylor, which were discovered two decades ago, will ever come to the point of publication as promised, when so many similar promises have been indulged in without fulfillment. Other unpublished Crane letters include letters to Joseph Conrad (excepting the two reproduced here) and the ones to Lily Brandon Munroe which were recently said to be "contemplated" for publication. There are twenty-four letters (five incomplete) and one telegram to Ripley Hitchcock as well as Crane inscriptions in presentation copies now in the Berg Collection of the New York Public Library, and one of these letters to Hitchcock receives first publication here. A cache of six hundred Crane letters (or copies?) is owned by L.C.D.R. Melvin Schoberlin, promised for future deposit at a university library, and I am indebted to him for his kind gift of a photoduplicate copy of Crane's reply to the Philistine Society. Legal and other obstacles prohibit release now of the thirteen Crane letters in the possession of Syracuse University Library, letters which no biographer has yet been permitted to quote from. Of these the seven to Miss Nellie Crouse were promised for publication twenty years ago.

I have collected from inaccessible periodicals and books as many of the already published Crane letters as are now available, so far as I know. (About twenty-one of these were previously published in books.) Fifty-seven letters in this first collection receive their first publication here. Three discoveries—an inscription to Hamlin Garland and two letters to Copeland & Day—were contributed by Mr. Josiah K. Lilly. The New York Public Library, the Yale University Library, and the Huntington Library each contributed one or two letters not before published. Twelve letters dealing with the publication of *The Black Riders* were contributed by Mr. H. B. Collamore; a few of these letters had received previous publication. Twenty-seven letters selected from a set of thirty-three unpublished letters, chiefly the letters to Willis Hawkins, are the gift of Mr. Clifton Waller Barrett. Crane's letters to Miss Amy Leslie, other than the ones reproduced here, are presumably lost, and what letters Thomas Beer used for his biography are reported to be no longer among his papers. I have reprinted eighteen letters from Beer's *Stephen Crane* (1923). Mr. Odell S. Hathaway kindly contributed nine new letters. Dartmouth College Library granted me use of its Crane letters and inscriptions, nine in all, and I owe a special debt of gratitude to Mr. Harold G. Rugg, of Dartmouth College Library, for his constant help and many kindnesses. This collection of one hundred and twenty letters had its beginning in the set of Crane letters Mr. Barrett gave me, and I am most deeply grateful to him.[2]

---

[2] Not included in this collection are eleven letters that came to me while the book was on press: two letters to Phillips of McClure, Phillips, and Company, one of which is very interesting as a commentary on *The Red Badge*; an important letter to John N. Hilliard (dated January 2, 1896) dealing with *The Red Badge*; a letter to McClure; a letter to Pinker written at Brede Place; five letters to William Dean Howells; and a letter written while Crane was in St. Louis (dated January 30, 1894).

TO ODELL HATHAWAY [1]

[December 25, 1887?]
Asbury Park, New Jersey

Hello: central:
hello:
Give me tough Hathaway, Middletown
Well, old man, I hope you are having a merry, merry X'mas. I
expect to stop up and see you as I promised but cant tell for
sure yet. Johnnie wrote me that he was afraid he could'nt show
up, but would try. I expect to go to P. J.[2] in a few days and on
my way back will stop and see you
I heard from Puzey and I also heard a voice from Mich. say he
had not left my overcoat on the route. Write me here at A.P.
Merry Xmas to you and all your friends.

Yours sincerely
Stephen Crane

Xmas morning
Asbury Park

TO ODELL HATHAWAY [1]

My dear "Tough"
I thought I would enjoy writing to you to-
day, as, I am home with lots of friends, yet, longing for some of
my old companions at Old Claverack.[2] I am smoking a cigar
after a 10.00 AM breakfast of roast pigeon and gooseberries

---

[1] The original letter is in the possession of Mr. Odell S. Hathaway, Jr.,
and is reproduced with his permission, here for the first time.

[2] P. J.—Port Jervis, New York, where William Crane lived.

[1] The original letter is in the possession of Mr. Odell S. Hathaway, Jr.,
and is reproduced with his permission, here for the first time.

[2] Claverack—the Hudson River Institute at Claverack, New York,
where Crane had been schooled during the previous year.

yet I wish to God I was puffing on a cigarette butt after a 7.00
AM breakfast of dried-beef and oat meal at H.R.I. If you see
Tuttle give him my kindest regards and tell him to write. Good-
bye, old man, write to me. I dont forget my friends and you
will always have my best wishes.

Yours ever

Stephen Crane

Asbury Park [3] [New Jersey]
Sunday, June 15, 1890

TO ODELL HATHAWAY [1]

[September or October 1890]

[Lafayette College]

Dear Boys,

I send you a piece of the banner we took away from
the Sophemores last week. It dont look like much does it? Only
an old rag, ain't it? But just remember I got a *black and blue
nose*, a barked shin, skin off my hands and a lame shoulder, in
the row you can appreciate it.[2] So, keep it, and when you look
at it think of me scraping about twice a week over some old
rag that says "Fresh '94" on it.

Stephen Crane

TO MISS HELEN TRENT

[A tall darkly pretty girl, Helen Trent was already betrothed when
Crane fell in love with her. The next summer he fell in love with a
married woman, Lily Brandon Munroe. Neither of these romantic

---

[3] Crane was here for the summer reporting "shore news" for the *New
York Tribune*'s representative, Townley Crane, Stephen's brother.

[1] The original letter is in the possession of Mr. Odell S. Hathaway, Jr.,
and is reproduced with his permission, here for the first time.

[2] This incident occurred shortly after Crane entered Lafayette College in September. This tug of war for the flag was probably the inspirational source of the contest between the enemy flag-bearers in *The Red
Badge of Courage.*

infatuations was reciprocated. His affair with Miss Trent forms one strand of *The Third Violet*, as Wilson Follett points out. Earlier, while at the Hudson River Institute, Crane was in love with Miss Harriet Mattison, a redhead; she died, and then there was a tall dark girl from Sioux City, and later another redhead, Jennie Pierce, whom he loved "madly" at seventeen. He said that if he ever met a woman with golden hair he would marry her. He found her at Jacksonville, Florida, in November 1896 and he married her the next year—Cora Taylor, who lived with him as wife during his last years in England. Beer makes no mention of three women who played an important part in Crane's life: Lily Brandon and Nellie Crouse, who were pursued by Crane, and Amy Leslie, who seems to have been in love with Crane—at any rate she pursued him!

The three notes to Helen Trent are reprinted from *Stephen Crane*, by Thomas Beer, in *Hanna, Crane, and The Mauve Decade* (1941), pp. 256–7. John Berryman gives an account of Helen Trent in his *Stephen Crane* (1950), pp. 28–9.]

[Lake View, N.J.] [1]
September 18, '91

Dear Miss Trent:

I have found out something that you should know at once and will be up this evening to tell you.

Yours,

S. C.

TO HELEN TRENT

[undated leaf from
yellow notebook]

Your window was lighted all last night but they said you were not in. I stood and looked at your window until a police-man came and made me go away. But I came back and looked until my head was just a sponge of lights. Please do not treat me like this. Nothing else counts but that.

---

[1] Lake View was Edmund Crane's home, later at Hartwood, a hamlet of Sullivan County not far from Port Jervis, where William Crane lived.

TO HELEN TRENT

[September 20, 1891]
You have the most beautiful arms I ever saw.[1] You never should have to wear dresses with sleeves. If I could keep your arms nothing else would count. It would not matter if there was nothing else to hope for in the world or if there was no more world. In dreams, don't you ever fall and fall but not be afraid of anything because somebody safe is with you? I shall be here tomorrow. I must get back to Ed's house, now.

TO ODELL HATHAWAY [1]

Dear old man:

Are you dead? Why dont you write to a fellow? I think you owe me a letter, you terrier. I received a letter from the Rushville Indian. He is well, and evidently happy. He says he is "going to be married to a girl whom" he "really loves" See?

I often think of you, old man, and wonder what has become of you and if you ever think of the old times at C.C. and remember your old friends.

Write to me, now, damn you.

Yours always truly
Stephen Crane

Lake View, N. J.
Feb. 10, 92

---

[1] This love-note transposes into the poem in *The Black Riders*, No. X:
Should the wide world roll away,
Leaving black terror,
Limitless night,
Nor God, nor man, nor place to stand
Would be to me essential,
If thou and thy white arms were there,
And the fall to doom a long way.

[1] The original letter is in the possession of Mr. Odell S. Hathaway, Jr., and is reproduced with his permission, here for the first time.

TO ACTON DAVIES

[New York City]
[May 29, 1892]

Dear Acton:

Please send me $5 by this bearer whose name is only Smith. Am going to Ed's[1] at Lakeview and need some grub. Other wise I shall eat the front door, his baby and the cat.

S. C.

TO THE MANAGER OF THE AMERICAN PRESS ASSOCIATION [1]

The New Jersey Coast News Bureau, *To* Manager
J. Townley Crane, Manager, The American Press
Stephen Crane, Secretary, Asso. NY
Edgar C. Snyder, Treasurer.

Asbury Park, N. J.,
August 25 *1892*

My dear sir:

I am going south and, also, west this fall and would like to know I could open up a special article trade with you.[2] I have written special articles for some years for the

---

[1] Edmund Crane. Stephen's family knew nothing of his privations. He told Karl Harriman in 1899: "I was foolishly proud back then. I hated to borrow money from my brothers who were not too well off. I borrowed too much which I have never paid back. The sane thing would have been simply to have lived with Will or Ed constantly and trusted to fortune for some luck in paying them back. They have never asked me for a cent and that hurts like hellfire." (My source here is a letter written by Thomas Beer, January 30, 1923.)

[1] The original of this letter is in the possession of the Huntington Library (HM 3996) and is here reprinted, by permission of the Trustees of The Henry E. Huntington Library and Art Gallery, for the first time.

[2] Crane did not go west until 1895, and then for the Bacheller syndicate.

Tribune and other papers. Much of my work has been used by
the various press associations, and I would like to deal directly
with you if possible. Kindly let me know if it would be worth
my while to send you copy for consideration.

Yours very truly

Stephen Crane

TO THE LIBRARIAN OF CONGRESS [1]

[about January 18, 1893]

Librarian of Congress:

Enclosed find a printed copy of the
title page of a book [2] written by me, and one dollar, for which
please send a copy of the record of the copyright which is
applied for, to

Stephen Crane

1064 Eastern Boulevard

N. Y.

TO ODELL HATHAWAY [1]

[1893?]

[Hartwood, Sullivan County, N.Y.]

Hello, you old devil. I was going through here today on the
Ontario & Western and thought I would drop you a line. How's
things anyhow. You never answer a mans letters so thought

---

[1] This letter was first published in *Stephen Crane: A Bibliography*, by
Ames W. Williams and Vincent Starrett (John Valentine, 1948), p. 13.

[2] The book was *Maggie*, but it was copyrighted without the title
Maggie. Crane's typewritten title-page had simply: *A Girl of the Streets,/
A Story of New York./—By—/Stephen Crane.* The Librarian received
Crane's request for copyright on the 19th; Crane's handwritten letter has
the letterhead of the Pendennis Club.

[1] The original letter is in the possession of Mr. Odell S. Hathaway, Jr.,
and is reproduced with his permission, here for the first time.

you might be dead. Write to me at Hartwood Sullivan County, NY, or I'll come down and wipe you off the earth, the same as I used to at H.R.I.

Yours as ever
Stephen Crane

TO LILY BRANDON MUNROE [1]

[1064 Avenue A]
[March 1893]

Dearest L. B.,

I am sure that you have not concluded that I have ceased to remember. The three months which have passed have been months of very hard work to S. Crane. I was trying to see if I was worthy to have you think of me. . . . Well, at least, I've done something. I wrote a book. . . .[2] And I? I have merely thought of you and wondered if you cared that they said these things. Or whether you have forgotten?

TO MRS. ARMSTRONG

[April 2, 1893]

Thank you very much for letting me keep these so long.[1] I have spent ten nights writing a story of the war on my own responsibility but I am not sure that my facts are real and the books won't tell me what I want to know so I must do it all over again, I guess.

---

[1] This letter is reprinted from *Stephen Crane,* by John Berryman, p. 45. Copyright 1950 by William Sloane Associates.

[2] The book, according to Berryman (p. 52), was *Maggie.*

[1] The Century's *Battles and Leaders of the Civil War.* This note to Mrs. Armstrong is, as Beer says, "the birth notice" of *The Red Badge of Courage.* Crane had now written the first draft; the story as yet had no name. Reprinted from Beer, p. 281.

[1893]

[Inscribed on a copy of *Maggie*]

It is inevitable that you will be greatly shocked by the book but continue, please, with all possible courage, to the end. For it tries to show that environment is a tremendous thing in the world and frequently shapes lives regardless. If one proves that theory one makes room in Heaven for all sorts of souls, notably an occasional street girl, who are not confidently expected to be there by many excellent people.

It is probable that the reader of this small thing may consider the author to be a bad man; but obviously that is a matter of small consequence to

The Author

TO HAMLIN GARLAND

[1893 [1]]

[Inscribed across the cover of a copy of *Maggie*]

It is inevitable that you will be greatly shocked by this book but continue please with all possible courage to the end. For it

---

[1] Crane repeated this inscription almost word for word in the presentation copy of *Maggie* inscribed to the Reverend Thomas Dixon (1895?) and again in the copy inscribed to Hamlin Garland (1893). Crane wrote to Button from San Antonio, Texas, on March 12, 1895.

Reprinted from *23 Books: The Stories behind Them*, by John T. Winterich (1939), p. 124.

[1] A note about this copy of *Maggie* in the holograph of Hamlin Garland reads: "The first copy Crane sent to me, probably about Oct. '92 H. G." Garland must be incorrect in this dating, as *Maggie* was not published until "sometime between late February and May 1893, since a printed copy was reviewed by Hamlin Garland in the June 1893 issue of *The Arena*." (Williams: *Bibliography*, p. 14.)

In *Stephen Crane* (1950) John Berryman says that the copy of *Maggie* which Crane posted to Garland "just said: 'The reader of this book must tries to show that environment is a tremendous thing in the world and frequently shapes lives regardless. If one proves that theory one makes room in Heaven for all sorts of souls (notably an occasional street girl) who are not confidently expected to be there by many excellent people.

It is probable that the reader of this small thing may consider the Author to be a bad man, but, obviously, this is a matter of small consequence to

The Author

TO JOHN NORTHERN HILLIARD [1]

[about summer of 1893]

. . . As far as myself and my own meagre success are concerned, I began the battle of life with no talent, no equipment, but with an ardent admiration and desire. I did little work at school, but confined my abilities, such as they were, to the diamond. Not that I disliked books, but the cut-and-dried curriculum of the college did not appeal to me. Humanity was a

inevitably be shocked, but let him keep on till the end, for in it the writer has put something important'" (p. 64). If this quotation is correct, Crane inscribed two copies of *Maggie* to Garland, but it may be that the discrepancy is to be accounted for by supposing that Garland is misquoting the above copy.

The original is in the possession of Mr. Josiah K. Lilly and is reproduced with his permission, here for the first time.

[1] Crane knew Hilliard personally—well enough to borrow from him a suit of clothes to use for his appearance at the dinner William Dean Howells gave him in the spring of 1893. By 1895 Hilliard was associated with the *Rochester Union and Advertiser*. Hilliard published three of Crane's letters in the *New York Times, Supplement,* July 14, 1900. Only one of these is identified in Hilliard's article as having been written to him—namely, the letter written probably in 1897 from England. He says that the present letter was written "two years after [Crane's] leaving college, when his name was first becoming known . . . when he was struggling for a precarious living in New York City writing local reports and sketches for the newspapers . . . and working at odd times on his story of the civil war."

much more interesting study. When I ought to have been at recitations I was studying faces on the streets, and when I ought to have been studying my next day's lessons I was watching the trains roll in and out of the Central Station. So, you see, I had, first of all, to recover from college. I had to build up, so to speak. And my chiefest desire was to write plainly and unmistakably, so that all men (and some women) might read and understand. That to my mind is good writing. There is a great deal of labor connected with literature. I think that is the hardest thing about it. There is nothing to respect in art save one's own opinion of it.

TO HOLMES BASSETT [1]

[1893?]

[Inscribed on a copy of *Maggie*]

This work is a mudpuddle, I am told on the best authority. Wade in and have a swim.

TO LILY BRANDON MUNROE [1]

[143 East 23rd Street
New York City]
[Fall of 1893]

Dearest:

Although I do not now know what I am to you. . . . Many months—or a thousand years: I hardly know—have passed

---

[1] Bassett, in Ottawa, must have been surprised upon receiving this copy of *Maggie* to discover that his friend was an author.
Reprinted from Beer, p. 288.

[1] Crane thought he would be going to Europe soon and he begged Lily Brandon to write him—"Even though you can only consistently be cold, do me this grace. . . ." In March of 1894 he wrote her again:

Don't forget me, dear, never, never, never. For you are to me the only woman in life. I am doomed, I suppose, to a lonely existence of since we met and were comrades; I can readily see that, in that time, I have, perhaps, become a memory to you, a mere figure in a landscape of the past. And it is well for you if it [is] so, and for it I must be glad. Yet you, to me, are still a daily vision. . . . Your face is a torturing thing. . . . It is beyond me to free myself from the thrall of my love for you; it comes always between me and what I would enjoy in me—always—like an ominous sentence—the words of the parrott on the death-ship: "We are all damned."

And yet, would I escape from it? Not I. It is the better part. . . . I would not give up one small remembrance of your companionship. Yet, with it, I suffer and I wished you to know it because you are a woman and though [you] may value me as a straw, you will comprehend. . . . For, surely, it is a small thing. I ask nothing of you in return. Merely that I may tell you I adore you; that you are the shadow and the light of my life;—the whole of it.

TO HOLMES BASSETT [1]

[February 24, 1894]

. . . I have just sold another book and my friends think it is pretty good and that some publisher ought to bring it out when it has been shown as a serial. It is a war-story and the syndicate people think that several papers could use it.[2]

---

futile dreams. It has made me better. . . . And to it I owe whatever I have achieved and the hope of the future . . . goodbye, beloved. These letters are reprinted from Berryman, pp. 45–6.

[1] As Beer gives his name; whereas Berryman calls him Bassett Holmes (p. 138). Bassett was an Englishman. "Met him in a whorehouse in New York when we were kids" (Crane in a letter to Sanford Bennett, August 29, 1899).

[2] According to Beer (p. 288), Crane had sold *The Red Badge* to Irving Bacheller, but the words "syndicate people" could also be taken to refer to the McClure, Phillips, and Company. (See page 216.)

TO A FRIEND

[Hamlin Garland lent Crane fifteen dollars to get back from the typewriter agency one part of the manuscript of *The Red Badge of Courage*—there in hock as security for the cost of typing it. But Garland's account in *Roadside Meetings* is not the whole story. Another account, appearing in the *Bookman* for May 1912, is here retold for the first time—in the following letter to Dicon. This fellow journalist borrowed a check for fifteen dollars from his boss and gave it to Crane. When the canceled check with Crane's endorsement came back to Dicon's boss, he felt he had been tricked because he had himself refused to make Crane this very loan. Dicon didn't get any more commissions.]

[late in February 1894]

Dear Dicon:

Beg, borrow or steal fifteen dollars. [McClure's] [1] like the Red Badge and want to make a contract for it. It is in pawn at the typewriter's for fifteen.

Thine,
Steve

TO HAMLIN GARLAND [1]

111 West 33d St., City
Wednesday P.M. [April 18, 1894]

Dear Mr. Garland:

I have not been up to see you because of various strange conditions—notably, my toes are coming through one shoe and I have not been going out into society as much as I might. I hope you have heard about the Uncut Leaves affair.[2] I tried

---

[1] The unnamed publisher was either McClure or Bacheller. Hamlin Garland also lent Crane fifteen dollars for recovery of one half the manuscript of *The Red Badge*. (The typist's bill was thirty dollars.) Cf. Crane's letter to Garland on November 15, 1894.

[1] From *Roadside Meetings*, pp. 201–2. The originals of Crane's letters to Garland are at the University of Southern California Library.

[2] John Barry read Crane's poems before the Uncut Leaves Society at Sherry's on April 14, Crane refusing to read them himself. He waited

to get tickets up to you but I couldn't succeed. I mail you last Sunday's *Press*.[3] I've moved now—live in a flat. People can come to see me now. They come in shoals and say I am a great writer. Counting five that are sold, four that are unsold, and six that are mapped out, I have fifteen short stories in my head and out of it. They'll make a book. The Press people pied some of Maggie, as you will note.[3]

Yours sincerely

Stephen Crane

TO HAMLIN GARLAND [1]

111 West 33d St.,

May 9, 94.

Dear Mr. Garland:

I have not written you because there has been little to tell of late. I am plodding along on the Press [2] in a quiet and effective way. We now eat with charming regularity at least two times per day. I am content and am writing another novel which is a bird.[3] That poem, "The Reformer," which I showed you in behind Daly's Theater, was lost somehow, so I dont think we can ever send it to the *Arena*. I can't remember a line of it.

I saw " *Hannele*." Its reason for being is back somewhere in the Middle Ages, but as an irresponsible, artistic achievement, its great. I sat and glowed and shivered.

When anything happens, I'll keep you informed. I'm getting lots of free advertising. Everything is coming along nicely now.

---

down the street for Louis Senger and Corwin Linson to report on the reception his poetry made on the society. The *Tribune* quoted Crane as saying that he "would rather die than do it." One is reminded of Crane's Whilomville story *The Making of an Orator*. The one time Crane did make a speech was at the banquet honoring him on December 19 the next year, the banquet given by the Philistine Society.

[3] The *New York Press* of Sunday, April 15, 1894.

[1] Reprinted from *Roadside Meetings*, by Hamlin Garland, pp. 200–1.

[2] The *New York Press*. Edward Marshall was Sunday Editor.

[3] *George's Mother*. See letter to Garland of November 15, 1894.

I have got the poetic spout so that I can turn it on or off.[4] I wrote a decoration day thing for the *Press* which aroused them to enthusiasm. They said, in about a minute, though, that I was firing over the heads of the soldiers. I am going to see your brother soon. Don't forget to return to New York soon for all the struggling talent miss you.[5]

Yours as ever,
Stephen Crane

TO ODELL HATHAWAY [1]

Hartwood, Sul Co, N.Y.[2]
Sept 7 [1894]

My dear Odell:

It was a perfectly shameful thing in me not to have answered your letter sooner but it was a difficult thing to write letters at camp and since my arrival here at Hartwood tonight has been my first real opportunity. I was very glad to hear from you but I felt ashamed too because it recalled to me those days when you used to make weekly demands that I come to Middletown to visit. God always interferes when I try to stop off at Middletown. I have never succeeded in seeing any more of it than can be percieved from the railroad tracks altho the Powelson used occasionally to ask me after you quit, and one might think that God would not seriously oppose anything that a Powelson was in. I have been wondering what has

---

[4] Crane wrote his first poems in the spring of 1893. He brought Garland then a dozen poems written on legal-cap paper and in Garland's presence he jotted down some poems that were in his head but had not yet been drawn off. Gradually the "poetic spout" dried up, but now a year later he has it again so that he can "turn it on or off." What inspired that first visitation of the poetic ghost was his hearing Emily Dickinson's poetry read to him by William Dean Howells, in March or April 1893.

[5] Garland was now in Chicago; he remained in the West all this year.

[1] The original letter is in the possession of Mr. Odell S. Hathaway, Jr., and is reproduced with his permission, here for the first time.

[2] At Edmund Crane's home; Edmund moved from Lake View probably in the fall of 1893, some time prior to the summer of 1894.

become of the Sioux Indian and the other stars of the third hall
at Claverack. If you have received any letters from them let me
know. In the meantime I shall soon make a violent struggle to
reach Middletown. And at any rate I remain always grateful to
you for your remembrances of the old days at H.R.I.

Yours_____
Stephen Crane

TO COPELAND & DAY [1]

Interlaken Camp—
Parker's Glen
Pike Co., Penn.

Messrs Copeland and Day:—

Dear sirs:—

I would like to hear from you concerning my
poetry. I wish to have my out-bring all under way by early fall
and I have not heard from you in some time. I am in the dark
in regard to your intentions.

Yours very truly
Stephen Crane

Aug. 23 [1894]

[1] Publishers (in Boston) of experimental poetry; described by
Ames W. Williams as being among the first of American publishers at
the turn of the century to issue works of literary merit in an attractive
format. *The Black Riders, and Other Lines* was published in April or May
1895. Crane expected Copeland & Day to bring out the book this year,
1894. In *Month at Goodspeed's,* 9 (1937), 10–14, excerpts of eight of
Crane's letters to Copeland & Day appeared in an article entitled: "Letters of a Shortstop." (An error is made here in the claim that *The Black
Riders* was published in the autumn of 1894.) Prompted no doubt by
the success of *The Red Badge of Courage,* a second edition was issued in
1896, limited to fifty copies and printed in green ink.
The originals of the eight letters described in *Month at Goodspeed's*
are in the possession of Mr. H. B. Collamore and are reproduced with his
permission, here in full for the first time. (One of the eight letters, this
first one of August 23, was printed in full in *Month at Goodspeed's.*)

September 9, 1894

Dear Sirs:

We disagree on a multitude of points. In the first place I should absolutely refuse to have my poems printed without many of those which you just as absolutely mark "No." It seems to me that you cut all the ethical sense out of the book. All the anarchy, perhaps. It is the anarchy which I particularly insist upon. From the poems which you keep you could produce what might be termed a "nice little volume of verse by Stephen Crane," but for me there would be no satisfaction. The ones which refer to God, I believe you condemn altogether. I am obliged to have them in when my book is printed. There are some which I believe unworthy of print. These I herewith enclose. As for the others, I cannot give them up—in the book.

In the second matter, you wish I would write a few score more. It is utterly impossible to me. We would be obliged to come to an agreement upon those that are written.

If my position is impossible to you, I would not be offended at the sending of all the retained lines to the enclosed address. I beg to express my indebtedness to you and remain

Yours sincerely,

Stephen Crane

---

[1] The original of this letter is in the possession of Mr. H. B. Collamore; it is reproduced here with his permission. It first appeared in the *Literary Observer*, 2 (June–July 1934), 57.

TO COPELAND & DAY

143 East 23d St
[October 31, 1894]

Messrs Copeland and Day
Dear Sirs: I enclose copy of title poem.[1]

Sincerely
Stephen Crane

Please note change of address.

TO HAMLIN GARLAND [1]

143 East 23d St, NYC

My dear friend:

So much of my row with the world has to be silence and endurance that sometimes I wear the appearance of having forgotten my best friends, those to whom I am indebted for everything. As a matter of fact, I have just crawled out of the fifty-third ditch into which I have been cast and I now feel that I can write you a letter that won't make you ill. McClure was a Beast about the war-novel and that has been the thing that put me in one of the ditches. He kept it for six months until I was near mad. Oh, yes, he was going to use it; but

---

[1] The title poem of *The Black Riders, and Other Lines*:
> *Black riders came from the sea.*
> *There was clang and clang of spear and shield,*
> *And clash and clash of hoof and heel,*
> *Wild shouts and the wave of hair*
> *In the rush upon the wind:*
> *Thus the ride of Sin.*

(James Joyce's poem "I Hear an Army," published in *Chamber Music*, 1907, bears a striking resemblance to Crane's poem.)

[1] Reprinted from *Roadside Meetings*, by Hamlin Garland, p. 201.

—Finally I took it to Bacheller's. They use it in January in a shortened form.[2] I have just completed a New York book [3] that leaves Maggie at the post. It is my best thing. Since you are not here, I am going to see if Mr Howells will not read it.[4] I am still working for the *Press.*

Yours as ever
Stephen Crane

Thursday Nov 15*th* [1894]

TO COPELAND & DAY

♯143 East 23d St., N.Y.C.
Dec. 10, 94

Messrs Copeland and Day:

Dear sirs: I would like to hear something from you in regard to the poems.

Also, I have grown somewhat frightened at the idea of old English type since some of my recent encounters with it have made me think I was working out a puzzle. Please reassure me on this point and tell me what you can of the day of publication.

Yours sincerely
Stephen Crane

---

[2] Irving Bacheller's syndicate was founded in late 1894, but it was probably in the planning stage much earlier. According to Beer, Crane sold *The Red Badge* for ninety dollars to Bacheller on February 24, 1894. It was syndicated, in shortened form, in early December, a month sooner than Crane expected. It appeared first in the *Philadelphia Press* (December 3–8) and then in the *New York Press* (December 9), as well as in several other newspapers which have not been identified.

[3] This is *George's Mother.* In his letter to Garland in May of this year Crane also refers to it.

[4] Garland was in Chicago. Howells, in fact, preferred *George's Mother* to *The Red Badge.*

TO COPELAND & DAY [1]

‡143 East 23d St. City
15 Dec. 94.

Messrs Copeland and Day

Dear sirs:—There has been no necessity for you to wait impatiently to hear from me for I have answered each of the letters sent to me and at any rate, you have had opportunities to inform me of it since the 31st Oct. The type, the page, the classic form of the sample suits me. It is however paragraphed wrong. There should be none. As to punctuation, any uniform method will suit me. I am anxious to know the possible date of publication.

Yours sincerely
Stephen Crane

TO A FRIEND [1]

[Port Jervis, New York]
[December 1894]

[Recipient unknown]

. . . If you hear that I have been hanged by the neck till dead on the highest hill of Orange County you may as well know that it was for killing a man who is really a pug—No, by the legs of Jehovah! I will not insult any dog by comparing this damned woman to it. There is a feminine mule up here who has roused all the bloodthirst in me and I don't know where it will end. She has no more brain than a pig and all she

[1] The original handwritten letter is in the possession of Mr. H. B. Collamore and is reproduced with his permission, here for the first time. This applies also to the letters of October 31 and December 10.

[1] This letter is reprinted from Beer, pp. 289–90, where it is incorrectly given as belonging to "some date of late November 1894." But *The Red Badge* had not appeared by then; it did not appear until the second week of December in the *New York Press*; it began to appear serially on December 3 in the *Philadelphia Press*. Hence this letter, as the postscript indicates, was written some time after first publication of *The Red Badge*.

does is to sit in her kitchen and grunt. But every when she grunts something dies howling. It may be a girl's reputation or a political party or the Baptist Church but it stops in its tracks and dies. Sunday I took a 13 yr. old child out driving in a buggy. Monday this mule addresses me in front of the barber's and says, "You was drivin' Frances out yesterday" and grunted. At once all present knew that Frances and I should be hanged on twin gallows for red sins. No man is strong enough to attack this mummy because she is a nice woman. She looks like a dried bean and she has no sense, but she is a nice woman. Right now she is aiming all her artillery at Cornelia's [2] new hat. I have been deprived by heaven of any knowledge of hats but it seems to be a very kindly hat with some blue flowers on one side and a ribbon on the other. But we rustle in terror because this maggot goes to and fro grunting about it. If this woman lived in Hester Street some son or brother of a hat would go bulging up to her and say, 'Ah, wot deh hell!' and she would have no teeth any more, right there. She is just like those hunks of women who squat on porches of hotels in summer and wherever their eye lights there blood rises. Now, my friend, there is a big joke in all this. This lady in her righteousness is just the grave of a stale lust and every boy in town knows it. She accepted ruin at the hands of a farmer when we were all 10 or 11. But she is a nice woman and all her views of all things belong on the tables of Moses. No man has power to contradict her. We are all cowards anyhow. Bacheller thinks I had best start for Nevada as soon as possible, maybe before Christmas, but I should like to be with the family, of course.[3]

P.S. Somebody has written clean from California about The Red Badge.

---

[2] Mrs. William Crane. The Port Jervis gossip reappears in *The Third Violet*, in Section XIX of *The Monster*, and Chapter xxi of *The O'Ruddy*. As Wilson Follett points out, "Crane pilloried her over and over again, where she fitted the story and where she did not." Introduction to *Work*, III, xvi.

[3] Crane did not leave for the West until the first week of February 1895

TO COPELAND & DAY [1]

143 East 23d St., N.Y.C.

Dear sirs: I enclose a copy of a recent review in the Philadephia Press.[2] I have a good many notices but none of them are particular. Most of them call me a prominent youth. Another review that I would like to have used was published in the Arena Magazine some time in '92 I think. It was written by Garland.[3] I suppose it could readily be found at the Arena office. Some parts of it would make good extracts

Sincerely yours

Stephen Crane

Sunday [January 6, 1895]

---

[1] The original letter is in the possession of Mr. H. B. Collamore and is reproduced with his permission, here for the first time.

[2] Crane sent Copeland & Day a handwritten copy of Holland's review: "The Work of Stephen Crane." It appeared in the *Philadelphia Press* during the serial appearance of *The Red Badge,* and on the same day there was also an editorial comment on Crane's fiction. Some months before this, Holland had published a letter about *Maggie* in the *Press* and predicted that Crane "would surely make a name for himself in American literature." "He was a shy, almost nervous young man when I saw him and talked with him about the first of his works of fiction which had been published only a few days." That refers to *Maggie,* published in March or April 1893. "At that time *I saw the manuscript* of the story that is now running in 'The Press' as a serial. Then Mr. Crane had some purpose of publishing it in the first instance complete in book form." Berryman says that it is not known whether anyone ever saw the original manuscript of *The Red Badge,* but Holland saw it and Hamlin Garland saw it, in April 1893; and furthermore, a year later, Irving Bacheller saw it. Holland, in "The Work of Stephen Crane," said of *Maggie:* "It contained the evidences of great power, of real imagination, and a sort of poetic quality as well which would be sure to take him out of the list of the perfunctory realists."

[3] Garland's review in the *Arena* appeared in June 1893. Copeland & Day brought out an ad announcing publication of *The Black Riders* and quoted here some of Garland's remarks about *Maggie* made in his *Arena* review: "With such a technique already in command, with life mainly before him, Stephen Crane is to be henceforth reckoned with . . . a man who impresses the reader with a sense of almost unlimited resource."

143 East 23d, NYC
[January 10, 1895]

Dear sirs:

The notice by Mr Garland is in the June 93 number of the Arena on page 12 of the book notices.

I had no dedication in mind for the volume [2] but on second thoughts I would like to dedicate it to Hamlin Garland in just one line, no more:

TO HAMLIN GARLAND

My friend, the artist,[1] is very busy but if you will send him here an exact rendering of the words of the cover, he may submit something shortly.

The book I wrote some time ago is difficult to procure but if I can get one I will send it to you.

Sincerely yours
Stephen Crane

---

[1] This letter is in the possession of Mr. Josiah K. Lilly and is reproduced with his permission, here for the first time.

[2] *The Black Riders* (Crane's second published book) was dedicated to Garland without Garland's knowing about it. See Crane's letter to him on July 17, 1895.

[1] Frederic C. Gordon, the artist friend who did the decorations for *The Black Riders.* Crane lived with him during part of the previous year and finished writing *The Red Badge* in Gordon's studio in the old Art Students' League building in October. Gordon's original cover design for *The Black Riders* is described in his letter to Copeland & Day. (The original is in the possession of Mr. H. B. Collamore. It was reproduced in Ames Williams's *Bibliography,* p. 16.)

Messrs. Copeland & Day

Gentlemen—

In another package I mail you a design for cover of Mr. Crane's poems. It is drawn twice the dimensions of the book. The same de-

143 East 23d St.

[Monday] Jan 14, 94 [1895 [2]]

Dear sirs: I start for the west on a very long and circuitous newspaper trip on the last day of this week.[3] I end ultimately in the City of Mexico. I will probably not return before the book is issued. If you can send me more proofs this week, I would like it. I will try to establish a means of cummunication with you. Any answer to a letter of mine will have to be sent very promptly or it will not reach me, as I travel quickly from city to city.

I send you a list of personal friends who would like to get that notice of the poems. I can use many more if you will send them to me in the west. Kindly preserve the list and return it to me when you have finished with it.

Yours sincerely

Stephen Crane

Will you please send, as I requested, the size of the cover, the exact lettering upon it, and, if possible, the probable thickness of the book. The artist needs it.

---

sign, with title and author's name omitted is intended for the back of the book.

The orchid, with its strange habits, extraordinary forms and curious properties, seemed to me the most appropriate floral motive, an idea in which Mr. Crane concurred before he left New York. I have just mailed him a tracing of the design.

Will you kindly let me know whether it suits your requirements.

Very truly yours,

F. C. Gordon

[1] The original handwritten letter is in the possession of Mr. H. B. Collamore and is reproduced with his permission, here for the first time.

[2] Crane misdated this.

[3] Berryman neglected this letter and the one to Copeland & Day written on January 18. Crane did not begin his trip until the last week of January, about the 28th. Berryman says that Crane "lingered at least until January 10th" (p. 95).

TO COPELAND & DAY

143 East 23d St.

Dear sirs: The artist wishes to know what you mean by the phrase: "Both sides the same" in relation to the book cover.

My journey to the west is delayed for ten days

Yours sincerely

Stephen Crane

Friday [January 18, 1895 [1]]

Please dont destroy Ms.[2]

Crane

TO THE REVEREND THOMAS DIXON

[about January 1895]

[Inscribed on a copy of *Maggie* [1]]

It is inevitable that this book will greatly shock you, but continue, pray, with great courage to the end, for it tries to show

---

[1] The postmarked envelope is dated January 19, but Friday of this week in January 1895 fell on the 18th. This letter is not among the eight letters listed in *Month at Goodspeed's*. The original is in the possession of Mr. H. B. Collamore and is reproduced with his permission, here for the first time.

[2] The handwritten manuscript of one of the poems, No. II in *The Black Riders* ("Three little birds in a row"), answers perfectly Conrad's description of Crane's "regular, legible, perfectly controlled handwriting." It is written on paper measuring 7⅞ by 4⅝ inches, and it is without any correction. It was used by the printer. (This manuscript is in the possession of Mr. H. B. Collamore.) Crane's first batch of poems, written in three days shortly after his visit in March or April 1893 with William Dean Howells, was written on legal-cap paper, according to Hamlin Garland's recollection of the manuscript Crane brought him.

[1] Reprinted here for the first time from the *Bookman* of May 1895, where it appeared in an unsigned article. The copy with this inscription written across the cover was addressed to the Reverend Thomas Dixon "a few months ago, before the author went West on a journalistic trip to Nebraska." Crane began his trip west as a writer for Irving Bacheller's syndicate about January 28 or during the first week of February. My con-

that environment is a tremendous thing in the world, and often shapes lives regardlessly. If one could prove that theory, one would make room in Heaven for all sorts of souls (notably an occasional street girl) who are not confidently expected to be there by many excellent people.

TO CLARENCE LOOMIS PEASLEE [1]

Lincoln, Nebraska
February 12, 1895

. . . As far as myself and my own meagre success are concerned, I began the war with no talent, but an ardent admiration and desire. I had to build up. I always want to be unmistakable.[2] That to my mind is good writing. There is a great deal of labor connected with literature. I think that is the hardest thing about it. There is nothing to respect in art, save one's own opinion of it.

jecture about this inscription is that it was Clarence Peaslee who made it known to the *Bookman*. He did the same thing with the letter Crane wrote him from Nebraska on February 12, 1895, making it public about eighteen months later in the *Monthly Illustrator*. Crane's inscribed copies of *Maggie* presented to Hamlin Garland and to Dr. Lucius L. Button of Rochester differ from this inscription to Dixon only in a few phrasings and by a last sentence not quoted here by the *Bookman* or perhaps not included by Crane in this version.

[1] Peaslee was Crane's fraternity brother at Syracuse University, spring of 1891. He printed this much of the letter in the *Monthly Illustrator*, 13 (1896) 28. A letter that Hilliard quoted in the *New York Times, Supplement*, July 14, 1900, p. 466, seems practically a copy of this one. (See the letter to Hilliard here dated as summer of 1893.) In Beer the letter to Peaslee is incorrectly given as of February 13.

[2] By "unmistakable," Crane means *lucid*. In his letter to Hilliard (1897) he says: "I endeavored to express myself in the simplest and most concise way." Again: "My chiefest desire was to write plainly."

TO DR. LUCIUS L. BUTTON [1]

Mahncke Hotel
San Antonio, Texas
March 12, 1895

My dear Button: [2]

I am about to venture into Mexico and sever my relations with the United States postal service so it will cost you five cents to answer this note—Hotel Iturbide, City of Mexico—

I would tell you of many strange things I have seen if I was not so bored with writing of them in various articles. This note is merely an attempt to cajole a letter out of you.

There is one thing however—I met a most intolerable duffer in New Orleans. No doubt his ingenuous Akron spirit was amazed at many scenes but for my own part I felt that he should have controlled his emotion.

It is hard to feel kindly toward a man who makes you look like an unprecedented idiot and while I had only a general and humane objection to his making an ass of himself, I felt differently about myself.

He enthusiastically requested me to stop off on my way home in the spring and visit him. I modestly replied that while I appreciated his generosity and his courage, I had to die early in the spring and I feared that I would have to hurry home for

---

[1] The original of this letter is in the possession of Dartmouth College Library and is reproduced by permission of the Trustees of Dartmouth College, here in full for the first time. (Berryman quotes parts of this letter, p. 101, but not accurately.)

[2] It was through Dr. Button that Crane met Nellie Crouse, in a house on 34th Street in New York City, and then a year after this single meeting with her he wrote her seven letters in the winter of 1895-6, during a period of three months. She, too, came from Akron, Ohio.

On March 8 Crane was in New Orleans. He sent the manuscript of *The Red Badge of Courage* to Ripley Hitchcock, editor at Appleton's, from New Orleans on March 8.

Beer describes Crane's scarce letters from San Antonio as "almost childish" (p. 293).

the funeral but I had an open date in 1997 and would be happy to see him in hell upon that occasion.

Well, at any rate, I lie, for I was considerate of him, treated him well at times, and was careful of his childish innocence. But there should be a tariff on that kind of an export from Akron, O.

Tell Tommie Parson that this is a straight tip upon the quality of his rivals, named Butler who let it be known that he was from Akron, O., although I dont see why he should. He told me that he knew your friends there or your friends, who have escaped or are about to escape or are planning to escape, or are about to plan to escape from there.

He had fingers like lightning rods and on the street he continually pointed at various citizens with the exclamation: "Look at that fellow!" People in New Orleans don't like that sort of thing, you know.

I am off for Mexico tonight.

Yours as ever
S. C.

P.S. Be good!

TO ODELL HATHAWAY [1]

The American Club
City of Mexico
My dear Wick:

This is to say that I am well and am going to ascend Popocatapetl. Wether I will be well afterward is a matter for speculation. Give my adieus in a general manner to Middletown.

Yours Sincerely
Stephen Crane

Hotel Iturbide
City Mexico
March 30, 1895

[1] The original letter is in the possession of Mr. Odell S. Hathaway, Jr., and is reproduced with his permission, here for the first time.

TO A YOUNG BOY

[San Antonio, Texas]
[April 1895]

[Edward Grover, a sixteen-year-old boy, ran away from his Chicago home to become a cowboy. Crane, finding him sobbing and penniless on the Alamo Plaza, took him to a restaurant, fed him, and paid his fare on a homebound train. An uncle met him at St. Louis and wired Crane the money to repay him. Crane's letter, undated, is reprinted from Beer, page 294. Crane used the word *kid*, as Beer explains, long before it was popular in fiction.]

Dear Deadeye Dick:

Thanks for sending back my money so fast. The hotel trun me out, as my friends of the Bowery say and I was living in the Mex diggings with a push of sheep men till my boss in New York wired me money. Now, old man, take some advice from a tough jay from back East. You say your family is all right and nobody bothers you. Well, it struck me that you are too young a kid and too handsome to be free and easy around where a lot of bad boys and girls will take your pennies. So better stay home and grow a mustache before you rush out into the red universe any more.

Yours sincerely,
Stephen Crane

Wm. H. Crane
Attorney & Counselor at Law,
Port Jervis, N.Y.
Rooms 1 & 2 Farnum Building

Port Jervis, N.Y.
May 29 [1895]

Dear sirs: If it is convenient for you at this time I would greatly like a settlement in the matter of *The Black Riders.*

Sincerely yours
Stephen Crane

The Hartwood Club

Port Jervis, N.Y.
June 8, '95

Messrs Copeland and Day

Dear Sirs: I returned from Mexico some days ago but have come up here for a time because I am not in very good health. I would be glad to learn of the Black Riders. I see they are making some stir. My address will be % Lantern Club, 126 Williams St. NYC.

Yours Sincerely
Stephen Crane

---

[1] The original letter is in the possession of Mr. H. B. Collamore and is reproduced with his permission, here for the first time.

[1] This is letter No. 7 in the *Month at Goodspeed's* article. No. 8 is a short note of August 3, 1895, written from Parker's Glen, Pike County, Pennsylvania, asking Copeland & Day to forward a copy of *The Black Riders* to a friend. As Crane puts it: "Dear sirs: Please forward a 'Black Riders' to the enclosed gentleman." These letters are in the possession of Mr. H. B. Collamore and are reproduced with his permission, here for the first time.

TO HAMLIN GARLAND [1]

Lantern Club
126 William St.,
New York City
[July 17, 1895]

Dear Mr. Garland:

I have lost your address and so for certainty's sake send this to the Arena. I am just returned from my wanderings in Mexico.[2] Have you seen *The Black Riders*. I dedicated them to you but I am not sure that I should have done it without your permission? Do you care? I am getting along better—a little better—than when I last saw you. I work for the Bachellers.[3]

TO COPELAND & DAY [1]

#126 Williams St
[Lantern Club]
New York City
[1895]

Messrs Copeland and Day
    Dear sirs
        I cant seem to light on a copy of Maggie.

I have considerable work that is not in the hands of publishers. My favorites are eight little grotesque tales of the woods which I wrote when I was clever.[2] The trouble is that they only sum 10000 words and I can make no more.

---

[1] Reprinted from *Roadside Meetings*, by Hamlin Garland, p. 202.

[2] It would appear from Crane's statement that he did not return from Mexico until mid-July, but he had returned more than a month earlier. The letter of June 8 to Copeland & Day is important therefore, since it corrects this one. Crane's trip to the West lasted just four months, from the first week in February to the first week in June.

[3] The Bacheller and Johnson syndicate.

[1] The original of this letter is in the possession of Mr. Josiah K. Lilly and is reproduced with his permission, here for the first time.

[2] His Sullivan County sketches.

If you think you can make one of your swell little volumes of 10000, the tales would gain considerable lengthy abuse no doubt.

Mr Howells wishes the Black Riders to review in Harper's Weekly. Jordan of Current Literature wishes it for the same reason. If you could send me a few at the Lantern Club, I would like them. I am particularly anxious to see the green ones.[3]

I see they have been pounding the wide margins, the capitals and all that but I think it great.

Yours sincerely
Stephen Crane

TO LILY BRANDON MUNROE

[Lantern Club, N.Y.C.]
[about mid-July 1895]

My dear L. B.:

Copeland and Day of Boston which [for wish] to reprint those old Sullivan County tales of mine and there is no one in the world has any copies of them but you. Can you not send them to me?[1]

Are you coming north this summer? Let me know, when you send the stories. I should like to see you again.

Yours as ever,
S. C.

---

[3] Printed subsequently to the original edition, bound in gray. The edition printed in green ink and limited to fifty copies has the date *1895* on the white paper label pasted on the spine. A third edition of *The Black Riders* was issued jointly by Copeland & Day and William Heinemann in 1896. Cf. Williams's *Bibliography*, pp. 16–17.

[1] Copeland & Day did not publish them. They were not published in book form until 1949, when Melvin Schoberlin brought out *The Sullivan County Sketches*. Three of them appeared in the collected *Work of Stephen Crane*, edited by Wilson Follett, published by Knopf, 1925–7.

TO WILLIS BROOKS HAWKINS

[Willis Brooks Hawkins, editor of the Brains Publishing Company and a charter member of the Lantern Club, was Crane's best friend. The Lantern Club was the literary hangout for a group of newspapermen and aspiring writers meeting in an old shanty near the Brooklyn Bridge for lunches and poker games and Saturday night sessions of readings and criticisms of manuscripts submitted by one or another of its members. The members included Edward Marshall, Ned Townsend, Don Seitz, Irving Bacheller as president, Hawkins, and Crane. All good fellows, as Bacheller said, "but able borrowers," and the ablest of them all no doubt was Stephen Crane. Hawkins was always helping him out of tight spots with money, an overcoat, or just good advice. His literary underwriter, Hawkins was also one of the four executors of a will that Crane drew up in 1897, and he got the best part of Crane's literary estate—the gift of the original manuscript of *The Red Badge of Courage*, which Crane sent him early the preceding year as an expression of gratitude. "Thought maybe you'd like it." Hawkins probably felt proud to appear beside his famous friend in *The Lanthorn Book*, a collection of tales and verses "Read at the Sign o' the Lanthorn" and published in 1898.

Writing to Hawkins put Crane in the mood to discuss anything but a literary idea. He was more inclined to describe what happened while sailing a catfish boat on the lake at Hartwood, mention some girls in the camp at Parker's Glen, or recount experiences with a bicycle when he was a boy in military school. They did not discuss literature; they knew each other too well for that. When Crane did pour out his literary soul, it was to a woman he knew only slightly and to another woman he knew not at all.

Here, beginning with this letter of August 9, 1895, are twenty-eight letters to Willis Hawkins selected from the Stephen Crane Collection of Mr. Clifton Waller Barrett. The last one was written in mid-April 1897, Crane writing to his friend from Greece. This set of Crane's letters to Hawkins is reprinted—here for the first time—with the permission of Mr. Barrett.

Hawkins wrote a running commentary on these Crane letters for a Chicago collector who first purchased them, but his account—evidently lost—has not come to light.]

Parker's Glen
Pike Co., Penn.
August 9, '95

My dear Willis:

I am cruising around the woods in corduroys and feeling great. I have lots of fun getting healthy. Feel great.

If anything in the way of notices comes out and you see it, send them to me here for I feel out of the world.[1]

There are six girls in camp and it is with the greatest difficulty that I think coherently on any other subject.[2]

Wish you could come up some Sunday. Only—it is with the greatest trouble that any one can reach here. Four deadly miles up the mountain from the Erie's station at Parker's Glen. If you would care to do it let me know and I will tell you how to do it.

My remembrances to Mrs. Hawkins and to Florence.

Yours, as ever,
S. C.

---

[1] Review notices of his book of poems, *The Black Riders, and Other Lines,* published in May.

[2] Crane had an eye for pretty girls. In a letter of January 9, 1891, written almost immediately after arriving at the Delta Upsilon house at Syracuse University, he told a friend:

". . . I hope you may all come here sometime although the fellows are somewhat slow . . . there are certainly some dam pretty girls here, praise be to God. Not as nice as they are in Newburgh, however. . . . [This is a] dandy city at least, and I expect to see some fun here. . . ."

The original of this letter of 1891 is in the possession of the Syracuse Chapter of Delta Upsilon and is here quoted in part with the permission of Lester G. Wells, Alumni Historian of the Syracuse Chapter of Delta Upsilon and Curator of the Stephen Crane Collection at Syracuse University Library. It was quoted more fully in the Syracuse University *Alumni News* for October 1946, in an article by Wells: "Stephen Crane—Syracusan Extraordinary."

Crane camped at Interlaken the previous summer, 1894; the camp was at Twin Lakes, back of Milford, Pennsylvania.

TO WILLIAM DEAN HOWELLS

[Inscribed in a copy of *The Red Badge of Courage* [1]]

To W. D. Howells this small and belated book as a token of the veneration and gratitude of Stephen Crane for many things he has learned of the common man and, above all, for a certain re-adjustment of his point of view victoriously concluded some time in 1892.

August 17, 1895   Stephen Crane

TO WILLIS BROOKS HAWKINS

Parker's Glen
Pike Co., Penn.
August 18, '95

My dear Willis:

The Philistine people [1] have written to me about the notice of *The Red Badge of Courage* which they wish to bring out in their September number. What shall I say in it. I dont know how to write those notices. Can you advise me

---

[1] Not presented to Howells until 1896. The original presentation copy is in the possession of the New York Public Library and is here reprinted by permission of the Henry W. and Albert A. Berg Collection.

[1] Harry P. Taber and Elbert Hubbard of *The Philistine: A Periodical of Protest,* published at East Aurora, New York. Crane's poems appeared in nearly every issue of the *Philistine* during 1895. A year before the magazine began actual publication (the first issue was in June), Hubbard had bought two articles of Crane, one on slum charities and the other expounding a social theory. Both articles were lost by Hubbard on a train.

Mr. Barrett's collection of letters to Hawkins provides the first full account of Crane's dealings with Hubbard and the *Philistine*. Beer says nothing about this affair except to mention Hubbard, p. 291, and the Philistine banquet, p. 305. These new letters bring to light furthermore an intimate friendship. Berryman says (p. 23) that "Crane had perhaps never any *intimate* friends."

concerning a little notice. [I meant to say *will* you.] I hope you
are awfully well. Did you get my last letter. My remembrances
to all the lanterns.² I am getting mighty anxious to hear the
Apache Scalp Dance again. I will down however in about 2
weeks more.

Yours as always
S. C.

TO WILLIS BROOKS HAWKINS

Office of The Press,
Philadelphia,
Sept. 6, [1895]

Dear Willis:

It is dramatic criticism and nuthin else.¹ I've taken
it and am to go to work at once. I will however be in New York
on Tuesday night for the dinner, and will talk at length to you.
I wrote to Mr. Howells ² today asking him to come to the dinner.

Yours as ever
S. C.

---

² Members of the Lantern Club.

¹ As we see by the letter that follows, Crane's attempt to hire himself
out as a dramatic critic to the *Philadelphia Press* did not succeed. The
Press had accepted in March his one piece of dramatic criticism: "Grand
Opera in New Orleans." Later when in England he and Conrad proposed
writing a Western play, *Predecessor,* and supposedly the two collaborated
in writing another play, *Ghost,* but the only play by Crane that saw print
was *Blood of the Martyr,* in the *Sunday New York Press* in 1898.

² William Dean Howells. The famous dinner with Howells took place
in 1893. These 1895 letters to Hawkins discuss another literary dinner,
the Philistine affair. On both occasions Stephen Crane attended in borrowed clothes. It was in John Hilliard's suit that Crane listened to Howells read Emily Dickinson's poetry in March or April 1893.

TO WILLIS BROOKS HAWKINS

2840 Ridge Ave.
Philadelphia

Dear old man:

Things fell ker-plunk. Stranded here in Phila. Dont you care! Nice town. Got lots of friends, though, and 23,842 invitations to dinner of which I have accepted 2.

The Press wanted me bad enough but the business manager suddenly said: "Nit"

Yours as ever
S. C.

Tuesday. [September 10, 1895]

TO WILLIS BROOKS HAWKINS

2840 Ridge Ave.,
Philadelphia
Sept. 18, [1895]

My dear Willis:

I am going to stay down for a few more days. If you see anything for me in New York holler quick. I am with some friends, pretty good time but I am engaged at last on my personal troubles in Mexico.[1]

Yours as ever
S. C.

---

[1] The "personal troubles" Crane was writing had to do with his having been chased in Mexico by a "fashionable bandit" named Ramón Colorado, the episode which he recast in *Horses—One Dash!* This letter to Hawkins dates the composition of that sketch and identifies the place where it was written. It was published as *One Dash—Horses!* in the *Philadelphia Press* on January 4 and 6, 1896.

TO WILLIS BROOKS HAWKINS

165 W 23d [New York City]
[October 1895]

My dear Willis: [1]

Can you bring over a poker contingent to-
night. The place is all torn to shreds—I'm moving to Hartwood
but would be glad to welcome a poker party.

S. C.

TO WILLIS BROOKS HAWKINS

165 West 23d [New York City]
[October 1895]

My dear Willis:

By all means you fellows come here tonight.
Looked for you this afternoon in the Downing Build'g. This
will be my last game—perhaps. Expect to skip for the country.
Dont let the game fall through.

Yours
S. Crane

TO ODELL HATHAWAY [1]

The Hartwood Club
Hartwood Sul Co, N.Y.
Oct 21st, 1895

My dear Wick:

My brother William H. is running for Surrogate
of Orange County on the Democratic ticket and although I

---

[1] Written on a Western Union telegraph blank. See also Crane's note
to Willis to bring the boys over "for a little fiesta de poke" written in
April 1896.

[1] The original letter is in the possession of Mr. Odell S. Hathaway, Jr.,
and is reproduced with his permission, here for the first time.

know you fellows dont care so much for politics I am immensely interested in seeing the boy make a creditable record for himself wether he gets elected or not. The other man is Howell from here and he isn't so nice. Surrogate isn't much of a political office any how, and you can swallow all the rest of the Republican ticket if you like. Be careful, though, about the mechanical part of it. Understand you know that this is merely a broad general hint and I know too that any kind of a man will do just as he damned pleases in the matter, but—you see how it is. Let me hear wether this makes you made or not. I am going to gun for W.W.W. and A.A., too.

Yours as ever
Stephen Crane

TO ODELL HATHAWAY [1]

Hartwood, N. Y.
Oct 23d, 95

My dear Wick:

I am delighted at your good-nature in the election business. Will is a good fellow and very honest and clever. I would like to snare Arly and Bill Woodward but dont quite know how to go about it as I dont feel that I know them as well as I do you and anyhow I hate to monkey about politics. I used to think that distinquished merit had some weight but it isn't worth a damn, relatively speaking. The man who hustles is the man who gets there and if some honest person is opposing a thief, he wants to be busy or the thief will snow him under, which is, after all, what everybody knows.

I am working pretty well here. Better than in New York. Missed my first partridge today. Crash.

Yours as ever
Stephen Crane

---

[1] The original letter is in the possession of Mr. Odell S. Hathaway, Jr., and is reproduced with his permission, here for the first time.

TO WILLIS BROOKS HAWKINS

Hartwood, Sul. Co., N.Y.
Nov. 1st, 1895

My dear Willis:

My correspondence—incoming—has reached mighty proportions and if I answered them all I would make Hartwood a better class office and my brother a better class postmaster for you know he is a postmaster, justice-of-the-peace, ice-man, farmer, mill-wright, blue stone man, lumber-man, station agent on the P.J.M. and N.Y.R.R. and many other things which I now forget. He and his tribe can swing the majority in the township of Lumberland. By that reference to my correspondents I meant the fellows before the war. They're turning up. Heaven send them somebody to appreciate them more although it is true I write two or three perfunctory little notes each day.[1]

There has been an enormous raft of R. B. of C. reviews and Appleton and Co. have written me quite a contented letter about the sale of the book.[2] Copeland and Day have written for my New York sketches and Appleton and Co. wish to put

---

[1] Perhaps it is this correspondence Beer had in mind when saying that Crane's correspondence is uninteresting. One of these letters dated from Hartwood on February 6 (probably 1896) answered a request for a photograph:

Dear sir:

I don't thing [*sic*] it possible to get my photograph. They have been mostly amateur things.

Very truly yours,
Stephen Crane

This note is reprinted from *Meditations of an Autograph Collector*, by Adrian Joline, published by Harper in 1902, p. 14. The original is in the possession of the Huntington Library.

[2] On December 24 he quoted the Appleton editor: "Mr. Hitchcock tells me that the book does not sell much in New York. It has gone to about 4500, though, and many of them have been sent west." Quoted from Beer, p. 302.

my new story in their Zeit-Geist series, which I leave you alone to pronounce. Devil take me if I give you any assistance.

That's enough about books.

On the bicycle question, I refuse to listen to you. In the old days at military school I once rode a wheel—a high one—about three miles high, I think. An unsmiling young cadet brought one into the armory one morning and as I was his senior officer I took it away from him. I mounted by means of a friend and rode around and around the armory. It was very simple.

When I wished to dismount however I found I couldn't. So I rode around and around the armory. Shafer, who was champion of Pennsylvania in those old high-wheel days, watched me and said I did some things on that wheel which were impossible to him. A group of cadets gathered in a corner and yelled whenever I passed them. I abjured them at intervals to let me off that wheel but they only hollered. At last, I ran into a bench and fell neatly on my head. It broke the machine, too, praise God. Some days later I whipped the boy who had loaned it me. Not for that mind you, but for somethingelse.

I am shooting a good deal. I beat my brother the last time out. That's a good deal.

I have another brother who is running for surrogate of Orange County and I haven't a doubt but that he will achieve a magnificent defeat. For he is a bold Democrat and they're rare birds in Orange.

Give my remembrances cordially to all your people and say that I regret the Apaches and the Pilgrims. Remember me too at the Lantern.

Yours as always
Stephen Crane

TO AN EDITOR OF "LESLIE'S WEEKLY" [1]

[about November 1895]

. . . I can't do any sort of work that I don't like or don't feel like doing and I've given up trying to do it. When I was at school few of my studies interested me, and as a result I was a bad scholar. They used to say at Syracuse University, where, by the way, I didn't finish the course, that I was cut out to be a professional base-ball player. And the truth of the matter is that I went there more to play base-ball than to study. I was always very fond of literature, though. I remember when I was eight years old I became very much interested in a child character called, I think, Little Goodie Brighteyes, and I wrote a story then which I called after this fascinating little person. When I was about sixteen I began to write for the New York newspapers, doing correspondence from Asbury Park and other places. Then I began to write special articles and short stories for the Sunday papers and one of the literary syndicates, reading a great deal in the meantime and gradually acquiring a style. I decided that the nearer a writer gets to life the greater he becomes as an artist, and most of my prose writings have been toward the goal partially described by that misunderstood and abused word, realism. Tolstoï is the writer I admire most of all. I've been a free lance during most of the time I have been doing literary work, writing stories and articles about anything under heaven that seemed to possess interest, and selling them wherever I could. It was hopeless work. Of all human lots for a person of sensibility that of an obscure free lance in literature or journalism is, I think, the most dis-

---

[1] Part of this letter was quoted by Ripley Hitchcock in his Introduction to *The Red Badge of Courage* (1900). It first appeared in *Leslie's Weekly* for May 28, 1896, and it is here reproduced in full for the first time. The article in which it appeared—"The Personality and Work of Stephen Crane," by J. Herbert Welch—is not listed in Ames Williams's *Bibliography*.

couraging. It was during this period that I wrote "The Red Badge of Courage." It was an effort born of pain—despair, almost; and I believe that this made it a better piece of literature than it otherwise would have been. It seems a pity that art should be a child of pain, and yet I think it is. Of course we have fine writers who are prosperous and contented, but in my opinion their work would be greater if this were not so. It lacks the sting it would have if written under the spur of a great need.

But, personally, I was unhappy only at times during the period of my struggles. I was always looking forward to success. My first great disappointment was in the reception of "Maggie, a Girl of the Streets." I remember how I looked forward to its publication, and pictured the sensation I thought it would make. It fell flat. Nobody seemed to notice it or care for it. I am going to introduce Maggie again to the world some time, but not for a good while.[2] Poor Maggie! she was one of my first loves.

I suppose I ought to be thankful to "The Red Badge," but I am much fonder of my little book of poems, "The Black Riders." The reason, perhaps, is that it was a more ambitious effort. My aim was to comprehend in it the thoughts I have had about life in general, while "The Red Badge" is a mere episode in life, an amplification. A rather interesting fact about the story is that it lay for eight months in a New York magazine office waiting to receive attention. I called on the editor[3] time and again and couldn't find out whether he thought it a good story or whether he intended to publish it or not, so at last I took it

---

[2] Crane's viewpoint that literature is the product of "a great deal of labor," as he said in his letter to John N. Hilliard in 1893, is re-echoed here. Again in his letter to Hilliard in 1897 (?) Crane repeats parts of this letter to *Leslie's Weekly*. The letter was probably addressed to J. Herbert Welch, since it appeared in an article by him in *Leslie's Weekly* for May 28, 1896; Welch says that Crane *said* or *wrote* this "the other day," but his letter must be dated much earlier, since *Maggie* was being revised in February 1896. It was published in early June 1896.

[3] McClure.

away. Now that it is published and the people seem to like it
I suppose I ought to be satisfied, but somehow I am not as
happy as I was in the uncertain, happy-go-lucky newspaper
writing days. I used to dream continually of success then. Now
that I have achieved it in some measure it seems like mere
flimsy paper.

TO WILLIS BROOKS HAWKINS

[Hartwood, N.Y.]
[about November 7, 1895]

My dear Willis:

I always considered Field [1] to be a fine simple
spirit and I am glad his death makes you so sad.

I never thought him a western barbarian. I have always believed the western people to be much truer than the eastern
people. We in the east are overcome a good deal by a detestable superficial culture which I think is the real barbarism.
Culture in it's true sense, I take it, is a comprehension of the
man at one's shoulder. It has nothing to do with an adoration
for effete jugs and old kettles. This latter is merely an amusement and we live for amusement in the east. Damn the east! I
fell in love with the straight out-and-out, sometimes-hideous,
often-braggart westerners because I thought them to be the
truer men and, by the living piper, we will see in the next fifty
years what the west will do. They are serious, those fellows.
When they are born they take one big gulp of wind and then
they live.

Of course, the east thinks them ridiculous. When they come
to congress they display a child-like honesty which makes the
old east laugh. And yet—

Garland will wring every westerner by the hand and hail
him as a frank honest man. I wont. No, sir. But what I contend

---

[1] Eugene Field, who died on November 4.

for is the atmosphere of the west which really is frank and honest and is bound to make eleven honest men for one pessimistic thief. More glory be with them.[2]

The novel is one-third completed.[3] I am not sure that it is any good. It is easy work. I can finish a chapter each day. I want you to see it before it goes to the Appletons.

Sometimes I go out sailing in a little boat here. The people are expecting my death shortly for the little boat leans like a shingle on a house—when she tacks—and the November winds are very strong.

My brother William went down in the Democratic wreck. Poor boy.

It is singular that the Republicans won in every place where it was to the glory of God that they should lose, and lost in every place where it was to the glory of God that they should win.

I am very contented here. For a while I felt incarcerated but not now.

Good-bye. My remembrances always to your Greene Ave castle.

Your friend—ever
Stephen Crane

---

[2] An inscribed presentation copy of *George's Mother* (1896) reads: "To Hamlin Garland of the great honest West from Stephen Crane of the false East." In *The Great Gatsby*, F. Scott Fitzgerald uses this theme, though here the West is actually as false as the East. In Garland's *Afternoon Neighbors*, published in 1934, we find Garland shifting his viewpoint. He now dislikes the Middle West!

[3] This is *The Third Violet*, tentatively called "The Eternal Patience" (cf. Williams, p. 127); it was serialized a year later in the *New York Evening World*, Nov. 4–14, and published in book form in 1897. At the end of October he had written "seven chapters in the rough and they have given me the proper enormous interest in the theme." Now about a week later it is "one-third completed." In his November 12 letter to Hawkins we learn that it is "exactly half finished," and then on November 19 it is "two-thirds done." On December 27 he shipped the new novel to Hitchcock to have the manuscript typed. He didn't keep to the beginning speed of a chapter per day but he wrote twenty-six chapters during November and December, and perhaps it was because it all came too easy for him

TO WILLIS BROOKS HAWKINS

Hartwood
Nov. 8 [1895]

Dear Willis:

I sent down to Port Jervis to-day to get hung up for fifty cents worth of tobacco and on the same train with the tobacco came the enclosed interesting cummunications.[1] My dress suit took to the woods long ago and my 1895 overcoat is not due until 1896. I have not owned a pair of patent leather shoes in three years. Write me at once and tell me how to get out of the thing. Of course I am dead sore but I think if you will invent for me a very decent form of refusal, I will still be happy up here with my woods.

Yours as always
S. C.

---

that he was dubious about it. *In name* the hero of *The Third Violet* echoes Willis Hawkins, though with the difference that the hero, William Hawker, is an impressionist painter.

[1] These "communications" were (1) a letter dated November 5 from the Committee for the Philistine Society inviting Crane to attend a proposed dinner to take place at the Iroquois Hotel in Buffalo in about one month, and (2) a letter from Elbert Hubbard urging him to come and praising *The Red Badge*: " 'The Red Badge' is a strong work thoroughly well sustained. I congratulate you on it." The committee letter said: "As soon as we receive your acceptance stating the date that suits you best we will send our invitations to 200 of the best known writers, publishers and newspapermen of the United States and England. . . . We believe that aside from the charming friendly intercourse of the occasion [the actual dinner turned out to be anything but *that*], that the dinner will be of very great value to your books and will lead to a wider recognition of your talent." Evidently Crane (as we see in his next letter to Hawkins) thought so too. Crane made handwritten copies of these letters and sent them to Hawkins at the Lantern Club.

I have made no corrections of Crane's misspellings in these letters. (Crane was as poor a speller as Hemingway is.)

TO WILLIS BROOKS HAWKINS

My dear Willis:

No, you hadnt answered my last letter. Sometimes I dont need a reply because I know you are there and everything is all right. But this time I did need a reply because my sudden escape that day I was supposed to go to your house was upon my conscience very heavily and your majestic silence was a great trouble to me. However, I am perfectly contented with your reply and the way in which you appropriate 50% of the blame. I had been carefully abusing myself for the whole affair and was quite astonished and over-joyed when you volunteered.

I am writing a story—"The Little Regiment" for McClure. It is awfully hard. I have invented the sum of my invention in regard to war and this story keeps me in internal despair. However I am coming on with it very comfortably after all.[1]

The dinner scheme mingles my emotions. In one sense, it portends an Ordeal but in the larger sense it overwhelms me in pride and arrogance to think that I have such friends.[2]

By the way, you ought to see the effect of such things upon

---

[1] It was published in *McClure's Magazine* in June the next year and as the title piece to a volume of that name, in 1896 by Appleton and 1897 by Heinemann. In contrast to the "easy work" of evolving *The Third Violet*, the difficulties he encountered in composing *The Little Regiment* recall the labor of pain which *The Red Badge* cost him. Crane finished the story at the end of February 1896.

[2] The author of these illusions suggests his counterpart Henry Fleming in *The Red Badge*, for the actual dinner at Buffalo was a vulgar orgy of chaos and stupid bickering among the thirty hosts collected in a private room of the Genesee House—not at all the glorious tribute of friends that Crane here anticipates with "pride and arrogance." After the event Crane saw himself as the deluded hero, the dupe of his own vainglorious notions, and it is because of this change of vision that this Philistine affair has importance in any account of Crane's life. (Beer slights the whole thing.) It marked the turning-point in Crane's outlook. The anecdote of the Philistine banquet is written up in the *Bookman*, 69 (July 1928), 478, by Claude Fayette Bragdon.

my family. Aint they swelled up, though! Gee! I simply cant
go around and see 'em near enough. It's great. I am no longer
a black sheep but a star.

Yours, always

S. C.

Hartwood

Tuesday. [November 12, 1895]

TO THE COMMITTEE FOR THE PHILISTINE SOCIETY [1]

Hartwood, N.Y.

Nov. 15, 1895

To Mr. Elbert Hubbard, Mr. Harry P. Taber, Mr. Eugene R.
White, Mr. Wm. McIntosh, Mr. Walter Blackburn Harte,
Mr. S. G. Blythe, Mr. John Northern Hilliard, Mr. Philip
Hale, Mr. Nelson Ayres, Mr. L. H. Bickford, Mr. Marshall
Cushing of the Society of the Philistines.

Gentlemen:

The only obstacle in the way of my accepting an
invitation at once so cordial and so kind is the fact that an ac-

---

[1] The Committee for the Society of the Philistines wrote Crane on
November 10, from East Aurora, New York:

To Mr. Stephen Crane:

Recognizing in yourself and in your genius as a poet, a man whom
we would like to know better, The Society of the Philistines desire to
give a dinner in your honor early in the future. If this meets with
your approval we should be glad if you will let us know upon what
date you could conveniently come to us.

This November 10 invitation letter and Crane's November 15 reply
were printed later this year in a pamphlet entitled *The Members of the
Society*, published by Hubbard's Roycroft Printing Shop, 1895. The
Philistine's invitation, says Berryman (p. 153), "had not mentioned his
novel." But Hubbard had praised *The Red Badge* in his November 5 letter. The accounts by Berryman and Williams on this Philistine affair are
incomplete, as no mention is made of the November 5 letters from Hubbard and the committee.

For photoduplicate copy of these November 10 and 15 letters I am indebted to Melvin Schoberlin.

ceptance, it seems to me, is a tacit admission of my worthiness in the circumstances. Believe me, this sense of embarrassment that I should be at all considered as a fit person for such distinction is my solitary discomfort. But I have industriously blunted this sense and can say that it will deal me great pleasure to dine with the Society of the Philistines on Thursday evening, Dec. 19th.

I beg to thank you, gentlemen, and pray believe me that I am ever

Very Sincerely Yours,
Stephen Crane

TO WILLIS BROOKS HAWKINS

Hartwood, N.Y.
[about November 15, 1895]

My dear Willis:

Upon my soul when I first read your letter I was ashamed that I had written you about it at all. Then when I reflect I find I wrote you because the letter delighted and charmed me and I had to whoop it up to somebody. But heavens, to think you would allow me to make a victim of you! For, blast it all, on the strength of your letter I have accepted the invitation. At first, as I said, I was dismayed at your letter but, confound it, you might understand that I blush for myself more still when I think I was low enough to grab at your generosity.

I told the Philistines that any date in late November or early December would suit me. When they write, you shall hear from me at once. I shall go and I shall have a dandy time. I know and am satisfied that it will do me an immense amount of good. My chest, bad luck to it, measures 35 inches—scant—and my leg is a 33—worse luck. And foot—rot it—is a seven. There! It is over. I feel as if I have told you that I am a damned thief.

Heaven send you rest, Willis, and in your old age may you remember how you befriended the greatest literary blockhead in America from himself.

The novel is exactly half finished. It seems clever sometimes and sometimes it seems nonsensical.[1] I hope to show it you in less than two months. The Evening Post has come out very grandly in support of the Black Riders. And the Boston papers have said some fine things about the Red Badge.

What do you suppose made the Philistines do this dinner thing? Was it because I wrote for their magazine? You could have knocked me down with a gas-pipe when I got their bid. Until today I was very miserable about it for I of course was resolved to refuse the offer. But, bad luck to me again. I was delighted with your letter and accepted it "within-side" of thirty minutes.[2]

The woods up here are all dun and dusk and purple save where there are pines or white birches. The little lake is like blue crystal.

> I am as always Willis
> Your good friend
> Stephen Crane

---

[1] *The Third Violet,* tentatively called "The Eternal Patience." It was serialized in November 1896 in the New York *Evening World* and in *Inter Ocean* and published in book form by Appleton and Heinemann in 1897.

[2] Elbert Hubbard without asking permission printed Crane's letter of acceptance in the Buffalo newspapers, and Crane in commenting on this public appearance of his private letter wrote to Miss Nellie Crouse that he would have been more hypocritical in phrasing it had he known it was to appear in print.

TO WILLIS BROOKS HAWKINS

Hartwood, N.Y.
Nov. 15th [i.e., November 17, 1895] [1]

Dear Willis:

Herein enclosed letter of Hubbard.[2] Write to me quick and tell me that you don't think I am a villian. Would you come out to Buffalo for the dinner?

I am getting frightened already. Imagine me representing a "cause."

Yours always
Stephen

TO WILLIS BROOKS HAWKINS

Hartwood
Nov. 19 [1895]

My dear Willis:

I have no late news from Buffalo, although Hubbard sent me his picture some days ago. He is a clever-looking duck. I hope by all means you can come to the Buffalo dinner. For heaven's sake begin to think about it now and then by the time the day comes around it will seem easy.

There is a clipping bureau in Boston which is said to only send in it's bills once in three months, so when they wrote me the other day I took them up. I got forty-one new reviews of the Red Badge. And, oh, say, most of 'em were not only favor-

---

[1] Crane misdated his letter. The Hubbard letter he enclosed is dated November 16, and therefore Crane must have written this one on the 17th or the 16th. Willis Hawkins answered this letter from Crane probably on the same day he received it, the 18th. Crane is constantly misdating events. In February 1900 he wrote an editor of the *Rochester Post-Express* that he was "precisely" twenty-nine on his last birthday, whereas he was in fact then only twenty-eight.

[2] Hubbard wrote that the dinner was intended to be far more than just "a pleasant meeting and dinner with you. But it is more than this—you represent a 'cause' and we wish in a dignified, public (and at the same time) elegant manner to recognize that cause."

able but passionately enthusiastic. They didn't skirmish around and say maybe—perhaps—if—after a time—it is possible—under certain circumstances—but.[1]

No; they were cock-sure. The above is a fair sample of New York literary criticism. The fellows in Boston, ten of them,— had a real nice fit. In the west, the Chicago Post and the Minneapolis Tribune were the best but there were a lot of other good ones. About six in the patch are roasts. One is a copy of the Tribune's grind. New York, throughout, has treated me worse than any other city. Damn New York. Except the Evening Post. The Evening Post has just reviewed The Black Riders beautifully.

There—I'm through talking about them but then you know there is nobody here whom one can talk to about them at all. It sounds sort of priggish, somehow. And it is I have no doubt excepting that it is right to be elated when almost all the writers and reviewers seem to have really read the thing.

The new novel is two-thirds done.[2] I gave the first eighteen chapters to my brother Teddie to read. He finished them up without a halt. He is an awful stuff in literature. I am a little dubious about his performance. Seems to me it throws rather a grimly humorous light on the situation. Understand, he thinks my style wouldn't be used by the devil to patch his trousers with. I think he—Teddie—discovered the fellow and the girl in the story and read on to find out if they married. He hung around for a time asking for more chapters but I sent him away.

Dont you forget to keep deciding every day that you are coming to the Buffalo thing.

I lost my temper to-day—fully—absolutely—for the first time in a good many years. I sailed the cat-boat up the lake today in the stiffest breeze we've had in moons. When I got near to

---

[1] Two scrapbooks of reviews of Crane's works, compiled by William Crane, are in the Crane Collection of Mr. H. B. Collamore.

[2] *The Third Violet*; Crane sent it to Ripley Hitchcock at Appleton's on December 27.

the head of the lake, the boat was scudding before the wind in a manner to make your heart leap. Then we got striking snags—hidden stumps, floating logs, sunken brush, more stumps,—you might have thought ex-Senator Holman of Indiana was there. Anything that could obstruct, promptly and gracefully obstructed. Up to the 5th stump I had not lost my philosophy but at the 22d I was swearing like cracked ice. And at the appearance of the 164th, I perched on the rail, a wild and gibbering maniac. It is all true. I cant remember when I was so furiously and ferociously angry. Never before, I think.

Teddie has a Belton setter named Judge. When the girls run Judge out of the kitchen, his soul becomes so filled with hate of the world, that outside, he pounces on the first dog he meets. This is all right if it happens to be one of the hounds. They are only pups. He whales them and they roar. But sometimes the first dog he meets is the collie and the collie, after recovering from his surprise, simply wipes up the place with him. But this causes no change in Judge's way. Little dog, or big dog, hound or collie, put him out of the kitchen and he pounces on the first one. This is the way I felt up the pond. But there was nobody there.

Dont you miss the Buffalo dinner.

Yours always

S. C.

TO WILLIS BROOKS HAWKINS

Dec. 20 [for November 20, 1895]

Dear Willis: Date for dinner Wednesday, Dec 18.[1]

Don't say at Lantern Club that you are coming.

Other invitations there supposed to be complimentary.

Do you follow me?

Yours as ever

S. C.

---

[1] The Philistine Society banquet took place on Thursday, December 19, in Buffalo, not at the Iroquois Hotel as originally planned, but at the Genesee House.

TO WILLIS BROOKS HAWKINS

Hartwood
Nov. 25 [1895]

My dear Willis:

I have been frantically hustling of late to make some money but I haven't achieved a cent mainly because I want it so badly. Frank Leslie's Weekly wrote me that my story was very stunning but that the tale "When Greek meets Greek" was going to run until February and they didnt feel justified in buying a serial at this moment. Irving Bacheller had tried hard to accept a story of mine, he said, but he said that he couldn't. Stone and Kimball wrote me that they wanted something for the Chap-book and I immediately fired something at them. I hope for the Lord's sake it goes, but it would be my luck if it didnt.[1] I send you a clipping which may convey a general impression of Red Badge notices—outside of New York.[2]

I have send [for *sent*] a little story to Irving [3] but it is so tiny—the Lantern Club will grab every cent. I tell you these things to convey a sense of how loyally and stoutly I have tried to pull you out of the hole you slid yourself into. When you dont write I begin to think you are disgusted with me. Adios.

Yours as ever
Stephen Crane

---

[1] In March 1896 the *Chap-book* published *In the Night*, a poem.

[2] In the Port Jervis *Union*: "An Extraordinary Work." This article quotes many other newspaper reviews of *The Red Badge* (none of which is listed in the Williams *Bibliography*).

[3] Irving Bacheller. Crane was working for the Bacheller syndicate this year; Bacheller was also a member of the Lantern Club.

[Hartwood, N.Y.]
[about December 15, 1895]

My dear Willis:

You harrow me a little bit. My transportation is to be by the Erie. I was hoping all along that you were going to go by the Erie. You were to be the moral reinforcement which I sought. I cant come to N.Y., because it requires "dough." I have mapped out my two or three shekels so that I will return home smiling but broke and in the smoking-car. I bought to-day one full dress shirt and what goes with it. I have a damn fine hat. I have no overcoat save that little gauze one which you may remember. Nor no dress-suit. My brother has (had) a pair of patent leathers and I am sleeping with them under my pillow. I've got 'em.

There is a peach of a row on in Buffalo. The Saturn Club, the Browning Clubs, etc., have heard somehow of me and—Hubbard says—are planning to dine me. All the *Philistines* are hot. Wrote swearing letters to and fro to each other. Hubbard enclosed letters to me without comment. I of course wrote him that it would naturally be hard for me to offend people who only intended to be kind but that for my very short stay I would consider that I had engaged myself to the *Philistines*. I didnt see what else to do when I could percieve by their letters that the *Philistines* were likely to be very much injured. They called the others a "god damned lot of old tabies."

I enclose you copy of a London letter.[1]

In the matter of the Saturn Club—I don't deride a dinner from the Saturn Club. No. But then I have to proceed by the atmosphere when I get there.

And now, Willis, old man, when I get in all this flumy-

---

[1] The London letter was not enclosed in Crane's letter to Hawkins, or perhaps Hawkins failed to preserve it.

doodle business and see you behind there moving the scenes and knowing all the time what a damned fool I am and what a ridiculous hole I'm in, I get fair feeble-minded with dwelling upon it. I leave it all to you. For my part I wish the whole thing was in Ballywhoo because while I look forward to it as probably the greatest pleasure of my life, I feel as if I were astride of your shoulders. And if I could stop the thing now I would.

Yours alway

S. C.

I go to Port Jervis on Sunday. My address—Port Jervis, N.Y. c/—W. H. Crane [2]

TO WILLIS BROOKS HAWKINS

["In Honor of Mr. Stephen Crane" the Society of the Philistines printed a banquet menu-folder presenting three dozen tributes and regrets of authors and journalists unable to attend, including messages from William Dean Howells, Hamlin Garland, Louise Imogen Guiney, Bliss Carman, and Ambrose Bierce: "Were it not for the miles which separate us, I would be with you." There were notes from Richard Harding Davis, Ripley Hitchcock, and S. S. McClure, and a pert one from the editor of the *Albany Express*: "I have a profound admiration for a man who, casting to the winds rhyme, reason and metre, can still write poetry." From Amy Leslie of the *Chicago News* there was a more personal note: "My most gentle thoughts are tinged with envy of you who are so lucky as to meet Stephen Crane." There was also a verse parody of Crane by Hayden Carruth ("I saw a Man reading an Invitation"), and quotations from Crane's poems appeared on the back cover. Crane wrote this note to Willis two days after the banquet. He stayed on in East Aurora with Hubbard and Taber for four days.]

---

[2] William Crane lived at Port Jervis, Edmund Crane at near-by Hartwood.

Dear Willis:
                    I am coming to New York on Tuesday morning.
                                        Stephen Crane
East Aurora,
Saturday [December 21], 1895
[P.S.] *I wish I could too!*
        Elbert Hubbard

TO WILLIS BROOKS HAWKINS

[To commemorate the event Hubbard printed three pamphlets of
souvenir stuff—the letters of invitation and acceptance in *The Members of the Society*; the menu and additional responses and an unsigned new Crane poem ("I have heard the sunset song of the
birches," printed there for the first time) in *The Time Has Come*;
and in the May issue of Hubbard's *Roycroft Quarterly* as "A Souvenir and a Medley" tributes to Crane and seven poems by him.
Hubbard exploited the whole thing to the utmost. On New Year's
Eve Crane wrote Nellie Crouse a long letter and satirized the
Philistine affair in describing what happened at the dinner, but he
expressed himself quite differently in writing to Willis that same
night.]

                                        Hartwood, N.Y.
                                        Dec 31st [1895]
Dear Willis:
                    Back and retired once more to corduroys. I send
overcoat tonight. Pray heaven I have not got you into trouble
by keeping it too long. Write me your impressions of the dinner
as soon as you get time. Hubbard and Taber think you are
just the smoothest guy in the world. The reason I wrote you
that I would be in NY was because they told me my passes
would be over the Central but as it turned out, they were to
Port Jervis over the Erie. I am very anxious to hear wether
you are satisfied with the dinner. I did not drink much but the
excitement soon turned everything into a grey haze for me and
I am not sure that I came off decently.

I sent my new novel down to Appleton's yesterday.[1] Will let you know it's reception. If you see Colonel Floyd give him my kindest regards. I think you and him made the big hit at Buffalo. The agony of the Indians over the fact that you left the boat in the middle of the Fox River may have led you to think differently but it is true. Write me soon.

Yours as ever
Stephen Crane

TO CURTIS BROWN [1]

My Dear Curtis,

Thank you for your kind words and for *Sketch* clipping. I hear the damned book ("The Red Badge of Courage") is doing very well in England. In the meantime I am plodding along. I have finished my new novel—"The Third Violet"—and sent it to Appleton and Co., as per request, but I've an idea it won't be accepted. It's pretty rotten work. I used myself up in the accursed "Red Badge."

Yours as ever,
Stephen Crane

Hartwood, N.Y.
Dec. 31st, 1896 [for 1895] [2]

---

[1] Crane's December 27 note to Hitchcock—"I forward to you today *The Third Violet*"—was probably sent separately from the manuscript, this going off three days later.

[1] Literary agent; at this time Sunday editor of the *New York Press.*

[2] This 1896 date is incorrect for two reasons: he sent Hitchcock *The Third Violet* on either December 27 or the 31st from Hartwood in 1895; and he sailed on the *Commodore* from Jacksonville, Florida, on New Year's Day 1897. He couldn't therefore be writing to Curtis Brown from Hartwood on December 31, 1896.

Reprinted from *Contacts*, by Curtis Brown. Copyright 1935 by Harper & Brothers. Reproduced by permission of the publishers and Mr. Curtis Spencer Brown, here for the first time.

TO WILLIAM DEAN HOWELLS [1]

Hartwood, N.Y.
January 1st [1896]

Dear Mr. Howells:

Every little time I hear from some friend a kind thing you have said of me, an interest which you have shown in my work. I have been so long conscious of this, that I am grown uncomfortable in not being able to express to you my gratitude and so I sieze the New Year's Day as an opportunity to thank you and tell you how often I think of your kind benevolent life.

Sincerely yours
Stephen Crane

TO WILLIS BROOKS HAWKINS

Hartwood, N.Y.
January 27th [1896]

My dear Willis:

There are none of my friends whom I could treat so shamefully and none who can make me feel so utterly dejected over it afterward. But oh you dont know how that damned city tore my heart out by the roots and flung it under the heels of it's noise. Indeed it did. I couldnt breathe in that accursed tumult. On Friday it had me keyed to a point where I was no more than a wild beast and I had to make a dash willy-nilly. It was a disgraceful retreat but I think you will understand me. I feel myself perfectly capable of any sacrifice for you now with the sting of that retreat still upon me. But as

---

[1] Reprinted from *Life and Letters of William Dean Howells,* edited by Mildred Howells, Vol. II, p. 44. Copyright 1928 by Doubleday, Doran & Company, Inc.

to that past thing I will have to throw myself upon your mercy.
I am coming down again in about two weeks.

Yours invariably
S. C.

P.S.: I am expressing you the original ms of The Red Badge.
Thought maybe you'd like it.[1]

S. C.

[P.S.] DID you see Sunday's Times.[2]

TO RIPLEY HITCHCOCK [1]

Hartwood, N.Y.
January 27 [1896]

Dear Mr. Hitchcock:

I fear that when I meet you again I shall
feel abashed. As a matter of truth, New York has so completely
muddled me on this last visit that I shant venture again very

---

[1] What Crane sent him was the final handwritten manuscript containing a portion of an earlier draft written on the back sides of the loose sheets; Hawkins had the loose sheets bound into a notebook in order to preserve the manuscripts.

[2] In Sunday's *New York Times, Supplement,* January 26, Harold Frederic discussed *The Red Badge* in great detail and reported to American readers the sensation this war novel had caused in England. It was this article—"Stephen Crane's Triumph"—that turned the tide of response to *The Red Badge* here at home. Frederic's own novel, *The Damnation of Theron Ware,* appeared two months later, in March 1896.

[1] Editor of Appleton & Company. Hitchcock bought *The Red Badge* in December 1894 on the basis of the newspaper version then appearing serially in the Philadelphia and New York papers, from which Crane sent him clippings on December 18. The book was not published, however, until the next autumn because Crane's trip to Mexico had delayed correction of the proofs. On March 8, 1895 Crane sent Hitchcock the manuscript from New Orleans, just as he was about to go to Mexico, and he suggested that the word *Red* might be excised from the title—*The Red Badge of Courage*—since Hitchcock thought the title too long. "That would shorten it." What Crane sent Hitchcock was probably the typescript copy or page proof, rather than the actual handwritten manuscript. He was still reading page proof after his return from the West in June. On the same day as this letter to Hitchcock, written at Hartwood, Crane

soon. I had grown used to being called a damned ass but this sudden new admiration of my friends has made a gibbering idiot of me. I shall stick to my hills.

I think it is as well to go ahead with The Third Violet. People may just as well discover now that the high dramatic key of The Red Badge cannot be sustained. You know what I mean. I dont think The Red Badge to be any great shakes but then the very theme of it gives it an intensity that a writer cant reach every day. The Third Violet is a quiet little story but then it is serious work and I should say let it go. If my health and my balance remains to me, I think I will be capable of doing work that will dwarf both books.

Yours sincerely,
Stephen Crane

TO THE EDITOR OF THE "CRITIC" [1]

Editor of the Critic

Dear Sir: There is a very excellent photograph of me in the possession of Mr. King, the artist, c/ The Lantern Club, 126 William St., New York. It is a picture that has never been used for publication and is I think a very good portrait. I have forwarded him your letter with a request to send you a picture.

---

expressed the original handwritten manuscript of *The Red Badge* to Willis Hawkins.

Appleton's published *The Red Badge* on October 3, 1895, and brought out *Maggie* and *The Little Regiment* in 1896, and *The Third Violet* in 1897.

The original of this letter is in the possession of the New York Public Library and is reproduced by permission of the Henry W. and Albert A. Berg Collection, here for the first time.

[1] Written in response to an inquiry from the editor of the *Critic*, a weekly periodical; the issue of March 7, 1896 quotes from this letter in a very complimentary notice of Crane's work. The letter appeared in facsimile in the *Colophon* for 1930, and six months later in the *Colophon*, July 1931, Vincent Starrett appraised this remarkable autobiographical letter as possibly "the most important Crane discovery of recent years." The original handwritten letter is in the possession of Mr. C. W. Barrett and is reproduced here by his permission.

I began writing for newspapers when I was 16. At 18 I did my first fiction—for the N.Y. Sunday Tribune—sketches. At 20 I began *Maggie* & finished it when I was somewhat beyond 21. Later in the same year I began *The R. B. of Courage* and finished it some months after my 22nd birthday.[2] *The Black Riders* were written in that year. When I was 23, I devoted most of my time to travelling for the Bachellor and Johnson syndicate and in writing short stories for English magazines. This winter I wrote a novel: "The Third Violet," which is to be published by the Appletons. Beforehand, however, they are to bring out in connection with William Heineman a new edition of *Maggie*.[3] I am now finishing a novelette for S. S. McClure called The Little Regiment which represents my work at its best I think and is positively my last thing dealing with battle.

When I look back on this array it appears that I have worked but as a matter of truth I am very very lazy, hating work, and only taking up a pen when circumstances drive me.

I live at Hartwood very quietly and alone, mostly, and think a good saddle-horse is the one blessing of life.[4]

Sincerely yours,
Stephen Crane
P.S. If in doubt concerning
certain facts apply to
S. S. McClure.

Hartwood, N.Y.
Feb. 15, 96.

---

[2] See Crane's letter written in February 1900 to Joseph O'Connor, editor of the *Rochester Post-Express*.

[3] Crane began rewriting *Maggie* this month for Appleton's edition, which appeared in June. He sent Hitchcock six edited chapters on February 15 "to see if they suit." He remarked that the book seemed to him to wear "quite a new aspect from very slight omissions." On May 29 he asked Hitchcock: "are you bringing out *Maggie* soon?"

[4] Crane was an excellent rider. In December during his visit with Elbert Hubbard he fell in love with a little brown horse, Peanuts, and purchased him with money earned from the sale of a short story. Peanuts was clever, playful, tricky; you never knew what he was going to do next. And that was why Crane had special affection for him. He was as unpredictable as his master.

TO LILY BRANDON MUNROE [1]

[Hartwood, New York]
Feb. 29, 1896

You know, when I left you [1892], I renounced the clever school in literature. It seemed to me that there must be something more in life than to sit and cudgel one's brains for clever and witty expedients. So I developed all alone a little creed of art which I thought was a good one. Later I discovered that my creed was identical with the one of Howells and Garland and in this way I became involved in the beautiful war between those who say that art is man's substitute for nature and we are the most successful in art when we approach the nearest to nature and truth, and those who say—well, I don't know what they say. Then that they can't say much but they fight villainously and keep Garland and I out of the big magazines. Howells, of course, is too powerful for them.

If I had kept to my clever Rudyard-Kipling style, the road might have been shorter but, ah, it wouldn't be the true road. The two years of fighting have been well-spent. And now I am almost at the end of it. This winter fixes me firmly. We have proved too formidable for them, confound them. They used to call me "that terrible, young radical," but now they are beginning to hem and haw and smile—those very old coons who used to adopt a condescending air toward me. There is an irony in the present situation that I enjoy, devil take them for a parcel of old, cringing, conventionalized hens.

---

[1] Reprinted from the Introduction by Melvin Schoberlin, p. 19, to *The Sullivan County Sketches*. Copyright 1949 by Syracuse University Press. Reprinted by permission of the publisher and the author.

TO WILLIS BROOKS HAWKINS

> Cosmos Club
> Washington [1]
> Mch 15 [1896]

Dear Willis:

It was a woman! Dont you see? Nothing could so interfere but a woman. How sorry I am that I treated you so badly and yet how full how absolute is the explanation—a woman. I shall want to know at once how angry you are. I am sure, of course that you have been very much offended but it is a woman, I tell you, and I want you to forgive me.

> Yours as ever
> Stephen Crane

Mch 15

TO WILLIS BROOKS HAWKINS

> Cosmos Club
> Washington, D.C.
> March 31 [1896]

My dear Willis:

You are the only friend I ever had who possessed the decency to forgive me for being an ass and your value has doubled in my eyes. I intend to come back to New York this week. Washington pains me. By the way, the three who I would like to see at the dinner are my brother, for one,

---

[1] McClure sent Crane to Washington to do a book on political society. (See Crane's letter of the next month to Wallis McHarg from Hartwood.) Crane once remarked that he "was a socialist for two weeks but when a couple of socialists assured me I had no right to think differently from any other socialist and then quarrelled [*sic*] with each other about what socialism meant, I ran away."

William H. Crane, Port Jervis, N.Y., Col. Floyd, and Underwood Johnson of the Century.

Will probably see you at lunch on Saturday.

Very much yours
S. C.

TO WALLIS McHARG [1]

Hartwood, New York [2]
[early April 1896]

. . . When people see a banker taking a glass of beer in a cafe, they say, There is Smith. When they behold a writer taking a glass of beer, they say, Send for the police! No great law of nature can be proved from this but it pretty often hits me that people are ingenious blockheads. I have been to Washington about a book on political society for Mr. McClure but I came straight back.

TO WILLIS BROOKS HAWKINS

[165 West 23rd Street, New York City]
[early April 1896]

Dear Willis: [1]

I am returned. Can—will—you bring the boys over for a little fiesta de poke tonight. Charley, Fairman & you will do if you cannot raise more.

Yours
S. C.

---

[1] A schoolboy chum whose life Stephen had saved one Sunday by pulling him out of the surf.

[2] In Beer's account this letter is dated March 1896, which indicates that Beer did not have access to the Crane-Hawkins letters, as the one of March 31 to Hawkins was written in Washington, D.C. Crane's letter to McHarg was written from Hartwood in early April. (Further letters from Crane to McHarg, according to Beer, are lost.) This letter is reprinted from Beer, p. 307.

[1] Another occasion for poker-playing took place in June, this time with Stephen as host to Fairman, Hawkins, and D. "Dysenpith" (?). Fairman is here named Bill, but it seems likely that he is the same Leroy Fairman

TO THE EDITOR OF THE "NEWARK SUNDAY CALL" [1]

[165 West 23rd Street, New York City]
[April 29, 1896]

I was born in Newark on the 1st of November, 1871. The house was No. 14 Mulberry place. My father was the Rev. J. T. Crane, D.D., presiding elder of the Newark district. The family moved from there to Bound Brook. My great great great grandfather was one of the seven men who came and solmenly [*sic*] founded Newark.[2] He was Jasper Crane. His farm came into the southwest corner of Market and Broad. His son, Stephen Crane, moved to Elizabeth, where my grandfather and my father were born. During the Revolution the Cranes were pretty hot people. The old man Stephen served in the Continental Congress (for New Jersey), while all four sons were in the army. William Crane was colonel of the Sixth regiment of New Jersey infantry. The Essex militia also contained one of the sons. I am not much on this sort of thing or I could write more, but at any rate the family is founded deep in Jersey soil (since the birth of Newark), and I am about as much of a Jerseyman as you can find.

Sincerely yours,
Stephen Crane

we hear about in the Amy Leslie affair. The names of the poker contingent are written on the cardtable cover used on this occasion in June, and Stephen, while keeping the score, doodled and, like Stephen Dedalus in Joyce's *Portrait of the Artist as a Young Man*, scribbled his name on the tablecover over and over again! "Stephen Crane, Chauncey Depew, Stephen Crane, Chauncey Depew, Stephen Crane." This paper tablecover, preserved by Hawkins, is in the Barrett Collection.

[1] Written in answer to a request for some record of himself and his people. Published in "A Genuine Jerseyman," *Newark Sunday Call*, May 3, 1896, p. 20. (Not listed in the Williams *Bibliography*.) This letter is reproduced from the *Newark Sunday Call* here for the first time.

[2] H. G. Wells said that Crane was "A New Englander of Puritan lineage." And Edward Garnett made the same mistake. On Crane's lineage see also the letter to Joseph O'Connor, editor of the *Rochester Post-Express*, February 1900.

TO ELBERT HUBBARD [1]

[about spring of 1896]
165 West 23d St.,
New York City

My dear Hub:

I've been a rampant wild ass of the desert with my feet never twice in the same place but at last I am settled down finally & feel that my first occupation should be the writing of a profound apology to you for my curious silence. I expect to be in East Aurora in about 2 weeks—at least if I am still at liberty to purchase that noble horse? At that time we will chew the rag at great length and finally decide all these contested points.

Yours always,
S. C.

TO A FRIEND [1]

[Inscribed in a copy of *George's Mother*]

To my friend Eddie
in memory of our days
of suffering and trouble
in 217th St.

Stephen Crane
New York City
June 14. [1896]

---

[1] The original is in the possession of Dartmouth College Library and is reproduced here by permission of the Trustees of Dartmouth College. It is printed in *A Stephen Crane Collection*, by Herbert Faulkner West (Dartmouth College Library, 1948), p. 14.

[1] E. J. Edwards? This friend gave Crane a place to sleep at his room on 217th Street, New York City, during the early part of 1892. (Cf. Berryman, pp. 34–5.)

The original inscribed presentation copy is in the possession of Dartmouth College Library and is reproduced by permission of the Trustees of Dartmouth College.

TO HAMLIN GARLAND
[165 West 23rd Street]
New York City
[July 1896]

Dear Mr. Garland:
Just heard you were in town. I want you to dine tonight with me at the Lantern Club. Sure! Roosevelt expects to be there.[1] He wants to meet you. Don't fail. I will call here at six —again.[2]

Yours
Crane

TO MISS BELLE WALKER [1]
141 East 25th St.
New York City
Sept. 8th [1896]

Dear Miss Walker:
I think the motif of the story is properly strong. "You will never hold the cross toward me." That, I think is very effective. One thing I must say at once: Take the diamond out of that man's shirt immediately. Dont let him live another [2] day with a diamond in his front. You declare him to be very swell and yet you allow him to wear a diamond as if he were a saloon proprietor or owned a prosperous livery stable. It is of the utmost importance that you remove the diamond at once for our fin de siecle have keen eyes for that sort of a mistake.

[1] Theodore Roosevelt, Commissioner of Police. The Lantern Club, at 126 Williams Street, had several other famous guests, including Mark Twain. Crane dined at Roosevelt's home this July. (Cf. Berryman, pp. 144–5.)

[2] Crane left this note at Garland's hotel, inscribing it in a copy of *George's Mother*: "To Hamlin Garlin / of the great honest West / From Stephen Crane / of the false East. / New York City / July, 1896."
Reprinted from *Roadside Meetings*, by Hamlin Garland, pp. 202–3.

[1] The original is in the possession of Dartmouth College Library and is here reprinted by permission of the Trustees of Dartmouth College.

[2] The word *editors* is written above the line, meaning "another editor's day."

Frankly I do not consider your sketch to be very good but even if you do me the honor to value my opinion, this need not discourage you for I can remember when I wrote just as badly as you do now. Furthermore there are many men far our superiors who once wrote just as badly as I do today and no doubt as badly as you.

Yours sincerely

Stephen Crane

TO CORA TAYLOR

[The woman Crane married in Greece—an extraordinary woman and a faithful wife. Of New England stock, she had married, when very young, Captain Donald William Stewart, C.M.G., and then, separating from him, she came to Jacksonville, Florida, as mistress of a yachtsman who set her up in business. She ran the Hotel de Dream in Jacksonville, where Crane met her. He inscribed this copy of *George's Mother* to her at this time of their first meeting there. When Crane went to Greece she followed him and nursed him back to health. They went to England *as* man and wife, setting up house first at Ravensbrook, Oxted, Surrey, and later at Brede Place, a semi-medieval mansion. Stephen died on June 5, 1900, and Cora came to America for the funeral and visited at Port Jervis. She returned to England and stayed there about a year. On returning to America she re-established herself at Jacksonville, presiding there in a mansion modeled upon Brede Place. She died in 1910, and her tombstone in Jacksonville's Evergreen Cemetery is inscribed: "Cora Crane / 1868–1910." There is an account of her later life in Jacksonville—"Cora Comes Back"—in *The St. Johns,* by Branch Cabell and A. J. Hanna (1943).]

[Inscribed in a copy of *George's Mother*]

To an unnamed sweetheart
    Stephen Crane
Nov. 4/96 [for November 14, 1896?] [1]

---

[1] The date of Crane's inscription, it seems logical to suppose, was November 14 rather than 4, for Crane was in Cambridge (as Berryman re-

TO MISS CATHERINE HARRIS [1]

[Jacksonville, Florida]

[November 12, 1896]

Thank you very much for your letter on Maggie. I will try to answer your questions properly and politely. Mrs. Howells was right in telling you that I have spent a great deal of time on the East Side and that I have no opinion of missions. That— to you—may not be a valid answer since perhaps you have been informed that I am not very friendly to Christianity as seen around town. I do not think that much can be done with the Bowery as long as the . . . [blurred] . . . are in their present state of conceit. A person who thinks himself superior to the rest of us because he has no job and no pride and no clean clothes is as badly conceited as Lillian Russell. In a story of mine called "An Experiment in Misery" I tried to make plain that the root of Bowery life is a sort of cowardice. Perhaps I mean a lack of ambition or to willingly be knocked flat and accept the licking. The missions for children are another thing and if you will have Mr. Rockefeller give me a hundred street cars and some money I will load all the babes off to some pink

ports) writing up a football game for the *Journal* on November 7. Berryman's version of the mystifying November 4 inscription to the "unnamed sweetheart," who was certainly Cora Taylor, forces him to conjecture that Crane returned from Jacksonville by November 7 and then went back there again! There is no reason for not altering Crane's inscription date, since almost everything he dates is likely to be incorrect. We know that he was in Jacksonville by November 12, since he then wrote to Miss Catherine Harris from there. His letter to Curtis Brown from Hartwood on December 31 is dated 1896, whereas it should be 1895 for if it were 1896 it would mean that Crane disappeared from Hartwood on New Year's Eve and sailed the next morning in the *Commodore*. It would furthermore say that Crane went to Jacksonville by November 4, was in Cambridge on the 7th, went back to Jacksonville on the 1st of January from Hartwood the night before!

The original inscribed copy of *George's Mother* is in the possession of Dartmouth College Library and is reproduced here by permission of the Trustees of Dartmouth College.

[1] Reprinted from Beer, pp. 312–13.

world where cows can lick their noses and they will never see
their families any more. My good friend Edward Townsend—
have you read his "Daughter of the Tenements"?—has another
opinion of the Bowery and it is certain to be better than mine.
I had no other purpose in writing "Maggie" than to show people to people as they seem to me. If that be evil, make the most
of it.

TO WILLIS BROOKS HAWKINS

[Amy Leslie, ex-actress and since 1889 dramatic critic on the *Chicago Daily News,* gave Crane some money on November 1, 1896,
and sued him for recovery of it in early January 1898. She claimed
that he had repaid her only $250 of the original $800 loaned him.
This letter of November 29 is important because it reveals that Amy
Leslie was in love with Crane and that Crane had the burden of
appeasing a broken-hearted woman. My interpretation of this affair
differs from Berryman's account, which lacks this letter. Hence
his version: "whether there had been a love affair does not appear. . . ." In *Stephen Crane,* pp. 146–7, 178.]

Jacksonville, Fla.,
Nov. 29, 1896

Mr. Willis B. Hawkins,
141 East 25th St.,
New York City.

My dear Willis:
                            I am here in Jacksonville and feeling very
good. I am very much obliged to you for allowing me to plant
certain responsibilities upon your noble shoulders and I know
that you will carry it out with every consideration for your old
friend. By the way, I have planted another responsibility upon
your noble shoulders. I have just written to my brother Will
that in case my journey was protracted by casuses [*sic*] which
you can readily imagine, I wish you to serve with Mr. Howells,
Mr. Garland and Mr. Hitchcock as my literary executors.
     In case you see Amy from time to time encourage her in

every possible way. Of course feminine nature is mighty peculiar and she might have that singular ability to get rid of mournful emotions which is possessed by a great many of her sex, but I was positively frightened for the girl at the moment of parting and I am afraid and worried now.[1] I feel that no one hardly could need a friendly word more than this poor child, and I know you are just the man to do it in a right way if the chance presents itself. Hooke fastens his intellect so securely to some damned molecule that he loses sight of a broad question and I do not think he is very efficient as a bracer. It broke my heart to leave the girl but I could feel comparatively easy now if I could feel that she had good friends. There is not one man in three thousand who can be a real counsellor and guide for a girl so pretty as Amy, and this will present itself to your mind no doubt as a reason for supposing that Charley would not be very capable in the position. Her sister [2] is a good hearted sort of a creature, but she is liable to devote most of her attention to herself and besides that Amy is mentally superior to her in every way. The sister is weak, very weak, and so I am sure that she would be of no help to Amy in what is now really a great trouble. I do not want to bore you with any of my affairs but I am obliged to feel that you are about the only man who could possibly help me and do it in the way that would count for some good, so just remember this and when you think some times of your friend remember that he has left behind him one to whom he would count favors done as favors done to himself. By my remarkable use of bad English in parts of this letter you can see that I am dictating [3] and you know very well that I am

[1] Miss Amy Leslie was almost twenty years older than Crane, who had his twenty-fifth birthday on November 1 this year.

[2] Mrs. O'Brien, with whom Amy Leslie lived on West 25th Street.

[3] Crane's typewritten letters, of which this is one, are rare. (The original is in the possession of Mr. C. W. Barrett.) On this same day Crane wrote his brother William from Jacksonville about his taking off for Cuba: "I was off to Cuba before I had a chance to even inform you of it from New York. I fooled around town for over a month expecting to go at any time. . . ." Then he suddenly "received orders to skip and I left New York that very night." He spent October in New York City waiting for

not used to dictation because my brain is too slow, but I have
no doubt you will be able to make out what I mean.

Yours always

Stephen Crane

My best to old Bill Fairman.

TO WILLIS BROOKS HAWKINS

Jacksonville, [Florida]

Dec. 24, 1896

[Western Union]

[Willis B. Hawkins
c/o Brains Publishing Co
141 E. 27 St.]

Leave soon. Telegraph frankly Amy's mental condition. Also
send fifty if possible Will arrange payments from Appleton.
Troubled over Amy

TO WILLIS BROOKS HAWKINS

St. James Hotel

Jacksonville, Fla

1/7 [January 7, 1897]

[Western Union]

Willis B. Hawkins
c/o Brains Publishing Co
141 E 27 St.

Thanks awfully old man [1] greeting to club send mail here

Crane

---

orders to go to Jacksonville, but he did not notify his brother about this
delay until he had arrived in Jacksonville. He arrived there about November 10.

[1] Hawkins probably had wired Crane some money as soon as news
reached him that Crane had been saved in the *Commodore* disaster.

TO WILLIS BROOKS HAWKINS

Grand Hotel D'Angleterre
Athens (Greece)
[about April 18, 1897]

Willie: [1]

Have mailed at 25th St—one hundred for Amy

Yours

S

A draft on Cooks.

TO WILLIS BROOKS HAWKINS [1]

Grand Hotel D'Angleterre
Athens (Greece)
April 27 [1897]

Dear old man:

I enclose a pony [2] for Amy. Give her my love.

---

[1] Crane apparently dispatched two notes to Hawkins the same day, for another one reads:

Dear Willie:

Have mailed you Cooks draft for one hundred for Amy

C

The envelope for this note is addressed to Hawkins at the Bacheller Syndicate, 141 East 25th Street, New York City.

"I am going to Greece for the Journal," Crane wrote to some friend, "and if the Red Badge is not all right I shall sell out my claim on literature and take up orange growing." (Quoted from Beer, p. 318.)

[1] The original of this letter is in the possession of Dartmouth College Library and is reproduced here by permission of the Trustees of Dartmouth College.

[2] Slang for £25. According to Berryman, Crane had paid back four hundred dollars to Amy by February 5; and now, on April 27, he sent another hundred. In Miss Leslie's suit against Crane she charged that he had repaid her only $250 of the $800 loaned him. This much ($250) is accounted for by Crane's wire to Hawkins on December 24, 1896 ($50), in his letter of April 18 ($100), and in his letter of April 27 ($100). An-

Tell her there is lots more coming. Just off again to see fight. I love Amy.

Yours
S.

Tell Fairman go to hell.[3]

[Enclosure] $100 ck.

TO MR. HARRIS [1]

[Inscribed on a copy of *The Third Violet*]

Dear Mr. Harris:

    This book is even worse than any of the others.

Stephen Crane

London,
June, 1897

TO SANFORD BENNETT

[Paris, France]
[September 2, 1897]

. . . Frederic and Mr. Heinemann [1] have been urging me to stay in England for a time. So my wife—after practicing nine

---

other five hundred is accounted for by Crane's having deposited with Hawkins that sum for installment payments to Amy. According to Berryman, this sum was deposited with Hawkins on November 25, 1896, but the source of his information is not cited. In Berryman, p. 147, this letter of April 27 is inaccurately quoted.

[3] Miss Leslie's agent was Leroy Fairman. Possibly this was the same "Bill" Fairman who was Crane's friend and crony at poker games that Crane and Hawkins played.

[1] A friend of Harold Frederic, the novelist.

The original inscribed presentation copy is in the possession of Dartmouth College Library, and the inscription is reproduced here by permission of the Trustees of Dartmouth College.

[1] Harold Frederic, agent of the *New York Times* in England and author of *The Damnation of Theron Ware*, published in the spring of 1896. Heinemann published Crane's works in England.

days I can write that without a jump—and I will be hunting a
house or an attic in London pretty soon.[2]

TO WILLIAM CRANE [1]

c/o William Heineman[n]
21 Bedford St., W.C.
London
Sat., Oct. 29. [1897]

My dear William:

I got your letter this morning. I have been
wanting to write you for some time about the library but have
been quite too busy. For my part I would gladly give to you
power to choose my part of the library. Take an encyclopaedia
and as many histories as possible and then let the others have a
chance. It cant matter so much to me and I feel that I have

---

[2] It is not known whether Crane actually married Cora Taylor, and
the only evidence that he did is this letter. Frederic was not married to
the woman he lived with in England, and with this example Crane, if he
did not marry Cora, must have felt more inclined to settle in England than
in America. (Berryman's version that no marriage actually took place is
convincingly argued, p. 190.)

Arnold Henry Sanford Bennett, a Canadian gentleman, had married a
Frenchwoman in 1896; she died in 1899, and Crane remarked in a letter
about him: "Destiny sets an alarm clock so as to be up early and strew
bañana peels in front of him. If he trusts a friend, he is betrayed. If he
starts a journey, he breaks an ankle. If he loves, death comes to her without a smile." Beer reports that Bennett "was so shy that he dropped the
name Arnold after the popularity of Arnold Bennett began." In "Mrs.
Stephen Crane," *American Mercury,* 31 (March 1934), 289. Beer quotes
this portion of Crane's letter to Bennett in *Stephen Crane,* p. 325.

[1] The original of this letter is in the possession of Dartmouth College
Library and is reproduced here by permission of the Trustees of Dartmouth College. In *A Stephen Crane Collection,* by Herbert Faulkner West
(1948), this letter is misdated 1898.

not treated the others very fairly in the matter. If you go to Asbury Park, look up my two swords—I wore them at Claverack —and keep them for me.[2]

I have been in England, Ireland, Scotland, Wales, France, Turkey and Greece. I have seen Italy but never trod it. Since I have been in England I have been in dreadfully hard luck. I have been here four months and one month I was laid up by the carriage accident. In the working three months I have earned close to 2000 dollars but the sum actually paid in to me has been only £ 20. 17 s. 3 d—about 120 dollars. In consequence I have had to borrow and feel very miserable indeed. I am not sure that I am not in trouble over it.

McClures, with security of over 1000 dollars against my liability of four hundred, refuse to advance me any money. And yet they think they are going to be my American publishers.[3]

---

[2] Claverack—the Hudson River Institute, where Crane had gone to military school. A year before this letter Crane had sent William directions for disposing of his personal things. Just before going filibustering in the *Commodore,* before leaving for Florida in 1896, Crane made out his will; and then on November 29 he wrote Willis Hawkins that he wished him "to serve with Mr. Howells, Mr. Garland and Mr. Hitchcock as my literary executors." In a letter to William written on the same day (November 29, 1896) he gave directions for his will: Peanuts, his horse, was not to be sold. A third of his estate was to go to William, another third to Edmund, and the remainder was to be divided between his other two brothers, Townley and Wilbur (Beer, p. 313). Crane just before he died in 1900, however, made out another will leaving Cora his personal things and (until she should remarry) his income; one half of his estate was to be divided between Edmund and William, and the other half was to go to his namesake, Stephen Crane (Edmund's son, born in 1900). William, as in the 1896 will, was again made executor. The will of 1900 was made in England and filed in Goshen, Orange County, New York. (No mention is made of it in Beer or in Berryman.)

In August 1897 the *Bookman* (London) announced: "Mr. Stephen Crane has settled down in this country for an indefinite period. . . ." Crane had arrived from Greece in June, bringing Cora Taylor with him.

[3] One of the reasons Crane made arrangements with the American literary agent Paul Revere Reynolds was to get himself "out of the ardent grasp of the S. S. McClure Co." See his letter to Reynolds later this year and his letter to Garland for November 15, 1894.

I am working now on a big novel.[4] It will be much much
longer than The Red Badge. My next short thing after the
novelette (The Monster) was The Bride Comes to Yellow Sky.[5]
All my friends come here say it is my very best thing. I am so
delighted when I am told by competent people that I have
made an advance. You know they said over here in England
that The Open Boat (Scribner's) was my best thing. There
seem so many of them in America who want to kill, bury and
forget me purely out of unkindness and envy and—my unworthiness, if you choose. All the hard things they say of me
affect me principally because I think of mine own people—you
and Teddie and the families. It is nothing, bless you. Now Dick
Davis [6] for instance has come to like the abuse. He accepts
it as a tribute to his excellence. But he is a fool. Now I want you
to promise to never pay any attention to it, even in your
thought. It is too immaterial and foolish. Your little brother is
neither braggart or a silent egotist but he knows that he is going on steadily to make his simple little place and he cant be
stopped, he cant even be retarded. He is coming.

Sometimes I think you and old Ted worry about me and you
may well worry! I have managed my success like a fool and a
child but then it is difficult to succeed gracefully at 23. However I am learning every day. I am slowly becoming a man. My
idea is to come finally to live at Port Jervis or Hartwood. I am
a wanderer now and I must see enough but—afterwards—I
think of P. J. & Hartwood.

---

[4] *Active Service*, begun at the suggestion of Harold Frederic but put
aside; finished the next year in Havana, Cuba, except for the last chapters, which had to be rewritten. It was published in 1899. In his letter
to Reynolds in December 1897, Crane says that his new Greek novel is
not yet begun.

[5] On September 9th he wrote to Edmund from Ireland: "finished a
novelette of 20,000 words–'The Monster.'" *The Bride Comes to Yellow
Sky* was also done at Ravensbrook, during September or October, and
by February he had finished *The Blue Hotel*.

[6] Richard Harding Davis

Ted wrote to me that he wanted to go to Klondike. At least he hinted at a desire. In less than a week, I happened to get a letter from the Bachellers asking me to go there. I do not believe there is exactly too much money in it for me but there will be enough to clear all heavy expenses and so I have accepted the offer in the hope that I may be able to do some small service to Ted—if he really means it.

I go to the Soudan in about a month.[7] The English forces are surely going to Khartoom [*sic*]. Perhaps I may be able to write you from there. That would be nice. I wanted badly to go to India to see the frontier row there but English papers discouraged me. They said it would be all over before I could get there. That was eight weeks ago and the war is still in full blast. The Afridis have thrashed the life out of the Englishmen on one or two occasions but we dont hear about it. That is the Englishman's strong point. However I hope there will be some good fighting in the Soudan before long.

I am sorry about the arm. Perhaps, after a time, it will regain its strength. So Helen has a sweetheart?[8] I got her letter but she didn't mention it. That reminds me—my stamp collection! If Townley[9] hasn't hocked it, it is now valuable. He had a good claim on it in a way. He gave me the start and, afterward, contributed largely. Try to get it at Asbury Park. Give Helen charge of it and then she and I can be partners. She had better then get a good catalogue that gives valuations.

The Irish Notes and so on, which appear in the Journal are written really for The Westminster Gazette and The Saturday Review.

I suppose it would be the proper thing for me to write long

---

[7] Crane never went to the Klondike, nor did he go to Khartoum. The closest he ever got to Africa was in writing about it in his first short story or sketch, published while he was at Syracuse University in the May issue of the *University Herald* for 1891. The setting of this sketch, *The King's Favor*, is British South Africa.

[8] Helen, William's daughter, was now about sixteen. She later visited Crane at Brede Place; she died in the spring of 1921.

[9] Townley was an older brother.

descriptions home of what I see over here but I write myself so completely out in articles that an attempt of the sort would be absurd.

I am just thinking how easy it would be in my present financial extremity to cable you for a hundred dollars but then by the time this reaches you I will probably be all right again. I believe the sum usually borrowed was fifteen dollars, wasn't it? Fifteen dollars—fifteen dollars—fifteen dollars. I can remember an interminable row of fifteen dollar requests.

Tell Cornelia [1] I still refer to her as the most delicately perfect cook—upon a given material—of the world and I have dined in all the best places of Paris and England. Give her my steadfast love.

I should like to see this famous pony. It appears to me that Edna might write and describe it. [2]

Yours loving brother
S.

TO JOSEPH CONRAD [1]

Ravensbrook,
Oxted,
Surrey.
Nov 11 [1897]

My dear Conrad:

My first feat has been to lose your note and so I am obliged to send this through Heineman [*sic*]. [2] I have

---

[1] William Crane's wife. Cora Taylor was also a wonderful cook. Among Crane's British guests (including Henry James), she was famous for her biscuits.

[2] The pony mentioned here is not Crane's own horse; Peanuts was sold by William, probably during 1900.

[1] The original is in the possession of Dartmouth College Library and is reproduced here by permission of the Trustees of Dartmouth College. It received previous book publication in *Two Letters from Stephen Crane to Joseph Conrad,* First Editions Club (London), 1926.

[2] William Heinemann, the publisher.

read the proof sheets which you so kindly sent me and the book
is simply great. The simple treatment of the death of Waite is
too good, too terrible. I wanted to forget it at once. It caught
me very hard. I felt ill over that red thread lining from the
corner of the man's mouth to his chin. It was frightful with the
weight of a real and present death. By such small means does
the real writer suddenly flash out in the sky above those who
are always doing rather well. In the meantime I have written to
Bacheller and told him to be valiant in the matter of "The Nigger"—I have also written some other little notes to America.[3]

I am afraid you must write to me soon so that I can finally
nail your address and put it away in my little book. I was very
stupid. Are you quite sure you could not come down for a
Sunday luncheon with Mrs. Conrad? Say your own date, barring this next one. We could then keep you as long as you
would stay.

Did not we have a good pow-wow in London?

Faithfully yours
Stephen Crane

---

[3] *The Nigger of the "Narcissus,"* begun in the autumn of 1896, was
finished February 19, 1897, and appeared in Henley's *New Review* that
year, and in book form in December. Crane immediately upon his first
arrival in London from New York asked to be introduced to the author of
The Nigger of the "Narcissus." They met in October. In a letter to Edward Garnett on December 5 Conrad writes: "I had Crane here last Sunday. We talked and smoked half the night. He is strangely hopeless about
himself. I like him." Conrad thought that the two stories Crane showed
him were excellent, but he preferred *A Man and Some Others* to *The
Open Boat*—though this "boat thing interested me more." In *Joseph Conrad: Life and Letters,* by G. Jean-Aubry (Doubleday, Page, 1927), I,
pp. 166, 211. See also Conrad on Crane in his Introduction to *Stephen
Crane.*

TO HENRY D. DAVRAY [1]

Telegrams—
Crane, Oxted.

Ravensbrook,
Oxted,
Surrey.
England
Nov 11. [1897]

M. Henry D. Davray

Dear Sir: I am today taking the liberty of sending you a copy of a little book of mine—The Black Riders—in hopes that some happy accident will persuade you to read it. My importunity is not without it's darker side. My dearest wish is to see these simples translated [*sic*] into French.[2] Some of my other books have recieved German and Russian translations but, let alone translations, the British public nor even my own American public will not look at The Black Riders. Thus my letter to you is in the nature of an appeal. I wish the distinction of appearing just for a moment to the minds of a few of your great and wise artistic public. I do not know if this will appear absurd to you. At any rate, I send you the book. You will tell me? Perchance, there would be a publisher who would print it. What I wish is the distinction. My American publishers, who own the copyrights, would readily agree. I hope I do not bore you too much? If you reply to this letter I shall be delighted.

Faithfully yours
Stephen Crane

---

[1] The original handwritten letter is in the possession of Mr. H. B. Collamore and is reproduced by his permission, here for the first time.

[2] There is no record of *The Black Riders* in a translation into French. Crane perhaps met Henry Davray in Paris, on his return from Greece. Crane sent him an inscribed copy of *The Black Riders*, dated Nov. 11, 1897.

TO EDWARD GARNETT [1]

Telegrams—   *Ravensbrook,*
Crane, Oxted.   *Oxted,*
                                                       Surrey.
                                              Nov 16 [1897]

Dear Mr. Garnett:

       I am sorry that I could not get over to you on Tuesday and sorry too that I have let so much time pass without saying so. Will you come over for luncheon at two on Sunday?

Faithfully yours
Stephen Crane

TO PAUL REVERE REYNOLDS [1]

[Crane met Reynolds early in 1896 when *The Red Badge of Courage* suddenly swept America. He met him at a luncheon given by Irving Bacheller, arranging then for Reynolds to be his literary agent.]

Ravensbrook,
Oxted,
Surrey.
[Nov.—?—1897]

Dear Mr. Reynolds:

       Good: Now we can do something. I will allow you ten percent on the sales and refer everything to you,

---

[1] British critic. He wrote "An Appreciation" of Crane which appeared in the *Academy* on December 17, 1898—the best essay, this side of H. G. Wells's appraisal of 1900, that Crane received during the next two decades of writings on him.

The original handwritten letter is in the possession of the Yale Collection of American Literature and is reproduced by permission of the Yale University Library, here for the first time.

[1] This letter and subsequent ones to Paul Revere Reynolds, Crane's American agent, are reproduced—most of them here in full for the first time—from *Paul Revere Reynolds*, by Frederick Lewis Allen. Copyright 1944. Reprinted by permission of the author and Mr. Paul Revere Reynolds, Jr.

giving you the clear field which is your right. You will have the whole management as in the theatrical business.

Now one of the reasons of this thing is to get me out of the ardent grasp of the S. S. McClure Co. I owe them about $500, I think, and they seem to calculate on controlling my entire out-put. They have in their possession "The Monster" (21,000 words) and "The Bride Comes to Yellow Sky" (4500) both for the American rights alone. The American rights alone of "The Monster" ought to pay them easily, minus your commission. No; perhaps it wouldn't pay them fully but it would pay them a decent amount of it. Then the American rights of "The Bride"—I judge to be worth $175.

As for my existing contracts there are only two. I. To write an article on an engine ride from London to Glasgow for the McClures. II. To give them my next book. Of course these would go on as if I had not called in your assistance.

Robert McClure here in London told me he thought you had "The Monster" in New York but I judge, if that were so, that you would have mentioned it in your letter this morning. I will write to Phillips and ask him to let you have it under the agreement that the money minus your commission shall be paid to them. Then *if* the money for "The Monster" goes far toward paying my debt, you can ask them about "The Bride."

"The Bride Comes to Yellow Sky" is a daisy and don't let them talk funny about it.

Now as for the newspaper business we can do large things. The *Herald* pays me $100 per article of between 3000 and 4000 words. The *World* has never paid me over $50 and expenses but could be brought to $75 or $100, I think.[2] Now that of course is a big graft to play as long as I am here in Europe. As for the *Journal* I have quite a big misunderstanding with them and can't get it pulled out straight. They say I am overdrawn. I say I am not. I have sent them an installment of my Irish Notes that I am doing here for the *Westminster Gazette*

---

[2] Crane, according to Cora (in a letter written by her in late 1900), "got high prices for his work, at least £10—a thousand words."

and would send them more if it were possible to hear from them. I would send you the Irish Notes and also my London Impressions from the *Saturday Review*—for the *Journal,* if we could get some definite statement from them. My idea was that they would go in with that stuff on the editorial page. Twenty-five dollars per installment would be enough. If the *Journal* will explain why they say I am over-drawn I am the last man in the world to kick and will pay the a/c in work.

Then on the other hand instead of fooling with the big newspapers, here is another scheme. You might go to Curtis Brown, Sunday Editor of the *Press* and say how-how from me. Then tell him this *in the strictest confidence,* that a lady named Imogene Carter whose work he has been using from time to time is also named Stephen Crane and that I did 'em in about twenty minutes on each Sunday, just dictating to a friend.[3] Of course they are rotten bad. But by your explanation he will understand something of the manner of the articles I mean to write only of course they will be done better. Ask him if he wants them, signed and much better in style, and how much he will give. Then if he says all right you might turn up a little syndicate for every Sunday. You can figure out that I should get about £ 10 per week out of it. Then—you do the business—I do the writing—I take 65 per cent and you take 35. The type-writing expenses in New York we share alike. You do a lot of correspondence, that's all—and keep your eyes peeled for new combinations.

Write me at once. Good luck to you.

Yours very truly
Stephen Crane

---

[3] The "friend" is Cora Taylor, known as "the first woman war correspondent," under the name of "Imogene Carter." Only two dispatches signed by that name are located. Cf. Ames W. Williams in the *New Colophon,* April 1948, p. 116.

TO PAUL REVERE REYNOLDS

> *Ravensbrook,*
> *Oxted,*
> *Surrey.*
> [December 1897]

Dear Reynolds:

I send you the child story of the Greek business. McClure has a call on it. He should give $300 for it—at least. The English rights are sold.

I have made a proposition to McClure that he advance £ 200 on the 1st of January for the book rights of my new Greek novel—not yet begun.[1] If he takes that offer he may want to hold back on payment for this story. I wouldn't have done it if I was not broke. For heaven's sake raise me all the money you can and *cable* it, *cable* it sure between Xmas and New Year's. Sell "The Monster"! Don't forget that—cable me some money this month.[2]

> S. C.

TO ACTON DAVIES [1]

> *Ravensbrook,*
> *Oxted,*
> *Surrey.*
> [Dec.—?—1897]

. . . Will you see if X and Y could let me have what they borrowed last May. I took X's not for $300 and Y owes me about $250. I hate to press nice fellows but it costs me more to

---

[1] *Active Service.*

[2] *The Monster* was rejected by the *Century*, Richard Watson Gilder protesting to Reynolds that they "couldn't publish that thing"—not with half the mothers in America expectant!

[1] Reprinted from Beer, p. 331.

live over here than I was led to believe and some of these Comache braves seem to think I am running a free lunch counter. Seven men have been staying over Sunday.[2]

TO JOHN NORTHERN HILLIARD

[This letter has critical importance. It is more illuminating of Crane's intentions as artist than any other single letter. From letter to letter Crane repeats himself, rephrasing the same statement or expanding upon it. Here his saying "I endeavored to express myself in the simplest and most concise way" echoes his letter to Clarence Peaslee on February 12, 1895, when he wrote: "I always want to be unmistakable. That to my mind is good writing." And this in turn repeats what he wrote to Hilliard in 1893. His view of the creative process as involving "an effort born of pain" is differently phrased in his letter to an editor of *Leslie's Weekly* (1895). The same statement is made in his letter to Hilliard in 1893. His letter to Joseph O'Connor of the *Rochester Post-Express* (February 1900) duplicates in its last sentences the opening part of this letter to Hilliard.

Of the three letters by Crane that Hilliard published in the *New York Times, Supplement,* July 14, 1900, this is the only one he identifies as having been written to him. Hilliard since 1895 was an editor on the *Rochester Union and Advertiser.*]

[*Ravensbrook,*
Oxted,
Surrey]
[1897?]

. . . I have only one pride—and may it be forgiven me. This single pride is that the English edition of "The Red Badge" has been received with praise by the English reviewers. Mr. George Wyndham, Under Secretary for War in the British Government, says, in an essay, that the book challenges comparison with the most vivid scenes of Tolstoi's "War and Peace" or of Zola's "Downfall"; and the big reviews here praise it for just what I intended it to be, a psychological portrayal of fear. They

---

[2] Acton Davies in New York collected nothing from Crane's friends.

all insist that I am a veteran of the civil war, whereas the fact is, as you know, I never smelled even the powder of a sham battle. I know what the psychologists say, that a fellow can't comprehend a condition that he has never experienced, and I argued that many times with the Professor. Of course, I have never been in a battle, but I believe that I got my sense of the rage of conflict on the football field, or else fighting is a hereditary instinct, and I wrote intuitively; for the Cranes were a family of fighters in the old days, and in the Revolution every member did his duty. But be that as it may, I endeavored to express myself in the simplest and most concise way. If I failed, the fault is not mine. I have been very careful not to let any theories or pet ideas of my own creep into my work. Preaching is fatal to art in literature. I try to give to readers a slice out of life; and if there is any moral or lesson in it, I do not try to point it out. I let the reader find it for himself. The result is more satisfactory to both the reader and myself. As Emerson said, "There should be a long logic beneath the story, but it should be kept carefully out of sight." Before "The Red Badge of Courage" was published, I found it difficult to make both ends meet. The book was written during this period. It was an effort born of pain, and I believe that it was beneficial to it as a piece of literature. It seems a pity that this should be so—that art should be a child of suffering; and yet such seems to be the case. Of course there are fine writers who have good incomes and live comfortably and contentedly; but if the conditions of their lives were harder, I believe that their work would be better. Bret Harte is an example. He has not done any work in recent years to compare with those early California sketches. Personally, I like my little book of poems, "The Black Riders," better than I do "The Red Badge of Courage." The reason is, I suppose, that the former is the more ambitious effort. In it I aim to give my ideas of life as a whole, so far as I know it, and the latter is a mere episode, or rather an amplification. Now that I have reached the goal, I suppose that I ought to be contented; but I am not. I was happier in the old days when I was always dreaming of the thing I have now attained. I am disappointed with success, and I am tired of abuse. Over here, happily, they don't treat you as if you were a dog, but give every one an honest measure of praise or blame. There are no disgusting personalities.

TO JAMES GIBBONS HUNEKER [1]

[Ravensbrook,
Oxted,
Surrey]
[1897?]

. . . They [Englishmen] will believe anything wild or impossible you tell them and then if you say your brother has a bathtub in his house they—ever so politely—call you a perjured falsifier of facts. I told a seemingly sane man at Mrs. Garnett's that I got my artistic education on the Bowery and he said, "Oh, really? So they have a school of fine arts there?" I had, you see, just told Mrs. Garnett [2] while this mummy listened all about the Bowery—in so far as I could tell a woman about the Bowery—but that made no difference to this John Bull. Now I am going to wave the starry flag of freedom a little even if you condemn the practice in one who knows not Balzac and Dostoy—what'shisname. You Indians have been wasting wind in telling me how "Unintrusive" and "DELICATE" I would find English manners. I don't. It has not yet been the habit of people I meet at Mr. Howells or Mr. Phillips or Mrs. Sonntag's to let fall my hand and begin to quickly ask me how much money I make and from which French realist I shall steal my next book. For it has been proven to me fully and carefully by authority

---

[1] American music critic and writer.
This letter appears in *Stephen Crane*, by John Berryman, p. 199.
[2] Wife of Edward Garnett, the British literary critic.

that all my books are stolen from the French. They stand me against walls with a teacup in my hand and tell me how I have stolen all my things from De Maupassant, Zola, Loti and the bloke who wrote—I forget the book.[3]

TO PAUL REVERE REYNOLDS [1]

[*Ravensbrook,
Oxted,
Surrey*]
Jan. 14 [1898]

Dear Reynolds:

I enclose you a thousand words on the Alfridi business. It might go to the *Press* and be syndicated, or else to the *Journal*.

I received your letter yesterday and promptly cabled you that McClure was not concerned in the matter. When I sent him "The Monster" I owed him a lot of money but when I paid him up, I went to see Robert McClure here and he agreed

---

[3] Garnett insisted that Crane must have read French authors, and Crane replied: "I never read a word of French in my life." But he admitted, when Garnett asked him about Maupassant, that he had read Henry James's critical essays on the French authors, or at least one essay (perhaps the one on Maupassant). Ford Madox Hueffer remembers Crane saying: "Oh well, I've read ol' man James's—" Beer quotes a letter Crane wrote to a woman, discussing Zola's *Nana*: "this girl in Zola is a real streetwalker. I mean, she does not fool around making excuses for her career. You must pardon me if I cannot agree that every painted woman on the streets of New York was brought there by some evil man. Nana, in the story, is honest. . . . Zola is a sincere writer but—is he much good? He hangs one thing to another and his story goes along but I find him pretty tiresome" (Beer, p. 318).

[1] This letter and the next one to Paul Revere Reynolds are reprinted here from *Paul Revere Reynolds*, by Frederick Lewis Allen (privately printed, 1944), pp. 56–8. (All other letters to Reynolds quoted here are likewise from this book.)

that "The Monster" was released. He said he would inform the N.Y. office to that effect or even write the same to you, if I liked. I said I did like but it seems the affair was bungled. McClure's claim on the story was one which I gave him through courtesy and honor—no other. Your final manipulation of the novelette I consider very brilliant and I am sorry to see it handicapped by that Scotch ass.

In all the months I have been in England I have never received a cent from America which has not been borrowed.[2] Just read that over twice! The consequences of this have lately been that I have been obliged to make arrangements here with English agents of American houses but in all cases your commission will be protected. This is the best I could do. My English expenses have chased me to the wall. Even now I am waiting for you to cable me my share of the Monster money and if there is a fluke I am lost.

Don't kick so conspicuously about the over-charge on the damned manuscripts. If I was a business man, I would not need a business man to conduct my affairs for me. I will try to do better but if I shouldn't, don't harangue me. The point is of minor importance.

I have withheld the "Death and the Child" story from an English sale because I think you can hit one of the three big fellows with it. "The Five White Mice" is sold in England.[3]

Faithfully yours,

Stephen Crane

---

[2] Amy Leslie added to his troubles by bringing suit against him for $550, which she alleged Crane had misappropriated. Cf. "Stephen Crane Sued," *New York Daily Tribune,* January 4, 1898.

[3] *The Five White Mice* was published in the New York *World* on April 10, 1898, and in *The Open Boat and Other Stories,* 1898, published by Heinemann and, in America, by Doubleday & McClure. *The Monster* was sold to *Harper's Magazine,* published there in August this year.

TO PAUL REVERE REYNOLDS

[*Ravensbrook,*
Oxted,
Surrey]
Feb. 7 [1898]

Dear Reynolds:

I am sending you by the Majestic (Wednesday) a new novelette, "The Blue Hotel." To my mind, it is a daisy. I have left every solitary right free—English book, English serial, American book, American serial—so that you can sell the story to Harper's Magazine for the volume. You might gently intimate to them that $500 is about the price I am led to expect for a story of ten thousand words. As for "Death and The Child" it is to go in the McClure book. So is "The Five White Mice."

Besides it would be absurd to conjoin "Death and The Child" with "The Monster." They don't fit. It would be rotten. Now, "The Blue Hotel" goes in neatly with "The Monster" and together they make 32,000. Very little more is needed for a respectably sized $1.00 book, and that can be readily submitted within the next six weeks.

If the Harpers take this story, try to get them to produce that 50£ which is to be paid for the book rights. I shall need every sou for the next two months. And if it hadn't been for your handsome management of the Harpers I would have been stumped absolutely. As you see, I am buckling down and turning out stuff like a man. If you hold your fine gait it will only be a short time before we are throwing out our chests.

There are a few odds and ends of affairs, such as the Journal business and so on that I wish you would get settled up. A ten pound note even fills me with awe.

You must understand as my confidential agent that my settlement in England cost me in the neighborhood of $2000 worth of debts. Your payments from the Harpers knocked a comfortable hole in them but I must have about $1200 more. This would have been simple if it were not for that black-mail at Appleton's.[1]

However, now that I am in it, I must beat it and I feel that with your help the affair will not be too serious. I will bombard you with stuff. Then, if you sell Harper's "The Blue Hotel," cable the money instantly.[2] I have got big matters to attend to this month. Get me through this and I am prepared to smile.

In a cable-gram, never mind the word "dollars." I will understand that you always speak in U.S. money. My replies should also be understood in U.S. terms.

Yours faithfully
S. C.

TO JOSEPH CONRAD [1]

Ravensbrook
Oxted, Surrey.
March 17th [1898]

My dear Conrad,

I am enclosing you a bit of original ms. under the supposition that you might like to keep it in remembrance

---

[1] This refers to the Amy Leslie affair, Crane being sued for recovery of money she lent him.

[2] It went to Scribner's, and Crane wrote Reynolds frantically: "Try to sell it as soon as possible. I must have some money by the first of April." But *Scribner's* declined *The Blue Hotel*, and so did the *Atlantic Monthly*. Then Reynolds sold it to Robert Collier for $300, in April. But it did not see print until November 26 to December 3, when it appeared in *Collier's Weekly*. Harold Frederic in December 1897 had advised Crane to throw away *The Monster*.

[1] Reprinted from *Two Letters from Stephen Crane to Joseph Conrad* (First Editions Club, London, 1926). This letter first appeared in Conrad's Introduction to *Stephen Crane* (1923), but Conrad misdated it as 1899. Since the printed heading is Ravensbrook, the correct date is 1898. Crane was at Brede Place in 1899, moving there on January 16.

of my warm and endless friendship for you.[2] I am still hoping
that you will consent to Stokes'[3] invitation to come to the
Savage on Saturday night.

Cannot you endure it?

Give my affectionate remembrances to Mrs. Conrad and my
love to the boy.

Yours always,
Stephen Crane

You *must* accept, says Cora and I, our invitation to come home
with me on Sat. night.

TO JOSEPH O'CONNOR [1]

[*Ravensbrook,
Oxted,
Surrey*]
[1898?]

. . . The one thing that deeply pleases me in my literary
life—brief and inglorious as it is—is the fact that men of sense

---

[2] Crane first met Conrad in London in October 1897, and the next
month he visited the Conrads at their Essex home. Crane's November 11
letter mentions the good "pow-wow" they had in London, and on
March 19 they had another one—on Saturday, two days after this letter
reminding Conrad of Stokes's invitation to meet at the Savage. Here
Crane talked about a plot for a story, "The Predecessor," and proposed
that Conrad join him in writing it as a play instead of a story. Conrad
came down to Ravensbrook that night. Nothing came of the intended
collaboration, however. Crane's gift to Conrad of "a bit of original ms."
recalls his gift to Willis Hawkins of the original manuscript of *The Red
Badge of Courage*, made on January 27, 1896.

[3] John Stokes, a cousin of the Duke of Norfolk.

[1] Crane wrote two letters to O'Connor, literary editor of the *Rochester
Post-Express*; the second and longer one was written in February (?)
1900. Both letters were published on April 18, 1900, in the *Post-Express*,
p. 4. This letter, which I have dated 1898, was published also in the *New
York Times, Supplement*, July 14, 1900, p. 466, in an article on Crane by
his friend John Northern Hilliard. But he misquoted one part of it.
Hilliard says it was written "shortly after the publication of *The Red*

believe me to be sincere. "Maggie," published in paper covers, made me the friendship of Hamlin Garland and W. D. Howells, and the one thing that makes my life worth living in the midst of all this abuse and ridicule is the consciousness that never for an instant have those friendships at all diminished. Personally I am aware that my work does not amount to a string of dried beans—I always calmly admit it. But I also know that I do the best that is in me, without regard to cheers or damnation. When I was the mark for every humorist in the country I went ahead, and now, when I am the mark for only 50 per cent of the humorists of the country, I go ahead, for I understand that a man is born into the world with his own pair of eyes, and he is not at all responsible for his vision—he is merely responsible for his quality of personal honesty. To keep close to this personal honesty is my supreme ambition. There is a sublime egotism in talking of honesty. I, however, do not say that I am honest. I merely say that I am as nearly honest as a weak mental machinery will allow. This aim in life struck me as being the only thing worth while. A man is sure to fail at it, but there is something in the failure.

Badge of Courage and *The Black Riders* when ridicule and personalities were volleyed across the net of criticism." Hilliard's dating (1896–7), however, is incorrect. O'Connor began editing his column for the *Post-Express* in 1898; consequently this letter must be dated then or after 1898, but not before. The *Literary Digest* for June 23, 1900 reprinted this letter and part of the long one saying that both letters were written "to the same gentleman." His identity has not before been brought to light. (For this information I am indebted to Miss Gladys Love, of the Rochester Public Library, and Miss Evelyn O'Connor.) In Williams's *Bibliography*, p. 12, this letter is quoted, but the full source is not given. Crane's letter was reprinted in the *Academy* for August 11, 1900, p. 116. It was made available again in Vincent Starrett's Introduction to *Men, Women and Boats* (1921), p. 20.

TO SANFORD BENNETT

[London, England]
[late March 1898]

Sorry not to have seen you. I have raised the wind and sail tomorrow.[1] Nothing I can do for Harold.[2] Barr will look after him.[3] Write me at Hartwood, N.Y., care of Edmund Crane. Shall get myself taken in the Navy if possible.

TO MRS. BOLTON CHAFFEE

[It was rumored while Crane was in Cuba that he had eloped with the wife of General Chaffee, the hero of El Caney, and had fled with her to San Francisco. General A. R. Chaffee was in fact unmarried.

[1] Crane sailed for Cuba, and so swiftly was he out of England "that guests came down to Oxted and were surprised to find him gone." Beer goes on to say that it was only after Crane had sailed that the New York *World* "cabled to secure his services," and then in New York he stopped in at the *World* offices but not until he had tried a naval recruiting bureau in hopes of joining the Navy. On May 23 from Key West he wrote his friend Robert Barr: "You should see the jay who runs the table here. He is straight out of a dime novel, moustache and all, with bunches of diamonds like cheap chandeliers on each hand. Now I owe Harold [Harold Frederic] an apology for laughing when he said they would tear me in pieces the minute my back was turned. Hi, Harold! I apologize! Did you know me for a morphine eater? A man who had known me for ten years tells me that all my books are written while I am drenched with morphine. The joke is on me." (In Beer, pp. 339–40.)

Crane sent the *World* twenty dispatches between April 27 and July 9, and then back in New York City Crane was refused an advance by Pulitzer's paper; so Crane signed up with the *Journal* and sent twenty dispatches from Cuba to the *Journal* between August 5 and November 9. (Their publication is listed by Ames W. Williams in the *New Colophon* for April 1948.) "I'm going to Greece for the *Journal*," Crane wrote to somebody in July (?), "and if the Red Badge is not all right I shall sell out my claim on literature and take up orange growing."

[2] Harold Frederic; ill now, he had a stroke in August and died on October 19.

[3] Robert Barr, who completed Crane's unfinished novel, *The O'Ruddy*, after Crane died.

Mrs. Bolton Chaffee had been Crane's guest three months before at Oxted. What started the gossip was his being seen with her on the veranda of Chamberlain's Hotel at Old Point Comfort.]

[Cuba]
[1898]

. . . You must be careful about feeding runaway dogs. Mr. Bemis [1] informs me that you and I are sinners and that we have flown to San Francisco. They have promoted you to the rank of Mrs. Brigadier General Chaffee. Perhaps it is not known to you—and it has not long been known to me—that my name in New York is synonymous with mud. Give my regards to your husband and tell him the cigars made many correspondents happier. [2]

TO PAUL REVERE REYNOLDS [1]

[Havana, Cuba]
[October (?) 1898]

My dear Reynolds:

Did you get my story: "The Price of the Harness"? I am worried for fear it is lost. Cable.

I am now sending you a *peach*. I love it devotedly. Sell to

---

[1] Floyd Bemis, a Southerner. In March 1893 Crane was pointed out to him "as an eccentric who spent all his time in dives of the Bowery and was the outcast son of an Episcopal Bishop" (Beer, p. 280).

[2] This incident occurred on July 13, and Crane's letter was probably written several months later (reprinted from Beer, p. 353). Crane was absent from England for nine months; he returned there in the first week of January, sailing in the *Manitou*. John T. Winterich errs in saying: "At the end of 1899 he was back in England"—even if his dating is a misprint for 1898. (In Introduction to the Folio Society edition of *The Red Badge of Courage*, 1951, p. 15.)

[1] Crane, now in Cuba as war correspondent, "was writing story after story, article after article, and sending them on [to his American agent] with brief penciled scrawls on cheap ruled pad paper; sometimes his vehement notes were written in a shaky hand on old telegraph blanks.

anybody if the price is grand enough. Otherwise remember that *Blackwood's* have a call on me. Send all letters here.

Crane.

I *love* this story.

TO PAUL REVERE REYNOLDS

Havana
Oct. 20 [1898]

My dear Reynolds:

I enclose a "personal anecdote" thing for McClure. Hit him hard. Hit him beastly hard. I have got to have at least fifteen hundred dollars this month, sooner the better. For Christ's sake get me some money quick here by cable.

The "Intrigue" lot goes to Heinemann.[1]

Yours,
Crane

TO PAUL REVERE REYNOLDS

Havana
Nov. 3rd. [1898]

My dear Reynolds:

Just received letter concerning "The Price of the Harness." If Blackwood can't take it for Dec. ask them

Always they glowed with enthusiasm over his work and appealed for instant payment:

[undated]

My dear Reynolds:

Now this is IT. If you don't touch big money for it I wonder!

And again:

Havana, Sept. 27. [1898]

Cable me when you make sale and how much. English copy goes to Blackwood.

Reprinted from *Paul Revere Reynolds*, by Frederic Lewis Allen, p. 61.

1 The "Intrigue" lot was a batch of love-poems.

to give it to Pinker.[1] Somebody must have it. With Pinker it is worth £ 36. We can't lose it.

Damn Walker. The name of the story is "The Price of the Harness" because it *is* the price of the harness, the price the men paid for wearing the military harness, Uncle Sam's military harness; and they paid blood, hunger and fever. Let him if he likes conjure some inflammatory secondary title. He is a fool.

Crane

TO MRS. WILLIAM SONNTAG

[New York City [1]]
November 28, 1898

Mrs. William Sonntag,

How do you persuade anybody to anything by cables and letters? I am very anxious to have Mrs.

---

[1] James Pinker, his London agent, with whom Crane had a contract at forty pounds per thousand words. *The Price of the Harness* appeared this December in *Cosmopolitan* and in *Blackwood's Edinburgh Magazine.* On its first appearance the story was called "The Woof of the Thin Red Threads," Crane taking that title from a phrase he had written in Part V of the story. The final title of *The Red Badge of Courage,* similarly, derived from a phrase struck off in writing the ninth chapter.

Crane had been on the verge of death in the fighting at San Juan and was now recuperating at the Hotel Pasaje in Havana. Cora heard nothing from him and was distressed by a Florida newspaper that somebody sent her—it claimed that Stephen Crane was missing. She wrote Reynolds for news of Crane's whereabouts and added: "I fear that we will lose our house here if I cannot get money to pay some pressing debts. . . . I have been served with two summons, so you can see how bad matters really are. If you can collect any money due to Mr. Crane please cable it to me without delay. This being so helpless in a foreign land together with my fears for Mr. Crane is almost driving me mad." Quoted from *Paul Revere Reynolds,* by Frederick Lewis Allen (1944), pp. 59–60.

[1] Crane left Havana in mid-November and spent a month in New York City. He hunted for a house, had luncheon with Howells, and cocktails with James Huneker. Leaving a theater with Mrs. Sonntag, a white-haired woman of forty-three and a cripple, Crane was accosted by a policeman and would have been booked on a trumped-up charge had not a priest (Mrs. Sonntag's cousin) intervened. On December 20 he cabled

Crane come to this country. Mrs. Crane is very anxious to have me come back to England. We are carrying on a duel at long range, with ink.

TO DR. CHARLES LITTLE [1]

Brede Place, Brede, Northiam, Sussex.
England
Feb. 6th. '99

Dear Doctor Little:—

I am quite sure that you will not remember me at all since I was merely a student of yours at Syracuse University and one of many hundreds. I distinctly confess that I had not the ability to impress myself upon you

---

Cora; some letters of late December to Mrs. Sonntag, Mr. Appleton, and Edward Garnett are dated from Hartwood. So he must have visited Edmund Crane before sailing for England on the *Manitou* early in January. In one of his late 1898 letters he expressed his decision to leave America: "I am going to stay in England for some time. It seems that in New York, outside the immediate circle of men who know me well, I am some kind of Simon Legree who goes around knocking women into the gutter and then walking on them. If I was a grocery boy or a hired man or a bank clerk no one would give a cuss what I did. But I am a writer so all bets are doubled." (This letter has not been previously printed.)

The letter to Mrs. Sonntag was first published in Beer's article "Mrs. Stephen Crane," *American Mercury,* 31 (February 1934), 291–2.

[1] History, which Dr. Little taught at Syracuse University, was Crane's favorite subject. But Crane was an indifferent student, and no semester grades were posted after his name at the end of the single semester he survived at Syracuse, spring of 1891. The dean of the university suggested that it would not be wise for him to return that fall unless he underwent a change of intention.

Dr. Little was the Reverend Charles J. Little, A.M., D.D., L.L.D. He was Professor of History and Logic at Syracuse University, 1885–91.

The original of this letter was typed, probably by Cora. It is in the possession of the Yale Collection of American Literature and is reproduced by permission of the Yale University Library, here for the first time.

through my mental endowments but I remember your telling me once that I impressed myself upon you through a resemblance to "John" whom you knew when you were at Dickinson College. After a certain examination in the French Revolution you called me to the desk and told me to beware—that I was going very wrong indeed. It has stuck in my mind for years that some of the information you had recieved of me was quite false. Candidly, I was worse than I should have been but I always had a singular faculty of having it said that I was engaged in crimes which are not of my accomplishments. Indeed, this singular faculty has followed me out of college into real life.

As to my little career, I'm sure I have nothing to say unless it be to the man who expressed such a generous interest in my welfare so long ago. True, it was mainly because I resembled "John" but I have never forgotten what you said to me. I am not one of the foolish ones who would say to you that your talk to me directed or changed my life but I *would* say to you that I remember with so much gratitude the words you spoke, they have been to me so much of a strength in life that my first fear is that amid your interest in the hundreds of students who year by year pass under your eye, you have totally forgotten your one-time interest in me,

It is a little thing to talk about but I have written several little books which have editions in New York, London, Paris, Leipsic, Vienna and in the English colonies.

It is indeed such a little thing to talk about that I would not bring it to your attention if I was not in the hopes of recalling to your mind the man who resembled "John" and to tell you that some silly talent of mine has been brought to light. In closing, I can only hope that you will remember the lad who resembled "John" and remember, also, that he often tells about his fireside the tale of the man who exhorted him—somewhat without accurate knowledge in regard to crime—but with such kindliness and interest—indeed almost affection—that the lad has almost made it a part of his creed of conduct.

I hope that you will be disposed to answer this note even if it is only three lines but anyhow remember there is one who will always be grateful to you.

Yours faithfully
[signed] Stephen Crane

TO ELBERT HUBBARD [1]

Brede Place
Brede
Northam, Sussex
May 1st '99

My dear Hubbard:

        I wrote I think sometime in '97 suggesting that you reprint in the *Philistine* two little articles of mine which appeared here in the *Westminster Gazette*.[2] I have just been reading them again and I like them. I send you copies and if you are not a duffer you will consider them good and human enough even for your blinding *Philistine*. Send me the *Philistine* or I will set fire to East Aurora by cable.

    I have been working up some grievances against you. I object strongly to your paragraphs about Rowan. You are more wrong than is even common on our humble incompetant [*sic*] globe. He didn't do anything worthy at all. He received the praise of the general of the army and got to be made a lieutenant col. for a feat which about forty newspaper correspondents had already performed at the usual price of fifty dollars a week and expenses. Besides he is personally a chump

---

   [1] This letter first appeared in the *New Colophon* for January 1948, Part I, p. 33.

   [2] The two little articles appeared under the title "With Greek and Turk" in the *Westminster Gazette* for June 14 and 18, 1897. Hubbard did not reprint them. His *Philistine* published two other Crane pieces this year: *Old Man Goes Wooing* (in July) and *Fishing Village* (in August).

and in Porto Rico where I met him he wore a yachting cap as part of his uniform which was damnable. When you want to monkey with some of our national heroes you had better ask me, because I know and your perspective is almost out of sight.[3]

When I think of you I rejoice that there is one man in the world who can keep up a small independent monthly howler without either dying, going broke, or becoming an ass.

Yours always
Stephen Crane

TO A BOOK REVIEWER [1]

[Brede Place,
Brede,
Northam, Sussex]
[late in 1899 (?)]

. . . No thanks. If the Whilomville stories [2] seem like Little Lord Fauntleroy to you you are demented and I know that you are joking, besides. See here, my friend, no kid except a sick little girl would like Lord Fauntleroy unless to look at Birch's pictures for it. The pictures are all right.

TO JOSEPH O'CONNOR

[This important letter is reproduced here in full for the first time since its original publication in the *Rochester Post-Express* on April

---

[3] The sham hero whom Crane is ridiculing here is A. S. Rowan of *A Message to Garcia.*

[1] This letter is reprinted from Beer, p. 292.

[2] Crane's Whilomville stories, starting in August 1899, ran for one year in *Harper's Magazine*, one story per issue to August of 1900 inclusive. The collection, in the press at the time of Crane's death in June, appeared in mid-August 1900.

18, 1900. Crane wrote it a few weeks before this, and the recipient
was Joseph O'Connor. It appeared in a column entitled "Literary
Notes," and O'Connor was editor of that column. Part of this letter
and another one appearing in the same issue of the *Post-Express*
(written probably in 1898, when O'Connor began literary editor-
ship of the *Post-Express*) were reprinted in the *Literary Digest* of
June 23, 1900, eighteen days after Crane died. Hilliard published
this second letter as one of three Crane letters in "Stephen Crane:
Letters to a Friend," *New York Times, Supplement,* July 14, 1900.
It has always been assumed that all three letters were addressed to
Hilliard. E. W. Chubb in *Stories of Authors* (1910), reprinted excerpts from this letter of February 1900, and from the one I have
dated as 1898. The Williams *Bibliography* cites Chubb only, instead
of the original source, the *Post-Express*.]

[*Brede Place*
Brede
Northam, Sussex]
[about February 1900]

Occasionally interested persons have asked me if Stephen
Crane was a nom de guerre; but it is my own name. In childhood, I was bitterly ashamed of it, and now, when I sometimes
see it in print, it strikes me as being the homliest named in
created things. The first Stephen Crane to appear in America,
arrived in Massachusetts from England in 1635. His son, Stephen Crane, settled in Connecticut, and the Stephen Crane of
the third American generation settled in New Jersey on lands
that now hold the cities of Newark and Elizabeth. When the
troubles with England came he was president of both Colonial
Assemblies that met in New York. Then he was sent by New
Jersey to the Continental Congress, and he served in that body
until just about a week before the Declaration was signed,
when the Tories made such trouble in New Jersey that he was
obliged to return and serve as speaker in the colony's assembly.
He died in the old homestead at Elizabeth when the British
troops were marching past to what happened to be the defeat
at Trenton. His eldest son commanded the Sixth New Jersey
Infantry during the Revolution and ultimately died the rank-

ing major-general in the regular army from an old wound received in the expedition to Quebec. The second son became the ranking commodore in the navy at a time when the title of admiral was unknown. The youngest son, while proceeding to his father's bedside, was captured by some Hessians, and upon his refusing to tell the road by which they intended to surprise a certain American outpost, they beat him with their muskets, and then having stabbed him with their bayonets, they left him dead in the road. In those old times the family did its duty. Upon my mother's side everybody as soon as he could walk, became a Methodist clergyman—of the old ambling-nag, saddlebag, exhorting kind. My father was a Methodist minister, author of numerous works of theology, and an editor of various periodicals of the church. He was a graduate of Princeton, and he was a great, fine simple mind. As for myself, I went to Lafayette college but did not graduate. I found mining-engineering not at all to my taste. I preferred baseball. Later I attended Syracuse university, where I attempted to study literature, but found baseball again much more to my taste. My first work in fiction was for the New York "Tribune," when I was about eighteen years old. During this time, one story of the series went into "The Cosmospolitan." At the age of twenty I wrote my first novel—"Maggie." It never really got on the market, but it made for me the friendship of William Dean Howells and Hamlin Garland, and since that time I have never been conscious for an instant that those friendships have at all diminished.

After completing "Maggie," I wrote mainly for the New York "Press" and for the "Arena." In the latter part of my twenty-first year I began "The Red Badge of Courage," and completed it early in my twenty-second year. The following year I wrote the poems contained in the volume known as "The Black Riders." On the first day of last November [1] I was pre-

---

[1] November 1, 1899. Stephen was then "precisely" 28 years old, *not* as he here so positively asserts "precisely 29 years old." Calendars and clocks, though time meant everything to him, never seemed to belong to

cisely 29 years old and had finished my fifth novel, "Active Service." I have only one pride and that is that the English edition of "The Red Badge of Courage" has been received with great praise by the English reviewers. I am proud of this simply because the remoter people would seem more just and harder to win.

TO AN UNKNOWN RECIPIENT [1]

[*Brede Place,*
Brede,
Northam, Sussex]
[1900]

. . . My mother was a very religious woman but I don't think that she was as narrow as most of her friends or her family. . . . My brothers tell me that she got herself into trouble before I was old enough to follow proceedings by taking care of a girl who had an accidental baby. Inopportune babies are not part of Methodist ritual but mother was always more of a Christian than a Methodist and she kept this girl at our house in Asbury until she found a home somewhere. Mother's friends were mostly women and they had the famous feminine aversion to that kind of baby. It is funny that women's interest in babies trickles clean off the mat if they have never

---

his world. It was as though he could not reckon himself according to clock-time. He was but 28 when he died at Badenweiler on June 5, 1900. Three writers or more (including Spiller and Pattee) say that he died at 29; the *Academy* for 1900 reported him dying at 31; and over half a dozen (including Mencken and Herzberg) state that Crane died at 30.

[1] My version of this letter consists of two portions quoted in Beer, pp. 245–6 and 239, which I have pieced together here. Willis Clarke, a young admirer who visited Crane during his last days, took down in short-hand these reminiscences. This "letter" consists of what he transcribed. The letters Crane wrote in 1900 show no signs of what Berryman describes as "his curt dying letters from Brede," which somehow is supposed to have connection with the style of Crane's story *A Man by the Name of Mud* (Berryman, p. 301).

met papa socially. . . . After my father died, mother lived in
and for religion. We had very little money. Mother wrote articles for Methodist papers and reported for the [New York]
Tribune and the [Philadelphia] *Press*. Every August she went
down to Ocean Grove and reported proceedings at the Methodist holy show there. . . . My brother Will used to try to
argue with her on religious subjects such as hell but he always
gave it up. Don't understand that mother was bitter or mean
but it hurt her that any of us should be slipping from Grace
and giving up eternal damnation or salvation or those things.
You could argue just as well with a wave. . . . She was always
starting off when she felt well enough to some big prayer meeting or experience meeting and she spoke very well. Her voice
was something like Ellen Terry's but deeper. She spoke as
slowly as a big clock ticks and her effects were impromptu.[2] . . .
It is in me to think that she did some good work for the public
schools. One of my sisters was a teacher [3] and mother tried for
years to get women placed on the school boards and to see that
whisky was not sold to boys under age. . . . I used to like
church and prayer meetings when I was a kid but that cooled
off and when I was thirteen or about that, my brother Will told
me not to believe in Hell after my uncle had been boring me
about the lake of fire and the rest of the sideshows. . . . Once
when I was fourteen an organ grinder on the beach at Asbury
gave me a nice long drink out of a nice red bottle for picking
up his hat for him. I felt ecstatic walking home and then I was
an Emperor and some Rajahs and Baron de Blowitz all at the
same time. I had been sulky all morning and now I was perfectly willing to go to a prayer meeting and Mother was tickled
to death.[4] And, mind you, all because this nefarious Florentine
gave me a red drink out of a bottle. I have frequently wondered

---

[2] Crane, who himself worked against time, describes his mother in
terms of a clock.

[3] Agnes, who was fifteen years older than Stephen.

[4] For Crane's imaginative reconstruction of this personal incident see
George's Mother.

how much mothers ever know about their sons, after all. She would not have found it much of a joke. . . . They tell me that I got through two grades in six weeks which sounds like the lie of a fond mother at a teaparty but I do remember that I got ahead very fast and that father was pleased with me. He used to take me driving with him to little places near Port Jervis where he was going to preach or bury somebody. Once we got mixed up in an Irish funeral near a place named Slate Hill. Everybody was drunk and father was scandalized. . . . He was so simple and good that I often think he didn't know much of anything about humanity. Will, one of my brothers, gave me a toy gun and I tried to shoot a cow with it over at Middletown when father was preaching there and that upset him wonderfully.[5] He liked all kinds of animals and never drove a horse faster than two yards an hour even if some Christian was dying elsewhere. But it is a big job to be presiding elder in a Methodist Conference. He worked himself to death, my people thought.

TO HIS NAMESAKE [1]

[*Brede Place,
Brede,
Northam, Sussex*]
[1900]

My dear Stephen:

      I need not say to you that I welcomed your advent with joy. You and I will struggle on with the name together and do as best we may. In the meantime, I would re-

---

[5] This incident reappears in Crane's story *Lynx Hunting*. The original episode is retold by Helen R. Crane in "My Uncle, Stephen Crane," *American Mercury*, January 1934.

[1] Stephen, born this year, was the son of Edmund, Crane's brother, now living in Port Jervis, New York. Stephen was a twin; he died in the spring of 1921. Crane in his will had left him one half his estate. Cora saw little Stephen when she visited at Edmund's house in June 1900.

mind you to grow up, as much as possible, like your gentle, kindly, lovable father, and please do not repeat the vices and mistakes of

Your devoted uncle,
Stephen Crane

FROM ROBERT BARR TO AN UNKNOWN RECIPIENT [1]

Hillhead, Woldingham
Surrey
June 8, 1900

I was delighted to hear from you, and was much interested to see the article on S. Crane you sent me. It seems to me the harsh judgment of an unappreciative commonplace person on a man of genius. Stephen had many qualities which lent themselves to misapprehension, but at the core he was the finest of men, generous to a fault, with something of the old time recklessness which used to gather in the ancient literary taverns of London. I always fancied that Edgar Allan Poe revisited in the earth as S. Crane, trying again, succeeding again, failing again, and dying ten years sooner than he did on the other occasion of his stay on earth.

When your letter came I had just returned from Dover, where I stayed four days to see Crane off for the Black Forest.[2]

---

[1] Barr's letter was first printed in Vincent Starrett's Introduction to *Men, Women and Boats* (Modern Library, 1921); and therefore the claim of John N. Birss, in the *Saturday Review of Literature,* November 25, 1933, that this letter "has escaped Crane's biographers and bibliographers" is incorrect. Birss dug it up from its original source (the *New York Herald*), but failed to acknowledge Starrett's reproduction of this letter a dozen years previously.

[2] Crane, his health wrecked by exposures endured in Cuba, died of consumption on June 5 at a Bavarian health resort in the Black Forest, at Badenweiler, Germany. Conrad also went to Dover, after staying with Crane during his last day in England. "Went to see Crane yesterday at Dover. Been with him 20 minutes. Supported move from Brede pretty

There was a thin thread of hope that he might recover, but to me he looked like a man already dead. When he spoke or rather whispered, there was all the accustomed humor in his sayings. I said to him that I would go over to the Schwarzwald in a few weeks, when he was getting better, and that we would take some convalescent rambles together. As his wife was listening he said faintly, "I'll look forward to that," but he smiled at me and winked slowly, as much as to say, "You damned humbug, you know I'll take no more rambles in this world." Then, as if the train of thought suggested what was looked on before as the crisis of his illness, he murmured, "Robert, when you come to the hedge—that we must all go over—it isn't bad. You feel sleepy—and—you don't care. Just a little dreamy curiosity—which world you're really in—that's all."

Tomorrow, Saturday, the 9th, I go again to Dover to meet his body. He will rest for a little while in England, a country that was always good to him, then to America, and his journey will be ended.[3]

I've got the unfinished manuscript of his last novel here beside me, a rollicking Irish tale, different from anything he ever wrote before. Stephen thought I was the only person who could finish it, and he was too ill for me to refuse. I don't know what to do about the matter, for I never could work up another man's ideas. . . .[4]

From the window beside which I write this I can see down in the valley Ravensbrook House, where Crane used to live and where Harold Frederic, he, and I spent many a merry night

---

well. I was awfully shocked of course and had to put on jolly manners. He may yet escape." (*Life and Letters*, I, p. 294, letter from Conrad to John Galsworthy.)

[3] Crane was buried in Elizabeth, New Jersey.

[4] As late as November 23, 1900, Cora wrote her agent that "Mr. A. E. W. Mason is finishing the story." It was, however, Barr who finished *The O'Ruddy*. It was published in 1903 by Frederick A. Stokes, and in England by Methuen & Co., in 1904. During the next seventeen years no work of Crane appeared in England or America.

together. . . . Stephen died at three in the morning, the same
sinister hour that carried away our friend Frederic nineteen
months before. . . .[5]

I feel rather like the last of the Three Musketeers the other
two gone down in their duel with death. I am wondering if,
within the next two years, I also will get the challenge. If so, I
shall go to the competing ground the more cheerfully that two
such good fellows await the outcome on the other side.

                                                  Robert Barr

---

[5] Frederic (misspelled in Barr's letter as Frederick) and Stephen
Crane died at the same "sinister hour" as F. Scott Fitzgerald.

BIBLIOGRAPHY

Several Crane bibliographies have been published: in 1923 by Vincent Starrett, in 1930 by B. J. R. Stolper, and in 1948 by Ames W. Williams and Vincent Starrett: *Stephen Crane: A Bibliography* (Glendale, Calif.: John Valentine).[1] The Williams-Starrett bibliography lists 114 biographical or bibliographical writings about Crane; most of this material has to do with the life; almost nothing is represented from surveys of American literature and critical studies of modern fiction; and several important biographical pieces are neglected. The critical pieces in this bibliography consist chiefly of contemporary reviews (1893–1900), numbering 115 in all. Of these the best are George Wyndham's exposition of *The Red Badge* in the *New Review*, 14 (January 1896), 30, and the *Critic*, 24 (November 30, 1895), 363, and H. G. Wells's summary of Crane in the *North American Review* (August 1900), CLXXI, 233–42.

I

NOVELS, SHORT STORIES, AND POEMS

1893 *Maggie: A Girl of the Streets: A Story of New York.* [Written in December 1891 and published, at the author's expense, under the pseudonym "Johnston Smith," in yellow paper wrappers. Not until the 1896 edition did *Maggie* appear in regular binding and with Crane's name.]

1895 *The Black Riders and Other Lines.* [Poems.]

The Red Badge of Courage: An Episode of the American Civil War. [Published in October by Appleton and

---

[1] In addition to these three books there are check-lists on Crane in *Stephen Crane and the Stephen Crane Association* (1926); in *Bulletin of Bibliography* (1935), check-list of Crane's short stories and essays compiled by Claude Jones; and in the *Literary History of the United States* (1948), III, 458–61.

in England by Heinemann, in December—in the week
of November 30, 1895. Heinemann published it in the
Pioneer Series in a paper-wrapper edition and in a
cloth-bound book with the title-page dated 1896. There
were fourteen American printings in 1896.]

1896   *George's Mother.* [Ames Williams says that "prior
to publication Crane tentatively called this work *A
Woman Without Weapons.*"]

Maggie. [Published by Appleton and by Heinemann.
Reprinted by Heinemann in *Bowery Tales,* 1900; in
Maggie and Other Stories, edited by Henry Hazlitt,
Knopf, 1931; in a Modern Library edition, by Vincent
Starrett, 1933; in *Twenty Stories,* edited by Carl Van
Doren, Knopf, 1940; in *Great Short American Novels,*
edited by William Phillips, Dial Press, 1946; and in
Selected Prose and Poetry, edited by W. M. Gibson,
Rinehart, 1950. *Maggie* appeared with *George's Mother*
in *Bowery Tales* and in Hazlitt's edition: *Maggie to-
gether with George's Mother and The Blue Hotel.*]

*The Little Regiment and Other Episodes of the Amer-
ican Civil War.* [Published by Appleton and the next
year by Heinemann. It was issued, like *The Red Badge,*
both in cloth binding and in paper wrappers in The
Pioneer Series.]

1897   *The Third Violet.* [A novel.]

1898   *The Open Boat and Other Tales of Adventure.* [Pub-
lished by Doubleday & McClure Co., and by Heinemann.]

Pictures of War. [Published by Heinemann. The stories
are the same as in *The Little Regiment,* but here *The
Red Badge* is added.]

1899   *War is Kind.* [Poems.]

Active Service: A Novel. [Published by Frederick A.
Stokes and by Heinemann.]

The Monster and Other Stories. [Published in New York and London by Harper. Reissued, with four additional stories, in 1901.]

II
WORK PUBLISHED POSTHUMOUSLY

1900 *Whilomville Stories.* [Published in New York—in August—and in London by Harper.]

Wounds in the Rain: War Stories. [Published in October by Frederick A. Stokes and in England by Methuen & Co.]

1901 *Great Battles of the World.* [Published in Philadelphia by Lippincott and in London by Chapman & Hall.]

1902 *Last Words.* [Published only in England—by Digby, Long & Co.]

1903 *The O'Ruddy: A Romance.* [Coauthor: Robert Barr.]

1921 *Men, Women and Boats.* Edited with an Introduction by Vincent Starrett. [Boni & Liveright and then the Modern Library.]

1925–7
The Work of Stephen Crane. Twelve volumes, edited by Wilson Follett, with Introductions by various friends and admirers. [Alfred A. Knopf. The Introductions to Volumes II and XII by Robert H. Davis and Charles Michelson respectively are of biographical value, and the Introductions to Volumes I, IX, and X, by Joseph Hergesheimer, Willa Cather, and H. L. Mencken respectively are of critical value. The *Work*, a limited and expensive edition, has long been out of print. It omits some works such as Crane's first printed story, *The King's Favor* (*Syracuse University Herald*, May 1891),

several *Sullivan County Sketches, The Blood of the Martyr* (a play, published by the Peter Pauper Press in 1940), *Legends* (in the *Bookman*, May 1896) and *A Lost Poem* (published by Harvard University Press, 1932, and appearing in *Golden Book*, February 1934); etc.]

1930 *The Collected Poems of Stephen Crane.* Edited by Wilson Follett. [Alfred A. Knopf. Reissued six times since 1930.]

1931 *Maggie together with George's Mother and The Blue Hotel.* Edited with an Introduction by Henry Hazlitt. [Alfred A. Knopf. Out of print in 1937.]

1933 *Maggie and Other Stories.* Edited with an Introduction by Vincent Starrett. [Modern Library.]

1940 *Twenty Stories.* Edited with an Introduction by Carl Van Doren. [Alfred A. Knopf. Reissued in 1945 by World Publishers. This edition is no longer in print.]

1949 *The Sullivan County Sketches of Stephen Crane,* edited with an Introduction by Melvin Schoberlin, pp. 1–20. [Syracuse University Press.]

1950 *Selected Prose and Poetry.* Edited with an Introduction by W. M. Gibson. [Rinehart.]

1951 *The Red Badge of Courage.* Edited with an Introduction by R. W. Stallman. [Modern Library, College Edition. Other editions with introductions include Ripley Hitchcock's (Appleton, 1900, 1917), Guy Empey's (Appleton, 1917), Max Herzberg's (Appleton, 1925, 1926; Modern Library, 1925; Pocket Books, 1942); Joseph Hergesheimer's (Volume I of the *Work*); Joseph Conrad's (in Heinemann's Pioneer Series, 1925, reprinted as "His War Book" in *Last Essays*, Dent, 1926); Carl Van Doren's, Heritage Press, 1944; John T. Winterich's (Folio Society, 1951); and R. W. Stallman's (Modern Library, Random House, 1951).]

III

BOOKS AND ARTICLES ON STEPHEN CRANE: BIOGRAPHICAL AND BIBLIOGRAPHICAL

1914 Hamlin Garland: "Stephen Crane as I Knew Him," *Yale Review*, N.S., 3 (April 1914), 494–506.

1923 Thomas Beer: *Stephen Crane: A Study in American Letters*. With an Introduction by Joseph Conrad. Reprinted in *The Borzoi Reader*, edited by Carl Van Doren, 1936. Knopf. Reprinted in *Hanna, Crane, and the Mauve Decade*, by Thomas Beer, 1941. Knopf.

1928 Irving Addison Bacheller: *Coming up the Road*, pp. 276–9, 292–3. Bobbs-Merrill.

1930 Hamlin Garland: "Stephen Crane," *Roadside Meetings*, pp. 189–206, 393. Macmillan.

1937 Ford Madox Ford: "Stephen Crane," *Portraits from Life*, pp. 21–37. Houghton Mifflin.

1939 Lyndon Upson Pratt: "A Possible Source of *The Red Badge of Courage*," *American Literature*, XI, 1–10.

H. T. Webster: "Wilbur F. Hinman's *Corporal Si Klegg* and Stephen Crane's *The Red Badge of Courage*," *American Literature*, XI, 285–93.

1945 W. L. Werner: "Stephen Crane and *The Red Badge of Courage*," *New York Times Book Review*, September 30, p. 4.

1948 Ames W. Williams and Vincent Starrett: *Stephen Crane: A Bibliography*. With an Introduction by Vincent Starrett, pp. 7–12. Glendale, Calif.: John Valentine.

1950 John Berryman: *Stephen Crane*. (American Men of Letters Series) William Sloane. Methuen, 1951.

1954 R. W. Stallman: "Some Additions to the Canon of Stephen Crane," *P. M. L. A.*, 69 (1954).

IV

Books and Articles on Stephen Crane: Critical

1898 Edward Garnett: "Mr. Stephen Crane: An Appreciation," *Academy*, LV, 483–4. Reprinted, in expanded form, in *Friday Nights*, by Edward Garnett, pp. 201–17. Knopf, 1922; Cape, 1922, 1929.

1900 H. G. Wells: "Stephen Crane from an English Standpoint," *North American Review*, CLXXI, 233–42. Reprinted in *The Shock of Recognition*, edited by Edmund Wilson, pp. 661–71. Doubleday, Doran, 1943.

1919 Harriet Monroe: "Stephen Crane," *Poetry: A Magazine of Verse*, XIV, 148–52.

1925 Joseph Conrad: "His War Book: A Preface to Stephen Crane's *The Red Badge of Courage*." (Pioneer Series) Heinemann. Reprinted in *Last Essays*, by Joseph Conrad, pp. 175–83. Dent, 1926.

1928 Robert Littell: "Notes on Stephen Crane," *New Republic*, LIV, 391–2.

1929 Wilson Follett: "The Second Twenty-Eight Years: A Note on Stephen Crane," *Bookman*, LXVIII, 532–7. Reprinted for the Stephen Crane Association, by Monroe F. Dreher, 1930.

Gorham B. Munson: "Prose for Fiction: Stephen Crane," *Style and Form in American Prose*, pp. 159–70. Doubleday, Doran.

1934 Harry Hartwick: "The Red Badge of Nature," *The Foreground of American Fiction*, pp. 21–44 and *passim*. American Book Co.

1935 Ford Madox Ford: "Technique," *Southern Review*, I, 20–35.

1940   Russell Nye: "Stephen Crane as Social Critic," *Modern Quarterly*, XI, 48–54.

1944   John C. Bushman: *The Fiction of Stephen Crane and its Critics*. University of Illinois dissertation (unpublished).

Jean Elizabeth Whitehead: *The Art of Stephen Crane*. Cornell University dissertation (unpublished).

1946   Horace Gregory and Marya Zaturenska: "A Note on Stephen Crane," *A History of American Poetry: 1900–1940*, pp. 133–7. Harcourt, Brace.

V. S. Pritchett: "Two Writers and Modern War," *The Living Novel*, pp. 166–78. Chatto & Windus.

1948   Robert E. Spiller: "Toward Naturalism in Fiction," *Literary History of the United States*, edited by Robert E. Spiller, Willard Thorp, and others, II, 1020–6 and *passim*. Macmillan.

1949   H. L. Mencken: "Stephen Crane," *A Mencken Chrestomathy*, pp. 496–7. Knopf.

1952   R. W. Stallman: "Stephen Crane," *Critiques & Essays on Modern Fiction*, edited by John Aldridge, pp. 244–69. Ronald Press.

A NOTE ON THE

T Y P E

IN WHICH THIS BOOK IS SET

THE TEXT *of this book is set in* Caledonia, *a Linotype face that belongs to the family of printing types called "modern face" by printers—a term used to mark the change in style of type-letters that occurred about 1800. Caledonia borders on the general design of Scotch Modern, but is more freely drawn than that letter.*

The book was composed by The Plimpton Press, Norwood, Massachusetts. Printed and bound by The Haddon Craftsmen, Inc., Scranton, Pennsylvania. The typography and binding are by W. A. Dwiggins.

WAD